TAG-Translate

# Tala Abu-Ghazleh

## Dictionary of Patent Terms

## معجم طلال أبو غزالة
## لبراءة الاختراع

English- عربي

المملكة الاردنية الهاشمية

رقم الايداع لدي دائرة

المكتبة الوطنية

٢٠١٢/٨/٢٩١٥

٣٤٠/٣

معجم طلال أبوغزاله لبراءات الاختراع - عمان

شركة طلال أبوغزاله للترجمة والتوزيع والنشر

الطبعة الأولى: ٢٠١٢

عدد الصفحات: ٣٠٤ صفحه

ر.أ: ٢٠١٢/٨/٢٩١٥

الواصفات: /المعاجم // براءات الاختراع

❖أعدت دائرة المكتبة الوطنية بيانات الفهرسة والتصنيف الأولية

ISBN: 978-9957-559-01-4 (ردمك)

ISBN: 978-9957-559-02-1 (ردمك) Book - E

# مقدمة

مع بزوغ أنظمة جديدة وتكنولوجيا حديثة لم يعد يكفي للفوز بالغنيمة أن تتمكن من إنتاج المعرفة فحسب، بل يجب عليك أن تكون قادراً على حمايتها وأن تطبقها.

هذا الأمر يفسر سبب إعتبار أن براءة الإختراع هي مقياس دقيق للإبداع والإصرار والمقدرة على إبتكار فكرة جديدة وكذلك المقدرة على بناء المعرفة، ولهذا فإذا لم تكن قادراً على إبتكار المعرفة وتقديم براءات الإختراع فمن المستحيل أن تتمكن من إنشاء شركات التكنولوجيا المتقدمة.

من هنا ولأهمية هذا الحقل في مكونات الملكية الفكرية جاء معجم أبوغزاله لبراءات الإختراع وبما تضمنه من محاور ومصطلحات شملت نحو عشرين ألف كلمة ومصطلح، ومن بين ما جاء فيها محور الجدل المستمر حول فكرة البراءة ومشروعيتها وتطبيقها.

ومحور آخر يتناول «البراءات الخضراء» التي أخذت بالتزايد واستوجبت الإهتمام كظاهرة تلبي الحاجات الإنسانية الحيوية، إضافة إلى محاور الفكر وحوكمة البراءات وإدارة محافظ البراءات وتحليل المعلومات المتصلة بالبراءات وتدقيق البراءات، ومن المحاور الأساسية الأخرى محور يتضمن أبرز الجرائم الخاصة بالبراءات وآخر للتقاضي والتحكيم بالنزاعات حول البراءات.

ومن المؤكّد أن علم البراءات شهد تطوراً ملحوظاً مع التطور التكنولوجي غير المسبوق، فكان لا بد لنا ومن واقع

مسؤولياتنا كمجموعة عالمية تهتم وتتحمل مسؤولية تطوير الملكية الفكرية في البلاد العربية أن نبادر لإصدار هذا المعجم المتخصص إلى جانب معجم أبوغزاله للملكية الفكرية، وبمعلومات أوفى واشمل عن قطاع براءات الإختراع لقناعتنا بأهمية البراءات في تشجيع الإبداع والإبتكار والتجديد وزرع الثقة في نفوس المبدعين والمخترعين من كافة القطاعات ففيها ضمان للحقوق وبذلك تحقق هدف أن تاخذ الملكية الفكرية دورها في التنمية والتطور والإقتصادي والإجتماعي، ونسهم بدورنا في حماية وحفظ الإبداعات الإنسانية في مجتمعاتنا العربية.

لقد سعدت بهذا الإصدار العلمي المهني الجديد السادس إلى جانب معاجم مهنية أخرى أصدرتها المجموعة:

معجم طلال أبوغزاله للمحاسبة والأعمال.
معجم طلال أبوغزاله للملكية الفكرية.
معجم طلال أبوغزاله لتقنية المعلومات.
معجم طلال أبوغزاله القانوني.
معجم طلال أبوغزاله للمتلازمات اللفظية.

أختم القول: «أننا حين نحقق إنجازاً يصبح تطلعنا ومهمتنا السعي إلى إنجاز ونجاح آخر».

طلال أبوغزاله
رئيس مجموعة طلال أبوغزاله

# INTRODUCTION

With the emergence of new state-of-the-art technologies, it is no longer enough to generate knowledge in order to be a winner; rather, you should be able to protect and apply such technologies.

This explains the reason for considering patents the accurate measurement of innovation.

Logically, if you are unable to generate knowledge and create inventions, it will be impossible for you to establish technology-based companies.

For this reason, and due to the importance of this field in terms of Intellectual Property, the Talal Abu-Ghazaleh Dictionary of Patent Terms was born, comprising twenty thousand entries.

"Green patents" are increasing and deserve to be acknowledged as a phenomenon that meets vital human needs. In addition, the fields of patents governance, patents portfolios management, analysis of patent-related information and the auditing of patents all merit our attention. Other areas include patent-related crimes, in addition to litigation and arbitration of patent disputes.

It goes without saying that patent science has witnessed remarkable development along with unprecedented technological advancements. Accordingly, and fulfilling our responsibility as an international group is concerned with the development of

Intellectual Property in the Arab countries, we introduce this publication in addition to Talal Abu-Ghazaleh Intellectual Property Dictionary, which contains in-depth information about patents since we believe in the patents role in encouraging innovation and enhancing confidence among innovators and inventors from all sectors. This will help protect rights and ensure that Intellectual Property plays its role in socio-economic development. We are therefore aiming to contribute to the protection and safeguarding of human innovations in our Arab communities.

I am extremely happy with this new sixth professional scientific publication which was issued by Talal Abu-Ghazaleh Organization. Other valuable publications include:

❖❖Talal Abu-Ghazaleh Accountancy & Business Dictionary
❖❖Talal Abu-Ghazaleh Intellectual Property Dictionary
❖❖Talal Abu-Ghazaleh ICT Dictionary
❖❖Talal Abu-Ghazaleh Legal Dictionary
❖❖Talal Abu-Ghazaleh Collocations Dictionary

Finally, I believe that achieving one success will always motivate us to look for other achievements and areas to excel.

**Talal Abu-Ghazaleh**
**Chairman of Talal Abu-Ghazaleh Organization**

# TAG-Org OFFICES


**General Administration (Amman-Jordan)**
Email: tagi@tagi.com

**AFAGHNISTAN**
**Kabul**
Email: afganistan@tagi.com
Email: afghanistan@agip.com

**ALGERIA**
**Algeria**
Email: algeria@agip.com

**BAHRAIN**
**Manama**
Email: tagco.bahrain@tagi.com
Email: bahrain@agip.com

**CHINA**
**Shanghai**
Email: china@agip.com

**CYPRUS**
**Nicosia**
Email: cyprus@agip.com

**EGYPT**
**Cairo**
Email: tagco.cairo@tagi.com
Email: egypt@agip.com

**INDIA**
**New Delhi**
Email: india@agip.com

**IRAQ**
**Baghdad**
Email: tagco.iraq@tagi.com
Email: iraq@agip.com
**Erbil**
Email: tagco.erbil@tagi.com
Email: erbil@agip.com

**JORDAN**
Email: agip@agip.com
**Amman-AGIP**
Email: jordan@agip.com
**Amman-Jordan Office**
Email: tagco.amman@tagi.com

**KUWAIT**
**Kuwait**
Email: tagco-kuwait@tagi.com
Email: kuwait@agip.com

**LEBANON**
**Beirut-TAGI**
Email: tagco.beirut@tagi.com
**Beirut-AGIP**
Email: lebanon@agip.com

**Libya - Jordan**
Email: libya@agip.com

**MOROCCO**
**Casablanca**
Email: morocco@agip.com

**OMAN**
**Muscat**
Email: tagco.oman@tagi.com
Email: oman@agip.com

**PAKISTAN**
**Karachi**
Email: pakistan@agip.com

**PALESTINE**
**Gaza**
Email: tagco-gaza@tagi.com
Email: gaza@agip.com
**Ramallah**
Email: tagco.ramallah@tagi.com
Email: westbank@agip.com

**QATAR**
**Doha**
Email: tagco.qatar@tagi.com
Email: qatar@agip.com

**SAUDI ARABIA**
**Riyadh**
Email: tagco.riyadh@tagi.com
Email: ksa@agip.com
**Khobar**
Email: tagco.khobar@tagi.com
**Jeddah**
Email: tagco.jeddah@tagi.com

**Abha**
Email: tagco.abha@tagi.com

**SUDAN**
**Khartoum**
Email: tagco.sudan@tagi.com
Email: sudan@agip.com

**SYRIA**
**Damascus**
Email: tagco-syria@tagi.com
Email: syria@agip.com

**TUNISIA**
**Tunisia**
Email: tunisia@agip.com

**TURKEY**
**Ankara**
Email: turkey@agip.com
**Istanbul**
Email: can.koc@karincaymm.com.tr

**United Arab Emirates**
**Abu-Dhabi**
Email:
tagco.abudhabi@tagi.com
**Dubai (TAGI)**
Email: tagco.dubai@tagi.com
**Dubai (TAGIP)**
Email: uae@agip.com
**Ras Al-Khaimah**
Email: tagco.rak@tagi.com
**Al-Ain**
Email: tagco.alain@tagi.com
**Jabal Ali**
Email: agip.jebelali@agip.com
**Um Al-Quwain**
Email: tagco.rak@tagi.com
**Sharjah**
Email: tagco.sharjah@tagi.com
**Ajman**
Email: tagco.sharjah@tagi.com

**YEMEN**
**Sana'a**
Email: tagco-yemen@tagi.
Email: yemen@agip.com
**Arab Society of Certified Accountants (ASCA)**
Email: info@ascasociety.org
**Arab Society for Intellectual Property (ASIP)**
Email: info@aspip.org
**Licensing Executive Society Arab Countries (LES-AC)**
Email: les@lesarab.org
**Arab Knowledge Management Society (AKMS)**
Email: akms@akms.org
**Arab Intellectual Mediation Society (AIPMAS)**
Email: info@aipmas.org

**Talal Abu-Ghazaleh Knowledge Society (TAG-Knowledge) Amman-Jordan Office**
Email: tag-knowledge@tagorg.com

**Talal Abu-Ghazaleh Graduate School of Business**
**Talal Abu-Ghazaleh Graduate School of Business (TAGSB)**
Email: info@tagcb.edu.jo
**Talal Abu-Ghazaleh Research Center (TAG-Research)**
Email: tagresearch@tagorg.com
**Talal Abu-Ghazaleh University Management Advisory Services (TAG-Universities)**
Email: taguniversity@tagorg.com

**Academies:**
**Talal Abu-Ghazaleh Academies (TAG-Academies)**
**Talal Abu-Ghazaleh Professional Training (TAG - Training Academy)**
Email: tagitraining@tagitraining.com
**Talal Abu-Ghazaleh Finance and Banking Academy (TAG-Banking Academy)**
Email: tag-cima@tagi.com
**Talal Abu-Ghazaleh Languages Academy (TAG-Lingual)**
Email: taglingual@tagorg.com

**Talal Abu-Ghazaleh Confucius (TAG-Confucius)**
Email: info@tagconfucius.com
**Talal Abu-Ghazaleh Cambridge International Center (TAG-CAMBRIDGE)**
Email: tagcic-amman@tagorg.com
**Arab Omani Management Training Institute**
Email: araboman@tagorg.com

## Liaison Offices:
**Montréal - Canada**
Email: nsalame@tagorg.com
**New York- USA**
Email: rar@robinrolferesources.com
**Edinburgh- UK**
Email: jsmall@tagi.com
**Buffalo- USA**
Email: egress@tagcb.edu.jo
**Paris- France**

## TAG-Org offices under establishment
**Currently to be established /activated**
- Iran
- Malta
- Moscow
- Hong Kong
- Nigeria

**In the near future:**
Azerbaijan
Kazakhstan
South Korea
Malaysia
Lagos
South Africa – Johannesburg or Cape Town
Kenya – Nairobi
Benin
Ivory Cosat
Brazil
Chile

# TAG-Org WEBSITES

**Talal Abu-Ghazaleh Organization (TAG-Org)**
www.tagorg.com
**Services:**
Talal Abu-Ghazaleh & Co. International (TAGI)
www.tagi.com
Talal Abu-Ghazaleh Intellectual Property TMP Agents-TAGIP(AGIP)
www.agip.com
Talal Abu-Ghazaleh Legal (TAG- Legal)
www.tag-legal.com
Talal Abu-Ghazaleh & Co. Consulting ( TAG-Consult)
www.agcon.com
Talal Abu-Ghazaleh Information Technology International (TAG-ITI)
www.tagiti.com
Talal Abu-Ghazaleh Valuation ( TAG-Value)
www.tagvaluation.com
Talal Abu-Ghazaleh Projects (TAG-Advisors)
www.abughazalehprojects.com
Talal Abu-Ghazaleh Translation Distribution and Publishing (TAG-Translate)
www.tagtranslate.com
Talal Abu-Ghazaleh Real Estates Management and Development (TAG-Aqarat)
www.tag-aqarat.com
Talal Abu-Ghazaleh Capital Services (TAG-Capital)
www.tag-capital.com

Talal Abu-Ghazaleh Recruitment and Human Resources Development (TAG-Recruit)
www.tagirecruitment.com
Talal Abu-Ghazaleh Profeessional Training Group (TAGTRAIN)
www.tagitraining.com
Talal Abu-Ghazaleh Arabic Encyclopedia (TAGIPedia)
beta.tagipedia.org
Talal Abu-Ghazaleh Cambridge IT Skills Center (TAG-Cambridge)
www.agcaitc.com
Talal Abu-Ghazaleh University (TAGIUNI)
www. tagiuni.com
Talal Abu-Ghazaleh & Co. International Domains (TAG-Domains)
www.tagidomains.com
Talal Abu-Ghazaleh Intellectual Property Renewals (AGIP-Renew)
www.ag-ip-renewals.com
Arab Society of Certified Accountants (ASCA)
www.ascasociety.org
Arab Society for Intellectual Property (ASIP)
www.aspip.org
Licensing Executive Society – Arab Countries (LES-AC)
www.lesarab.org
Arab Knowledge and Management Society (AKMS)
www.akms.org
Talal Abu-Ghazaleh Knowledge Society (TAG-KS)
www.tagks.com

Arab Organization for Quality Assurance in Education (AROQAE)
www.aroqa.org
Arab Intellectual Property Mediation Society (AIPMAS)
www.aipmas.org
Organization of States Research and Education Network (ASREN)
www.asrenorg.net
Talal Abu-Ghazaleh University (TAGIUNI)
www.tagiuni.com
Talal Abu-Ghazaleh Graduate School College of Business (TAGSB)
www.tagcb.edu.jo
Talal Abu-Ghazaleh University College of Business (TAGUCB)
www.tagucb.edu.com
Talal Abu-Ghazaleh Research Center (TAG-Research)
www.tagrsc.com
Talal Abu-Ghazaleh University Management Advisory Services (TAG-Universities)
www.taguniconsult.com
Talal Abu-Ghazaleh Academies (TAG-Academy)
www.tag-academies.com
Talal Abu-Ghazaleh Tenders (TAG-Tenders)
www.tagtenders.com
Talal Abu-Ghazaleh Finance and Banking Academy (TAG-Banking Academy)
www.tagbankingacademy.com
Talal Abu-Ghazaleh Information & Communication Technology Academy ( TAG-ICT Academy)
www.tagictacademy.com

Talal Abu-Ghazaleh Academy for Languages (TAG Lingual)
www.tag-languages.com
Talal Abu-Ghazaleh Cambridge International Center ( TAG-Cambridge)
www.tag-cic.com
Talal Abu-Ghazaleh Educational Consulting (TAG-Education)
www.tageducational.com
Talal Abu-Ghazaleh Confucius (TAG-Confucius)
www.tagconfucius.com
Talal Abu-Ghazaleh Chinese Visa Section (TAG-Visa)
www.tag-visa.com
Talal Abu-Ghazaleh Chinese Visa Section (TAG-Visa)
www.tag-visa.com
Talal Abu-Ghazaleh E-Solutions ( TAG E Solutions)
www.tagesolutions.com
Talal Abu-Ghazaleh International Press and Publishing ( TAG-Publish)
www.tagpublication.com
Talal Abu-Ghazaleh International Advertising ( TAG Media)
www.tagorgmedia.com
Talal Abu-Ghazaleh IP News Agency ( TAG-IP News)
www.ag-ip-news.com
Talal Abu-Ghazaleh Education News Agency ( TAG Educa News)
www.tageducanews.com
Talal Abu-Ghazaleh Information Technology International News Agency ( TAG-IT News)
www.tagitnews.com

**JORDAN:**

General Administration
TAG-Org Building, No. 26, Prince Shaker bin Zaid Street, Shmeisani, Amman
PO Box: 921100, Amman 11192, Hashemite Kingdom of Jordan
Telephone: (+ 962-6) 5100 900
Fax: (+ 962-6) 5100 901
Email: tagi@tagi.com

الأردن
الإدارة العامة
مبنى مجموعة طلال أبوغزاله، رقم 26، شارع الأمير شاكر بن زيد، الشميساني، عمان، الاردن
صندوق البريد: 921100، عمان 11192، المملكة الأردنية الهاشمية
هاتف: 5100900 (9626+)
فاكس: 5100901 (9626+)
البريد الإلكتروني: tagi@tagi.com

**Chairman's Office**

51 El Hegaz Street, 10th Floor, Mohandseen, Cairo, Egypt
P.O.Box: 96 Imbabah, Cairo 12411, Egypt
Tel: (+ 202) 33002200
Fax: (+ 202) 33045256
E-mail: sla@tagi.com

مكتب الرئيس

51 شارع الحجاز، الطابق العاشر، المهندسين، القاهرة، مصر
ص.ب: 96 إمبابة 12411، القاهرة، مصر
هاتف: 33002200(202+)
فاكس: 33045256 (202+)
البريد الإلكتروني: sla@tagi.com

# A

| | |
|---|---|
| aal | طبقة مواءمة وضع التحويل غير المتزامن |
| ab | جسم مضاد |
| abacus | أداة للعد |
| abandoned patent | براءة مهجورة او متخلى عنها |
| abatement of pain | تخفيف الألم |
| abatement of rent | إلغاء الإيجار |
| abdomen | بطن |
| abdominal | بطني |
| abdominal belt | حزام للبطن |
| abdominal corset | مشد للبطن |
| abdominal pad | وسادة لتدعيم البطن |
| abduction | إبعاد |
| aberrant | زائغ |
| abies koreana | التنوب الكوري |
| abietic acid | حمض الأبيتيك |
| abiotic | غير حيوي |
| aboriginal people's invention | اختراع خاص بشعب أصيل |
| aboriginal technology | تقنية أصيلة. تقنية الشعوب الأصلية |
| above boiling point | فوق نقطة الغليان |
| abr | معدل البت المتاح |
| abrasion | كشط |
| abrasion | سحجة (الجمع سحجات) |
| abrasive | كاشط |
| abrasive | مادة كاشطة |
| abrasive cloth | قماش سنفرة |
| abrasive paper | ورق سنفرة |
| abs | امتصاص |
| abs. | مطلق |
| abscissa | إحداثي سيني (أفقي) |
| absolute | نقي |
| absolute cartesian coordinate system | نظام الإحداثيات الديكارتي المطلق |
| absolute discharge | إفراج مطلق |
| absorb | يمتص |
| absorb | يمتص، يتشرب |
| absorbability | القابلية للامتصاص، القابلية للتشرب |
| absorbable | قابل للامتصاص |
| absorbance | امتصاص |
| absorbed | ممتص، مُستغرق |
| absorbency | المتصية، كون الشيء ممتصا أو ماصا |
| absorbent | ماص |
| absorbent | مادة ماصة |
| absorbent | ممتص، ماص، شيء ممتص |
| absorbent cotton | قطن ماص |
| absorbent wadding | حشوة ماصة |
| absorber | جهاز امتصاص؛ وحدة امتصاص |
| absorber | ممتص، متشرب |
| absorber of pollutive material | ممتص للمادة الملوثة |
| absorbing | ممتص |
| absorbing device | جهاز امتصاص |
| absorbing oil | زيت امتصاص |
| absorptiometry | قياس الامتصاص |
| absorption | امتصاص |
| absorption band | شريط الامتصاص |
| absorption coefficient | معامل الامتصاص |
| absorption columns | أعمدة امتصاص |
| absorption control | التحكم في الامتصاص |
| absorption mean free path | متوسط المسار الحر للامتصاص |
| absorption of technology | استيعاب التكنولوجيا |
| absorption spectrum | طيف الامتصاص |
| absorptive | ممتص، ماص |
| absorptivity | المتصية، كون الشيء ممتصا |
| abstract | ملخص تجريدي |
| abstract datatypes | أنواع البيانات المخصصة |
| abstract syntax | البناء التجريدي |
| absurd invention | اختراع سخيف |
| abt | تحويل كتلة وضع تحويل غير متزامن |
| abu dhabi fund for economic development | صندوق أبو ظبي للتنمية الاقتصادية |
| abundance | غزارة؛ وفرة |
| abusing patent | براءة تعسفية. براءة يستخدمها صاحبها بغية استغلال الناس استغلالاً غير مشروع |
| abut (against) | يرتكز (على) |
| abutting concave portion | جزء ارتكاز محدب |
| abyssal plains | سهول بحرية سحيقة العمق |
| ac | تيار متردد |
| ac adaptor | محول التيار المتردد؛ مكيف التيار المتردد |
| ac power source | مصدر (طاقة) التيار المتردد |
| academic achievement | تحصيل دراسي |
| academic paper | ورقة أكاديمية، ورقة علمية |
| academic patent | براءة أكاديمية |
| academy | أكاديمية |
| acceding defendant | خصم متدخل |
| acceleratability | قابلية الشيء للتسريع |
| acceleratable | قابل للتسريع |
| accelerate | يسرّع؛ يعجّل |
| accelerate | يُسرِّع، يعجل |
| accelerated | مُسرَّع، معجل |
| acceleration | تسريع، تعجيل |
| acceleration of gravity | عجلة الجاذبية |
| acceleration voltage | جهد تعجيل |
| accelerator | مادة مسرعة؛ مادة معجلة: تعمل على تسريع التفاعل |
| accelerator | مُسرِّع، معجل |
| accelerometer | مقياس تسارع؛ مقياس سرعة |
| accelerometer | جهاز قياس السرعة |
| acceptable technology | تقنية مقبولة. تقنية تستوفي المتطلبات التي تتطلبها قوانين التجارة الالكترونية |
| acceptor | مستقبل |
| acceptor human framework | إطار بشري لمستقبل |

| | |
|---|---|
| access | وصول (أو إمكانية وصول)، مدخل |
| access | إذن الوصول |
| access control list (acl) | قائمة التحكم في الوصول |
| access control system | نظام التحكم في إذن الوصول |
| access nodes | عقد الوصول؛ نقاط الوصول: نقاط وصول على شبكة تقوم بتفعيل الاتصال |
| access number | رقم وصول |
| access point | نقطة دخول |
| access privileges | امتيازات الوصول |
| access provider | مزود الوصول: شركة لتزويد المستخدم بحق الوصول إلى الإنترنت أو شبكة |
| access restrictions | قيود على إذن الوصول إلى شيء |
| access to database | إذن الوصول إلى قاعدة بيانات |
| access to information | إذن الوصول إلى المعلومات |
| access to knowledge | قناة الوصول إلى المعرفة |
| access to network | إذن الوصول إلى الشبكة |
| access to patent database | إذن الوصول إلى قاعدة بيانات براءتية ( براءات الاختراع ) |
| access to patent information | إذن الوصول إلى معلومات ( تتعلق ببراءات الاختراع ) براءتية |
| access to raw log files | الوصول إلى ملفات سجلات الصفوف: الوصول إلى إحصائيات الموقع بشكل خطي (سطور نصوص) بأقصى سرعة |
| accessibility | قابلية الشيء لمنح شخص إذناً للوصول إليه |
| accessible | يمكن إعطاء إذن لشخص للوصول إليه |
| accessible government | حكومة إلكترونية مفتوحة |
| accessible knowledge | معرفة يمكن الوصول إليها |
| accessible patent database | قاعدة بيانات يمكن الوصول إليها |
| accessible technology | تقنية يمكن الوصول إليه |
| accession | دنو، اقتراب |
| accession #; accession number | رقم الوصول |
| Accessories ; peripherals; auxiliaries | ملحقات؛ لواحق |
| accident insurance underwriting | إصدار سندات التأمين ضد الحوادث |
| accidental exposure to radiation | تعرض صدفي للأشعة |
| accidental invention | اختراع صدفي( اختراع غير مقصود او عرضي) |
| accidental inventor | مخترع بالصدفة |
| accl | كلوريد أسيتيل |
| accommodation (rental of temporary -) | محال الإقامة (تأجير محال إقامة مؤقتة) |
| accommodation bureaux [apartments] | مكاتب تأجير محال الإقامة [شقق سكنية] |
| accommodation bureaux [hotels, boarding houses] | مكاتب تأجير محال الإقامة [فنادق ونزل] |
| accommodation reservations (temporary -) | حجز محال الإقامة (حجز محال إقامة مؤقتة) |
| accomplice | شريك في جريمة |
| according to the method | وفقاً للطريقة المحددة في |
| regulated in | |
| account for | يفسر؛ يعلل: هو المسئول عن (عند التعليل)؛ هو ما يمثل (عند مقارنة نسب مختلفة) |
| accountability | محاسبة؛ مسئولية |
| accounting | محاسبة؛ علم المحاسبة |
| accounting machines | آلات حاسبة |
| accounting solutions | حلول محاسبة |
| accounts (drawing up of statements of -) | حسابات (تحرير كشوف الحسابات) |
| accumulator boxes | صناديق المركم |
| accumulator jars | جِرار المركم |
| accumulator tank | خزان تجميع |
| accumulators | مراكمات |
| accupoint control buttons | أزرار تحكم Accupoint |
| accupoint ii control buttons | أزرار نُقْطَةٌ وَخْزِيَّة 2 |
| accupoint ii secondary button | زر ثانوي نُقْطَةٌ وَخْزِيَّة 2 |
| accupoint ii-pointing device | جهاز تأشير 2 نُقْطَةٌ وَخْزِيَّة |
| accused | متهم |
| acetabulum | تجويف حقي |
| acetamidophenylboronic acid | حمض أسيتاميدو فينيل بورونيك |
| acetic acid-soluble palladium | بالاديوم قابل للذوبان في حمض الأسيتيك |
| acetone | أسيتون |
| acetonitrile | أسيتو نيتريل |
| acetylators | عوامل إضافة مجموعة أسيتيل؛ مؤستلات |
| acetylchloride | كلوريد أسيتيل |
| acetylene | أسيتيلين |
| acetylene burners | مواقد أسيتيلينية |
| acetylene cleaning apparatus | جهاز التنظيف الأستيليني |
| acetylene flares | شعلات أسيتيلينية |
| acetylene generators | مولدات أسيتيلينية |
| acetylene tetrachloride | رابع كلوريد الأسيتيلين |
| acetyl-nitrocellulose | سليولوز أسيتيل - نيترو |
| achieve | يحقق؛ ينجز |
| achromatic | أكروماتي؛ لا لوني |
| acid addition salts | أملاح الإضافة لحمض |
| acid chloride | كلوريد الحمض |
| acid hydrolysis | التحليل المائي الحمضي |
| acid hydrometers | هيدرومترات الأحماض |
| acid proof chemical compositions | تركيبات كيميائية مضادة للحمض |
| acid pump | مضخة حمض |
| acid scavenger | عامل كسح حمض |
| acid solubility | الذوبانية في الحمض |
| acid tanks | خزانات حمض |
| acidic amino acids | أحماض الأمينو الحمضية |
| acidified | حمضي؛ محمَّض |
| acidifier | عامل تحميض؛ محمِّض |
| acidify | يحوله إلى حمض: يحوله ليصبح حامضا |
| acidimeters for batteries | مقاييس حمضية البطاريات |
| acidity regulators | منظمات الأحماض |
| acidizing | تحميض |

| | |
|---|---|
| acid-labile | متحول بالحمض |
| acid-leach treatment | معالجة نض بحمض |
| acid-leached glass | زجاج منضوض بحمض |
| acid-leached sample | عينة منضوضة بحمض |
| acidulant | عامل تحميض؛ محمِّض |
| acidulated water | ماء محمض |
| acidulated water for recharging batteries | ماء محمض لإعادة شحن البطاريات |
| ack | إشعار بالاستلام؛ رسالة تأكيد وصول |
| acknowledgment | إشعار بالاستلام؛ رسالة تأكيد وصول |
| acne | حب الشباب |
| acne rosacea | العدة الوردية |
| aconitine | أقونيتين |
| acorn | بلوطة |
| acoustic alarms | منبهات صوتية |
| acoustic couplers | مقرنات صوتية؛ قوارن صوتية |
| acoustic signal | إشارة صوتية |
| acoustic velocities | سرعات صوتية |
| acoustic wave speeds | سرعات الموجة الصوتية |
| acoustical | متعلق بالصوت؛ صوتي |
| acoustical diaphragms | أغشية صوتية |
| acoustical panel | قاطوع (جاهز الصنع) عازل للصوت |
| acoustical tile | بلاطة عازلة للصوت |
| acquired neuromyotony | التشنج العضلي التوتري العصبي المكتسب |
| acquirer company | شركة أكوايرر |
| acquisition | استحواذ |
| acquisition of data | رصد بيانات: تجميعها |
| acquisitions | حيازات |
| acqusition of technology | الحصول على التكنولوجيا |
| acronym | اختصار بالحروف الأولى |
| acrylic | أكريليكي |
| acrylic resins | راتنجات أكريلية |
| acrylonitrile | أكريلو نيتريل |
| act | يفعل، يتصرف، يمثل، تمثيل، مرسوم، تشريع، قانون |
| act on | يؤثر في كذا |
| actinic radiation | إشعاع أكتيني |
| actinium | أكتينيوم |
| actinometers | مقاييس شدة الإشعاع (اكتينومترات) |
| action | تأثير، نشاط، فعل، دعوى قضائية |
| action potential | جهد الفعل |
| action potential conduction block | إعاقة نقل جهد الفعل |
| actionable data | بيانات قابلة للتحقيق |
| action-oriented thinking | تفكير ميال للفعل |
| actions | إجراءات؛ عمليات؛ أحداث |
| activatability | القابلية للتنشيط |
| activatable | قابل للتنشيط |
| activate | ينشط، يجعل الشيء حساسا للضوء أو ذا نشاط إشعاعي |
| activated attapulgite | أتابيولجيت منشَّط |
| activated carbon | كربون منشط |
| activated carbons | كربونات منشَّطة |
| activation | تنشيط |
| activator | منشط |
| activator | منشط |
| activator support | مادة حاملة لمنشط |
| activator-support | مادة حاملة لمنشط |
| active | نشط؛ فعال (مكون، دواء، مادة إلخ)؛ العامل الفعال؛ المكون الفعال؛ نشط، فعال |
| active basic | قاعدة نشطة |
| active catalyst | محفز فعال |
| active component of fluidized bed catalytic cracking catalyst | مكوِّن فعَّال في محفِّز التكسير الحفزي عند استخدام طبقة متميعة |
| active inducement | تحفيز نشط |
| active inducement to infringe | تحريض فعال للانتهاك. قيام شخص بتحفيز آخر تحفيزاً مؤثراً لانتهاك حق فكري. |
| active ingredient | مكون فعال |
| active moiety | جزء فعال |
| active patent | براءة فعالة |
| active principle | المادة الفعالة |
| active star | شبكة نشطة |
| active state | حالة فعالة |
| active wnt signaling | إصدار إشارات Wnt نشط |
| actively | بنشاط؛ على نحو نشط؛ بفعالية؛ نشاط |
| activity | نشاط |
| activity sensor | جهاز إحساس بالحالات النشطة المحيطة |
| acts | إجراءات |
| acts | تصرفات، مراسيم، تشريعات، قوانين |
| actual downhole fluid flow behavior | السلوك الفعلي لتدفق السائل أسفل البئر |
| actuarial services | خدمات تقييم المخاطر المالية |
| actuate | يشغل ميكانيكيا |
| actuate (by) | يشغل (بواسطة) |
| actuation | تشغيل |
| actuator | مشغِّل (بشري): شخص قائم بالتشغيل |
| actuator | مشغِّل (آلي): وحدة تشغيل |
| actuator | مشغل ميكانيكي |
| acupuncture | الوخز بالإبر |
| acupuncture needles | الإبر المستخدمة في العلاج بالإبر الصينية |
| acute | حاد |
| acute angle | زاوية حادة |
| acute leukemia | سرطان الدم الحاد |
| acute lymphatic leukemia (all) | سرطان الدم الليمفاوي الحاد |
| acute myeolid leukemia (aml) | سرطان الدم شبه النخاعي الحاد |
| acute myocardial infarction (ami) | احتشاء عضلة القلب الحاد: تجلط عضلة القلب الحاد |
| acute synovitis | التهاب الغشاء الزلالي الحاد |
| acute zoster pain | ألم العقبولة الحاد |
| acyclic | لاحلقي |
| acylazide | أسيل أزيد |
| acyloxy | أسيل أوكسي |
| acyloxyalkyl halides | هاليدات أسيل أوكسي ألكيل |
| ad | السنة الميلادية |

| | |
|---|---|
| ad allowable | الحد الأقصى الممكن لنفقات الدعاية |
| a-d converter | محول A-D أو محول من قياسي إلى رقمي |
| ad damnum | بدل العُطل والضَّرر |
| ad hoc arbitrator | محكم خاص |
| ad hoc arbitrators | محكمون خاصون |
| ad noting | ملاحظة إعلان |
| adamantan | أدامانتان |
| adapt (for) | يهيئ؛ يعد (لـ) |
| adaptable | قابل للتهيئة؛ قابل للتعديل |
| adaptable robotics | روبوتية قابلة للتكيف |
| adapter ; adaptor | مهايئ؛ موائم؛ مكيف |
| adaptive | تكيفي |
| adaptive control | أداة تحكم تكيفية |
| adaptive technology | تقنية تكييفية. يطلق هذا التعبير على التقنيات التي تستخدم في مساعدة أصحاب الإعاقات |
| adaptor molecules | جزيئات مهايئة |
| adcc | تسمم الخلايا المتوقف على جسم مضاد |
| added security | أمن مضاف |
| adding machines | آلات تجميع |
| addition polymerization | بلمرة بالإضافة |
| addition salt | أملاح إضافة |
| additional award | قرار إضافي. قرار تصدره هيئة التحكيم من تلقاء نفسها أو بناء على طلب من أحد الطرفين للفصل في مسألة لم يفصل فيها القرار الأساسي الصادر عنها بشأن النزاع |
| additional prior art | تقنية سابقة إضافية |
| additive | إضافة |
| additives | مادة إضافة؛ مضاف؛ مادة إضافية |
| additives | إضافات |
| additize | يدخل إليه مادة إضافة |
| additized fuel | وقود تم إدخال مادة إضافة إليه |
| additur | زيادة بدل العُطل والضَّرر |
| address book | دفتر العناوين |
| address mapping table (amt) | جدول تخطيط العناوين |
| address mask | قناع العنوان |
| address resolution | تحويل العنوان: تحويله من حقيقي إلى منطقي |
| address resolution protocol (arp) | بروتوكول تحويل العناوين |
| adduct | ناتج إضافة؛ مركب إضافة |
| adenocarcinoma | كارسينوما غدية |
| adenoid | غداني |
| adenovirus | فيروس غددي |
| adenylyl cyclase | الإنزيم الحلقي أدينيليل |
| adequate yearly progress (ayp) | التقدم السنوي الملائم |
| adhd | اضطراب نقص الانتباه وفرط الحركة |
| adhesion | تماسك؛ التصاق |
| adhesive bands | أشرطة لاصقة؛ رابطة لاصقة |
| adhesive plaster | لصقة |
| ad-hoc arbitration | تحكيم خاص |
| adiabatic | ثابت الحرارة؛ أديباتي |

| | |
|---|---|
| adiabatic expansion | تمدد ثابت الحرارة |
| adipocyte | خلية دهنية |
| adipose | دهني |
| adipose cell | الخلية الدهنية |
| adjacency | شيء متاخم، متاخمة |
| adjoin | يضم، يجاور، يحاذي؛ يرفع الجلسة |
| adjudged infringer | منتهك محكوم |
| adjust | يعدل؛ يضبط |
| adjust | يكيف، يتكيف |
| adjustability | قابلية الشيء للتكيف |
| adjustable | قابل للتكيف |
| adjustable wrench ; adjustable spanner | مفتاح ربط قابل للضبط: هذا المفتاح له طرف ثابت وطرف يمكن توسيعه وتضييقه |
| adjusting the exposure - exposure compensation | ضبط درجة الإضاءة – تعويض درجة الإضاءة |
| adjustment | توافق، أداة ضبط |
| adjustment shim | فلكة ضبط |
| adjutant (adjt) | أركان حرب الوحدة |
| adjuvant vaccine | لقاح مساعد |
| admin | إدارة؛ إداري؛ المدير |
| administrate (in association with) | يعطي (مع أو بالاشتراك مع أو في توليفة مع ) |
| administration | إعطاء (دواء، جرعة إلخ)؛ إدارة |
| administration | إدارة، تدبير شأن شئ |
| administration of testamentary trusts | إدارة صناديق الوصايا |
| administration route | طريقة الإعطاء |
| administrative domain | المجال الإداري |
| administrative license | ترخيص إداري. تصريح يصدر عن الجهات المعنية لتنظيم استعمال شئ ما. ووفقاً لاتفاقية التنوع البيولوجي، فمن الخصائص النمطية في سبيل تنظيم أنشطة الكائنات الحية المحورة فيما يتصل بالمسئولية عن الأضرار البيئية التي تسببها تلك الكائنات قامت بعض الأنظمة بتنفيذ قوانين خاصة توفر أساساً للمطالبة بتعويض عن الأضرار البيئية ومكافحة التلوث. كما قامت بعض الأنظمة الأخرى باستعمال نمط الترخيص الإداري، بما يتماشى مع خصائص الكائنات الحية المحورة والمسئولية الناشئة عن تحركاتها والتشريعات الخاصة بقطاعات الجينات أو التكنولوجيا الأحيائية كأنشطة تجارية تتعلق بالتعامل بالكائنات الحية المحورة (الاستيراد ـ النقل ـ البحث ـ الصنع ـ الإنتاج ـ النشر) وبما يتفق مع قانون البيئة وتكنولوجيا المعلومات. |
| administrative notes | ملاحظات إدارية |
| administrative receiver | حارس قضائي |
| administrative solutions | حلول إدارية |
| administrator | المدير |
| administrivia | معلومات إدارية |
| admiral | فريق بحري |

| | |
|---|---|
| admission | سماح، تسليم بـ قبول |
| admission control system | نظام التحكم في الدخول |
| admission of document | قبول مستند |
| admission of evidence | قبول دليل |
| admission of witness | قبول شاهد. قبول سماع شاهد في دعوى. |
| admit a crime | يعترف بالجريمة |
| admittance under coercion | اعتراف بالإكراه |
| admitte rifts with | يعترف بالخلاف مع كذا |
| admix | يخلط؛ يشوب؛ يمزج |
| admixing | خلط؛ مزج |
| admixture | 1. خليط؛ توليفة. 2. خلط؛ مزج |
| adoption agency services | خدمات وكالات التبني |
| adorants | مُعطرات |
| adrenergic | أدرينالييني الإثارة |
| adrenoceptor agonist | مساعد المستقبل الأدرينالي |
| adrenoleukodystrophy (ald) | سوء تغذية مادة الدماغ البيضاء الكظرية |
| adrenomyeloneuropathy | اعتلال الأعصاب النخاعية الكظرية |
| adry-lined construction | بناء بالجص |
| adsl | خط الاشتراك الرقمي اللاامتزامن |
| adsorb | يمتز |
| adsorb (onto) | يمتز (باستخدام) |
| adsorbability | القابلية للامتزاز |
| adsorbable | قابل للامتزاز |
| adsorbate de-hazed oil | الزيت الناتج عن الامتزاز والمزال منه الغبار |
| adsorbent | مادة ممتزة؛ مادة مازة؛ الممتزات |
| adsorption | امتزاز |
| adsorption of the fluid into the solvent | امتزاز المائع في المذيب |
| adult respiratory distress syndrome (ards) | متلازمة ضيق التنفس لدى البالغين (ARDS) |
| adult t-cell leukemia lymphoma | الورم الليمفاوي لسرطان الدم في الخلية T عند البالغين |
| adulterated milk | لبن مغشوش |
| advance directives | إرشـادات أو توجـيهات متـقـدمة |
| advance on the harvest | سلفة على المحصول |
| advance on the standing crop | سلفة على المحصولات الزراعية |
| advanced interactive excutive (aix) | الجهاز التنفيذي المتفاعل المتقدم |
| advanced networks and services (ans) | الشبكات والخدمات المتقدمة |
| advanced program-to-program communications | اتصالات برنامج إلى برنامج المتقدمة |
| advanced research projects agency (arpa) | وكالة مشروعات البحوث المتقدمة |
| advancing water flood front | موجة فيض المَاءِ المُتَقَدِّم |
| advantageously | على نحو مفيد أو من المفيد أن |
| adverse effects | آثار جانبية؛ آثار عكسية |
| adverse events | الحالات العكسية |
| advertisement boards | لوحات إعلانية |
| advertisement columns | أعمدة الإعلانات |
| advertising | الإعلان |
| advertising agencies | وكالات الإعلان |

| | |
|---|---|
| advertising by mail order | الإعلان عن طريق الطلبات البريدية |
| advertising material (updating of -) | مواد الإعلان (تحديث مواد الإعلان) |
| advertising matter (dissemination of -) | مواد الإعلان (نشر مواد الإعلان) |
| advertising patent portfolio | محفظة براءات متعلقة بالإعلانات |
| advertising platform | المنطلق الدعائي |
| advertising space (rental of -) | مساحات للإعلان (تأجير مساحات للإعلان) |
| advertorial | مقال دعائي أو دعاية على شكل مقال؛ مقال مدفوع الأجر |
| advice | مشورة |
| advisor | مستشار |
| advisory opinion | رأي استشاري صادر عن محكمة العدل الدولية. رأي قانوني غير ملزم |
| advocate | محامي (جنائي) |
| advocate | يدافع عن، يحامي عن، مؤيدون، مدافعون عن، محام |
| adware | 1. برامج الإعلانات المتطفلة/المزعجة 2. برامج الإعلانات التجسسية |
| adware detection | اكتشاف حزم البرمجيات الدعائية. رصد الحزم الدعائية التي ترسل إلى مستخدم الشبكة البينية دون طلب منه |
| aerate | يهوّي |
| aerate | يشبع الدم بالأكسجين |
| aerated water | مياه غازية |
| aerated water making apparatus | جهاز تصنيع المياه الغازية |
| aerating pumps for aquaria | مضخات التهوية الخاصة بأحواض الأحياء المائية |
| aeration | تهوية |
| aerator | جهاز تهوية |
| aerator | جهاز للإشباع بالأكسجين |
| aerial | هوائي |
| aerial | هوائي؛ جهاز هوائي |
| aerial | جوي |
| aerial and surface spreading of fertilizers | الرش الجوي والأرضي للأسمدة |
| aerial conveyors | وسائل النقل الهوائي: كالتلفريك مثلا |
| aerial perspective | منظور جوي |
| aerial robots | روبوت جوي |
| aerial surveying | مسح جوي |
| aerial vehicle | مركبات جوية |
| aerification | تهوية، تشبيع بالهواء، تشبع بالهواء |
| aerify | يهوي، يشبع بالهواء، يحول إلى بخار |
| aerobiosis | الحيهوائية، الحياة بوجود الهواء والأكسجين |
| aerocondenser | مكثف هوائي |
| aerodrome | مطار |
| aerodynamic | متعلق بالديناميكا الهوائية، أيرودنامي |
| aerodynamics | علم التحريك الهوائي؛ إيروديناميك |
| aerodynamics | الديناميكا الهوائية، الأيروديناميات |
| aerofoil (also airfoil) | منساب هوائي |
| aeroform | هوائي، غازي، وهمي |

| | |
|---|---|
| | علم الهواء |
| aerology | |
| aeromechanic | ميكانيكي جوي، خبير طيران |
| aeromechanics | ميكانيكا جوية، علم توازن الهواء وحركته |
| aeromedicine | الطب الجوي |
| aerometer | ميزان الهواء، أداة لقياس وزن الهواء وكثافته |
| aerometers | مقاييس كثافة الهواء |
| aeronautical | طيراني، متعلق بعلم الطيران |
| aeronautical apparatus | جهاز الطيران |
| aeronautical balloons | مناطيد الطيران |
| aeronautical engineering | هندسة الطيران |
| aeronautical engines | محركات الطيران |
| aeronautics | هندسة الطيران |
| aeroplane (also airplane) | طائرة |
| aeroplane engines | محركات الطائرة |
| aeroplanes | الطائرات |
| aerosol | الأيروسول: عقار سائل يستخدم كرذاذ عن طريق الاستنشاق |
| aerosol | الهباء الجوي، دخان |
| aerosol dispenser | جهاز توزيع الأيروسول |
| aerosol propellants | مواد دفعية للأيروسول |
| aerospace | فضائي، فضاء |
| aerospace engineering | هندسة فضائية |
| aerosphere | الهواء المحيط بالأرض |
| aerostatics | الأيروستاتيات، علم توازن الهواء والغازات وتوازن الأجسام المغمورة فيها |
| af academies | الكليات العسكرية |
| af authorities | هيئات القوات المسلحة |
| af technical institute | المعهد الفني للقوات المسلحة |
| affective disorder | اضطراب عاطفي |
| affective robot | روبوت عاطفي. روبوت معد على نحو يمكنه من محاكاة بعض المشاعر الإنسانية. |
| afferent axon | ليفة عصبية واردة |
| affibody | جسم أليف الارتباط |
| affidavit | إفادة كتابية مشفوعة بيمين؛ شهادة خطية بقسم |
| affinity | ألفة الارتباط (تُحسب بالمولار، بيكو مولار، غالبا) |
| affinity and avidity | الألفة والميل |
| affinity maturation | الوصول إلى الألفة |
| affinity matured ; affinity-matured | واصل إلى الألفة |
| affinity of antibodies for human il-17a | ألفة ارتباط الأجسام المضادة لـ IL-17A بشري |
| affinity of the antibody for non-human il-17a | ألفة ارتباط الجسم المضاد لـ IL-17A غير بشري |
| affinity purification | التنقية طبقا للألفة |
| affinity purify | ينقي طبقًا للألفة |
| affliction | إصابة |
| afford | يعطي؛ ينتج |
| aflp | واسمات تعدد شكل طول شظية مكبرة |
| african development bank | بنك التنمية الأفريقي |
| african development fund | صندوق التنمية الأفريقي |
| african regional intellectual property organization | المنظمة الإقليمية الأفريقية للملكية الفكرية. منظمة إقليمية تسعى إلى دعم مفهوم الملكية الفكرية في القارة السمراء. |
| afro-asian people's solidarity organizations | منظمة تضامن الشعوب الأفرو-آسيوية |
| after each run | بعد كل دورة (معالجة أو تجربة) |
| afterburner ; after-burner | وحدة الاحتراق اللاحق |
| after-cooling ; after cooling | التبريد اللاحق |
| after-effects | الآثار اللاحقة |
| aftermarket | إستراتيجية ما بعد التسويق: تُعنى بتقديم خدمات الصيانة والمتابعة في الغالب |
| after-shave lotion | غسول ما بعد الحلاقة؛ لوسيون ما بعد الحلاقة |
| afv | طلب إجازة |
| ag | أتو جرام |
| agar | آجار |
| agar-agar | أجار – أجار: غذاء هلامى لاستنبات البكتريا |
| agates | عقيق |
| age | يعتق؛ يعمر، عمر، عصر |
| ageing | تعتيق |
| agency | وكالة |
| agency of record (aor) | وكالة وسيطة؛ وكالة وكلاء؛ وكالة وكالات |
| agent | وكيل |
| agglomerates | نواتج تكتل |
| agglutinants for concrete | مواد ملصقة للخرسانة |
| agglutinants for paints | مواد ملصقة للطلاء |
| agglutinogen | مولد مواد ملصقة |
| aggregate | متكتل؛ متجمع؛ متراكم؛ تجمع؛ تكدس {للخلايا؛ إلخ}؛ يتجمع |
| aggregate formation | تشكيل متكتل |
| aggregation | تجمع؛ تكدس {للخلايا؛ إلخ} |
| aggressive cancer | سرطان سريع النمو. العكس indolent cancer |
| aggressive patent portfolio | محفظة براءات جرئية |
| aging | تعتيق |
| agitation | تقليب |
| agitators | وسائل تقليب؛ أدوات أو آلات تقليب |
| agonist | مساعد؛ مادة مساعدة؛ عامل مساعد |
| agonist antibody | جسم مضاد مساعد |
| agranulocytosis | فقد الكريات المحببة |
| agreement | اتفاق |
| agreement clause | بند تعاقدي |
| agricultural cooperative | جمعية تعاونية زراعية |
| agricultural credit | الإئتمان الزراعي |
| agricultural elevators | الروافع الزراعية |
| agricultural holding tax | ضريبة حيازة الزراعية |
| agricultural implements | المعدات الزراعية |
| agricultural lending | الإقراض الزراعي |
| agricultural machines | الآلات الزراعية |
| agricultural mechanisation | الميكنة الزراعية |
| agricultural rotation (policy, development) | الدورة (السياسة، التنمية) الزراعية |
| agro industries | الصناعات الزراعية |
| agro technology | تقنية زراعية |

| | |
|---|---|
| agrobacterium | بكتيريا نباتية |
| agro-physics | فيزياء زراعية |
| agrotechnology patent | براءة في مجال التقنية الزراعية |
| ai | إتاحة ذاتية |
| aid | عامل مساعد؛ مادة مساعدة |
| aid liability | دين المعونة المالية |
| aids related complex (arc) | المعقد المرتبط بالإيدز |
| aileron | جُنيح |
| air | هواء، يبث عبر الهواء |
| air academy | الكلية الجوية |
| air bags | الوسائد الهوائية: وسائل أمنية للاستخدام في العربات |
| air balloons | المناطيد الهوائية |
| air chief marshal | فريق أول طيار |
| air commodore | عميد طيار |
| air condensers | مكثفات هوائية |
| air conditioner | جهاز تكييف الهواء |
| air conditioning apparatus | جهاز تكييف الهواء |
| air conditioning apparatus installation and repair | تركيب وإصلاح جهاز تكييف الهواء |
| air conditioning installations | معدات تركيب مكيفات الهواء |
| air conditioning roof hatches relay | مرحل فتحات سقف مكيف الهواء |
| air control tower | برج المراقبة الجوية |
| air cooler | مبرد هواء |
| air cooling apparatus | جهاز تبريد الهواء |
| air cover | غطاء جوي |
| air cushion vehicles | المركبات الحوامة |
| air cushions | المخدات الهوائية؛ الوسائد الهوائية |
| air deodorising | تعطير الهواء |
| air deodorising apparatus | جهاز إزالة الروائح الكريهة من الهواء |
| air draft | دفع هوائي |
| air driers | مجففات هوائية |
| air dry ; air-dry | يجفف بالهواء |
| air duct | أنبوب هواء (في تكييف السيارة) |
| air ducting into the vehicle interior | أنابيب الهواء في داخل السيارة |
| air free stirring ; air-free stirring | تقليب مستمر بعيدا عن الهواء |
| air freshening | تجديد أو إنعاش الهواء |
| air freshening preparations | مستحضرات تجديد الهواء |
| air gun | مسدس هوائي |
| air intake | مدخل الهواء |
| air intake of the turbine | مدخل هواء التوربين |
| air link resource | مورد الربط الهوائي |
| air mail editions | طبعات ترسل بالجو |
| air marshal | فريق طيار |
| air mattresses | مراتب هوائية |
| air nailers | مسمرات هوائية |
| air pillows | وسائد هوائية |
| air pistols | مسدسات هوائية |
| air pumps | مضخات هوائية |
| air purification | تنقية الهواء |
| air strip | مطار حربي صغير |
| air tracker | رادار جوي |
| air transport | النقل الجوى |
| air valves | الصمامات الهوائية |
| air vehicle | مركبة هوائية |
| air vibrating | هز هوائي |
| air vice marshal | لواء طيار |
| airbrone | محمول جوًا؛ منقول بالهواء |
| air-conditionable vehicle | مركبة قابلة للتهيئة الهوائية |
| aircraft | طائرة |
| aircraft carrier | حاملة طائرات |
| airfield | مهبط المطار |
| airfield | مطار (حربي بخاصة) |
| airframe | هيكل الطائرة |
| airline | خطوط جوية |
| airlines | شركات خطوط الطيران الجوي |
| airospace patent | براءة في مجال الفضاء الخارجي. |
| airplane | طائرة |
| airplane maintenance and repair | صيانة وإصلاح الطائرات |
| airplanes | طائرات |
| airpouch | الجيب الهوائي |
| airships | مناطيد ذوات محركات؛ السفن الهوائية |
| airspeed (also air speed) | سرعة هوائية |
| air-spring bellows | منفاخ هوائي نابض؛ كير نابض |
| airtightness | إحكام الشّد |
| airtime ; air time | زمن البث |
| air-to-air missile (aam) | قذيفة جو -جو |
| air-to-surface missile (asm) | قذيفة جو-أرض |
| airway | مجرى هواء؛ مسلك هوائي |
| ais | نظام معلومات آلي |
| akinetic | غير متحرك؛ منعدم الحركة العضلية |
| aknldg | إفادة بالاستلام |
| alarm | جهاز التنبيه |
| alarm | ينذر، إنذار، جهاز إنذار |
| albite | ألبايت |
| albumin | ألبومين |
| albuterol | ألبوتيرول |
| alcohol burners | مواقد الكحول |
| alcohol starting material | مادة البدء المتمثلة في الكحول |
| alcoholate | كحولات |
| aldehyde | ألدهيد |
| alert | يرفع درجة الاستعداد |
| algae | طحالب |
| algicides | مبيدات الطحالب |
| alginic acid | حمض الألجينيك |
| algoneurodystrophy | ألم سوء التغذية العصبي |
| algorithm | الخوارزمية: طريقة حساب |
| algorithm | خوارزمية، لوغاريتم |
| alias | اسم مستعار: لعنوان انترنت أو بريد إلكتروني |
| alibi | حجة غياب؛ الدفع بالغيبة |
| alicyclic | دهني حلقي |
| alicyclic compounds | مركبات دهنية حلقية |
| alidade | جهاز المسح والرصد |
| alienation | نقل الملكية؛ تحويل الملكية |
| alighting | حط؛ هبوط |
| align | يحاذي، يصف، يضبط وضعية |

| | |
|---|---|
| align (with) | يحاذي مع |
| align the cartridges wizard | معالج محاذاة الخراطيش |
| alignability | قابلية الشيء لأن يتم ضبط وضعيته |
| aligned sequence amino acid residues | الوحدات البنائية للحمض أميني للمتواليات المتحاذية |
| aligned well production prediction models | نماذج تنبؤ متحاذية لإنتاج الآبار |
| alignment | محاذاة |
| alignment | ضبط وضعية |
| aliphatic | أليفاتي |
| aliphatic hydrocarbons | هيدروكربونات أليفاتية |
| aliquot | كمية متساوية؛ قُسامة |
| aliquote | تقسيم |
| alizarine dyes | أصباغ الإليزارين |
| alkali | قلوي: مادة قلوية؛ فلز قلوي |
| alkali earth metal ; alkaline earth metal | فلز أرضي قلوي |
| alkali metal hydroxide | هيدروكسيد فلز قلوي |
| alkaline | قلوي |
| alkaline earth component | مكون أرضي قلوي |
| alkaline earth metals | معادن أقلاء أرضية |
| alkaline metals | الفلزات القلوية |
| alkaline-earth metals | الفلزات الأرضية القلوية؛ فلزات التربة القلوية |
| alkalinize | يحول إلى الحالة القلوية |
| alkaloid | شبه قلوي |
| alkane | ألكان |
| alkene | ألكين |
| alkoxy silane grafted | مطعم بألكوكسي سيلان |
| alkyl | ألكيل |
| alkyl polyoxyethylene-polyoxypropylene block polymers | بوليمرات كتلية لألكيل بولي أوكسي إثيلين- بولي أوكسي بروبيلين |
| alkyl sulfonates | سلفونات ألكيل |
| alkylamine | ألكيلامين |
| alkylheteroaryl | ألكيل أريل غير متجانس |
| alkylheterocyclyl | ألكيل سيكليل غير متجانس |
| alkylnaphthenic hydrocarbons | هيدروكربونات محتوية على ألكيل نفثين |
| alkyloxy | ألكيل أوكسي |
| alkyne | ألكاين |
| alkynyl | ألكينيل |
| alleged infringer | منتهك مزعوم |
| allele | أليل |
| all-electric vehicle | مركبة كهربية كليا |
| allelic | أليلي |
| allergen | مولد للحساسية؛ مثير للحساسية |
| allergenic | مولد للحساسية؛ مثير للحساسية |
| allergen-induced asthmatic reactions | التفاعلات الربوية المستحثة بواسطة مولد الحساسية |
| allergic | مصاب بالحساسية |
| allergic | ناتج عن الحساسية |
| allergic conjunctivitis | الرمد الناتج عن الحساسية |
| allergic rhinitis | التهاب الأنف الناتج عن الحساسية |
| allergist | إخصائي الحساسية |
| allergy | الحساسية: مرض الحساسية؛ مرض فرط الحساسية |

| | |
|---|---|
| all-in-one main page | الصفحة الرئيسية للجهاز متعدد الإمكانات |
| allodynia | خلل الاستجابة (بخاصة للمؤثرات الخارجية) |
| allogeneic cell transplant | زرع خلايا من نفس المصدر |
| allograft | رقعة متجانسة؛ رقعة متماثلة |
| allograft rejection | رفض الجسم للرقع المتجانسة |
| allosteric modulators | المعدلات متباينة التجاسم |
| allotropic | تآصلي: موجود بشكلين مختلفين أو أكثر |
| allotropy; allotropism | تآصُل: وجود مادة (وبخاصة عنصر) بشكلين مختلفين أو أكثر. مثال: للكربون شكلان متآصلان هما الغرافيت والماس |
| allow to stir | يترك تحت التقليب |
| allow to warm | يتركه حتى يدفأ |
| alloys | خلائط؛ سبائك |
| alloys of common metal | سبائك (خلائط) من الفلزات غير النفيسة |
| all-season crops | محاصيل لكل الفصول: تزرع في كل الفصول |
| allspice | فلفل حلو |
| allyl | ألايل |
| allyl alcohol | كحول أليلي |
| almond confectionery | حلوى اللوز |
| almond milk for cosmetic purposes | ألبان اللوز المستخدمة في أغراض التجميل |
| almond oil | زيت اللوز |
| almond paste | عجينة اللوز |
| almond soap | صابون اللوز |
| alone or in combination with | بمفرده أو في توليفة مع |
| alopecia areata | القرع الجزئي |
| alpha (version) | ألفا (النسخة التطويرية) |
| alpha-amino acid; alpha amino acid | الحمض الأميني ألفا |
| alteration | تغيير؛ تعديل |
| alternate scanning | مسح متناوب |
| alternating current | تَيَّارٌ مُتَرَدِّدٌ |
| alternative dispute resolution clause | بند اللجوء إلى الوسائل البديلة لحل المنازعات |
| alternative dispute resolution lawyer | محامي مختص بالأطر البديلة لحل النزاعات |
| alternative embodiment | تجسد بديل. تجسد من بين تجسدات الاختراع الممكنة المختلفة |
| alternative embodiments of the inventions | تجسيدات بديلة للاختراع |
| alternative fuel | وقود بديل |
| alternative fuel vehicle | مركبة تزود بوقود بديل |
| alternative newsgroups hierarchy | هيكل المجموعات الإخبارية البديل |
| alternatively | كبديل لذلك؛ بصورة بديلة |
| alternatively or in addition | كبديل لذلك أو بالإضافة إليه |
| alternatively or in conjunction | كبديل لذلك أو بالإضافة إليه |
| altitude | ارتفاع |

| | |
|---|---|
| alum stones | أحجار الشب |
| alumina | ألومينا |
| alumina backbone | سلسلة ألومينا رئيسية |
| alumina blank | خام ألومنيا |
| alumina conveyor | ناقل ألومينا |
| alumina hydrosol | ألومينا به محلول مائي |
| aluminium | ألومنيوم |
| aluminium chloride | كلوريد الألومنيوم |
| aluminium foils | رقاقات الألومنيوم |
| aluminium hydrate | هيدرات الألومنيوم |
| aluminium iodide | يوديد الألومنيوم |
| aluminium paints | دهانات الألومنيوم |
| aluminium powder for painting | مسحوق الألومنيوم للاستخدام في الطلاء |
| aluminium silicate | سيليكات الألومنيوم |
| aluminium wire | سلك الألومنيوم |
| aluminosilicate glass | زجاج سيليكات الألومنيوم |
| aluminosis | السحار الألومنيومي: ترسب الألومنيوم في الرئة |
| aluminum industry | صناعة الألومنيوم |
| aluminum metaphosphate | ميتا فوسفات ألومنيوم |
| aluminum phosphate | فوسفات ألومنيوم |
| aluminum polyphosphate | بولي فوسفات ألومنيوم |
| aluminum-sodium phosphate; aluminum sodium phosphate; sodiumaluminum phosphate | فوسفات الألومنيوم الصوديوم |
| alveolar | حويصلي |
| alzheimer's disease | داء الزهايمر |
| amalgam | ملغم |
| amalgams | سبائك زئبق: للاستخدام في طب الأسنان |
| amateur inventor | مخترع هاوٍ |
| amber | عنبر |
| ambient air pressure | ضغط الهواء المحيط |
| ambient temperature | درجة الحرارة المحيطة |
| ambient well temperature | درجة حرارة البئر المحيطة؛ درجة الحرارة المحيطة للبئر |
| ambiguous patent claim | ادعاء خاص ببراءة غامض |
| ambroid bars | أصابع الغراء |
| ambroid plates | صفائح الغراء |
| ambulance stretchers | نقالات الإسعاف |
| ambulance transport | النقل للإسعاف |
| ambulances | سيارات الإسعاف |
| ambush | كمين |
| ambush | يوقع في كمين |
| ambush | كمين |
| amebiasis | داء الأميبة |
| amenorrhea | انقطاع الحيض |
| american innovators for patent reform | المبتكرون الأميركيون لإصلاح البراءات. جمعية أمريكية غرضها الإسهام في تحسين القوانين والتشريعات المنظمة لأوضاع البراءات. تأسست في 4 يونيو 2009 واتخذت نيويورك مقراً لها |
| american mobile phone system | النظام الأمريكي للهواتف المحمولة |
| american national | المعهد القومي الأمريكي |

| | |
|---|---|
| standards institute (ansi) | للمعايير القياسية |
| americium | أمريسيوم |
| amid | أميد |
| amidation | تكوين أميد |
| amido | أميدو |
| amine insertion (of, with) | إدراج أميني (باستخدام) |
| amino acid 23 n-terminal signal peptide | ببتيد إشارة لحمض أميني 23 عند الطرف N |
| amino acid residue | وحدة حمض أميني بنائية |
| amino acid residues | وحدات الحمض الأميني البنائية |
| amino acid salts | أملاح الأحماض الأمينية |
| amino acids | الأحماض الأمينية |
| amino polycarboxylic acids | أحماض أمينية عديدة الكربوكسيل |
| aminoazetidine | أمينو أزيتيدين |
| aminocarbonyl | أمينوكربونيل (كلمة واحدة) |
| aminothiazole regioisomer | أيزومر نطاقي لأمينو ثيازول |
| ammeters | الأميترات [مقياس التيار] |
| ammination | أمينة |
| ammonia | أمونيا: مادة قلوية متطايرة |
| ammonia gas | غاز الأمونيا |
| ammoniacal salts | أملاح الأمونيا |
| ammonium | أمونيوم |
| ammonium aldehyde | ألديهيد الأمونيوم |
| ammonium exchange | (عملية) تبادل أمونيوم |
| ammonium nitrate explosives | مفجرات نترات الأمونيوم |
| ammonium salts | أملاح الأمونيوم |
| ammoxidation | المعالجة بالأمونيا والأكسجين |
| ammunition | ذخيرة حربية |
| amnesia | فقدان الذاكرة |
| amnestic | نسياني |
| amnesty international, ai | منظمةالعفو الدولية |
| amoebic | أميبي |
| amorphous | غير متبلر؛ غير متبلور؛ غير بلوري (غير محددة الشكل) |
| amorphous material | مادة غير متبلرة |
| amorphous silica alumina | سيليكا الألومينا غير المتبلرة |
| ampa current | تيار AMPA |
| amperage | شدة التيار بالأمبيرات |
| amphibious airplanes | طائرات برمائية |
| amphibious tanks | دبابات برمائية |
| amphiphilic ; amphipathic | مزدوج الألفة: يألف الماء والمذيب العضوي |
| ampholytic | حمضي قلوي؛ أمفوليتي: متردد بين الحمضي والقلوي |
| amphoteric salts | أملاح حمضية قلوية |
| ampicillin | أمبيسيلين |
| ample | واسع، وفير |
| ampleness | اتساع، سعة، وفرة، إسهاب |
| amplifactory | توسعي، إسهابي، تضخيمي |
| amplified fragment length polymorphism (aflp) markers | واسمات تعدد شكل طول شظية مكبرة |
| amplifier | مكبِّر؛ مضخِّم |
| amplifier | مضخم |

| | |
|---|---|
| amplify | يكبّر؛ يضخم |
| amplify | يضخم |
| amplitude | سعة |
| amplitude | اتساع، وفرة |
| amply | بسعة، بوفرة |
| amprenavir | أمبرينافير |
| amps | المعيار المتطور للهاتف الجوال |
| ampul | أنبولة، وعاء زجاجي صغير |
| ampulla | قارورة، قازوزة، جراب |
| amu | وحدة كتلة ذرية |
| amusement | الترفيه |
| amusement arcade services | خدمات المباني الترفيهية |
| amusement parks | المتنزهات الترفيهية |
| amyl acetate | أسيتات الإميل |
| amyl alcohol | كحول الإميل |
| amyloid | نشواني |
| amyloid | نظير النشا |
| amyloid precursor protein (app) | البروتين المنتج للمادة النشوانية |
| amyloidosis | الداء النَّشَواني؛ داء شبيه النشا: مرض يتسم بترسيب مواد شبيهة بالنشا في خلايا الجسم وأنسجته وخاصة في الكبد أو الكلى، وقد يأتي مصاحبا لمرض مزمن مثل التهاب المفاصل الروماتيزمي أو الدَّرَن أو أورام النخاع العَظْمي. |
| amyotrophic | متعلق بالضمور العضلي |
| amyotrophic lateral sclerosis | تصلب جانبي ضموري |
| anabolic | بنائي |
| anaerobic | لاهوائي |
| anaerobic digestion | هضم لا هوائي |
| anaesthetic apparatus | جهاز تخدير |
| anaesthetic masks | كمامات تخدير |
| anaesthetics | مواد تخدير |
| analgesia | التسكين |
| analgesic | مسكّن |
| anallergic | غير مثير للحساسية |
| analog | تناظري |
| analog ; analogue | نظير (إنزيم أو مركب إلخ) |
| analog digital converter | محول تناظري رقمي |
| analogous art | تقنية مشابه |
| analogous prior art | تقنية سابقة مشابه |
| analogously (to) | بصورة مشابهة (لـ) |
| analogue circuit | دائرة متناظرة |
| analyses in laboratories | التحاليل في المعامل |
| analysis | تحليل |
| analysis (cost price -) | تحليل (تحليل سعر التكلفة) |
| analysis (financial -) | تحليل (تحليل مالي) |
| analysis for oil-field exploitation | تحليل ما يتعلق باستغلال حقول النفط |
| analysis of variance | تحليل التباين |
| analytical sem system with a motor control | نظام تحليلي مزود بتحكم دوار |
| analytical temperature rising elution fractionation (atref) | تقطير بالتجزئة للتصفية التتابعية الصاعدة لدرجة حرارة تحليلية. |
| analytics | تحليلات، هندسة تحليلية |
| anaphylaxis | صدمة الحساسية المفرطة: فرط الحساسية |
| anaplastic | فاقد للتمايز الخلوي: صفة لخلية فاقدة المعالم والخصائص المميّزة بسبب تسرطنها. |
| anaplastic | متعلق بجراحة التجميل |
| anaplastic oligodendroglioma | الورم الدبقي قليل التفرع فاقد التمايز الخلوي |
| anastomosis | تفمم |
| anchor | وسيلة تثبيت: بخاصة خطاف تثبيت |
| anchor | وسيلة تثبيت |
| anchor | مرساة: وسيلة تثبيت السفينة في مكانها |
| anchor | إرساء أو نقطة إرساء |
| anchor plates | صفائح تثبيت |
| anchor rod inspection | فحص قضبان الإرساء |
| anchor sector | قطاع تثبيت |
| anchorage | وسيلة تثبيت |
| anchorage | إرساء |
| anchovy | الأنشوجا |
| ancient invention | اختراع عتيق |
| ancillary | ثانوي؛ تابع |
| ancylostomiasis | داء الانكلستوما |
| andrew file system | نظام ملفات أندرو |
| androgenic | أندروجيني |
| anemometer | جهاز قياس سرعة الريح |
| anergy | تعطل |
| anesthetic | تخديري |
| aneurysm | أم الدم |
| angina | ذبحة |
| angina pectoris | ذبحة صدرية |
| angioedema | الأوديما الوعائية |
| angiogenesis | تكوين أو تكون الأوعية |
| angiography | تصوير الأوعية |
| angioneurotic edema | أوديما عصبية وعائية |
| angiopathy | اعتلال وعائي |
| angioplasty | تقويم أو ترقيع الأوعية |
| angiosarcoma | سركوما وعائية |
| angiotensin converting enzyme (ace) | إنزيم تحويل الموتر الوعائي |
| angle bracket | كتيفة زاوية |
| angle brackets | قوسي الزوايا |
| angle iron | مكواة بزاوية |
| angle of approach | زاوية اقتراب |
| angle of azimuth | زاوية سمت |
| angle of dip; dip angle | زاوية ميل |
| angle of repose | زاوية الإرتكاز |
| angle plate | لوح زاوي |
| angled away from the vertical | مائل بزاوية عن الاتجاه العمودي |
| angularly misalignment | سوء المحاذاة الزاوي |
| anhedonia | انعدام الشعور باللذة؛ عدم القدرة على الاستمتاع؛ وبخاصة جنسيا |
| anhydride | أنهيدريد |
| anhydrite | انهيدرايت: كبريتات الكالسيوم اللامائية |
| anhydrous | غير مائي |

| | |
|---|---|
| anhydrous ammonia | أمونيا لامائية |
| aniline dyes | أصباغ الأنيلين |
| animal | حيوان: وهناك صيغة ألطف هي: كائن حيواني |
| animal breeding | تربية الحيوانات |
| animal grooming | التنظيف والعناية بالحيوانات |
| animal litter | تبن الحيوانات |
| animal skins | جلود الحيوانات |
| animal training | تدريب الحيوانات |
| animals (boarding for -) | حيوانات (إيواء الحيوانات) |
| animals (slaughtering of -) | حيوانات (ذبح الحيوانات) |
| animated cartoons | الرسوم المتحركة |
| animated imagery | صورة محركة |
| anion exchange membrane | غشاء تبادل أنيوني |
| anion exchange resin | راتنج تبادل أنيوني |
| anion of a methyl | أنيون الميثيل |
| anionic | أنيوني |
| aniracetam | الأنيراسيتام |
| anise | يانسون |
| aniseed | بذر اليانسون |
| anisette | شراب اليانسون |
| anisotropic | مُتَبَايِنَ الخَوَاص |
| anisotropy | اللاتناحي؛ تباين الخواص اتجاهيًا (باختلاف المحور) |
| ankerite | انكرايت |
| ankle sprain | التواء الكاحل |
| ankylosing spondylitis | التهاب الفقرات المتصلبة؛ التهاب الفقرات المتيبسة |
| anneal | يلدن؛ يطوع |
| annealed | مُلدَّنة |
| annealed glass | زجاج ملدن: الزجاج الذي تم تعريضه لتبريد متحكم به لتقليل الإجهادات المتبقية وبالتالي يسهل قصه |
| annealing lehr | فرن تلدين (الزجاج) |
| annealing temperature | درجة حرارة التلدين |
| annihilate | يبيد |
| annotated | مزيَّل أو مزود بحواشي |
| announcement cards | بطاقات إعلانية |
| announcer | مذيع |
| annoybot | الروبوت المزعج |
| annul | يبطل، يجعله باطلا |
| annular | حلقي |
| annular drive ring | حلقة التدوير الحلقية |
| annular wire heater | جهاز تسخين سلكي حلقي |
| annulled arbitration award | حكم تحكيمي مُبطل |
| annulment | إبطال |
| annulment of arbitration awards | إبطال قرارات التحكيم |
| annulus | حيز حلقي؛ فراغ حلقي |
| annulus flow restriction device | جهاز تقييد التدفق خلال حيز حلقي |
| anode | أنود؛ مصعد؛ قطب موجب |
| anode batteries | بطاريات الأنود |
| anode beams | قضبان الأنود |
| anode exhaust gas line | خط غاز عادم الأنود |
| anode stems | سيقان الأنود |
| anodised | معالج بالطريقة الأنودية |
| anomaly | ظاهرة شاذة؛ حالة شاذة؛ شيء شاذ |
| anonymity | إخفاء الهوية |
| anonymous ftp | بروتوكل نقل الملفات مجهول الهوية |
| anonymous inventor | مخترع مغفول ذكر اسمه |
| anorexia | فقدان الشهية؛ قهم |
| anorexia nervosa | فقدان الشهية العصابي؛ الامتناع العصابي عن الطعام: حالة نفسية (تنتاب البنات عادة) تتسم بخوف المريض من تناول الطعام خشية البدانة. |
| anorthite | الانورثايت |
| anoxia | نقص أكسجين الأنسجة؛ أنوكسيا |
| answering (telephone -) [for unavailable subscribers] | الرد على الهاتف (الهاتف-) [للمشتركين غير المتواجدين] |
| answering machines | آلات الرد الآلي على الهاتف |
| antacid | مضاد الحموضة |
| antagonism (of the ... ) | التأثير المضاد (لـ ..) |
| antagonist | مضاد؛ عامل مضاد |
| antagonist antibodies | أجسام مضادة من نوع مضاد |
| antagonist antibody | جسم مضاد له تأثير مضاد |
| antagonization | تأثير مضاد |
| antagonize | يكون له تأثير مضاد ل؛ يقاوم؛ يضاد |
| antemortem | قبل الوفاة |
| antenna | هوائي |
| antenna rotator | مُدور الهوائي |
| antennas | هوائيات |
| anterolateral | الأمامي الوحشي |
| anterversion | التواء |
| anthelmintics | أدوية طاردة لديدان الأمعاء |
| anthracite | فحم الإنثراسيت |
| anthracosis | السحار الفحمي |
| anthrax warheads | رؤوس حربية تحمل الجمرة الخبيثة |
| anti shake indicator | مؤشر مقاومة الاهتزاز |
| anti-aircraft gun | مدفع مضاد للطائرات |
| antibiotics | مضادات حيوية |
| antibodies to lymphotoxin-alpha | أجسام مضادة لتوكسين ليمفي-ألفا |
| antibody | جسم مضاد |
| antibody antigen-binding site; antigen-binding site of antibody | موقع ربط جسم مضاد بمولد ضد |
| antibody constant region | منطقة ثابتة لجسم مضاد |
| antibody fab region | منطقة Fab لجسم مضاد |
| antibody fragments | شظيات (من) جسم مضاد |
| antibody humanization | جعل الجسم المضاد متوافقا مع البشري: تعديل الجسم المضاد ليتوافق مع البشر |
| antibody molecule vh or vl domain amino acid sequence ; sequence of amino acid of vh or vl domain of antibody molecule | متوالية حمض أميني لنطاق VH أو VL لجزيء جسم مضاد |
| antibody sandwich | الجسم المضاد المتداخل |
| antibody variable region | منطقة متغيرة لجسم مضاد |
| antibody-dependent cell- | تسمم الخلايا المتوقف على |

| | |
|---|---|
| mediated cytotoxicity (adcc) | جسم مضاد |
| anti-bogdonw | مضاد للتوقف الذاتي |
| anti-bribery clause | البند الخاص بمواجهة الرشوة. بند تعاقدي ينطوي على تعهد بعدم تقديم أي رشوة خلال تنفيذ العقد أو فيما يتصل به |
| anti-caking agents | عناصر مقاومة للتكتل |
| anticathodes | نظائر القطب السالب |
| anti-ccp | أجسام مضادة لـ CCP |
| anti-cd20 | أجسام مضادة لـ CD20 |
| anti-cheating patent | براءة مضادة للغش |
| anticholinergic | مضاد إفراز الكولين |
| anti-coagulant | مضاد للتجلط |
| anti-coking ability | القدرة على مقاومة تكوُّن الكوك |
| anticonvulsant | مضاد التشنجات |
| anti-corrosive bands | أشرطة مضادة للتآكل |
| anti-corrosive preparations | مستحضرات مضادة للتآكل |
| anti-corruption clause | البند الخاص الامتناع عن الفساد. بند تعاقدي ينطوي على تعهد بعدم القيام بأي ممارسات إفساد خلال تنفيذ العقد أو فيما يتصل به |
| anticryptogamic preparations | مستحضرات مضادة للنباتات اللازهرية |
| anti-cyclic citrullinated peptide (ccp) | أجسام مضادة لببتيد حلقي به |
| antibodies | مجموعة سيترولين |
| anti-dazzle devices | معدات مضادة للبهر |
| anti-dilution clause | بند عدم الإضعاف. بند تعاقدي يحمي المستثمر من أي إضعاف ناتج عن أي إصدار لاحق للأسهم بسعر أكثر انخفاضا من السعر الذي اشترى به المستثمر |
| anti-drugs department | مكتب مكافحة المخدرات؛ إدارةالمخدرات |
| anti-drugs squad | فريق مكافحة المخدرات |
| antiemetic | مضاد للقيء |
| antiepileptic | مضاد للصرع |
| anti-foam agent | عامل مضاد لتكوين رغوة |
| antifoams | مضادات المواد الرغوية |
| antifolate | مضاد حمض الفوليك |
| antifoulants | مضادات للاتساخ |
| anti-fouling paints | دهانات مضادة للاتساخ؛ دهانات مضادة لنمو الكائنات الفطرية |
| antifreeze | مادة مضادة للتجمد |
| anti-friction bearings | محامل مقاومة للاحتكاك |
| anti-frothing | مضاد للرغوة |
| antigen | مولد الضد؛ مستضد |
| antigen binding domain, antigen binding region, or antigen binding site | نطاق ربط مولد ضد، أو "منطقة ربط مولد ضد"، أو "موقع ربط مولد ضد": جزء من بروتين ربط مولد ضد يحتوي على وحدات حمض أميني بنائية (أو شقوق أخرى) تتفاعل مع مولد ضد وتساهم في نوعية وألفة بروتين ربط مولد الضد نحو مولد الضد. وبالنسبة لجسم مضاد يرتبط نوعيا بمولد |
| antigen-binding fragment | شظية ربط مولد ضد |
| antigen-binding site | موقع ربط مولد ضد |
| antigenecity | تكون مولد ضد |
| antigen-presenting cells (apc) | خلايا تقديم مولدات الضد |
| antigen-specific b cells | خلايا B الخاصة بمولد ضد معين |
| anti-glare | مضاد للبهر |
| anti-glucagon receptor antibody | جسم مضاد لمستقبل الجلوكاجون |
| anti-gravity patent | براءة مضادة للجاذبية |
| anti-horse-fly oils | زيوت مضادة لذبابة الخيل |
| anti-human fc antibody | جسم مضاد لـ Fc بشري |
| anti-human il-17 antibody | جسم مضاد لـ IL-17 بشري |
| anti-hypotensive agents | العوامل المضادة لانخفاض الضغط |
| anti-hypovolemic agents | العوامل المضادة لنقص حجم الدم |
| anti-idiotypic antibodies | أجسام مضادة للنمط الذاتي |
| anti-incrustants | مواد مانعة لتكوين القشور في الغلايات |
| anti-interference device | وسيلة مانعة للتداخل |
| anti-knock substances | مواد مانعة للدق |
| anti-lock braking system | نظام منع انغلاق المكابح |
| antimetabolites | مضادات للأيض |
| anti-micro rna molecules | جزيئات مضادة لـ RNA دقيقة |
| antimony | الأنتيمون |
| anti-myostatin | جسم مضاد للمايوستاتين |
| anti-neonatal fc receptor affibody | جسم أليف الارتباط مضاد لمستقبل Fc وليدي |
| antineoplastic | مضاد للأورام (الخبيثة) |
| antineoplastic drugs | العقاقير المضادة للأورام |
| antinephritic | مضاد لأمراض الكلى |
| antineuritic | مضاد لالتهاب الأعصاب |
| antinion | الجبين |
| antinuclear antibody ; anti-nuclear antibody | جسم مضاد للنَّوى |
| antio-riot police | شرطة مكافحة الشغب |
| anti-oxidant | مضاد للأكسدة |
| antioxidant ; anti-oxidant | مضاد للأكسدة |
| antiparasitic | مضاد للطفيليات |
| anti-patent | مناهض للبراءات |
| anti-patent lobby | تجمع استمالة مضاد للبراءات |
| anti-patent website | موقع شبكي مناهض للبراءات |
| antiperistalsis | الحركة الدودية للأمعاء في اتجاه عكسي؛ عكس الحركة الدودية |
| antipersiprant | مانع للعرق |
| antiphagocytic | مضاد للالتهام: مانع لالتهام الأجسام الغريبة بواسطة الخلايا الآكلة |
| antiphlogistine | مضاد للالتهاب: مادة تدخل في تركيب اللبخة وهي مهبطة للوجع والالتهاب |
| antiphthisic | مضاد للسُل الرئوي |
| anti-piracy agreement | اتفاق بشأن منع القرصنة |
| antipode | متقابلات |
| antipods | متقابلات |
| antipruritic | مضاد للهرش (الحكة) |
| antipyretic | مضاد للحمَّى؛ خافض لحرارة الحمَّى. |

| | |
|---|---|
| antique appraisal | تثمين التحف |
| antirabic | مضاد لداء الكلب |
| antirachitic | مضاد للكساح |
| anti-ragweed igg2a monoclonal antibody | جسم مضاد أحادي النسيلة IgG2a مضاد لعشبة الخنازير |
| antireflective | غير عاكس |
| antirheumatic | مضاد للروماتيزم |
| anti-rust treatment for vehicles | معالجة مضادة للصدأ في المركبات |
| anti-sa affibody | جسم أليف الارتباط مضاد لـ SA |
| antisense | مضادة لاتجاه النسخ: مضاد للتعبير الجيني |
| antisense oligonucleotide | أوليجو نيوكليوتيد مضاد لاتجاه النسخ؛ قليلات نيوكليوتيد مضادة للتعبير الجيني |
| antiseptic cotton | قطن مطهر |
| antiseptics | مطهرات |
| antiserum ; anti-serum | مصل مضاد |
| anti-shake (dis) | مضاد للاهتزاز (DIS) |
| anti-skid chains | سلاسل لمنع الانزلاق |
| anti-software-patent advocate | مؤيد مناهضة منح براءة عن برامج حاسبية |
| anti-solvent | مضاد إذابة |
| anti-spam software | برنامج مضاد للإزعاج |
| anti-splash tap nozzles | فوهات صنبور منع الرش |
| anti-spyware software | برنامج مضاد للأدوات التجسسية |
| antistatic preparations | مستحضرات لمنع الكهربائية الساكنة |
| antistatic; anti-static | مضاد للكهرباء الاستاتيكية |
| anti-surveillance software | برنامج مضاد للمراقبة |
| antisymmetry; anti-symmetry | عدم تماثل |
| anti-tacking ; anti-tack ; antitack | مضاد للالتصاق |
| anti-tank weapons | أسلحة مضادة للدبابات |
| anti-tarnishing chemicals for windows | كيماويات لمنع فقد النوافذ للمعانها |
| anti-tarnishing preparations for metals | مستحضرات لمنع فقد المعادن للمعانها |
| anti-theft alarm for vehicles | جهاز الإنذار المضاد لسرقة المركبات |
| anti-theft patent | براءة مضادة للسرقة |
| anti-theft warning apparatus | جهاز تحذير من السرقة |
| antithrombin | مانع للتجلط |
| anti-trombotic | مضاد للتجلط |
| anti-uric preparations | مستحضرات لتقليل حمضية البول |
| anti-viral | مضاد للفيروسات |
| antranilic acid | حمض الانترانليك |
| anvil | سندان |
| anvil | السندان: عظيمة السندان في الأذن |
| anxiolytic agent | عامل مزيل للقلق |
| anxiolytic effects | تأثيرات مزيلة للقلق |
| aor | منطقة المسؤولية |
| aorta | أورطي |
| apache web server | خادم أباتشي على الويب |
| apartment house management | إدارة المباني المؤلفة من عدة وحدات سكنية |
| apartments (renting of -) | غرف أو شقق سكنية (تأجير الغرف أو الشقق السكنية) |
| apas | اختبارات تقديم مولد الضد |
| apatite | أباتيت |
| apcs | خلايا تقديم مولد ضد |
| aperitifs | المشروبات فاتحة الشهية |
| apertometer [optics] | جهاز قياس فتحة العدسة [بصريات] |
| aperture | فتحة |
| apex of rice grain | قمة حبة الأرز |
| aphid | أرقة (نبات) |
| api | واجهة البرامج التطبيقية |
| api gravity | الوزن النوعي طبقا لـ API: الوزن النوعي طبقًا لمقاييس معهد البترول الأمريكي (API) |
| apical | قمي |
| apical surface (a) of cell monolayers | سطح قمة (أ) للطبقات الأحادية للخلايا |
| aplastic | لاتنسُّجي؛ متعلق بعَدَم التَّنَسُّج: غير قادر على النمو من جديد |
| aplastic anemia | فقر الدم اللاتنسجي |
| aplicable prior art | تقنية سابقة قابل للتطبيق |
| apolipoprotein | بروتين خالي من الدهن؛ بروتين غير دهني |
| apolipoprotein allele | أليل لصميم البروتين الدهني |
| apoptosis | موت الخلية، تلاشيها |
| apostille | شهادة توثيق أو تصديق |
| apparatus for artificial respiration | جهاز التنفس الصناعى |
| apparent bulk density | الكثافة الحجمية الظاهرية |
| apparent velocity | سرعة ظاهرية |
| appeal | طعن (قانون) |
| appeal hearing judges | قضاة جلسات الاستئناف |
| appellant | طاعن؛ طالب؛ مستأنف لدعوى |
| append | يلحق (بخاصة ملفا بنهاية ملف آخر) |
| appendicitis | التهاب الزائدة الدودية |
| appetite suppressants | مواد كابحة للشهية؛ مواد تحد من الشهية |
| apple attachment unit interface | واجهة وحدة مرفقات أبل |
| apple purée | بوريه التفاح (مهروس) |
| applet | برنامج صغير |
| appliance | أداة |
| appliances | أدوات |
| applicability | قابلية الشء للتطبيق |
| applicability test | اختبار التطبيقية |
| applicable | قابل للتطبيق |
| application | تطبيق، طلب |
| application key | مفتاح تطبيق |
| application layer | طبقة البرنامج |
| application program | برنامج تطبيق |
| application specific integrated circuits (asics) | الدوائر المتكاملة الخاصة بتطبيق محدد |
| applications | تطبيقات، طلبات |
| apply | يستخدم (وسيلة)؛ يطبق "كذا" على "كذا"؛ يعطي (دواء موضعي)؛ يدهن أو يوضع (كريم، إلخ) (موضعي) |

| | |
|---|---|
| applying disturbance (to fluid) | تسليط تشويش (على المائع) |
| applying finishes to textiles | القيام بتنشطيبات المنسوجات |
| appointed arbitrator | محكم معين |
| appointment clause | بند التعيين. بند تعاقدي ينص على قيام طرف بتعيين طرف آخر كوكيل أو موزع حصري أو مستشار أو غير ذلك |
| appraisal (antique -) | تثمين (تثمين التحف) |
| appraisal (art -) | تثمين (تثمين الأعمال الفنية) |
| appraisal (jewellery -) | تثمين (تثمين المجوهرات) |
| appraisal (numismatic -) | تثمين (تثمين القطع النقدية والميداليات والأوراق المالية) |
| appraisal (real estate -) | تثمين (تثمين العقارات) |
| appraisal (stamp -) | تثمين (تثمين الطوابع البريدية) |
| appraisals (business -) | تثمين (تثمين تجارى) |
| appreciate | يدرك |
| apprentice | صبي مهني؛ متمهن |
| apprenticeship | التمهن؛ التدريب على الصنعة |
| apprenticeship learning | التعليم المهني؛ التعليم الحرفي |
| approach | اقتراب |
| approach | طريقة؛ منهج |
| approach angle | زاوية الاقتراب |
| appropriate technology | تقنية مناسبة |
| approvals and consents clause | البند الخاص بالموافقات والتصريحات. بند تعاقدي يبين أن كلا من الطرفين قد استوفى الموافقات والتصريحات اللازمة لكي يبرم العقد ويكون إبرامه له صحيحا |
| approximate theory | خط نظري تقريبي |
| approximation sensor | مستشعر تقريبي |
| apr | تقرير معامل المواءمة |
| aprons | المئازر |
| aprons | وسائل لوقاية التروس: أجزاء من آلات |
| aprotic | غير مانح للبروتونات؛ لابروتوني |
| aq | مائي |
| aq ; aq. | مائي |
| aq. | مائي |
| aqua regalis | خليط من أنواع الماء المالكي |
| aquarelles | الرسومات بالألوان المائية |
| aquaria | أحواض تربية الكائنات المائية |
| aquarium | حوض سمك زجاجي |
| aquarium gravel | حصى أحواض تربية الكائنات المائية |
| aquarium heater | جهاز تدفئة أحواض تربية الكائنات المائية |
| aquarium hoods | أغطية أحواض تربية الكائنات المائية |
| aquarium lights | مصابيح إنارة أحواض تربية الكائنات المائية |
| aquarium sand | رمال أحواض تربية الكائنات المائية |
| aquatint | أكواتنت |
| aqueous surfactant micellar solution | محلول مائي لوحدة حيوية افتراضية خافض للتوتر السطحي |
| aqueous suspo emulsions | مستحلبات معلقات مائية |
| aqueous workup | المعالجة المائية |
| aquifer | مستودع ماء أرضي؛ مكمن مائي |
| aquit; release | يخلي سبيل |
| arab authority for agricultural investment and development, aaaid | الهيئة العربية للاستثمار الزراعي والتنمية |
| arab bank for economic development in africa | البنك العربي للتنمية الاقتصادية بأفريقيا |
| arab fund for economic and social development | الصندوق العربي للتنمية الاقتصادية والاجتماعية |
| arab fund for technical assistance of african and arab countries, aftaaac | الصندوق العربي للمساعدات الفنية للدول الأفريقية والعربية |
| arab gulf programme for united nations development organizations, agfund | برنامج الخليج العربي لدعم منظمات الأمم المتحدة الإنمائية |
| arable land | أرض صالحة للزراعة |
| arachis oil=ground | زيت الفول السوداني |
| aragonite | الأراجونايت |
| aralkyl | أرالكيل |
| aramco | شركة البترول العربية الأمريكية |
| arbitral advisory opinion | رأي استشاري تحكيمي. بيان غير ملزم صادر عن هيئة تحكيمية بإزاء مسألة عرضت عليها لتقديم ذلك الرأي. |
| arbitral award | حكم تحكيمي، قرار تحكيم |
| arbitrary unit | وحدة اختيارية |
| arbitration | تحكيم |
| arbitration award | حكم تحكيمي |
| arbitration clause | بند التحكيم. بند تعاقدي ينظم لجوء أطراف العقد إلى التحكيم بحسبانه وسيلة لحل أي نزاع قد يتمخض عن تنفيذ العقد أو يتصل بأي بند من بنوده. يشار له بشرط التحكيم ومشارطة التحكيم |
| arbitration code | ميثاق تحكيمي |
| arbitration code of ethics | ميثاق أخلاقي بشأن التحكيم |
| arbitration rules | قواعد التحكيم |
| arbitration services | خدمات التحكيم |
| arbitration tribunal | هيئة تحكيم |
| arbitrator | محكم |
| arbitrators | محكمون |
| arbitrator's neutrality | حياد المحكم. هو أن يكون المحكم طرفاً محايداً لا ينحاز لطرف على حساب الآخر، وعلى المحكم عند ترشيحه لأداء مهمته أن يثبت بقدر الإمكان مبدأ حياديته واستقلاله. |
| arbours ; arbors | المحاور |
| arc furnce | فرن قوسي |
| architectural consultation | استشارات معمارية |
| architecture | فن العمارة |
| architecture | بنية |
| archiving optimization | تحسين الأرشفة لأقصى مدى ممكن |
| are you on the net? | هل أنت متصل بالإنترنت؟ |
| area | منطقة؛ مساحة؛ سطح؛ نطاق، مكان،مجال |

| | |
|---|---|
| area ; region | منطقة |
| area of active scientific research | حقل يتسم ببحث علمي نشط |
| area of weakness | منطقة ضعف |
| area range | نطاق مساحي |
| area under the curve (auc) | المساحة تحت المنحنى |
| areal | مساحي |
| areas | مساحات، أماكن، مجالات |
| arenaceous rocks | بالصخور الرملية |
| argillaceous rocks | بالصخور الطينية |
| argillaceous sand | الرمل الطيني دقيق الحبيبات |
| argon | الأرجون |
| argon laser | ليزر به غاز أرجون |
| argument | معامل |
| arid | جاف |
| arithmetical tables | الجداول الحسابية |
| arkose | الاركوز |
| arm | ذراع |
| armament and ammunition authority | هيئة التسليح |
| armament solutions | حلول تسليحية |
| armatures | أعضاء الإنتاج الكهربائي |
| armchairs | المقاعد ذات المساند |
| armed organisation | تنظيم مسلح |
| armed robot | روبوت مسلح |
| armor cable | كبل مدرع |
| armored-car transport | النقل بالسيارات المصفحة |
| armour | المدرعات |
| armour plate | ألواح تدريع |
| armour plates | دروع |
| armour plating | تصنيع ألواح التدريع |
| armoured personnel carrier (apc) | ناقلة جنود مدرعة |
| armoured vehicles | مركبات مدرعة |
| arms | أسلحة |
| arms industry | صناعة الأسلحة |
| aromatherapy services | خدمات العلاج بالمركبات العطرية |
| aromatic heterocycle | حلقة غير متجانسة عطرية |
| aromaticity | عطرية: الخصائص العطرية |
| aromatics | العطريات: زيوت عطرية |
| aromatics = aromatic rings | الحلقات العطرية |
| arpanet | أربانت |
| arrack; arak | الأراك: مشروب كحولي آسيوي |
| arrangement | ترتيب |
| arrangement | ترتيبة |
| arranging and conducting of colloquiums | إعداد وإدارة الحلقات الدراسية |
| arranging and conducting of conferences | إعداد وإدارة المؤتمرات |
| arranging and conducting of congresses | إعداد وإدارة الاجتماعات العامة |
| arranging and conducting of seminars | إعداد وإدارة المنتديات |
| arranging and conducting of symposiums | إعداد وإدارة الندوات |
| arranging and conducting of workshops [training] | إعداد وإدارة ورش العمل [التدريب] |

| | |
|---|---|
| arranging newspaper subscriptions | إعداد اشتراكات الصحف |
| arranging of beauty contests | الإعداد لمسابقات الجمال |
| arranging of cruises | الإعداد للرحلات |
| arranging of tours | الإعداد للجولات السياحية |
| arrest | توقف (العضو عن العمل) |
| arrest warrant | مذكرة توقيف: أمر بالقبض على شخص |
| arrhythmia | عدم انتظام إيقاع القلب |
| arrhythmic | ناجم عن عدم انتظام إيقاع القلب |
| arrow mode | وضع السهم |
| arsenate | زرنيخات |
| arsenic | الزرنيخي |
| arsenic | الزرنيخ |
| arsenious acid | حمض الزرنيخ |
| arson | الحريق العمد |
| arsonist | مرتكب جريمة الحريق العمد |
| art | تقنية |
| art | منتج؛ مادة |
| art appraisal | تثمين الأعمال الفنية |
| art director | المخرج الفني |
| artefact ; artifact | مادة صناعية |
| arterial | شرياني |
| arterial blood pressure measuring apparatus | جهاز قياس ضغط الدم الشرياني |
| arterial hypertension | ارتفاع ضغط الدم الشرياني |
| arterial thrombus | جلطة شريانية |
| arteriosclerosis | تصلُّب الشرايين: حالة مرضية تتميز فيها جدران الشرايين بالغلظة والصلابة، فلا تسمح بمرور الدم بسلاسة، الأمر الذي يسبِّب الإصابة بضغط الدم المرتفع والسكتة الدماغية وأمراض القلب. |
| arteriosclerotic | متعلق بتصلب الشرايين |
| arteritis | التهاب الشريان |
| artery | شريان |
| artful | فني |
| arthalgias | آلام المفصل |
| arthitides | التهابات مفصلية |
| arthritis | التهاب المفاصل |
| article | رسالة: إحدى رسائل مجموعات الأخبار |
| article | منتج(مصنَّع) |
| article of manufacture | منتج مصنَّع |
| article of manufacture | منتج مصنع |
| artifical intelligence | الذكاء الصناعي؛ الذكاء الاصطناعي |
| artificial | اصطناعي |
| artificial breasts | النهود الصناعية |
| artificial coffee | القهوة الصناعية |
| artificial eyes | العيون الصناعية |
| artificial flowers | الزهور الصناعية |
| artificial fruit | الفواكه الصناعية |
| artificial garlands | أكاليل زهور صناعية |
| artificial honeycombs | أقراص العسل الصناعي |
| artificial insemination services | خدمات التخصيب الصناعي |
| artificial jaws | فكوك صناعية |
| artificial lakes | بحيرات صناعية |

| | |
|---|---|
| artificial limbs | أطراف صناعية |
| artificial minds | العقول الاصطناعية |
| artificial morality | أخلاقية اصطناعية |
| artificial morality of robots | أخلاقية اصطناعية للروبوت |
| artificial snow-making services | خدمات عمل الثلج الصناعي |
| artificial stone | أحجار صناعية |
| artificial teeth | أسنان صناعية |
| artificial turf | عشب صناعي |
| artillery | المدفعية؛ قوات المدفعية |
| artillery guns [= cannons] | المدافع |
| artillery preparations | تحضيرات النيران (المدفعية) |
| artisan creations | ابتكارات زخرفية. |
| artists (business management of performing -) | الفنانين (إدارة أعمال فناني الأداء) |
| aryloxyalkyl | أريل أوكسي ألكيل |
| arymy corps | فيلق |
| as a cream solid | في صورة مادة صلبة لونها أصفر شاحب |
| as a function of; as function of | في صورة دالة في |
| as a microfine powder for insufflation | في صورة مسحوق دقيق للاستنشاق |
| as a solid portionwise | في صورة مادة صلبة على أجزاء |
| as amber oil | في صورة زيت بلون بني مصفر |
| as defined | طبقا لما تم تعريفه |
| as defined by the appended claims | طبقا لما تم تحديده في عناصر الحماية الملحقة |
| as described above | طبقا لما تم وصفه أعلاه |
| as pale yellow liquid | في صورة سائل لونه أصفر باهت |
| asbestos | أسبستوس |
| asbestosis | داء الأسبستوس |
| ascariasis | داء الصفر؛ الاسكارية |
| ascas | محاسبة موقف التهيئة الآلية |
| ascii | آسكي: مجموعة رموز آسكي الشفرة القياسية الأمريكية لتبادل المعلومات" |
| ascii graphic | صورة آسكي |
| asciibetical order | ترتيب آسكي الأبجدي |
| asec | شركة هندسة النظم التحليلية |
| aseptic cotton | القطن المعقم |
| ash fouling | اتساخ بالرماد |
| ash melting point | نقطة انصهار الرماد |
| ash precipitates | رواسب الرماد |
| ashless | عديم الرماد |
| ashtrays | منافض رماد السجائر |
| ashworth score | مجموع نقاط آشورث |
| asic | دائرة كاملة محددة التطبيقات |
| asip | معالج محدد التعليمات والتطبيقات |
| aspect | سمة؛ جانب |
| aspect ratio | نسبة باعية |
| aspect ratio | نسبة الطول إلى العرض؛ نسبة الامتداد |
| asphalt | الأسفلت |
| asphalt paving | الرصف بالأسفلت |
| asphaltenes | مركبات الأسفلتين |
| asphalting | السفلتة: الرصف أو التعبيد بالأسفلت |
| aspirated supernatant | مادة طافية مستنشقة |
| assay | اختبار: تجربة؛ معايرة؛ مقايسة؛ تحليل |
| assay buffer | محلول منظم للاختبار |
| assemble | يجمع |
| assembled | مُجَمع |
| assembler | مجمع |
| assembly | تجمع، تجمع، المجمعة، مجموعة أجزاء آلية مجمعة، جمعية، جمعية تشريعية |
| assembly drawing | رسم تجميعي |
| assembly view | منظر تجميعي |
| assertive licensing | ترخيص تأكيدي |
| assess | يقيم |
| assessed valuation | تثمين تقديري: تقدير الضرائب على المال العقاري |
| assessed value | قيمة تقديرية: تثمين للعقار لأغراض الضرائب |
| assessment | تقييم |
| assessment report | تقرير التقييم |
| assessor | مقيم |
| assets | أصول |
| assign | يعيّن؛ يتنازل عن |
| assignability | القابلية للتنازل |
| assignable | قابل للتعيين، قابل للتنازل |
| assignable patent | براءة قابلة للتنازل، براءة يمكن التنازل عنها |
| assignation en référé provision | شرط أو بند تسهيل أو تسريع أو تعجيل الإجراءات |
| assigned | متنازل عنه |
| assigned numbers | تعيين الأرقام |
| assigned uplink traffic segments | الأجزاء المعينة لمرور اتصال صاعد |
| assignee | مُتنازل له؛ المتنازل له |
| assignment | تنازل |
| assignment agreement | اتفاق تنازل |
| assignment of patent application | تنازل عن طلب براءة |
| assignment of pre-employment works | التنازل عن أشغال ما قبل التوظيف |
| assignment system | نظام للتنازل |
| assignor | متنازل |
| assimilable | قابل للأيض (للتمثيل) |
| assist | يساعد |
| assistant | مساعد |
| assistive technology | تقنية مساعدة. يطلق هذا التعبير على التقنيات التي تستخدم في مساعدة أصحاب الإعاقات |
| associate | يساعد، مساعد |
| associate tenant | عضو مساعد مقيم |
| associated diabetic dyslipidemia | اختلال الدهون في الدم المتعلق بداء السكري |
| associated gas | غاز مرافق؛ غاز مصاحب |
| association | جمعية |
| association for computing machinery (acm) | اتحاد آليات الكمبيوتر |
| association of south east asian nations, asean | منظمة دول جنوب شرقي آسيا |

| | |
|---|---|
| astatine | الأستاتين |
| asthenia | الوهن |
| asthma | الربو |
| asthmatic tea | الشاي المخصص لمرضى الربو |
| astm | المواصفات الأمريكية لاختبار المواد |
| astm method d6822 | الطريقة D6822 وفقا لـ ASTM |
| astringents | مقابض الأوعية |
| astro-biology | البيولوجيا الفضائية |
| astro-chemistry | كيمياء فضائية |
| astrocyte | خلية نجمية |
| astrocytoma | الورم النجمي |
| astro-dynamics | ديناميات فضائية |
| astronautics | هندسة فضائية |
| astrophotography | الفوتوغرافيا الفلكية |
| asw | الحرب المضادة للغواصات؛ العمليات المضادة للغواصات |
| asylee | لاجيء: لأسباب سياسية أو دينية أو اضطهادية |
| asymetrical | اللاامتماثل؛ غير متماثل |
| asymmetric | غير متماثل |
| asymmetric carbon atom | ذرة كربون غير متماثلة |
| asymmetric center | مركز عدم تماثل |
| asymmetrical folds | الثنيات المحدبة والمقعرة غير المتماثلة |
| asymptomatic | مقارب |
| asymptomatic | عَديمُ الأَعْراض |
| asymptote | الخطّ المقارب |
| asynchronous transfer mode (atm) | نظام النقل غير المتزامن |
| asynchronous transmission | نقل غير متزامن؛ إرسال غير متزامن (للبيانات) |
| at 0 °c | عند درجة الصفر المئوي |
| at a high pressure | تحت ضغط مرتفع |
| at a high temperature | عند درجة حرارة مرتفعة |
| at an impeller speed | عند سرعة دفاعة مروحية |
| at commands | أوامر AT |
| at each occurrence | عند كل ظهور (لها) |
| at elevated pressure | تحت ضغط مرتفع |
| at high rpm | بسرعة دوران عالية |
| at off-design conditions | في ظروف خارج التصميم |
| at reflux; under reflux | عند الارتجاع |
| at room temperature | عند درجة حرارة الغرفة |
| at room temperature under a hydrogen balloon | تحت بالون من الهيدروجين |
| at spaced intervals | عند مسافات متباعدة |
| atactic | غير منتظم التكرار |
| ataxia | الاختلاج الحركي؛ الاضطراب الحركي؛ فقدان الانتظام: عدم اتساق الحركات الإرادية وفقدان السيطرة عليها بسبب خلل في الجهاز العصبي |
| atazanavir | أتازانافير |
| atelectasis | عدم تمدد الرئة؛ انكماش الرئة: عدم انتفاخ حويصلات الرئة بالهواء |
| athentication | توثيق؛ اعتماد |
| atherogenesis | تكون تعصدي |
| atherogenic | مسبب التعصدية |
| atheroma | التعصد (قلة سيولة الدم) |
| atheroma plaque | صفيحة عصيدية |
| atheromatous | عصيدي |
| atherosclerosis | التصلب العصيدي |
| atherosclerotic plaques | صفائح ناتجة من تصلب عصيدي |
| atlas | أطلس |
| atm | جوي |
| atm | وضع تحويل غير متزامن |
| atm | ماكينة الصراف الآلي |
| atmosphere of pressure | ضغط جوي |
| atmospheric chamber | غرفة ضغط جوي |
| atmospheric distillation | تقطير جوي |
| atmospheric distillation column | عمود تقطير تحت ضغط منخفض |
| and a vacuum distillation column | وعمود تقطير تحت ضغط منخفض |
| atmospheric pressure | الضغط المناخي |
| atmospheric sciences | علوم جوية |
| atom | ذرة |
| atomic | ذري |
| atomic absorption spectrometry | القياس الطيفي للامتصاص الذري |
| atomic absorption spectrophotometer | جهاز قياس طيف الامتصاص الذري |
| atomic clocks | الساعات الذرية |
| atomic magnetometers | مقياس للمغناطيسية ذري |
| atomic physics | فيزياء ذرية |
| atomic piles | المفاعلات الذرية |
| atomisers | بخاخ؛ مرذاذ |
| atomize | يحول إلى رذاذ |
| atomizer | جهاز ترذيذ |
| atopic | ناجم عن حساسية |
| atopy | الاستعداد للإصابة بالحساسية. قارن senstivity |
| atrial and ventricular arrhythmias | عدم انتظام الإيقاع الشرياني والبطيني |
| atrioventricular | أذيني بطيني |
| atrium | أذين |
| atrophy | ضمور |
| atropisomer | أيزومر بطيء التحول البيئي |
| att | مرفق |
| attach | يرفق (بخاصة يرفق ملفا في رسالة بريد إلكتروني) |
| attach (to) | يربط (بـ)، يوصل (بـ) |
| attaché cases | الحقائب الصغيرة: حقائب الوثائق والأوراق |
| attachements | مرفقات: ملفات مرفقة برسالة بريد إلكتروني |
| attachment | توصيل؛ ربط؛ إلحاق (جهاز بآخر مثلا) |
| attachment | جهاز ملحق |
| attending physician | طبيب معالج |
| attention deficit hyperactivity disorder | اضطراب فرط النشاط المصحوب بنقص الانتباه |
| attenuation | اضمحلال؛ توهين |

| | |
|---|---|
| attenuation per unit length of x-rays | الاضمحلال لكل وحدة طول من الأشعة السينية |
| attenuator operation, attenuate | إخفات الصوت؛ يخفت |
| attorney | وكيل ، محام |
| attorney at law | وكيل قانوني، محام |
| attorney docket number | رقم الحافظة |
| attorney general | المحامي العام |
| attorney's advice | مشورة محام |
| attorney-in-fact | وكيل |
| attractive force | قوة جاذبة |
| attractiveness-implementation difficulty (aid) analysis | تحليل العوامل المشجعة وصعوبة التنفيذ |
| attribute | سمة |
| attribution license | ترخيص نسبة |
| attrition | تفتت |
| au | أنجستروم |
| auc | المساحة تحت المنحنى |
| auction | يبيع بالمزاد العلني، مزاد |
| auctioneer | مأمور المزاد |
| auctioneering | البيع بالمزاد العلني |
| audibility | المسموعية، كون الشيء قابلا أن يكون مسموعا |
| audible | يمكن سمعُه |
| audible signals | إشارات يمكن سمعها |
| audience composition | تصنيف فئات الجمهور |
| audio and video | ملفات الفيديو والصوت |
| audio frequency | تردد سمعي |
| audio interface | سطح بيني سمعي |
| audio output device | جهاز مخرجات سمعية |
| audiovisual teaching apparatus | جهاز التعليم السمعي والبصري |
| audit | مراقبة؛ تدقيق |
| audit | تدقيق |
| auditing | مراجعة وتدقيق الحسابات |
| auditing solutions | حلول تدقيق |
| auditor | مدقق؛ ضابط إحصائيات التوزيع؛ شركة مراقبة التوزيع |
| auditor | مدقق |
| augers | أدوات الثقب اللولبي [عُدد يدوية] |
| augment | يزداد، زيادة |
| augmentability | القابلية للزيادة |
| augmentate | يزيد |
| augmentation | تعزيز - تدعيم |
| augmentation | إزدياد |
| auramine | أورامين |
| auranofin | أورانوفين |
| auricular fibrillation | الرجفان الأذيني الليفي |
| aurora | أورورا |
| authentic intellectual work | عمل فكري أصيل |
| authentic software | برنامج أصيل، برنامج موثوق فيه |
| authenticating works of art | إثبات أصالة الأعمال الفنية |
| authentication software | برنامج للتحقق من الأصالة. برنامج حاسوبي للتحقق من أصالة الأشياء والأشخاص. ومن أمثلته برامج التعرف إلى الصوت وبرامج التعرف إلى بصمة العين التي تديرها السلطات في المطارات للتثبت من شخصية المسافر |
| authority | مصلحة؛ هيئة؛ جهاز؛ إدارة؛ سلطة؛ مرجع |
| authorized | معتمد؛ مرخص له |
| authorized agents | وكلاء مفوضين |
| authorship agreement | اتفاق تأليف |
| auto | تلقائي؛ سيارة |
| autoantibodies | الأجسام المضادة الذاتية |
| autoantibody profiling | خصائص الجسم المضاد الذاتي |
| autoclave | أوتوكلاف؛ موصدة؛ جهاز تعقيم بالبخار المضغوط |
| autocrine | ذاتي الإفراز |
| auto-eject pull handle | مقبض سحبي للطرد الأوتوماتيكي |
| auto-generated | مولَّد تلقائيا |
| autogenous | ذاتي |
| autoignition temperature; auto-ignition temperature | درجة حرارة الاحتراق الذاتي |
| autoimmune | ذاتي المناعة |
| autoimmune cholangitis | التهاب قناة الصفراء ذاتي المناعة |
| autoimmune diseases | أمراض المناعة الذاتية؛ الأمراض ذاتية المناعة |
| autoimmune disorders | اضطرابات المناعة الذاتية؛ الاضطرابات ذاتية المناعة |
| autoimmune encephalomyelitis | التهاب الدماغ والنخاع ذاتي المناعة |
| autoimmune exocrinopathy | مرض الغدد خارجية الإفراز ذاتي المناعة |
| autoimmune hemolytic anemia | الأنيميا الحالة للدم ذاتية المناعة |
| autoimmune hepatitis type-1 | التهاب الكبد الوبائي ذاتي المناعة من النوع 1 |
| autoimmune hepatitis type-2 | التهاب الكبد الوبائي ذاتي المناعة من النوع 2 |
| autoimmune parathyreoidism | خلل التدرق ذاتي المناعة |
| autoimmune polyendocrinopathy-candidiasis-ectodermal dystrophy (apeced) | اعتلال الغدد الصماء المتعدد ذاتي المناعة-داء المبيضات -سوء التغذية المتعلق بالأدمة الظاهرة |
| autoimmune reactions | التفاعلات ذاتية المناعة |
| autoironic art | فن السخرية الذاتية |
| autolysis | تحلل ذاتي |
| automatability | قابلية الشيء أن يصبح أوتوماتيكيا |
| automatable | قابل لأن يكون أوتوماتيكيا |
| automate | جعل الشيء أوتوماتيكيا |
| automated | آلي؛ تم جعله أوتوماتيكيا |
| automated production | إنتاج آلي |
| automatic | آلي |
| automatic | أوتوماتيكي |
| automatic energy saving technology | تقنية المحافظة الأوتوماتيكية على الطاقة |
| automatic grapnels | خطافات آلية |
| automatic peptide synthesizers | وسائل تخليق الببتيد الآلية |
| automatic teller machine | آلة الصراف الأوتوماتيكي |

| | |
|---|---|
| automatically | تلقائيا: آليا |
| automation | جعل الشيء أوتوماتيكيا |
| automation system | نظام جعل الشئ أوتوماتيكيا |
| automatisms | خواص التشغيل الآلي |
| automative engineer | مهندس سيارات |
| automator | جاعل الشيء أوتوماتيكيا |
| automobile bodies | هياكل السيارات |
| automobile carpets | سجاد السيارات |
| automobile chains | سلاسل السيارات |
| automobile chassis | الهياكل المعدنية للسيارات |
| automobile hoods | أسقف السيارة |
| automobile lights | مصابيح السيارة |
| automobile tires; automobile tyres | إطارات السيارة |
| automobiles | السيارات |
| automotive industry | صناعة السيارات |
| autonomic | تلقائي؛ ذاتي |
| autonomous robot | روبوت ذو ذاتية |
| autonomous robot | روبوت ذاتي. روبوت يتمتع بقدرة عالية على التحرك على نحو مستقل |
| autonomous system (as) | نظام مستقل |
| autopsy | الصفة التشريحية |
| autoradiography | تصوير إشعاعي ذاتي |
| auto-reactive antibodies; self-reactive antibodies | الأجسام المناعية ذاتية التفاعل: أجسام مضادة ينتجها الجسم ويوجهها ضد نفسه |
| autoremailer | مرسل بريد إلكتروني آلي |
| autothermal | ذاتي الحرارة |
| aux | إضافي |
| auxiliary electrode | إلكترود إضافي |
| auxiliary exports | الصناعات المساعدة |
| auxiliary storage | مخزن ثانوي. مخزن على الخط يختلف عن الخزن في الذاكرة الرئيسية مثل القرص أو الشريط |
| avail | الزمن المعروض للبيع |
| availabilities (avails) | الوقت (أو الزمن) المعروض للبيع |
| availability | الإتاحة |
| average | يحسب متوسط |
| average dosage interval | متوسط الفترة الفاصلة بين الجرعات |
| average velocity | متوسط السرعة |
| average yield | متوسط العائد |
| average yield per cow | متوسط إدرار البقرة |
| aviaries | أماكن لتربية الطيور |
| aviation | طيران؛ ملاحة جوية |
| aviation aftermarket service | خدمة صيانة الطائرات |
| aviators | قائدو الطائرة |
| avidity | ميل (ارتباط)؛ ألفة (ارتباط) |
| avimer | أفيمر |
| aviso | مركب رسمي لنقل الرسائل |
| avo | آفو: يستخدم من أجل القياسات لبعض القيم التمثلية. يوجد أنواع للآفو: آفو مؤشر وآفو ديجيتال |
| avoid shock & vibration | تجنب الصدمات والاهتزازات |
| avoidant | انطوائي |
| award | قرار |
| awardability | حكم بالأولوية. حكم من يقرر الأولوية لصالح مخترع معين في حالة وجود نزاع قضائي بشأن عدد من البراءات حول الأولوية |
| awardable patent | براءة يمكن الموافقة عليها |
| aware | واع |
| awareness | وعي |
| awls | آلات الثقب؛ مثاقب |
| awnings | تندة |
| axial flow turbine | توربين محوري الدفق |
| axillary | إبطي |
| axis of rotation | محور الدوران |
| axle journals | مقاعد المحاور |
| azabenzotriazol | أزا بنزو تريازول |
| azadi | أزادي |
| azadicarboxylate | أزادي كربوكسيلات |
| azeotrope | يقطّر أزيوتروبياً |
| azeotropic | أزيوتروبي |
| azeotropic distillation | التقطير الأزيوتروبي |
| azeotropic mixture | خليط أزيوتروبي |
| azeotropping from toluene | الاستخلاص أزيوتروبيًا من التولوين |
| azeotropping with toluene | المعالجة أزيوتروبيًا بالتولوين |
| azepan | أزيبان |
| azetidin | أزيتيدين |
| azimuth | السمت |
| azimuth instruments | معدات قياس السمت |

# B

b&w أبيض وأسود
b.i.d مرتين يوميًا
b/o تعمل بالبطارية
b/s بت في ثانية
babies' bottles زجاجات رضاعة الأطفال
babies' diapers حفاضات الأطفال
babies' diapers of paper and cellulose [disposable] حفاضات الأطفال من الورق والسليولوز [للاستخدام لمرة واحدة]
babies' diapers of textile حفاضات الأطفال من القماش
babies' napkin-pants حفاضات الأطفال على شكل سراويل
babies' napkins فوط الأطفال
babies' napkins of paper and cellulose [disposable] فوط الأطفال من الورق والسليولوز [للاستخدام لمرة واحدة]
babies' napkins of textile فوط الأطفال من القماش
babies' pacifiers حلمات ماصة للأطفال
babies' pacifiers [teats] حلمات ماصة للأطفال [للرضاعة]
babies' pants سراويل الأطفال
baby baths [portable] أحواض استحمام الأطفال [أحواض محمولة]
baby carriages عربات الأطفال
baby carriages (covers for -) عربات الأطفال (أغطية لعربات الأطفال)
back ينسخ
back door الباب الخلفي
back extract استخلاص مرة أخرى؛ إعادة استخلاص
back extract يعيد استخلاص
back flush تدفق خلفي
back light الإضاءة الخلفية
back mixing مزج لاحق؛ الخلط الرجعي
back mutation طفرة عكسية
back non-entrance end of the container طرف عدم الدخول الخلفي للحاوية
back pressure ; backpressure الضغط العكسي
backboard لوح خشبي يوضع عند ظهر شيء
backbone سلسلة رئيسية
backbone cabal مجموعة الشبكة الكبيرة أو مج شبكة العمود الفقري
backbone network شبكة كبيرة؛ شبكة العمود الفقري
backcross to يحدث له تهجين رجعي في
backcrossing تهجين رجعي:تزاوج تبادلي مع (أب هجين؛ أب راجع إلخ)
back-end طرف خلفي
back-extract (with) يعيد استخلاص (باستخدام)
backfile data بيانات مؤرشفة
backgammon games العاب الطاولة
background الخلفية
background ركيزة
background خلفية
background check تدقيق أمني
background of the invention الخلفية التقنية للاختراع
background of the invention خلفية الاختراع
backing layer طبقة تبطين؛ بطانة أو طبقة دعم [حسب السياق]
back-lighting إضاءة خلفية
backlog الحطبة الخلفية، سناد، دعامة، تراكم
backout ; back out تراجع
backpacks الحقائب المحمولة على الظهر
backscatter تشتيت عكسي
backscatter visible light يشتت الضوء المرئي عكسياً
backsheet رقاقة خلفية
backslash الشرطة المائلة للخلف
backspace يتحرك (يتراجع) إلى الخلف
backspace key مفتاح التراجع للخلف
backspacing حذف خلفي
backspin التدويم الخلفي: حركة الكرة على نحو رحوي خلفي
backstay سنادة خلفية
backswept مرتد أو مائل للوراء
backteriologist عالم الجراثيم، عالم البكتيريا
backteroid جرثوماني، شبيه بالجرثوم
backtrack ينهج نهجا معاكسا
back-up software برنامج حماية
backward instructional design مردود تصميم العملية التعليمية
bacmid بلازميدة فيروس عصوي
bacon لحم خنزير مقدد أو مملح
bacterial expression التعبير الوراثي (عن كذا) في البكتيريا
bacterial leaf streak مرض التخطط البكتيرية
bacterial meningitis الالتهاب السحائي البكتيري
bacterial poisons السموم البكتيرية
bacterial preparations for medical and veterinary use مستحضرات بكتيرية للاستخدام الطبي والبيطري
bacterial preparations other than for medical and veterinary use مستحضرات بكتيرية للاستخدام في غير الأغراض الطبية والبيطرية
bacterial spoilage of milk التلف البكتيري للبن
bacterially expressed معبر عنه وراثيا في البكتيريا
bactericidal paints دهانات قاتلة للبكتيريا
bactericides مبيدات البكتيريا
bactericides (oenological-) [chemical preparations used in wine making] مبيدات البكتيريا (مبيدات البكتيريا الخاصة بصناعة النبيذ) [المستحضرات الكيميائية المستخدمة في صناعة الخمر]
bacteriological burden الإصابة البكتيرية
bacteriological cultures المزارع البكتيرية
bacteriological cultures (bouillons for -) المزارع البكتيرية (المرق المستخدم في المزارع البكتيرية)
bacteriological cultures (media for -) المزارع البكتيرية (الأوساط الخاصة بالمزارع البكتيرية)
bacteriological preparations for acetification المستحضرات البكتيرية المستخدمة في التخليل
Bacteriological المستحضرات البكتيرية للاستخدام

| | |
|---|---|
| preparations for medical and veterinary use | الطبي والبيطري |
| bacteriological preparations other than for medical and veterinary use | المستحضرات البكتيرية للاستخدامات غير الطبية والبيطرية |
| bacteriological weapons | أسلحة بكتريولوجية |
| bacteriology | علم الجراثيم، علم البكتيريا |
| bacteriophage | بكتيريا ملتهمة |
| bacteriostat | عامل مثبط لنمو البكتيريا |
| bacterize | يجرثم، يبكتر |
| baculiform | عصوي الشكل؛ على شكل عصا |
| baculovirus | الفيروسات العصوية |
| bad faith operation of a patent application | تسيير طلب براءة على نحو سئ النية |
| badges | شارات |
| badges [buttons] (ornamental novelty -) | شارات [أزرار] (شارات مزخرفة) |
| badges for wear, not of precious metal | الشارات المستخدمة في الملابس، ليست من المعادن النفيسة |
| badges of metal for vehicles | الشارات من المعادن للاستخدام في المركبات |
| badges of precious metal | الشارات من المعادن النفيسة |
| badian essence | عطر الباديان |
| badigeon | ملاط لسد الثقوب |
| badly established patent | براءة مؤسسة تأسيسا سيئ |
| badminton | تنس الريشة |
| baffle | حاجز: لتنظيم التدفق |
| bag filter | مرشح جيبي أو كيسي |
| bagasse | مُصاصة القصب التى تتبقى بعد استخلاص العصير، وتستعمل وقودًا وفى صنع الورق |
| bagasses of cane | لباب قصب السكر بعد عصره |
| bagasses of cane (agglomerated -) [building material] | لباب قصب السكر بعد عصره (اللباب المتكتل) [مواد بناء] |
| bagasses of cane [raw material] | لباب قصب السكر بعد عصره [مادة خام] |
| bagle | بيجلي: دودة فيروسية خطيرة |
| bagpipes | مزمار القربة |
| bags (conical paper -) | حقائب (حقائب ورقية مخروطية) |
| bags (game -) [hunting accessory] | حقائب (حقائب الألعاب) [ملحقات الصيد] |
| bags (garbage -) of paper or of plastics | حقائب (حقائب جمع القمامة) من الورق أو البلاستيك |
| bags (garment -) for travel | حقائب (حقائب الملابس) مخصصة للسفر |
| bags (mail -) | حقائب (حقائب البريد) |
| bags (net -) for shopping | حقائب (حقائب شبكية) مخصصة للتسوق |
| bags (nose -) [feed bags] | المخلاة (حقائب يوضع فيها العلف وتعلق في عنق الدابة) |
| bags (sleeping -) for camping | حقائب (حقائب النوم) المستخدمة في التخييم |
| bags (vacuum cleaner -) | حقائب (حقائب المكنسة الكهربائية) |
| bags (zip fasteners for -) | حقائب (السحاب المنزلق للاستخدام في الحقائب) |
| bags [envelopes, pouches] of leather, for packaging | حقائب [مظاريف، وأكياس] من الجلد ومستخدمة في التغليف |
| bags [envelopes, pouches] of paper or plastics, for packaging | حقائب [مظاريف؛ وأكياس] من الورق أو البلاستيك؛ ومستخدمة في التغليف |
| bags [envelopes, pouches] of rubber, for packaging | حقائب [مظاريف؛ وأكياس] من المطاط؛ ومستخدمة في التغليف |
| bags [envelopes, pouches] of textile, for packaging | حقائب [مظاريف؛ وأكياس] من القماش؛ ومستخدمة في التغليف |
| bags especially designed for skis and surfboards | الحقائب المصممة خصيصاً للزلاجات وألواح التزحلق على الماء |
| bags for campers | الحقائب الخاصة بهواة التخييم |
| bags for climbers | الحقائب الخاصة بهواة التسلق |
| bags for microwave cooking | الحقائب الخاصة بالطهي باستخدام الميكروويف |
| bags for washing hosiery | حقائب غسيل الملابس المحبوكة |
| bail | كفالة |
| bail entered | إتمام إجراءات الكفالة |
| bail payment | سداد الكفالة |
| bait (artificial fishing -) | الطعم (الطعم الاصطناعي الخاص بصيد الأسماك) |
| bait (fishing -) [live] | الطعم (الطعم الخاص بصيد الأسماك) [طعم حى] |
| bakers' bread baskets | سلال الخبز الخاصة بالخبازين |
| bakers' ovens | أفران الخبازين |
| baking | تكليس بالتحميص (في الكيمياء) |
| balance | الباقي |
| balance | يساوق، يحسب الفرق بين الميزات والسلبيات، يرصد الحساب، يتوازن، يتعادل، ميزان، وزن، توازن باقي الحساب |
| balance of payments | ميزان المدفوعات |
| balance shaft | عمود التوازن |
| balance weights for vehicle wheels | أثقال الموازنة الخاصة بعجلات المركبات |
| balanced data panel | مجموعة بيانات متوازنة |
| balanced line | خط (أوسلك ) متوازن |
| balancer | موازن |
| balances (precision -) | موازين (موازين بالغة الدقة) |
| balances [steelyards] | موازين [موازين قباني] |
| balancesheet | موازنة عامة |
| balancing apparatus | جهاز خاص بالوزن |
| balata | بلاطة [صمغ لزج جيد العزل مأخوذ من شجر البلاطة] |
| baler twine | دوبارة؛ لربط البالات |
| baling press | مكبس بالات |
| ball bearings | محامل ذات كريات |
| ball clay | طين لدن |
| ball mill | مطحنة بالكريات |
| ball rings for bearings | الحلقات الكروية في المحامل |
| ballast (v.) | فرش بالحصى : رصف |
| ballast (v.) | يوازن |
| ball-bearings | محامل كروية |
| balling guns | مسدسات متكورة تستخدم لإعطاء التحميلات للحيوانات |
| ballismus | حركة انتفاضية |

ballistic missiles صواريخ باليستية
ballistic weapons الأسلحة الباليستية
balloons مناطيد
balloons (air -) مناطيد (مناطيد هوائية)
balloons (dirigible -) مناطيد (مناطيد قابلة للتوجيه)
balloons (fabric impervious to gases for aeronautical -) مناطيد (قماش غير منفذ للغازات للاستخدام في المناطيد الطائرة)
balloons (meteorological -) مناطيد (مناطيد الأرصاد الجوية)
balloons (play -) مناطيد (مناطيد الألعاب)
ballot box صندوق اقتراع
balls for ball-point pens أطراف الأقلام على شكل كريات معدنية متحركة
balls for games الكرات المستخدمة في الألعاب
balls for games (small -) الكرات المستخدمة في الألعاب (الكرات الصغيرة)
balm of gurjun [gurjon, gurjan] for making varnish بلسم غورجين [غورجون، غورجان] لصنع الورنيش
balms for medical purposes بلسم للاستخدام في الأغراض الطبية [لتسكين الألم]
balneology علم الحمامات، علم استخدام الحمامات ومياه الينابيع المعدنية لأغراض طبية
balsam بلسم
balsam البلسم، مادة زيتية راتينجية عطرة تسيل من بعض الأشجار، مجزاعة
balsam (canada -) بلسم (بلسم كندا)
balustrading الدرابزين
bamboo الخيزران
bamboo curtains ستائر الخيزران
bamboo flutes الفلوت (آلة نفخ موسيقية) من الخيزران
banana fibers ألياف الموز
band قيد، رباط، شريط، عصابة، حزام، طوق، نطاق، نطاق من الذبذبات أو الأطوال الموجية، يربط بشريط أو عصابة، يتحد، يعتصب معتق من الذبذبات أو الأطوال الموجية.
band dryer مجفف شريطي
band saw مناشير شريطية
bandage ضمادة، يضمد
bandages أربطة
bandages (adhesive preparations for surgical -) أربطة (مستحضرات لاصقة للاستخدام في الأربطة الجراحية)
bandages (hygienic -) أربطة (أربطة صحية)
bandages (knee -) [orthopedic] أربطة (أربطة خاصة بالركبة) [جراحة العظام]
bandages (menstruation -) أربطة (أربطة خاصة بالحيض)
bandages (supportive -) أربطة (أربطة تجبير)
bandages (suspensory -) أربطة (أربطة تعليقية)
bandages [elastic] أربطة [مرنة]
bandages for dressings الأربطة المستخدمة في التضميد
bandages for joints [anatomical] أربطة للمفاصل [تشريح]
bandana باندانا: منديل مزدان بالرسوم
bandanas [neckerchiefs] مناديل مزدانة بالرسوم [مناديل للرقبة]
bandoliers أحزمة عريضة الكتف
bandoliers for weapons أحزمة عريضة للكتف مخصصة لحمل الأسلحة
bandonions آلة الباندونيون (آلة موسيقية)
band-pass filter مرشح إمرار نطاقي
bands أربطة؛ شرائط
bands (adhesive -) for pulleys شرائط (شرائط لاصقة) للاستخدام في البكرات
bands (anti-corrosive -) أربطة (أربطة مضادة للتآكل)
bands (expanding -) for holding sleeves أربطة (أربطة مطاطة) للاستخدام في مسك الأكمام
bands (hair -) أربطة (أربطة الشعر)
bands for wheel hubs أربطة محاور العجلات
bands of leather أربطة من الجلد
bands of metal for tying-up purposes أربطة من المعدن للاستخدام في أغراض الربط
bands of rubber for unscrewing jar lids أربطة من المطاط لفك أغطية الجِرار
bands, not of metal, for wrapping or binding أربطة، ليست من المعادن، تستخدم في اللف أو الربط
bands; band cells خلايا الدم البيضاء غير الناضجة (الخلايا المأطورة)
bandwidth عرض النطاق؛ سعة العرض الموجي (للاتصال الشبكي): وبخاصة عرض نطاق الترددات
bandwidth hog ملتهم لموارد الإنترنت، ملتهم لسعة العرض الموجي للاتصال الشبكي: كل من أو ما يستهلك مقدارا من موارد الإنترنت أكبر من القدرة التي يشارك بها عليها."
bandy متقوس
bang أزيز؛ صوت: إشارة على هيئة أزيز
banister درابزين
banister rail سياج درابزين
bank بنك؛ رُكام؛ ضفة
banned محظور: فُرض عليه حظر
banned party (outlawed) حزب محظور
banner راية
bar قضيب، يسد، يعترض، عائق، حاجز، عقبة، نقابة
bar abs بار مطلق
bar abs. بار مطلق
bar chart ; bar graph ; bar diagram منحنى بالأعمدة البيانية؛ مخطط بالأعمدة البيانية؛ خريطة الأعمدة البيانية: خريطة الاعمدة ( لوحة الاعمدة)؛ لوحة المراقبة
bar code reader جهاز قراءة شفرة أعمدة
bara بار مطلق
barb شوكة، يزود السهم بشوكة
barbecue شواية
barbecue grills الشوايات
barbecue grills (lava rocks for use in -) الشوايات (أحجار اللافا المستخدمة في الشوايات)

| | |
|---|---|
| barbed wire | الأسلاك الشائكة |
| bar-bells | الأثقال المستخدمة في رياضة رفع الأثقال |
| bare fiber | ليفة عارية |
| barg | بار بالمقياس |
| barge | صندل؛ مركب بضائع |
| barium | الباريوم |
| barium compounds | مركبات الباريوم |
| barium sulphate | كبريتات الباريوم |
| bark (quillaia -) for washing | لحاء (لحاء شجرة الكويلية) للاستخدام في الغسيل |
| bark coverings for sound insulation | أغطية من اللحاء تستخدم في عزل الصوت |
| barks | اللحاء |
| barks (raw -) | اللحاء (اللحاء الخام) |
| barley | الشعير |
| barley (crushed -) | الشعير (شعير مطحون) |
| barley (husked -) | الشعير (شعير مقشر) |
| barley meal | مجروش الشعير |
| barn | ردة الأرز |
| barn flakes | قشارات الردة |
| barnacles | القشريات البحرية: حيوانات قشرية تلتصق بالصخور والسفن والحيوانات وغيرها |
| barometer | البارومتر |
| baron | بارون |
| baroque building | المبنى الباروكي |
| barrages (weirs) | قناطر |
| barred | مزلج: مدعم بمزلاج أو أكثر، مسدود |
| barrel | ماسورة؛ أنبوب |
| barrel | ماسورة البندقية |
| barrel | برميل |
| barrel | برميل، ملء برميل، مقدار ضخم، أسطوانة، جزء اسطواني، أنبوبة قلم حبر |
| barrel hoops | الإطارات الاسطوانية |
| barrel organs | الأرغن اليدوي |
| barrels (gun -) | مواسير (مواسير الأسلحة) |
| barrels (rifle -) | مواسير (مواسير البندقية) |
| barrels [clock- and watchmaking] | إطارات الساعات [لصناعة ساعات الحائط وساعات اليد] |
| barrel-shaped | (على شكل) برميل (للطيات) |
| barrettes [hair-slides] | مشابك لشعر المرأة [بنس] |
| barricades | سدادات طرق |
| barrier | حاجز |
| barrier materials | مواد حاجزة |
| barriers (crash -) of metal for roads | حواجز (حواجز الاصطدام) من المعدن ومستخدمة في الطرق |
| barriers (floating anti-pollution -) | حواجز (حواجز طافية مضادة للتلوث) |
| bars (cutting -) | قضبان (قضبان القطع) |
| bars (latch -) of metal | قضبان (متراس الباب) من المعدن |
| bars (torsion -) for vehicles | قضبان (قضبان ملتوية) للاستخدام في المركبات |
| bars for metal railings | القضبان المستخدمة في القضبان المعدنية للسكك الحديدية |
| bart simpson | بارت سيمبسون، من رسم آسكي |
| baryta | باريتا [مركبات الباريوم] |
| baryta paper | ورق الباريتا |

| | |
|---|---|
| barytes | كبريتات الباريوم الطبيعية |
| basal | قاعدي |
| basal lamina | صفيحة قاعدية |
| basalioma | الورم القاعدي |
| base | قاعدة |
| base addition salt | ملح إضافة لقاعدة |
| base line | الخط القاعدي |
| base metal | معدن أساسي؛ معدن خسيس؛ |
| base number | عدد قاعدي |
| base oil | زيت أولي |
| base station | محطة قاعدة؛ محطة قاعدية |
| base yarn | خيط أساس |
| baseball gloves | قفازات البيسبول |
| baseband | النطاق الموجي الآساسي؛ سعة العرض الموجي الآساسي |
| baseband network | شبكة عريضة الأساس |
| based licensing | ترخيص ذو أساس |
| based on | على أساس؛ بالاعتماد على؛ استنادا إلى |
| base-labile | متحول بالقاعدة |
| baseline | القيمة الأولية؛ خط القاعدة؛ الخط الأساسي؛ البداية؛ خط المعايرة |
| basemat | الحصيرة الملاطية الأساسية |
| baseplate | صفيحة القاعدة؛ لوح القاعدة |
| bases [chemical preparations] | القواعد [مستحضرات كيميائية] |
| basestock | خام تغذية أساسي |
| basic | قاعدي |
| basic | أساسي |
| basic addition salt | ملح إضافة لقاعدة |
| basic drug | العقار الأساسي |
| basic encoding rules (ber) | قواعد التشفير الأساسية |
| basic fluid; base fluid | مائع اساسي |
| basic gallate of bismuth | الجالات القاعدية من البزموث |
| basic material ; basic substance | المادة القاعدية |
| basic nitrogen | نيتروجين قاعدي |
| basic rate interface (bri) | واجهة السرعة الأساسية |
| basicity | توافر قاعدة |
| basidial | دعامي، ذو دعامة |
| basifixed | قاعدي: متصل بالقاعدة أو مثبت بها |
| basify | يقوعد؛ يحول إلى قاعدة؛ يتم تحويله ليصبح قلويا |
| basin irrigation, perennial irrigation, tile irrigation | ري الحياض، ري دائم، ري مغطي (بالمواسير) |
| basins | أحواض |
| basophils | خلايا قاعدية |
| bass drum sticks | عصى الطبلة الكبيرة |
| basses [musical instruments] | آلات القرار [آلات موسيقية] |
| bassinettes | مهاد الأطفال شبيهة بالسلة |
| basting spoons, for kitchen use | ملاعق تطرية اللحم للاستخدام في المطبخ |
| batch | دفعة |
| batch processing | معالجة دفعية |
| batch reactor | مفاعل صهريجي |
| bate for dressing skins | النقع في كيماويات لمعالجة الجلود |
| bath | حمام؛ حوض استحمام |
| bath (therapeutic | الحمام (مستحضرات علاجية |

preparations for the -) للاستخدام في الحمام )

bath fittings تجهيزات الحمام
bath fittings (hot air -) تجهيزات الحمام (هواء ساخن لتجهيزات الحمام)
bath installations تركيبات الحمام
bath installations (sauna -) تركيبات الحمام (تركيبات الساونا في الحمام)
bath linen بياضات الحمام
bath mats حُصر الحمام
bath plumbing fixtures تجهيزات/مثبتات السباكة في الحمام
bath robes برانس الحمام
bath sandals صنادل الحمام
bath slippers خُفّ الحمام، "شبشب" الحمام
bath tubs أحواض الاستحمام
bath tubs for sitz baths أحواض الاستحمام للاستخدام في أحواض الاستحمام النصفية
bathe يغسل كذا (أو يشرّب )
bathing caps قلنسوة السباحة
bathing drawers سراويل السباحة
bathing suits أثواب السباحة
bathing trunks سراويل السباحة القصيرة للرجال
baths (baby -) [portable] أحواض الاستحمام (أحواض استحمام الأطفال) [قابلة للحمل]
baths (bird -) [structures of metal] أحواض الاستحمام (أحواض استحمام الطيور) [هياكل من المعدن]
baths (fixing -) [photography] مغاطس (مغاطس تثبيت) [في التصوير الفوتوغرافي]
baths (heaters for -) مغاطس (أجهزة تسخين المغاطس)
baths (oxygen -) مغاطس (مغاطس الأكسجين)
baths (salts for mineral water -) مغاطس (الأملاح المستخدمة في مغاطس المياه المعدنية)
baths (spa -) [vessels] مغاطس ( مغاطس ينابيع المياه المعدنية) [أوعية]
baths (toning -) [photography] مغاطس (مغاطس التلوين) [في التصوير الفوتوغرافي]
baths for galvanizing مغاطس للجلفنة
batons (conductors' -) المخصرة [عصا قائد الفرقة الموسيقية]
bats for games مضارب الألعاب المختلفة
battalion كتيبة
batteries (acidulated water for recharging -) بطاريات(ماء محمض لإعادة شحن البطاريات)
batteries (anti-frothing solutions for -) البطاريات (المحاليل المضادة للتجمد في البطاريات)
batteries (liquids for removing sulphates from-) بطاريات (السوائل المستخدمة في إزالة الكبريتات من البطاريات)
batteries (salts for galvanic -) بطاريات (الأملاح المستخدمة في البطاريات المجلفنة)
batteries for lighting بطاريات تستخدم في الإنارة
batteries for pocketlamps بطاريات للاستخدام في مصابيح الجيب اليدوية
batteries, electric بطاريات كهربائية
batteries, electric, for vehicles بطاريات كهربائية للاستخدام في المركبات
battery بطارية؛ سرية مدفعية
battery boxes علب البطارية
battery charger شاحن البطارية
battery jars أوعية البطاريات
battery life indicator مؤشر عمر البطارية
battery release latch مزلاج تحرير البطارية
battery slot فتحة البطارية
batting gloves قفازات ضرب الكرة
battleship بارجة
bauxite البوكسايت
bayonet سونكي؛ الحِرّاب؛ حربة (بندقية)
bayonet socket دواة سنانية
baz متغير
bbc نسخة كربونية صماء
bbl/d برميل / يوم
bboard لوحة الإعلانات
bbs لوحة الإعلانات
beach bags حقائب الشاطئ
beach clothes ملابس الشاطئ
beach shoes أحذية الشاطئ
beacon signals إشارات إرشاد لاسلكية
beacons فنارات
beacons of metal, non-luminous الفنارات غير مضيئة من المعدن
beacons, luminous الفنارات المضيئة
beacons, not of metal, non-luminous فنارات غير مضيئة ليست من المعدن
bead كرية
bead curtains for decoration ستائر بها خرز للزينة
beaker مانع تكسير [كيمياء]
beaker دورق
beak-irons [bick-irons] أطراف السندان المحددة
beam كمرة (كالكمرات الموجودة في السقف)
beam عارضة
beam شعاع أو حزمة (أشعة)
beams of electron حزم الإلكترونات
beams, not of metal عوارض ليست من المعدن
bean choke صمام اختناق فولي؛ صمام اختناق مُقحَم
bean meal غذاء الفول
beanie قبعة صغيرة لا حافة لها
beans (locust -) الخروب (بذور الخروب)
beans, fresh الفول الطازج
beans, preserved الفول المحفوظ
beard clippers ماكينات قص اللحية
beard dyes أصباغ اللحية
beards (false -) اللحى (اللحى الاصطناعية)
bearing محمل
bearing area منطقة تحميل
bearing brackets for machines كتائف الارتكاز في الماكينات
bearing face وجه تحميل
bearing license صادر عنه ترخيص
bearing material مادة المحمل
bearing race مضمار حمل
bearings (ball rings for-) المحامل (الحلقات الكروية في المحامل)
bearings [parts of machines] المحامل [أجزاء من الآلات]

| | |
|---|---|
| bearings for transmission shafts | المحامل المستخدمة في أعمدة نقل الحركة |
| beaters (carpet -) [not being machines] | مقارع (منافض السجاد) [ليست من الماكينات] |
| beaters, electric | خلاطات كهربائية |
| beaters, non-electric | خلاطات غير كهربائية |
| beating machines | ماكينات الخلط |
| beating to death | الضرب المفضي إلى الموت |
| beats | مواد مخفوقة |
| beauty masks | أقنعة التجميل |
| bed | مهاد |
| bed blankets | بطانيات الفراش |
| bed clothes | شراشف الفراش |
| bed covers | أغطية الفراش |
| bed covers of paper | أغطية الفراش من الورق |
| bed fittings, not of metal | تركيبات الفراش، ليست من المعدن |
| bed linen | بياضات الفراش |
| bed pans | قصريات الفراش للمرضى |
| bed vibrators | هزازات الأَسّرة |
| bedding | أغطية الفراش [فيما عدا البياضات] |
| bedding (feathers for-) | أغطية الفراش (ريش لأغطية الفراش) |
| bedding [except linen] | أغطية الفراش [فيما عدا البياضات] |
| beds | أَسّرة |
| beds (ex: fittings of metal for beds) | أساسات البناء (مثال: تجهيزات من المعدن لأساسات البناء) |
| beds (hospital -) | أَسّرة (أَسّرة المستشفيات) |
| beds (hydrostatic [water]-) for medical purposes | أَسّرة (أَسّرة هيدروستاتية [مائية]) للاستخدام في الأغراض الطبية |
| beds for household pets | فرش للحيوانات المنزلية |
| bedspreads | مفارش الأَسّرة |
| bedsteads | هياكل الأَسّرة |
| bedsteads [wood] | هياكل الأَسّرة [من الخشب] |
| bedwarmers | مدفئات الفراش |
| bee glue [propolis] for human consumption | شمع النحل [المستخدم لغلق خلايا النحل] للاستهلاك الآدمي |
| beech | خشب زان |
| beehives | خلايا النحل |
| beehives (comb foundations for -) | خلايا النحل (قواعد لخلايا النحل) |
| beehives (sections of wood for -) | خلايا النحل (قطع خشبية لخلايا النحل) |
| beer | البيرة |
| beer (apparatus for drawing up - ) under pressure) | البيرة (جهاز للسحب تحت الضغط) |
| beer (colorants for -) | البيرة (مواد ملونة من أجل-) |
| beer mugs | أكواب البيرة الكبيرة |
| beer preserving agents | عوامل حفظ البيرة |
| beer pumps | مضخات البيرة |
| beer vinegar | خل البيرة |
| beer wort | منقوع البيرة |
| beer-clarifying and preserving agents | عوامل تصفية البيرة وحفظها |
| beestinggs | السرسوب |

| | |
|---|---|
| beeswax | شمع العسل؛ شمع النحل |
| beet | البنجر |
| behave | يسلك، يتصرف |
| behavior | سلوك |
| behavioral robotics | روبوتية سلوكية |
| behavior-based robotics | روبوتية مرتكزة على السلوك |
| behcet's disease | داء بهجت |
| beige | مائل للصفرة |
| bellow | منفاخ |
| bellows | منفاخ [آلة] |
| bellows (fireplace -) [hand tools] | المنفاخ (منفاخ الحريق) [عُدد يدوية] |
| bellows [machines] | منفاخ [آلة] |
| bellows for musical instruments | منفاخ الآلات الموسيقية |
| bells | أجراس |
| bells (alarm -), electric | أجراس كهربائية (أجراس منبهة) |
| bells (signal -) | أجراس (أجراس الإشارة) |
| bells for animals | أجراس مخصصة للحيوانات |
| bells for bicycles, cycles | أجراس مخصصة للدراجات |
| bells for christmas trees | أجراس شجر أعياد الميلاد |
| belt clasps | مشابك الأحزمة |
| belt conveyor | سير ناقل |
| belt conveyors | ناقلات بالسيور |
| belt engaging roller | بكرة تتعشق مع سير |
| belt stretchers of metal | أدوات من المعدن لتوسيع السير |
| belt transmission | ناقل حركة |
| belting wax | شمع السيور |
| belts (dynamo -) | السيور (سيور المولد الكهربائي) |
| belts (grease for -) | سيور (شحم السيور) |
| belts (leather shoulder -) | أحزمة (أحزمة الكتف المصنوعة من الجلد) |
| belts (money -) [clothing] | أحزمة (أحزمة النقود) [ملابس] |
| belts (non-slipping preparations for -) | سيور (مستحضرات غير منزلقة للسيور) |
| belts (orthopaedic [orthopedic] -) | أحزمة (أحزمة التجبير) |
| belts (tool -) [holders] | أحزمة (أحزمة العُدد) [حوامل] |
| belts (weight lifting -) [sports articles] | أحزمة (أحزمة رفع الأوزان الثقيلة) [أدوات رياضية] |
| belts [clothing] | الأحزمة [ملابس] |
| belts for conveyors | سيور الناقلات |
| belts for machines | سيور الآلات |
| belts for motors and engines | سيور الموتورات والمحركات |
| belts for sanitary napkins [towels] | أحزمة للفوط الصحية [فوط] |
| belts of metal for handling loads | أحزمة من المعدن لشحن وتعبئة الحمولات |
| bench | نَضَد: مائدة تشكل جزءا من آلة |
| benches (vice -) not of metal | نضد (نضد الملْزَمة) ليست من المعدن |
| benches (vice -) of metal | نضد (نضد الملزمة) من المعدن |
| benches (work -) | نضد (نضد العمل) |
| benches [furniture] | نضد [أثاث] |
| benchmark | معايير قياسية |
| bending deformation | تشوه انحنائي |

| | |
|---|---|
| bending machines | ماكينات الثني |
| beneficiaries clause | بند تحديد المستفيدين من العقد |
| beneficiation | تجويد الخام |
| benefits | فوائد |
| benefits of agreement clause | البند الخاص بفائدة العقد. بند تعاقدي يحدد الجهات التي يكون للعقد أثر في مواجهتها |
| bengal lights | الأضواء البنجالية (ضوء أزرق فاتح براق، كان يستخدم للإشارة في السباق والآن يستخدم في الألعاب النارية) |
| benign | حميد |
| benign economy | اقتصاد مواتي |
| benign prostatic hyperplasia | فرط التنسج البروستاتي الحميد |
| bentonite | بِنْتونَيْت |
| benzaldehyde | بنزالدهيد |
| benzalkonium | بنزالكونيوم |
| benzamide | بنزاميد |
| benzene | البنزين |
| benzene (methyl -) | البنزين (بنزين الميثيل) |
| benzene derivatives | مشتقات البنزين |
| benzene-based acids | أحماض أساسها البنزين |
| benzenesulfenyl chloride | كلوريد بنزين سلفينيل |
| benzethonium | بنزيثونيوم |
| benzine | بنزين النفط (بنزين) |
| benzofused carbocycles | حلقات كربون ملتحمة مع مجموعة بنزو |
| benzoic acid | حمض البنزويك |
| benzoic sulphinide | سولفينيد البنزويك |
| benzol | البنزول |
| benzol (methyl -) | البنزول (بنزول الميثيل) |
| benzonitrile | بنزونيتريل |
| benzyl | بنزيل |
| benzylamine | بنزيلأمين |
| berets | البيريه (قبعة مستديرة تلبس في الرياضة والعطلات وفي الأغراض العسكرية). |
| bergamot oil | زيت ليمون البرجموث |
| berkeley internet name domain (bind) | مجال اسم انترنت بيركلي |
| berkeley software distribution (bsd) | توزيع برامج بيركلي |
| berkelium | البركليوم |
| berries | التوت |
| berths (sleeping -) for vehicles | الأسرة (أسرة النوم) الخاصة بالمركبات |
| beryllium [glucinium] | البريليوم [الجلوسينوم] |
| best fit | مواءمة؛ يوائم |
| best of breed | فائق التميز |
| best practices | أفضل الممارسات |
| best-fit | ملائم؛ مناسب؛ مواءمة |
| bet pore volume | حجم المسام وفقا لطريقة BET |
| bet total pore volume | حجم المسام الكلي وفقا لطريقة BET |
| beta basic hypercil | بيتا هيبرسيل أساسي |
| beta version | النسخة التجريبية بيتا |
| betain / betaine | بيتايين |
| betatrons | أجهزة البيتاترون: أجهزة تقوم بتسريع شعاع من الإلكترونات إلى سرعات عالية بواسطة حقل إلكتروني، يتم إنتاجه من خلال تغيير التدفق المغناطيسي |
| bevel | يشطف الحواف |
| beverage concentrates | نواتج تركيز مشروب |
| beverage preparation machines, electromechanical | آلات كهروميكانيكية لتحضير المشروبات |
| beverages (alcoholic -) [except beer] | مشروبات (مشروبات كحولية) [فيما عدا البيرة] |
| beverages (chocolate-based -) | مشروبات (مشروبات أساسها الشكولاته) |
| beverages (cocoa-based -) | مشروبات (مشروبات أساسها الكاكاو) |
| beverages (coffee-based -) | مشروبات (مشروبات أساسها القهوة) |
| beverages (distilled -) | مشروبات (مشروبات مقطرة) |
| beverages (flavorings [flavourings] for -) [essential oils] | مشروبات (مكسبات النكهة الخاصة بالمشروبات) [زيوت عطرية] |
| beverages (flavorings [flavourings], other than essential oils, for -) | مشروبات (مكسبات النكهة بخلاف الزيوت العطرية الخاصة بالمشروبات) |
| beverages (heat insulated containers for -) | مشروبات (أواني معزولة عن الحرارة خاصة بالمشروبات) |
| beverages (non-alcoholic-) | مشروبات (مشروبات غير كحولية) |
| beverages (preparations for making -) | مشروبات (مستحضرات لتصنيع المشروبات) |
| beverages (tea-based -) | مشروبات (مشروبات أساسها الشاي) |
| beverages (whey -) | مشروبات (مشروبات مصل اللبن) |
| beverages containing fruit (alcoholic -) | مشروبات محتوية على الفواكه (مشروبات كحولية محتوية على الفواكه) |
| beverages cooling apparatus | جهاز تبريد المشروبات |
| beverages for pets | مشروبات مخصصة للحيوانات الأليفة |
| bhp | قدرة حصانية (للكابحة) |
| bi-, di-, tri-, etc. | باي، داي، تراي، إلخ |
| biantennary sugar | سكر ثنائي القرن |
| biaryl group | مجموعة باي أريل |
| bias | تحيز |
| bias | قيمة منحرفة |
| biasing | انحيازي |
| biasing apparatus | جهاز توجيه |
| biasing means | وسيلة انحياز |
| biaxially oriented | الموجهة بشكل ثنائي المحور |
| biaxially oriented | موجه بشكل ثنائي المحور |
| bib | صدرية الطفل؛ صُدْرة الطفل: توضع تحت ذقن الطفل أثناء الطعام |
| bibody & tribody | جسم ثنائي & جسم ثلاثي |
| bibs of paper | صدرية الأطفال من الورق |
| bibs, not of paper | صدرية الأطفال [توضع تحت ذقن الطفل أثناء الطعام] ليست من الورق |

| | |
|---|---|
| bicarbonate of soda | بيكربونات الصودا |
| biceps femoris | العضلة ذات الرأسين الفخذية |
| bichloride of tin | ثاني كلوريد القصدير |
| bichromate of potassium | ثاني كرومات البوتاسيوم |
| bichromate of soda | ثاني كرومات الصودا |
| bicontinuous | ثنائية الاستمرار |
| bicycle assembling machines | ماكينات تجميع الدراجات الهوائية |
| bicycle bells | أجراس الدراجات الهوائية |
| bicycle brakes | فرامل الدراجات الهوائية |
| bicycle chains | سلاسل الدراجات الهوائية |
| bicycle dynamos | مولدات الدراجات الهوائية |
| bicycle frames | هياكل الدراجات الهوائية |
| bicycle handle bars | أذرع التوجيه في الدراجة الهوائية |
| bicycle lights | مصابيح الدراجات الهوائية |
| bicycle parking installations of metal | تركيبات انتظار الدراجات الهوائية من المعدن |
| bicycle pumps | مضخات الدراجة الهوائية |
| bicycle rims | إطارات الدراجة الهوائية |
| bicycle saddles | مقاعد الدراجات الهوائية |
| bicycle spokes | شعاع إطارات الدراجة الهوائية |
| bicycle stands | مساند الدراجة الهوائية |
| bicycle tires | إطارات الدراجات الهوائية |
| bicycles | الدراجات الهوائية |
| bicycles (stationary exercise -) | الدراجات الهوائية (الدراجات الثابتة المخصصة للتمرينات الرياضية) |
| bid | مرتين في اليوم؛ مزايدة |
| bidentate | ثنائية الترابط |
| bidentate | ثنائي السن |
| bidets | البيديه: شطّاف بالحمام |
| bidirectional : bi-directional | ثنائي الاتجاه |
| bidirectional data eyeglasses | نظارات بياناتية ذات اتجاهين |
| biemical oxygen demand (bod) | الأكسجين المستهلك حيوياً |
| bifunctional | مزدوج الوظيفة |
| big blue | العملاق الأزرق: نسبة إلى شعار آي بي إم IBM |
| big dummy's guid to the internet | دليل المبتدئين إلى الإنترنت |
| big red switch | المفتاح الأحمر الضخم |
| bile acid | حمض صفراوي |
| bile duct | قناة مرارية |
| bile salts | أملاح الصفراء |
| biliary cirrhosis | التشمع الصفراوي |
| biliary tract | مجرى صفراوي |
| bill of indictment | عريضة دعوى؛ قرار اتهام |
| bill-hooks | منجل |
| billiard balls | كرات البليارد |
| billiard cloth | قماش البليارد |
| billiard cue tips | حواف عصا البليارد |
| billiard cues | عصى البليارد |
| billiard table cushions | وسائد حافة طاولة البليارد |
| billiard tables | طاولات البليارد |
| billiard tables (coin- | طاولات البليارد (الطاولات التي |

| | |
|---|---|
| operated -) | تعمل بالعملة) |
| billion | مليار أو بليون |
| billion cubic feet (bcf) per day | مليار متر مكعب (Bcf) كل يوم |
| billposting | لصق الإعلانات |
| billposting (adhesives for -) | لصق الإعلانات (مواد للصق الإعلانات) |
| bimodal or multimodal polymers | البوليمرات ثنائية الصورة أو متعددة الصورة |
| bin | حاوية؛ صندوق؛ سلة |
| bin (silo) | صومعة؛ صوامع |
| binaphtalenyl | بينافتالينيل |
| binaries newsgroup | مجموعات الأخبار الثنائية |
| binary | ثنائي |
| binary data | بيانات ثنائية |
| binary file | ملف ثنائي |
| binary file transfer | نقل الملفات الثنائية |
| binary synchronous control (bisync) | التحكم الثنائي المتزامن |
| bind sth (to sth) | يربطه (بكذا) |
| bind to sth ; bind for sth | يرتبط بكذا |
| binder | آلة حصاد وربط (الحبوب) |
| binder | مادة رابطة؛ رابط |
| binders | مواد التجليد |
| binders (loose-leaf -) | مواد التجليد (إضبارة الأوراق السائبة خاصة بمواد التجليد) |
| binding | رابط؛ ربط |
| binding agent | عامل ربط؛ عامل رابط |
| binding agents for ice cream [edible ices] | مواد إلصاق للاستخدام في الحلوى المثلجة [مثلجات صالحة للأكل] |
| binding agents for making briquettes | مواد إلصاق لتصنيع طوب الآجر |
| binding apparatus for hay | جهاز ربط الكلأ المجفف |
| binding arbitration | تحكيم ملزم |
| binding assay | اختبار ارتباط |
| binding data analysis | تحليل بيانات الارتباط |
| binding law of the land | القانون السائد |
| binding member | عضو رابط |
| binding needles | إبر الخياطة |
| binding precedent | سابقة ملزمة |
| binding preparations for paints | مستحضرات الإلصاق في الدهانات |
| binding screws | براغي الربط |
| binding screws of metal for cables | براغي (مسامير) الربط من المعدن للكبلات |
| binding site | موقع ربط |
| binding specificity (for) | نوعية ارتباط (بـ أو نحو) |
| binding strips [bookbinding] | شرائح الربط [تجليد الكتب] |
| binding substances (foundry -) | مواد الربط (مواد الربط الخاصة بالمسابك) |
| binding thread of metal | خيوط الربط من المعدن |
| bindings of metal | مواد الربط من المعدن |
| binge eating disorder | اضطراب الإفراط في تناول الطعام |
| bingo cards | ورق لعب البنجو |
| binoculars | مناظير ثنائية |
| bins | الخانات أو البيانات |

| | |
|---|---|
| bins (dust -) | صناديق (صناديق لجمع الأتربة) |
| bins of metal | صناديق من المعدن |
| bins of wood or plastic | صناديق من الخشب أو البلاستك |
| bioactivity | نشاط حيوي |
| bioalcohol | كحول حيوي |
| bioassay in vitro | اختبار حيوي في المختبر |
| bioaugmentation | إضافة كائنات دقيقة تحت التربة؛ تطعيم التربة بالكائنات الدقيقة؛ التطعيم البيولوجي للتربة |
| bioavailability | الإتاحة الحيوية |
| biochemical catalysts | محفزات بيوكيميائية |
| biocide | مبيد حيوي |
| biocides | مبيدات حيوية |
| biodegradable | قابل للتحلل الحيوي,,قابل للتحلل البيولوجي، |
| biodiesel | ديزل حيوي |
| bio-diesel powered vehicle | مركبة تزود بالديزل الحيوي |
| bioengineering | هندسة حيوية |
| bio-fuel | وقود عضوي |
| biogas | غاز حيوي |
| biogenic amine neurotransmitter transporter reuptake blockers | مغلقات إعادة امتصاص المرسلات العصبية القائمة على أمينات بيولوجية المنشأ |
| biogenic sedimentary structures | البنيات الأولية الرسوبية العضوية |
| biography | سيرة ذاتية |
| bioisosteric | مماثل فراغي حيوي |
| biolistic | بالقذف البيولوجي |
| biolistic means | مسدس جيني |
| biolistic transformation | تحويل الخلايا بالقذف البيولوجي |
| biological activity | نشاط حيوي |
| biological assays | الاختبارات الحيوية؛ التجارب الحيوية |
| biological chemistry | كيمياء بيولوجية |
| biological expermiments | التجارب الحيوية |
| biological markers | الواسمات الحيوية |
| biological neural system | نظام عصبي بيولوجي |
| biological preparations [other than for medical or veterinary purposes] | مستحضرات بيولوجية [بخلاف المستخدمة في الأغراض الطبية أو البيطرية] |
| biological response modifiers | معدلات الاستجابة البيولوجية |
| biological samples for use in microscopy [teaching material] | عينات بيولوجية للاستخدام في الدراسة المجهرية [مادة تعليمية] |
| biological tests | الاختبارات الحيوية |
| biologically active protein | نشط حيويا |
| biologicals | احيائيات |
| bio-luminescent labels | علامات اللمعان الحيوي |
| bioluminescent materials | مواد بيولوجية مضيئة |
| biomass | كتلة حيوية |
| bio-mass | كتلة حيوية |
| biomass energy | طاقة الكتلة الحيوية |
| biomass heating | الكتلة الحيوية للتسخين |
| biomedical engineering | هندسة طبية |
| bio-nano generator | مولد نانو حيوي |

| | |
|---|---|
| bio-physics | فيزياء حيوية |
| bio-process | طريقة بيولوجية. أي طريقة تتضمن استعمال خلايا كاملة أو مكونات أخرى مثل الأنزيمات بغية إحداث تغييرات مادية أو كيمائية مرغوبة |
| biopsy | خَزْعَة؛ خَذْعَة؛ خِزْعَة؛ عينة حية: عينة حيوية لفحص الكائنات الحية (أخذ قطعة من الجزء المريض لفحصها مجهريًا) |
| bioreactor | مفاعل حيوي |
| bioremediation technology | تقنية استخدام الخلايا في إزالة عناصر التلوث من البيئة |
| biosynthetic pathway | مسار مخلق حيويا |
| biotage 75l | خرطوشة بيوتاج 75 لتر |
| biotech patenting | إصدار براءات بيوتكنولوجية |
| biotechnological patent | براءة بيوتكنولوجية |
| biotinylated | تم إدخال مجموعة بيوتين إليه؛ به مجموعة بيوتين؛ مضاف إليه مجموعة بيوتين |
| biotransformation | التحول الحيوي |
| biotrophic | تعيش على نسيج حى |
| biotype | نمط أحيائي |
| biped robot | روبوت ذو ساقين |
| biplane | طائرة مزدوجة الأجنحة |
| bipolar | ثنائي القطبية |
| biproduct | منتج ثانوي |
| bird baths | مغاطس الطيور |
| bird food | طعام الطيور |
| birdcages | أقفاص الطيور |
| birdlime | الدابوق: مادة لزجة تطلى بها الأغصان لصيد صغار الطير |
| birds (stuffed -) | طيور (طيور محنطة) |
| birds' feathers [clothing accessories] | ريش الطيور [إكسسوارات للملابس] |
| birefringent | ثنائي الانكسار |
| birefringent plate | لوح ثنائي الانكسار؛ صفيحة ثنائية الانكسار |
| biscuits | بسكويت |
| bisdn | الشبكة الرقمية للخدمات المتكاملة ذات نطاق التردد الواسع |
| bismuth | البزموث [أملاح أو إسترات حمض الجاليك] |
| bismuth (basic gallate of -) | البزموث (الجالات [ملح أو استر حمض الجاليك] القاعدية للبزموث) |
| bismuth (iii ) chloride | كلوريد البزموث (III) |
| bismuth nitrite | نيتريت البزموث |
| bismuth preparations | مستحضرات البزموث |
| bismuth subnitrate | تحت نيتريت البزموث |
| bispecific; bi-specific; dual specific; dual-specific | مزدوج النوعية؛ ثنائي النوعية |
| bispecific antibodies | أجسام مضادة مزدوجة النوعية |
| bispecific diabodies | أجسام مضادة ثنائية التكافؤ مزدوجة النوعية |
| bispecific igg-like format | صيغة مزدوجة النوعية شبيهة بـ IgG |
| bisphosphonates | بس فوسفونات |
| bi-substituted alkyl | ألكيل بها استبدال ثنائي |

| | |
|---|---|
| bisulfite | بيكبريتيت |
| bisulphate | بيكبريتات |
| bisulphite | ثاني كبريتيت |
| bisynchronous | متزامن ثنائيا |
| bit | لقمة الحفر |
| bit / bits | بت / بتات (وحدات البت) |
| bit error rate | معدل أخطاء البت |
| bite indicators [fishing tackle] | مؤشرات ابتلاع الطعم [عُدة صيد الأسماك] |
| bite sensors [fishing tackle] | أجهزة الإحساس بابتلاع الطعم [عُدة صيد الأسماك] |
| bitmap indexes | فهارس نقطية |
| bits | قطع |
| bits [hand tools] | فكّا الكماشة [عُدد يدوية] |
| bits [parts of hand tools] | القواطع [أجزاء من عُدد يدوية] |
| bits for animals [harness] | الشكائم المستخدمة للحيوانات [أطقم الفرس] |
| bits per second (bps) | بت لكل ثانية (بت /ثانية) |
| bitters | نوع من البيرة؛ شراب مُسكّر شبيه بالبيرة: يُعد هذا الشراب بتقطير بعض الأعشاب أو الأوراق أو الجذور المرة (لتسهيل الهضم) |
| bitty box | الكمبيوتر الصغير، للتهكم من PC |
| bitumen | القار؛ البيتومين |
| bitumen | قار، يحول إلى قار |
| bitumen froth | زبد البيتومين: زبد يحتوي على البيتومين |
| bitumen making machines | آلات تصنيع القار |
| bitumen varnish | ورنيش من القار |
| bituminous coatings for roofing | طلاء القار المستخدم في عمل الأسقف |
| bituminous products for building | منتجات القار للاستخدام في البناء |
| bivalent | ثنائي التكافؤ |
| bivalent analyte datmodel | نموذج ثنائي التكافئ لبيانات ناتج التحليل |
| bivalent antibody | جسم مضاد ثنائي التكافؤ |
| biw | مرتين في الأسبوع |
| bkg | ركيزة background [التجارب الكيميائية] |
| black & white | أبيض وأسود |
| black (lamp -) for industrial purposes | السواد (السُخام) للاستخدام في الأغراض الصناعية |
| black energy | طاقة سوداء |
| black hole | الثقب الأسود |
| black pudding | السجق الأسود [سجق لحم خنزير داكن جداً يحتوى على كمية كبيرة من الدم] |
| blackboards | ألواح سوداء [سبورة] |
| blacks [colorants or paints] | الأصباغ السوداء [مواد التلوين أو الدهانات] |
| bladders of balls for games | الأكياس الهوائية من الكرات المستخدمة في الألعاب |
| blade | نصل؛ شفرة: سكين بدون مقبض |
| blade holders [parts of machines] | حوامل النصل [أجزاء آلات] |
| blade sharpening [stropping] machines | آلات سن [شحذ] الأنصال |
| blade sharpening instruments | معدات سن الأنصال |
| blades (chaff cutter -) | أنصال (أنصال قاطعة للتبن) |
| blades [hand tools] | أنصال [عدد يدوية] |
| blades [parts of machines] | أنصال (أجزاء من آلات) |
| blades [weapons] | شفرات المدية [أسلحة] |
| blades for planes | أنصال المسحاج |
| bland | ملطف |
| blank | خام |
| blank solution | محلول خالي من المواد الفعالة |
| blank value | قيمة متعادلة |
| blanket contract | عقد شامل |
| blanket of chilled inert atmosphere | بدثار من هواء خامل مبرّد. |
| blankets (bed -) | بطانيات (بطانيات الفراش) |
| blast | إنفجار |
| blast- | خلايا أولية |
| blast furnaces | أفران صهر المعادن |
| blast furnaces (cement for -) | أفران صهر المعادن (أسمنت مستخدم في أفران صهر المعادن) |
| blast valve | صمام انفجار |
| blasted | ملفوح |
| blast-furnace, smelting, cast iron, steel, wrought iron | الفرن العالي، الصهر، الحديد الزهر، الحديد الصلب، الحديد المطاوع |
| blastocyte | خلية جرثومية |
| blastoma | ورم الخلايا الأولية |
| blaze | لحام بالنحاس |
| blaze the trails | يأخذ بزمام المبادرة |
| blc indicator | مؤشر BLC |
| bldrep | تقرير عن المصابين |
| bleaching | التبييض: (في صناعة الورق) عملية تلميع الألياف بإزالة المواد الملونة أو بإزالة لونها |
| bleaching (leather -) preparations | مستحضرات تبييض (مستحضرات تبييض الجلود) |
| bleaching chemicals | مواد كيميائية للتبييض |
| bleaching chemicals (fat- -) | مواد كيميائية للتبييض (مواد كيميائية للتبييض عالية الشحوم) |
| bleaching chemicals (oil- -) | مواد كيميائية للتبييض (مواد كيميائية زيتية للتبييض) |
| bleaching chemicals (organic- -) | مواد كيميائية للتبييض (مواد كيميائية عضوية للتبييض) |
| bleaching chemicals (wax- -) | مواد كيميائية للتبييض (مواد كيميائية شمعية للتبييض) |
| bleaching preparations [decolorants] for industrial purposes | مستحضرات تبييض [مزيلات اللون] للاستخدام في الأغراض الصناعية |
| bleaching preparations [laundry] | مستحضرات تبييض [لغسيل الملابس] |
| bleaching salts | أملاح التبييض |
| bleaching soda | صودا التبييض |
| bleed port | منفذ تسريب (سائل، مائع إلخ) |
| bleed port | منفذ تنفيس (غاز إلخ) |
| bleeding air | تصريف الهواء أو نفث الهواء |
| blend | خليط |
| blended butter | زبد من مصادر مختلفة |

| | |
|---|---|
| blending tanks | خزانات خلط |
| blind | ستارة |
| blind cover plate | لوح غطاء مصمت: أي بلا نافذة مركزية |
| blinded clinical trial; blind clinical trial | تجربة إكلينيكية مجهولة للمريض (معلومة للقائمين عليها) |
| blinder | وسيلة حجب |
| blinders [harness] | غمامات الفرس [أطقم الفرس] |
| blinding layer | طبقة غير مسلحة |
| blinds | ستائر |
| blinds (ladder tapes or webbing for venetian-) | ستائر (أشرطة متدرجة سلّمية أو قطع قماش منسوجة للاستخدام في الستائر) |
| blinds (slatted indoor-) | ستائر (ستائر مضلعة مستخدمة داخل المباني) |
| blinds [outdoor], not of metal and not of textile | ستائر [خارج المنزل] ليست من المعدن أو القماش |
| blinkers [harness] | غمامات الفرس [أطقم الفرس] |
| blinkers [signalling lights] | الأضواء الوامضة [أضواء للإشارة] |
| blister pack | عبوة حبيبات: مثل شريط دواء |
| blitz | غارة خاطفة |
| blitzkrieg | حرب خاطفة |
| blk&wht | أبيض وأسود |
| block | كتلة |
| block | وحدة: صندوق [في المخططات والرسومات] |
| block | إغلاق؛ سد؛ إنسداد؛ ترباس؛ يغلق؛ يسد |
| block capitals | حروف طباعية أو خط واضح أو حروف منفصلة |
| block copolymers | بوليمرات مشتركة كتلية |
| block decoding | فك تشفير الكتلة |
| block diagram | مخطط صندوقي؛ مخطط إطاري؛ رسم تخطيطي إطاري |
| block of data | كتلة بيانات؛ كتلة من البيانات |
| block polymers | بوليمرات كتلية |
| block scheduling | الجداول النمطية |
| blockade | إعاقة نشاط |
| blockers | مغلقات؛ محصرات |
| blocking buffer | محلول إعاقة منظم |
| blocks (building -) | الكتل المستخدمة في البناء (كتل البناء) |
| blog | مدونة؛ يدون |
| blog journalism | صحافة المدونات |
| blogger | مدون |
| blood brain barrier | حاجز المخ الدموي: هو حاجز يحمى الدماغ من المواد الكيميائة التي يحملها الدم |
| blood charcoal | فحم دموي (يستخدم كبيئة مناسبة لنمو البكتيريا لغايات التجارب) |
| blood collection | تجميع عينات الدم |
| blood dialysis | غسيل الكلى |
| blood glucose | تحليل السكر |
| blood glucose | سكر الدم (جلوكوز الدم) |
| blood glucose levels | مستويات السكر في الدم (مستويات الجلوكوز في الدم) |
| blood plasm concentration | التركيز في بلازما الدم |

| | |
|---|---|
| blood plasma | بلازما الدم |
| blood sausage | السجق الدامي [سجق لحم خنزير داكن جداً يحتوى على كمية كبيرة من الدم] |
| blood testing apparatus | جهاز اختبار الدم |
| blood-brain barrier | الحائل الدموي الدماغي |
| blood-brain barrier | الحاجز الدموي الدماغي |
| blooms [metallurgy] | قضبان فولاذية [علم الفلزات] |
| blotters | الورق النشاف |
| blouse fasteners | سحابات البلوزة |
| blow | ينفخ/يحترق/يهب |
| blow moulding; blow molding | قَوْلَبَةٌ بِالنَّفْخ |
| blowdown | تفريغ؛ تصريف |
| blowdown | وحدة تفريغ |
| blower | منفاخ؛ مُفجر |
| blowing | احتراق/انفجار |
| blowing engines | محركات النفخ |
| blowing head | رأس نفخ |
| blowing machines for exhaustion of dust, etc. | آلات النفخ لإزالة الأتربة .. الخ |
| blowing machines for the compression, exhaustion and transport of gases | آلات النفخ لضغط، وتفريغ ونقل الغازات |
| blowing machines for the compression, sucking and carrying of grain | آلات النفخ لضغط، وسحب وحمل الحبوب |
| blowing pressurized air | دفع هواء مضغوط |
| blowout preventer | مانع التدفق المفاجئ |
| blow-up perspective view | رسم منظوري مكبر |
| bludgeons | الهراوات |
| blue cheese | الجبن الركفور |
| bluebell | عشبة الجُرَيْس |
| blueing for laundry | الصباغ الأزرق للاستخدام في غسل الملابس |
| blueprint apparatus | جهاز الطباعة |
| blueprint cloth | قماش الطباعة |
| blueprint paper | ورق الطباعة |
| blueprints | نماذج مطبوعة |
| blues [colorants or paints] | الأصباغ الزرقاء [مواد تلوين أو دهانات] |
| bluetooth | مواصفات التوصيل اللاسلكي قصير المدي الذي يتيح لإمكانية الإتصال اللاسلكي المجاني (بإستخدام تقنية الراديو) بين مجموعة من الأجهزة بما فيها الهواتف المحمولة وأجهزة الكمبيوتر والطابعات وغيرها |
| bluff body | جسم عريض الواجهة |
| bluing for laundry | الصباغ الأزرق للاستخدام في الغسيل |
| blunt | غير حاد |
| blunt end ligation | إلحاق في الطرف الخامل |
| blu-ray | تقنية بلو-راي |
| bmg's rootkit | أسلوب أو تكنولوجيا لحماية الإسطوانات الموسيقية من القرصنة: أنتجته سوني وثبت فشله |
| bmp | صورة نقطية |
| board | لوحة، حافة، جانب، يكسو بألواح جانبية |

| | |
|---|---|
| board games | الألعاب باستخدام الألواح |
| boarding stairs of metal, mobile, for passengers | سلالم الارتقاء، متحركة ومن المعدن ومخصصة للركاب |
| boards (display -) | لوحات (لوحات العرض) |
| boards (floor -) | ألواح (ألواح أرضية) |
| boards (ironing -) | ألواح (ألواح الكي) |
| boards of metal (building-) | ألواح معدنية (ألواح معدنية للبناء) |
| boas [necklets] | أوشحة للرقبة من فرو أو ريش أو نسيج رقيق |
| boat hooks | خطافات القوارب |
| boats | قوارب |
| boats (engines for -) | قوارب (محركات القوارب) |
| boats (fire -) | قوارب (قوارب الإطفاء) |
| boats (motors for -) | قوارب (موتورات "ماكينات" القوارب) |
| bobbin | بكرة |
| bobbins for weaving looms | بكر لأنوال الغزل |
| bob-sleighs | زلاجات مزدوجة (للتنقل على الثلوج) |
| boc edwards auto 306 evaporation system (1 unit) | جهاز تبخير بالحرارة BOC Edwards – (عدد 1) |
| boc group | مجموعة بوك؛ مجموعة Boc |
| boc-piperazine | برازين محمي بمجموعة Boc |
| bodices [lingerie] | حمالات للثدي [ملابس تحتية للنساء] |
| bodies | هياكل |
| bodies for vehicles | هياكل المركبات |
| bodkins | مخرزات القماش |
| body | جسم |
| body boards | الألواح المستخدمة في السباحة |
| body cavities (appliances for washing -) | تجاويف الجسم (أجهزة لغسيل تجاويف الجسم) |
| body mass index | مؤشر كتلة الجسم |
| body of knowledge | حزمَة معرفة |
| body of liquid | كتلة من السائل |
| body portion | جزء أساسي |
| body waves | الموجات الاهتزازيَّة الداخليَّة |
| body weight | وزن الجسم |
| body-belt bomb | حزام ناسف |
| body-building apparatus | جهاز بناء الأجسام |
| body-training apparatus | جهاز التمرينات الجسدية |
| bog down | يتوقف تلقائيا؛ يتوقف ذاتيا |
| bogie | مجمع العجلات |
| bogies for railway cars | مجمعات العجلات في عربات السكة الحديدية |
| bogometer | مقياس الخطأ |
| bogon | خطأ |
| bogon filter | مرشح الخطأ |
| bogon flux | تدفق الخطأ |
| bogosity | مدى الخطأ |
| bogus | غبي؛ سخيف؛ غير مفيد؛ ردئ؛ ممتلئة بالأخطاء |
| bogus newsgroups | مجموعة أخبار سخيفة |
| bogus patent | براءة زائفة. |
| boil off | إزالة كذا بالغليان |
| boiler composition to prevent the radiation of heat | مُركّب الغلاية لمنع إشعاع الحرارة |
| boiler control instruments | أدوات التحكم في الغلاية |
| boiler pipes [tubes] for heating installations | مواسير [أنابيب] الغلاية للاستخدام في تجهيزات التدفئة |
| boiler scale collectors (machine -) | أجهزة تجميع قشور الغلاية (ماكينة تجميع قشور الغلاية) |
| boiler tubes [parts of machines] | أنابيب الغلاية [أجزاء من الماكينات] |
| boilers [other than parts of machines] | غلايات [بخلاف أجزاء الآلات] |
| boilers industry | صناعة المراجل البخارية |
| boiling range distribution | توزيع مدى درجات غليان |
| boilup vapor | بخار الغليان |
| boink | حفلة؛ اجتماع أعضاء مجموعة أخبار |
| boll worm | دودة اللوز |
| bolsters | مساند |
| bolt | برغي |
| bolted | يثبّت باستخدام براغي |
| bolting cloth | قماش الغربلة |
| bolts | براغي: مسامير ملولبة |
| bolts (lock -) | مزاليج (مزاليج القفل) |
| bolts [flat] | مزاليج [مسطحة] |
| bolus | جرعة (أو حبّة) كبيرة (دفعة واحدة) |
| bombard | يقصف (من الجو) |
| bombers | قاذفات؛ قاذفة (طائرات) |
| bonbons (explosive -) [christmas crackers] | بون بون (بون بون متفجر) [مفرقعات عيد الميلاد] |
| bond | رابطة |
| bond strength | مقاومة التماسك |
| bonding capacity | حجم أو قيمة الكـفالة |
| bonding strength | شدة ترابط |
| bone cement | ملاط العظم: للاستخدام في أغراض الجراحة والتجبير |
| bone charcoal | فحم العظام الحيوانية |
| bone gain | زيادة عظم؛ زيادة في العظم |
| bone loss | نقص عظم؛ نقص في العظم |
| bone marrow | نخاع العظم |
| bone meal | مسحوق عظام |
| bone metabolism | اضطرابات العظام |
| bone oil | زيت العظام |
| bone resorption diseases | أمراض ارتشاف العظام |
| bone turnover | دورة تجديد العظم؛ تحلل النسيج العظمى وتكون الجديد |
| book rests | حوامل الكتب |
| book rests [furniture] | حوامل الكتب [أثاث] |
| bookbinding | تجليد الكتب |
| bookbinding apparatus and machines | أجهزة وماكينات تجليد الكتب |
| bookbinding cloth | قماش تجليد الكتب |
| bookbinding cords | أشرطة تجليد الكتب |
| bookbinding material | مادة تجليد الكتب |
| bookbindings | تجاليد الكتب |
| bookends | مساند الكتب |
| booklets | كتيبات |
| bookmark | إشارة مرجعية |
| bookmarkers | المؤشرات (أشرطة توضع بين صفحات الكتاب للإشارة إلى موضع بعينه) |
| books | الكتب |

| | |
|---|---|
| books of cigarette papers | رُزَم من أوراق التبغ |
| boolean search | البحث المنطقي باستخدام boolean |
| booster | منشط وبخاصة جرعة منشطة |
| booster | معزز |
| boot | يشغل |
| boot camp | برنامج التشغيل Boot Camp |
| boot cream | ورنيش الأحذية |
| boot jacks | خالعة الأحذية ذات الرقبة |
| boot polish | ورنيش الأحذية الملمع |
| boot trees [stretchers] | قوالب الأحذية [أدوات توسيع الحذاء] |
| boot up | يشغل |
| boot uppers | الأجزاء العليا من الحذاء عالي الرقبة |
| bootable | قابل للتشغيل |
| boots | أحذية عالية الرقبة |
| boots (cement for -) | أحذية عالية الرقبة (ملاط للأحذية عالية الرقبة) |
| boots (grease for -) | أحذية عالية الرقبة (شحم للأحذية عالية الرقبة) |
| boots (heelpieces for-) | أحذية عالية الرقبة (كعوب للأحذية عالية الرقبة) |
| boots (iron fittings for-) | أحذية عالية الرقبة (التركيبات الحديدية في الأحذية عالية الرقبة) |
| boots (non-slipping devices for -) | أحذية عالية الرقبة (الوسائل المضادة للانزلاق في الأحذية عالية الرقبة) |
| boots (skating -) with skates attached | أحذية عالية الرقبة (أحذية تزلج) ملحق بها مزالج |
| boots (ski -) | أحذية عالية الرقبة (أحذية عالية الرقبة للتزحلق على الجليد) |
| boots (welts for -) | أحذية عالية الرقبة (حواشي للأحذية عالية الرقبة) |
| bootstap protocol | بروتوكول التشغيل |
| borax | بورات الصوديوم المائية |
| border dispute | نزاع حول الحدود |
| border gate protocol | بروتوكول عبّارة الحدود |
| border line | إطار الإعلان |
| border shears | أدوات قص الحافة |
| bordetella pertussis | السعال الديكي البورديتيلي |
| bore | تجويف: تجويف قطر الماسورة الداخلي عند وصف أنبوب حفر مثلا |
| bore | حفرة (البئر)؛ ثقب (البئر) |
| bore well | بئر ارتوازي |
| borehole | ثقب الحفر؛ بئر الحفر؛ بئر التنقيب |
| borer | حفار |
| borers (mine -) | الحفارات (حفارات المناجم) |
| boric acid | حمض البوريك |
| boride | بوريد |
| born digital document | مستند ولد رقميا |
| boron | بورون |
| borosilicate glass (e.g., pyrex, duran, simax, etc.) | زجاج سيليكات البورون (على سبيل المثال،Pyrex،Duran، Simax،إلخ) |
| boss | مسند |
| bossy | دكتاتوري |
| bot | روبوت |
| botrytis | المُعَنْقَدَة (جنس من الفطريات) |
| bottle capping machines | آلات تغطية الزجاجات |
| bottle caps of metal | أغطية الزجاجات من المعدن |
| bottle casings of wood | أغلفة الزجاجات من الخشب |
| bottle closures of metal | أدوات غلق الزجاجات من المعدن |
| bottle envelopes of cardboard or paper | أغلفة الزجاجات من الورق المقوى أو الورق |
| bottle envelopes of straw | أغلفة الزجاجات من القش |
| bottle fasteners of metal | روابط الزجاجات من المعدن |
| bottle filling machines | آلات تعبئة الزجاجات |
| bottle gourds | آنية زجاجية رفيعة الرقبة |
| bottle neck | مشكلة الزحام على الخادم |
| bottle openers | فتاحات الزجاجات |
| bottle racks | حوامل الزجاجات |
| bottle sealing machines | الآلات الخاصة بإحكام غلق الزجاجات |
| bottle stoppering machines | الآلات الخاصة بوضع السدادات على الزجاجات |
| bottle washing machines | آلات غسيل الزجاجات |
| bottle wrappers of cardboard or paper | مواد تغليف الزجاجات من الورق المقوى أو الورق |
| bottles | الزجاجات |
| bottles (corks for -) | زجاجات (سدادات فلينية للزجاجات) |
| bottles (refrigerating -) | زجاجات (زجاجات التجميد) |
| bottles (straw wrappers for -) | زجاجات (مواد تغليف من القش للزجاجات) |
| bottles [metal containers] for compressed gas or liquid air | زجاجات [آنية معدنية] للغاز المضغوط أو الهواء السائل |
| bottom hole | قاع البئر |
| bottom hole ; bottom-hole | قاع البئر؛ أسفل البئر |
| bottom line | خلاصة الأمر؛ العامل الأساسي المهم |
| bottom resistivity | المقاومية عند القاع |
| bottom support | المادة الحاملة السفلية |
| bottom trip anchor | الجزء الخلفي من مثبت |
| annulus | السقاطة في القاع |
| bottoms | مواد مترسبة؛ رواسب؛ مخلفات: مكونات ثقيلة heavier components تترسب في قاع المفاعل أو وعاء التفاعل |
| botyris-resistence-conferring part | جزء مانح مقاوم للمعنقدات |
| botyris-susciptible | عرضة للإصابة بالمعنقدات |
| bougies [surgery] | أدوات التوسيع [تستخدم في الجراحة] |
| bouillon | مرق |
| bouillon (preparations for making -) | مرق (مستحضرات لتصنيع المرق) |
| bouillon concentrates | أشكال مركزة من المرق |
| bouillon for bacteriological cultures | مرق للمزارع البكتيريولوجية |
| boulimia | النهم |
| bounce back | يرتد |
| bounce message | رسالة مرتدة |
| bound water | ماء مرتبط |

| | |
|---|---|
| boundary | حد الحقل |
| bounds (pl) | حدود الأرض |
| bovine species | أنواع/حيوانات الفصيلة البقرية |
| bow nuts for musical instruments | صواميل منحنية للاستخدام في الآلات الموسيقية |
| bow saws | مناشير قوسيه |
| bowling apparatus and machinery | أجهزة ومعدات آلية خاصة بلعبة البولينج |
| bowls (glass -) | طست (طست زجاجية) |
| bowls [basins] | طست [أحواض] |
| bows (paper -) | أقواس (أقواس ورقية) |
| bows for archery | أقواس خاصة بلعبة رماية القوس والسهم |
| bows for musical instruments | أقواس خاصة بالآلات الموسيقية |
| bows for the hair | عُقد أنشوطية للشعر |
| box | كمبيوتر، غالبا لفظ تهكمي |
| box fasteners of metal | أقفال الصناديق من المعدن |
| boxes (cigar -), of precious metal | علب (علب السيجار) من المعادن النفيسة |
| boxes (nesting -) | أقفاص (للإيواء) |
| boxes (nesting -) for household pets | صناديق [أقفاص] مخصصة لإيواء الحيوانات المنزلية |
| boxes (safety cash -) | صناديق (صناديق النقود المؤمنة) |
| boxes (sewing -) | صناديق (صناديق الخياطة) |
| boxes (soap -) | علب (علب الصابون) |
| boxes for matrices [printing] | علب المصفوفات النقطية [في الطباعة] |
| boxes for pens | علب أقلام الحبر |
| boxes for sweetmeats, not of precious metal | علب الفاكهة المحلاة، ليست من المعادن النفيسة |
| boxes of cardboard or paper | علب من الورق المقوى أو الورق |
| boxes of common metal | علب من المعادن غير النفيسة |
| boxes of glass | علب زجاجية |
| boxes of leather (hat -) | علب جلدية (علب جلدية للقبعات) |
| boxes of leather or leather board | علب من الجلد أو الجلد المقوى |
| boxes of metal, for dispensing paper towels | صناديق معدنية للتخلص من الفوط الورقية |
| boxes of precious metal | علب من المعادن النفيسة |
| boxes of precious metal for needles | علب من المعادن النفيسة للإبر |
| boxes of precious metal for sweetmeats | علب من المعادن النفيسة للفاكهة المحلاة |
| boxes of vulcanised fibre | علب من الألياف المقساة |
| boxes of wood or plastic | علب من الخشب أو البلاستيك |
| boxes, not of precious metal, for needles | علب ليست من المعادن النفيسة مخصصة للإبر |
| boxing gloves | قفازات الملاكمة |
| bp | دستور الأدوية البريطاني |
| bp | نقطة الغليان |
| Bp = base pair | زوج قاعدة |
| br | عريض |
| bracelets (identification-), not of metal, for hospital purposes | أساور (أساور تحديد الهوية) ليست من المعدن وتستخدم في المستشفيات |
| bracelets [jewellery, jewelry (am.)] | أساور [مجوهرات] |
| bracelets of metal (identification -) for hospitals | أساور من المعدن (أساور من المعدن لتحديد الهوية وخلافه) للاستخدام في المستشفيات |
| braces | حاصرتان |
| braces (fastenings for-) | حمالات البنطلون (إبزيمات تثبيت حمالات البنطلون) |
| braces for clothing [suspenders] | حمالات للملابس [حمالات للتعليق] |
| braces of metal for handling loads | دعامات من المعدن لتعبئة وشحن الحمولات |
| brachial plexopathy | اعتلال الضفيرة العضدية |
| brachiocephalic | عضدي رأسي |
| bracket | حامل؛ سناد |
| brackets | كتائف (مفرد كتيفة) |
| brackets (bearing -) for machines | كتيفات (كتيفات التحميل) في الآلات |
| brackets (picture frame -) | كتيفات (كتيفات إطار الصورة) |
| brackets for gas burners | كتيفات للمواقد التي تعمل بالغاز |
| brackets of metal for building | كتيفات من المعدن تستخدم في البناء |
| brads | مسامير صغيرة الرأس أو بدون |
| bradyarrhythmias | بطء النبض |
| bradykinesia | بطء الحركة |
| braiders [hand tools] | المجدلية [عدد يدوية] |
| braiding machines | آلات الجدل |
| braids | الجدائل |
| brain | يضرب على الرأس، دماغ، مخ، فهم، ذكاء |
| brain activity regulator | منظم نشاط المخ |
| brain chemistry | كيمياء الدماغ |
| brain dump | لغو؛ الإفراغ العقلي: كلام كثير غير مفيد ردا على سؤال بسيط |
| brain electric signaling | إعطاء إشارة كهربية مخية |
| brain electric stimulation | حث (تحفيز) كهربي للمخ/للدماغ |
| brain homogenate of both rats and mice | مادة متجانسة من أدمغة الجرذان والفئران |
| brain imaging | تصوير المخ |
| brain implant | زراعة مخ |
| brain mapper | راسم خرائط الدماغ |
| brain mapping | رسم خرائط الدماغ |
| brain regenerative capabilities | قدرات المخ على إعادة التوليد |
| brain scanner | ماسح ضوئي للمخ، ماسح ضوئي للدماغ |
| brain scanning | مسح للمخ، مسح للدماغ |
| brain stimulation | حث (تحفيز) المخ |
| brain topology | طوبولوجيا الدماغ |
| brain tumors | أورام المخ |
| brain wave measurement | قياس موجات الدماغ |
| braincase | علبة الدماغ |
| brain-computer interfaces (medi) | أسطح بينية بين المخ والحاسوب |
| brain-dead | معطل تماما؛ متوقف (للبرامج والمعدات المتوقفة) |
| brainfag | كلال الدماغ، الإجهاد العقلي |
| braininess | ذكاء |
| brainless | متبلد الذهن |
| brainless person | شخص مفتقر للذهن العميق |

| | |
|---|---|
| brainpower | القدرة العقلية |
| brainstorm | يقدح زناد الفكر، فكرة بارعة مفاجئة، قدحُ زناد الفكر |
| brainy | ذكي |
| brainy person | شخص ذو ذهن عميق |
| brake fluid | سائل الفرامل [الكابحات] |
| brake lining materials, partly processed | مواد بطانة الفرامل [الكابحات]، معالجة جزئياً |
| brake linings for vehicles | بطانات الفرامل [الكابحات] في المركبات |
| brake segments for vehicles | قطع الفرامل [الكابحات] في المركبات |
| brake segments other than for vehicles | قطع الفرامل [الكابحات] بخلاف المستخدمة في المركبات |
| brake shoes for vehicles | لُقم الفرامل [الكابحات] المستخدمة في المركبات |
| brakes for bicycles, cycles | الفرامل [الكابحات] المستخدمة في الدراجات الهوائية |
| braking system | نظام اختراق |
| bran | نُخالة |
| bran mash for animal consumption | مجروش النخالة للاستهلاك الحيواني |
| branch | فرع |
| branch boxes [electricity] | صناديق التفريع [طاقة كهربائية] |
| branches of the army | أفرع الجيش |
| branching pipes of metal | مواسير تفرّيع معدنية |
| brand conceptualization | البناء المفهومي للعلامة، بناء مفهوم عن علامة |
| brand driven innovation | ابتكار تسوقه قاطرة وضع المنتج. جهد ابتكاري غرضه تحسين المنتج التجاري يسير على هدى من وضع المنتج بالسوق وخصوصياته |
| brand growth | نمو العلامة |
| brand licensing | ترخيص علامة |
| brand promotion | ترويج العلامة |
| brand value | قيمة العلامة |
| branding irons | الميسم [أدوات يوسم بها] |
| brand's designability | قابلية العلامة للتصميم |
| brandy | براندي |
| brass, unwrought or semi-wrought | النحاس الأصفر، غير مشكل أو شبه مشكّل |
| brassards | قطع من القماش تحمل شارة أو علامة ترتدى على الذراع |
| brassieres | صديريات للثدي |
| brattice cloth (tarred -) | قماش الحواجز (قماش الحواجز المشبع بالقطران) |
| brazing (rods of metal for -) | لحام (قضبان معدنية للحام) |
| brazing alloys | سبائك لحام |
| brazing fluxes | صهور اللحام |
| brazing preparations | مستحضرات لحام |
| brb | سأعود ثانية |
| breach of duty | عدم القيام بالواجب |
| bread | الخبز |
| bread (diabetic -) | الخبز (خبز الحمية) [لمرضى السكري] |
| bread (ginger -) | الخبز (كعكة الزنجبيل) |
| bread baskets (bakers' -) | سلال الخبز (سلال الخبازين) |
| bread baskets [domestic] | سلال الخبز [منزلية] |

| | |
|---|---|
| bread bin | صندوق خزين الخبز |
| bread board | لوح تقطيع الخبز |
| bread cutting machine | آلة قطع الخبز |
| bread roll | قرص الخبز |
| bread toaster | جهاز تحميص الخبز الكهربائية |
| breadcrumbs | كسارات الخبز؛ قطع صغيرة من الخبز [لعمل الفتّة] |
| breadth parameter | متغير الاتساع |
| break | يفصل (كهرباء) |
| break (up) | يفصل (كهرباء) |
| break (up) | يكسّر؛ يفتت |
| break position | إعلان (يبث) بين برنامجين؛ موقع فاصل؛ موقع بين برنامجين |
| breakable | قابل للقطع |
| breakable mechanical link | وصلة ميكانيكية قابلة للقطع |
| breakably | 1. على نحو قابل للفصل<br>2. على نحو قابل للكسر |
| breakage of the si-c bond | قطع الرابطة Si-C |
| breaker | قاطع دائرة كهربائية؛ قاطع تيار. انظر circuit breakers |
| breaker | دورق |
| breakers | خافضات اللزوجة |
| break-in | بدء التشغيل |
| break-in | اختراق؛ تغلغل لصوص |
| breaking | توقف؛ فترات توقف عن العمل |
| breaking elongation | استطالة الكسر |
| breaking fracturing fluids | تخفيض لزوجة موائع التكسير |
| breaking strength | مقاومة الكسر أو القطع |
| breaking up large estates | تقسيم الملكيات الكبيرة |
| breakthrough | اقتحام |
| breakthrough discovery | اكتشاف مؤثر |
| breast drills | مثاقب الصدر |
| breast pumps | مضخات الصدر |
| breast-nursing pads | وسائد رقيقة للرضاعة |
| breasts (artificial -) | صدور (صدور صناعية) |
| breaststroke | صدر (في السباحة) |
| breath freshening sprays | رشاشات إنعاش التنفس |
| breathalyzer | جهاز قياس الكحول |
| breathing apparatus for underwater swimming | جهاز التنفس المستخدم في السباحة تحت الماء |
| breathlesness (dyspnea) | ضيق التنفس |
| brecanavir | بريكانافير |
| breccia | الرواهص ( البريشيا |
| bred stock | قطعان التربية (الماشية) |
| breeches [for wear] | البنطلونات القصيرة [للملابس] |
| breeches of firearms | مؤخرة الأسلحة النارية |
| breed | ينجب، يستولد |
| breeding (poultry for -) | تربية (طيور مخصصة للتربية) |
| brewer's rice | كسر الأرز |
| brewing machines | آلات تخمير الجعة |
| bricks | طوب |
| bricks (earth for -) | طوب (طين يصنع منه الطوب) |
| brickwork | بناء بالطوب |
| brickwork preservatives, except paints and oils | مواد حفظ أعمال البناء بالطوب، فيما عدا الدهانات والزيوت |
| bridge | جسر |

| | |
|---|---|
| bridge | قنطرة |
| bridge | قنطرة؛ جسر |
| bridge | ينشئ أو يكون قنطرة |
| bridge cables | كبلات الكباري |
| bridged and caged saturated ring groups | مجموعات حلقية مشبعة متخطاة ومحصورة |
| bridged group | مجموعة مجسَّرة: مجموعة كيميائية ذات جسر أو قنطرة |
| bridged metallocene compound | مركب ميتالوسين مجسَّر |
| bridgehead | رأس جسر |
| bridges (roller -) | جسور (جسور دوارة) |
| bridges for musical instruments | الأمشاط الخاصة بالآلات الموسيقية |
| bridging | توصيل (مع مركبات) |
| bridging group | مجموعة ربط |
| bridles [harness] | اللجام [أطقم الفرس] |
| bridoons | لجام |
| brief description of the drawings | وصف مختصر للرسومات |
| briefcases | محافظ جلدية مسطحة |
| brigade | لواء |
| brigadier (brig) | عميد |
| bright comedy | الكوميديا المرحة |
| bright field microscope | مجهر المجال المضيء |
| bright gold for ceramics | الذهب اللامع للاستخدام في الخزف |
| bright platinum for ceramics | البلاتينيوم اللامع للاستخدام في الخزف |
| brighteners | مواد ساطعة |
| brightening chemicals (color- [colour-] -) for household purposes [laundry] | كيماويات تزهيه (كيماويات تزهيه الألوان) للاستخدام في الأغراض المنزلية [غسيل الملابس] |
| brightening chemicals (color- [colour-] -) for industrial purposes | كيماويات تفتيح (كيماويات تفتيح الألوان) للاستخدام في الأغراض الصناعية |
| brightness range | نطاق درجات السطوع |
| brillouin optical time domain reflectometer | ومقياس الانعكاس الضوئي عبر نطاق الزمن لبريلوين |
| brine | محلول ملحي |
| bring sth to | يصل به إلى كذا؛ يدفعه إلى كذا |
| briquettes (combustible -) | قوالب (قوالب قابلة للاحتراق) |
| briquettes (wood -) | قوالب (قوالب خشبية) |
| bristles (animal -) [brushware] | شعور خشنة (شعور الحيوانات الخشنة) [فراشي] |
| british parliament | البرلمان البريطاني |
| brittle | هشاشة |
| broad band | موجة عريضة أو واسعة النطاق |
| broad molecular weight distribution | توزيع وزن جزيئي عريض: توزيع وزن جزيئي في نطاق عريض |
| broad singlet | مفردة عريضة |
| broadband | عريض النطاق |
| broadband network | شبكة عريضة الموجة |
| broadcast | بث؛ إرسال |
| broadcast planting | الزراعة بطريقة البذر |
| broadcast storm | عاصفة إرسال؛ عاصفة من الرسائل |
| broadcasting materials | مواد إذاعية |
| broadened | واسع |
| broader patent | براءة أوسع |
| brocades | أقمشة مطرزة |
| broke | فاقد الورق، الذي يتم التخلص منه خلال أي من مراحل التصنيع |
| broker | وسيط |
| broker clause | بند تحديد ما إذا كان هناك وسطاء |
| brokerage | وساطة |
| broket | قوس زاوية |
| bromide | بروميد |
| bromine | بروم |
| bromo-derivative | مشتق برومو |
| bromomethyl analogue | مناظر برومو ميثيل |
| bronchial carcinoma | الورم السرطاني الشعبي |
| bronchial leak | ارتشاح شعبي |
| bronchiectasis | توسع الشعب |
| bronchiolitis | التهاب الشعيبات |
| bronchitis (including chronic bronchitis) | التهاب الشعب الهوائية (وتشمل التهاب الشعب الهوائية المزمن) |
| bronchoconstriction | تضييق الشعب |
| bronchodilating preparations | مستحضرات توسيع الشعب الهوائية |
| bronchodilation | توسيع الشعب |
| bronchogenic carcinoma | سرطان الرئة |
| bronchopleural fistulae | ناسور شعبي |
| bronchopulmonary dysplasia | خلل التنسج الشعبي الرئوي |
| bronchospasm | تشنج شعبي |
| bronze | البرونز |
| bronze powder | مسحوق البرونز |
| bronzes [works of art] | تماثيل برونزية [أعمال فنية] |
| bronzes for tombstones | برونز للاستخدام في بلاط الأضرحة |
| bronzing lacquers | لاكيه البرونز |
| brooches [clothing accessories] | البروش [دبوس زينة للملابس] |
| brooches [jewellery, jewelry (am.)] | البروش [مجوهرات] |
| broom handles of metal | مقابض المكنسة اليدوية من المعدن |
| brooms | المكانس اليدوية |
| broth | مرق |
| broth | سائل رقيق |
| broth concentrates | أشكال مركزة من المرق |
| brouter | موجِّه القنطرة: يجمع بين وظيفتي القنطرة bridge والموجِّه router |
| brown oxide | أكسيد بني |
| brown rice /canned rice/ lightly miled rice | أرز مقشور، أرز معلب، أرز غير تام الضرب |
| brown-sequard syndrome | متلازمة براون سيكار |
| brownstock | الخام البني، معلق اللب غير المبيض |
| browse | يستعرض |
| browser | المستعرض |
| brush border | الحافة الفرجونية |
| brush goods | منتجات الفرش |

| | |
|---|---|
| brush mountings | حوامل الفرش |
| brushes | الفرش |
| brushes (dishwashing -) | فرش (فرش غسيل الأطباق) |
| brushes (dynamo -) | فرش (فرش المولدات) |
| brushes [parts of machines] | فرش [أجزاء من الماكينات] |
| brushes for cleaning body cavities | فرش لتنظيف تجاويف الجسد |
| brushes for cleaning tanks and containers | فرش لتنظيف الصهاريج والأوعية |
| brushes for footwear | فرش خاصة بلباس القدم |
| brushes, electric [except parts of machines] | فرش كهربائية [فيما عدا أجزاء الآلات] |
| brushes, electrically operated | فرش تعمل كهربائياً |
| brush-making (material for -) | تصنيع الفرش (مواد لتصنيع الفرش) |
| bryozoa | الحزازيات |
| bs | قياس بريطاني |
| btoa | برنامج بتواي |
| btu | وحدة حرارية بريطانية |
| btu per pound | وحدة حرارة بريطانية لكل رطل |
| btu/ib | وحدة حرارية بريطانية/ رطل |
| btw ; by the way | بالمناسبة |
| bubble | يمرر فقاعات (من غاز) |
| bubble breaker | مكسر الفقاعات |
| bubble breaker assembly | تجميعة مكسرة للفقاعات |
| bubble packs (plastic-) [for wrapping or packaging] | أكياس الفقاقيع (أكياس فقاقيع بلاستيكية) [للتغليف أو التعبئة] |
| bubble point | نقطة التفقع |
| bubbling | تمرير فقاعات |
| buccal administration | إعطاء في الشدق |
| buccal and sublingual | في الشّدق، وتحت اللسان |
| buccins [trumpets] | آلات موسيقية بالنفخ [أبواق] |
| buckets | دِلاء |
| buckles (shoe -) | إبزيمات (إبزيم الحذاء) |
| buckles [clothing accessories] | إبزيمات [إكسسوارات للملابس] |
| buckling | انبعاج؛ تقوّس؛ تحدّب |
| buckram | بَكْرَم [قماش قاسى للتجليد] |
| buckskin for cleaning | قطع من الجلد للتنظيف |
| budding inhibitors | مثبطات تبرعم |
| budding knives | سكاكين تطعيم النباتات |
| budgetary transaction | معاملة أو صفقة مؤثرة على الميزانية |
| budgeted expenditures | نفقات مضمنة في الميزانية |
| buffer | محلول منظم (للرقم الهيدروجيني PH) |
| buffer | دائرة وقائية؛ يعالج بمحلول منظم؛ ذاكرة التخزين المؤقت |
| buffer battery | بطارية دارئة (للتغذية المرتدة) |
| buffer vessel | وعاء حائل |
| buffers for railway rolling stock | مخففات الاصطدام في المعدات الدراجة على خطوط السكة الحديدية |
| buffers of rubber (shock-absorbing-) | مخففات الاصطدام من المطاط (ماص للصدمات) |
| bug | خطأ |
| buggy | ملئ بالعيوب |
| bugle(r) | البواق: النافخ في البوق |

| | |
|---|---|
| build rate equation | معادلة تغير الميل |
| build up | يتراكم |
| builders supply merchant | تاجر مواد بناء |
| building (framework for -), not of metal | البناء (سقالة للبناء)، ليست من المعدن |
| building (framework of metal for -) | البناء (سقالة للبناء من المعدن) |
| building (reinforcing materials of metal for -) | البناء (مواد داعمة مصنوعة من المعدن للبناء) |
| building automation solutions | حلول جعل المبنى أوتوماتيكيا |
| building automation system | نظام جعل المبنى أوتوماتيكيا |
| building blocks [toys] | وحدات البناء [ألعاب] |
| building boards of metal | ألواح البناء من المعدن |
| building cardboard [asphalted] | الورق المقوى المستخدم في البناء [مسفلت] |
| building games | ألعاب البناء |
| building glass | زجاج المباني |
| building management system | نظام إدارة الأبنية. |
| building materials industry | صناعة مواد البناء |
| building materials of metal | مواد بناء من المعدن |
| building materials, not of metal | مواد بناء ليست من المعدن |
| building or furniture fittings of nickel-silver | تجهيزات البناء أو الأثاث من نيكل - فضة |
| building panels of metal | الألواح المعدنية الرقيقة المستخدمة في البناء |
| building panels, not of metal | الألواح الرقيقة المستخدمة في البناء، ليست من المعدن |
| building paper | ورق البناء |
| building stone | حجر البناء |
| building system | نظام بناء |
| building technology | تقنية بناء |
| building timber | أخشاب المباني |
| buildings (fittings of metal for -) | المباني (تجهيزات المباني من المعدن) |
| buildings of metal | مباني من المعدن |
| buildings, not of metal | مباني ليست من المعدن |
| buildings, transportable, of metal | مباني معدنية قابلة للنقل |
| build-up | تزايد؛ تراكم |
| built machines | ماكينات مُصنعة من قبل |
| built-in | مدمَج؛ مضمَّن |
| built-in screen | شاشة مضمَّنة |
| bulbs | البصيلات |
| bulging deformation | تشوه انتفاخي |
| bulging step portion | جزء السدادة المرحلي (أو التدريجي) |
| bulimia | نهم |
| bulimia nervosa | حالة الشهوة العصبية للطعام |
| bulk | الجزء الرئيسي أو الأساسي من القوات؛ القلب |
| bulk density | كثافة حجمية |
| bulk form | صورة سائبة |
| bulk or global operating temperature | درجة حرارة التشغيل الكلية أو الشاملة |
| bulk sample capacitance | سعة عينة كلية |
| bulk separators | جهاز فصل الحجم |

| | |
|---|---|
| bulk starter | كتلة المادة البادئة |
| bulkhead | فاصل |
| bulking | تمدد حجمي |
| bulking agent | عامل تمدد حجمي |
| bulking agents | عوامل زيادة الكتلة والحجم؛ عوامل منفشة |
| bulky means | وسيلة كبيرة الحجم |
| bull bars | واقيات المصابيح الأمامية |
| bulldozer, earthmover | جرافة (جرافات): لشق الطرق |
| bulldozers | جرارات التسوية [بولدوزر] |
| bulletin board services | خدمة لوحات الإعلانات |
| bullet-proof waistcoats [vests (am.)] | صديريات مضادة للرصاص |
| bullheading | التوجُّه الرئيسي |
| bullous pemphigoid | شبيه الفقاع الفقاعي |
| bumper guard | واقي مصد |
| bumpers (vehicle -) | مصدات (مصدات للمركبات) |
| bumpers for automobiles | مصدات للاستخدام في العربات |
| bungs of metal | سدادات من المعدن |
| bungs, not of metal | سدادات ليست من المعدن |
| bunion pads | اللفافات الخاصة بالورم الملتهب في المفصل الكبير من إبهام القدم |
| buns | الكعك المحلى |
| bunting | قماش الرايات |
| buoys (marking -) | العوامات (عوامات لإرشاد السفن) |
| buoys (mooring -) not of metal | العوامات (عوامات الإرساء) ليست من المعدن |
| buoys (mooring -) of metal | عوامات (عوامات الإرساء) من المعدن |
| buoys (signalling -) | عوامات (عوامات التحذير والإشارة) |
| burble | يشتغل (بكفاءة منخفضة) |
| burden of proof | عبء الإثبات |
| bureau international des expositions | المكتب الدولي للمعارض |
| buried advertisement | إعلان محشور أو مطمور بين إعلانات أخرى |
| burkitt lymphoma | الورم الليمفاوي لبيركت |
| burn off | يفصل بالحرق |
| burner | موقد؛ ناسخ أقراص |
| burner grate | شعلة البوتاجاز |
| burners | مواقد [أفران] |
| burners (acetylene -) | مواقد (مواقد الأسيتيلين) |
| burners (gas -) | مواقد (مواقد بالغاز) |
| burners (germicidal -) | مواقد (مواقد مطهرة للميكروبات) |
| burners (incandescent -) | مواقد (مواقد وهاجة) |
| burners (laboratory -) | مواقد (مواقد معملية) |
| burners (perfume -) | مواقد (مواقد العطر) |
| burners for lamps | مواقد المصابيح |
| burning of songs onto blank cd | نسخ الأغاني على اسطوانات مضغوطة فارغة |
| burnout | الاحتراق النفسي |
| burns (preparations for the treatment of -) | حروق (مستحضرات لمعالجة الحروق) |
| burs (dental -) | مثاقب (مثاقب أسنان) |
| bursitis | التهاب كيسي |
| bus | ناقل |
| bus bars; busbars | قضبان التوصيل: وهي عبارة عن قضبان نحاسية تأخذ أشكال مختلفة وكذلك مساحة مقطع مختلفة حسب الحمل التصميمي وكذلك حسب الشركة المصنعة |
| bus topology | بنية الناقل |
| busbars | قضبان توزيع |
| buses (motor -) | الحافلات (الأتوبيسات) |
| bushel | بوشل |
| bushes | الأدغال |
| bushhammers | مطارق النقش |
| bushing | وصلة ازدواج |
| bushings ; bush | جلبة |
| business | عمل تجارية، نشاط تجاري |
| business banking | الخدمات المصرفية للشركات |
| business continuity solutions | حلول إدارة |
| business controls | أدوات تحكم تجارية |
| business environment | بيئة تجاريه |
| business greening | تخضر العمل التجاري. جعل العمل التجاري معززا للبيئة. |
| business idea | فكرة تجارية |
| business internships | فرص إلحاق بالتدريب العملي على الأعمال |
| business knowhow | دراية الكيفية التجارية |
| business logic | منطق العمل |
| business method patent | براءة منبثقة عن طريقة تجارية |
| business model | نموذج العمل |
| business model | نموذج تجاري |
| business solutions | حلول تجارية |
| business torts | دعاوى تجارية |
| business unit | وحدة الأعمال |
| busks (corset -) | أضلاع المشد [كورسيه] |
| busts of china, terra-cotta or glass | أواني الشرب من الصيني، أو التراكوتا أو الزجاج |
| busts of common metal | التماثيل النصفية من المعادن غير النفيسة |
| busts of precious metal | التماثيل النصفية من المعادن النفيسة |
| busts of stone, concrete or marble | التماثيل النصفية من الأحجار، أو الخرسانة أو الرخام |
| busts of wood, wax, plaster or plastic | التماثيل النصفية من الخشب، أو الشمع، أو الجص أو البلاستيك |
| busulphan | بيوسلفان |
| but/ib | وحدة حرارة بريطانية but لكل رطل |
| butanediol | بيوتان دايول |
| butchers' animals (skinning appliances and instruments for -) | حيوانات الجزارة (أدوات ومعدات سلخ الحيوانات) |
| butoxide | بيوتوكسيد |
| butoxy | بيوتوكسي |
| butt | تناكبي، |
| butter | الزبد |
| butter (chocolate nut -) | زبده (زبده بندق الشكولاته) |
| butter (cocoa -) | زبده (زبده الكاكاو) |
| butter (coconut -) | زبده (زبده جوز الهند) |
| butter (colorants for -) | زبده (مواد تلوين الزبد) |
| butter (peanut -) | زبده (زبده الفول السوداني) |

| | |
|---|---|
| butter dishes | أطباق الزبد |
| butter machines | ماكينات صنع الزبد |
| butter oil | زيت الزبد |
| butter powder | مسحوق الزبد |
| buttercream | زبده (قشدة الزبد) |
| butter-dish covers | أغطية أطباق الزبد |
| butterfly | فراشة (في السباحة) |
| butterfly nets | شباك صيد الفراشات |
| butterfly valves | صمامات الفراشة؛ الصمامات الخانقة ذات الأقراص |
| butterine | الزبد الصناعي |
| butternut | جوز أرمد |
| buttonhooks | أدوات التزرير [كلابات لتزرير القفازات والأحذية] |
| buttons | الأزرار |
| butts [parts of hides] | جلود الحيوان [أجزاء من الجلود المدبوغة] |
| butyl | بيوتيل |
| butyronitrile | بيوتيرو نيتريل |
| buzz word | الكلمة الرنانة |
| buzzers | الطنان [جهاز شبيه بالجرس الكهربائي] |
| buzzers, electric | طنان كهربائي |
| by forced air | بالهواء المضغوط |
| by gravity | بفعل الجاذبية |
| by hand | يدويا |
| by total weight of the composition | بالوزن من إجمالي وزن التركيبة |
| by-elections | انتخابات فرعية |
| bypass | وصلة جانبية |
| bypass | تمرير جانبي |
| bypass assembly | تجميعة مسار فرعي: تجميعة لمسار فرعي |
| by-pass line | خط تحويل جانبي |
| by-products of the processing of cereals | منتجات ثانوية لمعالجة الحبوب |
| byssinosis | السحار القطني |
| byte | البايت |

# C

| | |
|---|---|
| c.a. | حوالي |
| c/hr | درجة مئوية / ساعة |
| c1-20 alcohol | كحول به من 1 إلى 20 ذرة كربون |
| c1-4 alcohol | كحول به من 1 إلى 4 ذرات كربون |
| c1-4 alkyl group | مجموعة C1-4 ألكيل |
| c1-6 alkyl group | مجموعة C1-6 ألكيل |
| c-5 alkyl substitutions | مجموعات الاستبدال C-5 ألكيل |
| c5 asphaltenes content | محتوى مركبات أسفلتين C5 |
| c5-unsubstituted | ليس به استبدال عند الموضع 5 |
| ca. | حوالي |
| cabin | مقصورة |
| cable | كيبل |
| cable drum | اسطوانة أو بكرة كبل |
| cable jacket curing | معالجة غطاء الكابل |
| cable tv piracy | قرصنة تلفزة بطاقات الاشتراك |
| cache | ذاكرة وسيطة |
| cachet | برشامة |
| cachexia | ضعف عام؛ هزال |
| cachexia secondary to acquired immune deficiency syndrome (aids) | الهزال التالي للإصابة بمتلازمة نقص المناعة |
| cachexia secondary to infection or malignancy | الهزال التالي للإصابة أو المرض |
| cacoon | شرنقة |
| cad | تصميم بمساعدة الحاسب |
| cadaver | جثّة |
| cadrg | رسومات متسامتة رقمية قوسية مضغوطة |
| cafeteria feeding of rats | تغذية الجرذان بطريقة الاختيار الحر |
| caisson | مأطورة مجوفة |
| cakes | كعك |
| cakes | كتل؛ تكتلات |
| calcareous algae | والطحالب الكلسية |
| calcic feldspar | الفلسبارات الكلسية |
| calcification | تكلس |
| calcilutite | حجري وحلي كلسي |
| calcination | تحميص |
| calcination of the cobalt impregnated support preferably is conducted in air | يتم بشكل مفضل تحميص المادة الحاملة المشربة بالكوبالت في الهواء |
| calcinator | محمص |
| calcine | يكلس؛ يحل إلى كلس |
| calcined contact product | منتج مكلسن ناتج عن تلامس |
| calcining | تحميص |
| calcinosis | التكلس |
| calcite | الكالسايت |
| calcitization | الكلسنة |
| calcium monohydrogen phosphate (dcp) | فوسفات كالسيوم أحادية الهيدروجين |
| calcium sulfate dihydrate | ثنائي هيدرات كبريتات كالسيوم |
| calcium sulfate hemihydrate | نصف هيدرات كبريتات الكالسيوم |
| calcuation analysis | التحليل الحسابي |
| calculated molecular weight | الوزن الجزيئي المحسوب |
| calefacient | محر، مدفئ |
| calefaction | حموة، تسخين |
| calefactory | محر، محدث، حرارة |
| calender | وسيلة تمليس |
| calf | بطن الساق |
| calibrate | يعاير، يدرج |
| calibration | معايرة |
| calibration | معايرة، تدريج |
| calibration, industrial waste / management | المعيار، النفايات الصناعية، الإدارة الصناعية |
| calibre | عيار البندقية |
| call for votes (cfv) | دعوة الأشخاص |
| call list clear, p 10 | قائمة المكالمات مفرغة |
| call logs | سجلات المكالمات |
| call now motivators | محفزات "اتصلوا حالا"؛ محفزات للاتصال فوراً |
| call timers | عدادات المكالمات؛ موقتات المكالمات |
| call to action | الدعوة للاتصال؛ دعوة الجمهور للاتصال والشراء؛ فقرة الاستحثاث؛ الفقرة الاستحثاثية |
| call to action (cta) | فقرة الدعوة |
| caller ring back tone (crbt) | نغمة رنين المتصل |
| calling line identification (cli) | تعريف خط الإتصال: وهى الخدمة التي تمكن مستقبل المكالمة من الدخول على خط المتصل. ومثال على هذ الخدمة هو خدمة الرقم 1471 والتي تقدمها شركة الإتصالات البريطانية لعملائها كما هو الحال أيضا بالنسبة لخدمة إظهار رقم الطالب التي تقدم لمستخدمي الهاتف المحمول. |
| callus | جزء من الجلد أو اللحاء متصلب |
| calorific | حراري |
| calorific | مولد للحرارة |
| calorimeter | مقياس حراري؛ مقياس كمية الحرارة؛ مقياس الحرارة |
| calorimeter | مسعر، كالورمتر. جهاز لقياس كمية الحرارة الناشئة عن الاحتكاك أو الانفجار |
| calorimetric | مسعري |
| calorimetry | قياس الحرارة |
| calorimetry | المسعرية، الكالوريمترية: قياس كمية الحرارة |
| caltrop | كرة (مجازا) |
| cam | كاميرا |
| camber | يحدب، يحدودب، احدوداب |
| camcorder | كاميرا فيديو؛ كاميرا تسجيل |

| | |
|---|---|
| camelid dabs | أجسام مضادة نطاقية جملية |
| camelid germaline | سلالة جرثومية جَمَلي |
| camelid immunoglobulin variable domain | نطاق متغير جَمَلي لجلوبيولين مناعي |
| camelid variable domain | نطاق متغير جَمَلي |
| camelids | فصيلة الجمال |
| camelization | (1) التوافق مع العائلة الجملية.<br>(2) جعله متوافقا مع العائلة الجملية. |
| camera mode | وضع الكاميرا |
| camouflage | تمويه؛ يموه |
| campbell soup position | موقع شوربة كامبل |
| camphoric | كافوري |
| campus-wide information server (cwis) | خادم معلومات واسع النطاق. |
| canard | طائرة متقدمة الذيل |
| cancel | يلغي |
| cancers | أنواع سرطان |
| candidate | مرشح. |
| candidate leads | بروتينات LEADs مرشحة: بروتينات طافرة قيادية مرشحة |
| canine | الكلب |
| cannabinoid | شبيه القنب |
| cannabinoid receptors | مستقبلات شبيه القنّب |
| canonical | قانوني؛ معترف به؛ مقبول |
| canonical wnt signaling | إصدار إشارات Wnt مقبولة |
| canula | أنبوب دقيق |
| canvas | لوحة |
| cap | غطاء؛ سدادة؛ يتوج، يتم، يضع حدا أعلى لشيء، غطاء القنينة، قمة، ذروة، يرسم سقفا، يتم قمة، ذروة |
| cap rock; caprock | صخور غطاء للنفط |
| capabilities | قدرات |
| capability | قدرة |
| capable | قادر على |
| capacitator | مكثف كهربائي |
| capacitive coupling | تقارن تكاثفي |
| capacitive element | عنصر سعوي |
| capacitor | مكثف |
| capacity | طاقة، قدرة |
| capacity of exercise | الأهلية |
| capillary action | الفعل الشعري |
| capillary action | الخاصية الشعرية |
| capillary column | عمود شعيري |
| capillary voltage | فلطية شعرية |
| capital | رأس المال |
| capital costs | تكلفة رأس المال |
| capital expenditures | مصروفات رأسمالية |
| capital goods industries | صناعات رأسمالية |
| capital spending | نفقات رأسمالية |
| capital-intensive projects | مشروعات ذات كثافة رأس مالية عالية |
| capitulate | يستسلم بشروط معينة |
| caprine | ماعزي؛ متعلق بالماعز |
| caps | واسمات متوالية متعددة الشكل مكبرة مقسومة |
| capsular | عليبي، محفوظ في عليبة أو كبسولة |
| capsulate | محفوظ في عليبة أو كبسولة |
| capsule | كبسولة |
| capsule | عليبة، مركز، غشاء |
| capsule ( solid or soft ) | كبسولة ( صلبة أو رخوة) |
| captain (capt.) | نقيب |
| capture | يلتقط |
| capture | يرصد |
| capture | يحتجز |
| capture | يمسك بـ يقبض على |
| capture (a position, weapons etc.) | يستولى على (مكان أو أسلحة) |
| capture a series of still images | يلتقط سلسلة من الصور الثابتة |
| captured | ممسك به |
| captured text | نص ملتَقَط |
| capturer | ممسك بـ قابض على |
| capturing | الإمساك بـ القبض على |
| capturing sun's energy | الإمساك بطاقة الشمس |
| car | عربة، سيارة |
| car suspension | تعليق السيارة |
| car tracking | تعقب السيارات |
| carabinieri | الشرطة الإيطالية |
| carat | قيراط |
| carbaldehyde | كربالدهيد |
| carbamate intermediate | مادة الكاربامات الوسيطة |
| carbaminodoyl | كربامينودويل |
| carbide | كربيد |
| carbodiimide | كربو داي إيميد |
| carbon | كربون |
| carbon awareness | وعي الخطر الكربوني. الإلمام بخطر التلوث النجم عن زيادة الكربون. |
| carbon black | أسود الكربون |
| carbon credits | اعتمادات تخفيض الكربون: اعتماد الكربون يساوي خفض ثاني اوكسيد الكربون بطن واحد |
| carbon dioxide evolution | انبعاث ثاني أكسيد كربون |
| carbon efficient technology | تقنية اتصالات ومعلومات فعالة في مواجهة الخطر الكربوني |
| carbon nanotube batteries | بطاريات أنابيب النانو الكربونية |
| carbon nano-tube x-ray source array | مصفوفة مصدر أشعة سينية لأنبوب نانو كربوني |
| carbon residue | المتبقي من الكربون |
| carbon steel | صلب كربوني |
| carbon supersaturated and a low oxygen partial pressure environments | بيئات فائقة التشبع بالكربون ذات ضغط أكسجين جزئي منخفض |
| carbon tetrachloride | ترا كلوريد الكربون |
| carbonate | يحول إلى كربونات |
| carbonate rocks | صخور الكربونات |
| carbonated | محول إلى كربونات، مشبع بثاني أكسيد الكربون |
| carbonated beverages | المشروبات المكربنة |
| carbonation | التحويل إلى كربونات |
| carbon-carbon | كربون-كربون |
| carbon-carbon double bond | رابطة كربون-كربون مزدوجة واحدة على الأقل |

| | |
|---|---|
| carbon-carbon double bonds | روابط كربون-كربون مزدوجة |
| carbonitrile | كربو نيتريل |
| carbonization | التحويل إلى كربون |
| carbonize | يحول إلى كربون |
| carbonized | محول إلى كربون |
| carbonyl oxysulphide | كربونيل أوكسي كبريتيد |
| carbonylated | المحتوية على مجموعة كربونيل |
| carbonylation | إدخال مجموعة الكربونيل |
| carbonylative cyclization | تحويل إلى صيغة الكربونيل الحلقي |
| carboxy | كربوكسي |
| carboxy methyl celulose | سيليولوز كربوكسي ميثيل |
| carboxylate | كربوكسيلات |
| carboxylic acid | حمض كربوكسيلي |
| carboxylic acid bioisostere | متماثل تجاسمي حيوي لحمض كربوكسيلي |
| carboxylic acid esters | إسترات حمض كربوكسيلي |
| carboxy-terminal alpha-helical coiled-coil | ملف ألفا-حلزوني عند طرف الكربوكسي |
| carburized | مكربن |
| carburized transition metal-alumincompound | مركب فلز انتقالي مكربن-ألومينا |
| carcinogenic | مولد للكارسينوما؛ مسرطِنة |
| carcinoma | كارسينوما؛ ورم سرطاني بالأنسجة الظهارية |
| card | بطاقة |
| card to disc | من البطاقة إلى القرص |
| cardfile | بطاقة |
| cardiac arrhythmias | اضطرابات عدم انتظام إيقاع القلب |
| cardiac arrythmia | عدم انتظام إيقاع القلب |
| cardiac rapid delayed rectifier current ikr | التيار القلبي Ikr السريع الناتج من المقوم المتأخر |
| cardigan | سترة من الصوف المحبوك |
| cardinal points | نقط إشارية |
| cardiovascular | قلبي وعائي |
| cards | بطاقات |
| career officer | ظابط مهني |
| caret | علامة الإدراج، أو الإقحام |
| careware | المشاركة الخيرية: شكل من أشكال المشاركة يطالبك فيه منشئ البرنامج بسداد رسوم البرنامج إلى مؤسسة خيرية |
| cargo meal | مسحوق الأرز المبشور |
| cargo pants | سراويل بجيوب كبيرة |
| caribbean development bank | بنك التنمية الكاريبي |
| caribbean free trade association | الاتحاد الكاريبي للتجارة الحرة |
| carnauba wax | شمع كوبرنيكي |
| carotid | سباتي |
| caroxamide | كربوكساميد |
| carpal tunnel syndrome | متلازمة النفق الرسغي |
| carriage | انتقال |
| carriage return | عودة العربة: فاصل أسطر |
| carrier | مادة حاملة |
| carrier | ناقل |
| carrier | إشارة حاملة |
| carrier detect | الكشف عن الناقل |
| carrier medium | الوسط الحامل |
| carrier protein | بروتين حامل |
| carrier sense multiple access (csma) | الوصول المتعدد عبر تحسّس الناقل |
| carrier sense multiple access with collision avoidance (csma/ca) | الوصول المتعدد عبر تحسّس الناقل مع تجنب التصادم |
| carrier sense multiple access with collision detection (csma/ca) | الوصول المتعدد عبر تحسّس الناقل مع كشف التصادم |
| carrier wave | موجة حاملة |
| carrier-deposited catalyst | محفز تم ترسيبه على حامل |
| carrying capacity | قدرة الاستيعاب؛ سعة الحمل |
| carryon bags | حقائب يمكن حملها في وسائل النقل |
| carry-over | جزء محتجز (محمول في طور آخر ويرتحل معه) (في الفصل الطوري للغازات والسوائل) |
| carthage / venice film festival | مهرجان قرطاج/ فنيسيا السينمائي |
| cartilage | غضروف |
| cartoon strip | فيلم كارتون |
| cartridge | خرطوشة |
| carve | ينحت، ينقش |
| carve-out | انفصال جزئي |
| carver-style bench press; carver bench press | مكبس منضدي من نوع Carver |
| cascade | تسلسل العمليات التي تحدث بالجسم، وهو معنى يستخدم فقط في العلوم البيولوجية |
| cascade energy transfer | نقل طاقة تسلسلي |
| cascade impaction | تصادم تعاقبي |
| cascade impactor | صدامة تعاقبية |
| case | هندسة برامج بمساعدة الحاسب |
| case sensitivity | خاصية تحسس الأحرف: التمييز بين الأحرف الكبيرة والصغيرة في برنامج أو لغة برمجة |
| case-control studies | دراسات الحالات المُقارنة؛ دراسة حالات وشواهد |
| cased well | بئر مغلّف؛ بئر ذي تغليف |
| casein | كازيين |
| case-insensitive | متعلق بخاصية عدم تحسس الأحرف: عدم التمييز بين الأحرف الكبيرة والصغيرة في برنامج أو لغة برمجة |
| case-sensitive | متعلق بخاصية تحسس الأحرف: التمييز بين الأحرف الكبيرة والصغيرة في برنامج أو لغة برمجة |
| cash backed consitional vs cash backed conditional | دفع نقدي مقابل اصول عينية مقيمة ومحتجزة مقابل دفع ديون سائلة مشروطة بأجل |
| cashflow | تدفق نقدي |
| casing | غلاف؛ طبقة تغليف |
| casing | غلاف البئر؛ تغليف البئر |
| casing collar location (ccl) | موقع وصلات غلاف |

| | |
|---|---|
| casing failure | انهيار في الغلاف |
| casing housing | مبيت تغليف |
| casing string | خط أنابيب التغليف |
| cassette | مجموعة |
| cassette dosing, cassette doses | مجموعة جرعات |
| cassette dozing | عبوات جرعات |
| cast | طاقم الفيلم: الممثلين به |
| cast | يلقي، يبعث، يطرح، يسبك، يصب، يتقولب، يعقد عقدة، شكل، هيئة |
| cast / splint | جبيرة |
| cast iron | حديد الصب (حديد الزهر) |
| castellated | برجي |
| casting | صب |
| casting vote | صوت راجح |
| cast-iron | حديد الصب |
| castor oil | زيت الخروع |
| casualities | الخسائر في الأفراد؛ الضحايا |
| cataclastic rocks | صخور تهشمية |
| cataleptic states | حالات الإغماء التخشبي |
| catalog | فهرس |
| catalysis | حفز؛ تحفيز |
| catalyst | محفز |
| catalyst | مادة محفزة |
| catalyst carrier | مادة حاملة لمحفز؛ حامل محفز |
| catalyst deactivation | تثبيط المحفز |
| catalyst for the methane dry reforming reaction | محفز لتفاعل إعادة تشكيل جاف للميثان |
| catalyst support | مادة حاملة لمحفز؛ حامل محفز |
| catalystic cracking conditions | ظروف التكسير الحفزي |
| catalytic bed | الطبقة الحفزية؛ طبقة المحفز |
| catalytic conversion | تحويل حفزي |
| catalytic cracker | وحدة تكسير حفزي |
| catalytic cracker heavy cycle oil (hco) | زيت تدوير ثقيل بوحدة تكسير حفزي |
| catalytic cracking cycle oil | زيت تدوير للتكسير الحفزي؛ زيت تدوير التكسير الحفزي |
| catalytic reactor | مفاعل حفزي |
| catalytically active zero valence forms | صور ذات تكافؤ صفر نشطة حفزيًا |
| catalyze | يحفز |
| cataract | المياه البيضاء |
| cataract extraction | إزالة المياه البيضاء؛ استئصال المياه البيضاء |
| cataytic hydrogenation | هدرجة بالحفز |
| catch all email | تجميع كل رسائل البريد: عنوان صندوق بريدي رئيسي موحد لتجميع رسائل البريد التي لا تملك جهة لاستقبالها |
| catch basin / catchpit | حوض احتجاز |
| catechol | كاتيكول |
| catheter | قثطرة |
| catheter clearance | تصفية القسطرة |
| cathode | مهبط؛ كاثود |
| cathode exhaust air line | خط هواء عادم مهبطي |
| cathode feed air line | خط هواء تغذية مهبط |
| cathodic protection voltages | جهد حماية مهبطية |
| cation | كاتيون |
| cation exchange membrane | غشاء تبادل كاتيوني |
| cationic | كاتيوني |
| cations of alkaline or alkaline-earth metals | كاتيونات لفلزات قلوية أو فلزات قلوية أرضية |
| c-atoms | ذرات كربون |
| cauda equina syndrome | متلازمة ذيل الفرس |
| caught up | ارتفع معدل التجارة أو تجاوز الحد |
| causalgia | حراق |
| causality | السببية |
| caustic | كاوي |
| caustic | مادة كاوية |
| caustic contacting step | خطوة الملامسة بمادة كاوية |
| caustic potash | ألبوتاسا كاوية |
| caustic solution | محلول كاوي |
| caustic wash | غسول كاو |
| caution | تنبيه |
| cavity | تجويف |
| cavity | فجوة، تجويف |
| cbi | تدريس باستخدام الحاسب |
| cbr | معدل بت ثابت |
| cbs | هيكل تفاصيل التكلفة |
| cbt | تدريب باستخدام الحاسب |
| cc | سنتيمتر مكعب؛ نسخة صماء |
| cc / g | سنتيمتر مكعب / جرام |
| ccb | لوحة التحكم في التهيئة |
| ccd | عدسة تصوير |
| cce | بيئة تشغيل عامة |
| ccitt | اللجنة الاستشارية الدولية للتلغرافات والهواتف |
| ccitt | اللجنة الاستشارية الدولية للبرق والهاتف |
| cctv | دائرة تليفزيونية مغلقة |
| cd | قرص مضغوط |
| cdk4/6 | إنزيمي CDK4/6 : هما نوعان من الإنزيمات CDK4 و CDK6 |
| cdk4/6 kinase activity | نشاط إنزيمي CDK4/6 كيناز |
| cdm | نموذج بيانات المفهوم الأساسي |
| cdma | الوصول المتعدد بتقسيم الشفرة |
| cdr | مراجعة التصميم الحرج |
| cd-r | قرص مضغوط - قابل للتسجيل |
| cdrl | قائمة متطلبات بيانات العقد |
| cd-rom | قرص مضغوط |
| cd-rom drive | محرك أقراص مضغوطة |
| cd-rom/ fdd | محرك أقراص مضغوطة/أقراص مرنة |
| cd-rw | قرص مضغوط - قابل لإعادة الكتابة: قرص مضغوط من النوع القابل للكتابة عليه عدة مرات |
| cd-rw/dvd-rom drive | محرك أقراص مضغوطة قابلة لإعادة الكتابة وأقراص دي في دي |
| cdu | وحدة تقطير النفط الخام |
| cede | يتنازل (عن ملكية، قضية .. ) |
| cel column | عمود سيليت |
| celebral contusion | رضة بالمخ؛ رض مخي |
| celiac | بطني؛ جوفي |
| celite | سيليت |
| celite pad | طبقة سيليت |

| | |
|---|---|
| centraliser | جهاز تمركز |
| centralized digital documents storage | مخزن مستندات رقمية مركزي |
| centralized paper documents storage | مخزن مستندات ورقية مركزي |
| centralized storage | مخزن بيانات مركزي |
| centralized storage system | نظام تخزين مركزي |
| centralizer | جهاز تمركز |
| centrifugal compressor | ضاغط طرد مركزي |
| centrifugal retention capacity (crc) | سعة احتجاز الطرد المركزي |
| centrifugation | طرد مركزي |
| centrifuge | طرد مركزي |
| centrifuge | جهاز الطرد المركزي: يستخدم لفصل عينات البروتين والحامض النووى الديوكسى ريبوز بطريقة الترسيب. يمكن استخدام أنابيب ذات سعة 0.5 ملي لتر وحتى 30 ملي لتر ذات سرعة الطرد المركزى تصل الى 10000 لفة لكل دقيقة. |
| centripetal dryers | مجففات جاذبة نحو المركز؛ مجففات جذب مركزي |
| ceo | مدير تنفيذي |
| ceoi | تعليمات تشغيل إلكترونيات الاتصالات |
| cept | المؤتمر الأوروبي للبريد والاتصالات |
| ceramic | الخزف |
| ceramic balls | كريات خزفية |
| ceramic coping | غطاء خزفي (تلبيسة خزفية) |
| ceramics | الخزف والصيني |
| cereated glass | زجاج سيريتي |
| cerebellar | مخيخي |
| cerebellar degeneration | تنكس مخي؛ الضمور المخي |
| cerebral aging | تقدم العمر المخي |
| cerebral cortex | القشرة المخية |
| cerebral malaria | الملاريا المخية |
| cerebrovascular | المخية الوعائية |
| cermet | سرمت (فلز مخزف) |
| cern | سيرن: المعمل الأوروبي للفيزياء الجزئية |
| certificate | شهادة |
| certificate of all history | شهادة بجميع المواد المسجلة |
| certification | شهادة |
| certification programme and mark | برنامج وعلامة اعتماد |
| certified | مجاز |
| certified arbitrator | محكم معتمد |
| certified patent translator | مترجم براءات معتمد |
| certified software | برنامج مرخص |
| cervix carcinoma | الورم السرطاني بالعنق |
| ces | خدمة محاكاة الدائرة |
| cesium | سيزيوم |
| cession | التنازل (عن ملكية، قضية .. ) |
| ceteris paribus | في ظل ثبات العوامل الأخرى |
| cfc | هيدرو فلورو كربون |
| cfe | معدات موفرة من قبل المقاول |
| cfu | وحدة تشكيل مزرعة |
| cg | سنتي جرام |
| ch2cl2 | كلوريد ميثيلين |
| cell | خلية |
| cell culture chamber | غرفة استزراع خلايا |
| cell differentiation | تمايز الخلايا |
| cell line | سلالة خلية |
| cell stimulation | تنبيه (استثارة، تنشيط) الخلايا |
| cell surface human c-met receptor | مستقبل c-Met البشري عند سطح الخلية |
| cell surface target | هدف عند سطح الخلية |
| cell therapy | علاج الخلايا |
| cell-based assay | اختبار خلوي؛ تجربة خلوية، اختبار أساسه الخلية؛ تحليل خلوي |
| cell-mediated | تساهم فيه الخلية |
| cello browser | مستعرض تشيللو |
| cellphone ; cell phone | هاتف خلوي |
| cells | خلايا |
| cells population | مجموعة الخلايا |
| cell-switching | تبديل الخلية |
| cellular oxidative stress | إجهاد مؤكسد للخلايا |
| cellular pathways | مسارات خلوية |
| cellular response | الاستجابة الخلوية: الاستجابة المناعية التي تقوم بها الخلايا التائية lymphocytes T بواسطة المستقبلات المتوضعة على أغشيتها التي تكسبها الإستجابة النوعية للمستضدات . حيث تنتج كل خلية أثناء عملية النضج نوعا من المستقبلات خاصا بغشائها وبذلك فإن كل نوع منها |
| cellular viability | قدرة الخلايا على البقاء حية |
| cellulolytic enzymes | إنزيمات خلوية |
| cellulose | سليولوز |
| cellulosic biomass | كتلة حيوية سيلوزية |
| cellulosic ethanol commercialization | جعل الأيثانول السيليلوزي ذا طبيعة تجارية |
| cement | إسمنت |
| cement | لاحم (لاصق) |
| cementation | تثبيت بالأسمنت |
| cementation | تلاحم؛ لحم؛ لحام (تلاصق) |
| cementing | تثبيت بالأسمنت |
| cementum | ملاط الأسنان. مادة شبه عظمية |
| censensus | متطابقة تمامًا |
| censensus scoring | تسجيل إجمالي |
| censorship | الرقابة |
| center spread | صفحتا وسط المجلة |
| centerifuged to pellet cells | التعريض للطرد المركزي للحصول على كريات خلايا |
| centerline | خط مركزي |
| centimetre | سنتيمتر |
| central american common market, cacm | السوق المشتركة لأقطار أمريكا الوسطى |
| central command | مركز قيادة العمليات |
| central nerve system | الجهاز العصبي المركزي |
| central pain syndromes | متلازمات الألم المركزي |
| central processing unit, cpu | وحدة المعالجة المركزية، المعالج المركزي |
| central treaty organisaion, cento | منظمة الحلف المركزي |

| | |
|---|---|
| chaff | التبن |
| chagas disease | مرض شاجاس |
| chain | سلسلة |
| chain saw | منشار سلسلي |
| chain transfer agent | عامل نقل تسلسلي |
| chain-tooth saw | منشار عادي بأسنان |
| chalcogenide / sulphide glass | تشالكوجينيد / زجاج كبريتيد |
| chalconide | فلز كريم |
| chalicosis | السحار الترابي |
| challengability | القابلية للتحدي |
| challenge | اختبار مناعي |
| challenge | طعن (في قرار لجنة تحكيم، حكم إلخ)؛ تحدى |
| challenge assay | اختبار مناعي |
| challenge test | اختبار مناعي |
| challenged with endotoxin | إجراء اختبار مناعي عليها بإعطائها سم داخلي |
| chamber | غرفة |
| chambers | غرف |
| chamfer | يشطف الحواف |
| chamfered | مشطوف |
| change awareness | وعي التغيير |
| changer | مغيِّر |
| changing technology | تقنية متغيرة |
| channel | قناة |
| channel binding | ربط القناة |
| channel gain | كسب القناة |
| channel hopping | الوثب بين الأقنية |
| channel plate | لوح قنوي (على شكل مجرى) |
| channeling | تكون قنوات |
| channelopathies | اعتلال القنوات |
| chaotropes | عوامل أو مواد حالة للبروتين |
| chaotropic: pertaining to chaotropism | حالّ للبروتين |
| character | شخصية |
| character length | طول الحرف |
| character string | سلسلة أحرف |
| character-based | نصي؛ مرتكز على النص |
| character-based interface | واجهة نصية |
| characteristic | خاصية |
| characteristic | خاصية |
| characteristics | خصائص |
| characterization | تحديد خصائص؛ وصف خصائص |
| characterizing clause | البند المميز. بند يوضح الخصائص الجديدة في اختراع ما، يشيع ظهوره في الأطر الأوروبية والألمانية بشكل خاص |
| charcoal | فحم نباتي |
| charge (with) | يملء؛ يعبئ (وبخاصة أنبوب) (ب) |
| charge back costs | تكاليف إلغاء العملية الائتمانية |
| chart | مخطط |
| charter | قالب |
| chartered bank | مصرف مرخص؛ مصرف معتمد قانونا |
| chassis identification number | رقم القاعدة؛ رقم الهيكل؛ رقم الشاسيه |
| chat | محادثة؛ دردشة |

| | |
|---|---|
| cheapernet | الشبكة الأرخص |
| check box | مربع اختيار |
| check valve | صمامات منع ارتجاع |
| check valve | صمام فحص |
| checklist | قائمة المهام اللازمة |
| checklist/check list | قائمة المراقبة |
| cheese in brine | جبن محفوظ في محلول ملحي |
| cheesecloth | قماش جبني |
| cheksum | مراجعة البيانات النهائية |
| chelate | خلابي |
| chelate | مركب خلابي |
| chelate | يحول إلى الصورة الخلابية |
| chelating agent | عامل خلابي |
| chelator | مركب خلابي |
| chemical abstracts service registry (cas) | سجل دائرة المستخلصات الكيميائية |
| chemical decomposition | تحلل كيميائي |
| chemical energy | طاقة كيميائية |
| chemical engineering | هندسة كيمائية |
| chemical entity | مركب كيميائي |
| chemical oxygen demand (cod) | الأكسجين المستهلك كيميائياً |
| chemical pulp : | اللب الكيميائي: المادة الليفية التى يتم الحصول عليها بفصلها من المادة الخام بالمعالجة الكيماوية (الطبخ، إزالة اللجنين، التبييض) |
| chemical shift | إزاحة كيمائية |
| chemical weathering | التجوية الكيميائية |
| chemically formed sediments | صخور رسوبية كيميائية النشأة |
| chemically-treated solid oxide | الأكسيد الصلب المعالج كيميائياً |
| chemiluminescence | الاستضاءة الكيميائية؛ التألق الكيميائي |
| chemiluminescent | مُظهر يستخدم الاستضاءة الكيميائية |
| chemiluminescers | مواد لمعان كيميائي |
| chemisorbed | ممتز كيميائياً |
| chemisorption | امتزاز كيماوي |
| chemisorption | امتزاز كيميائي |
| chemistry | كيمياء |
| chemoattractant receptor-homologous molecule expressed on th2 cells, (such as a crth2 antagonist) | جزئ متجانس لمستقبل تجاذب كيميائي معبر عنه جينيا على خلايا TH2 (مثل مضاد CRTH2 |
| chemokine | كيموكين |
| chemokines | كيموكينات |
| chemoluminescent labels | علامات الاستضاءة الكيميائية |
| chemoluminescent materials | مواد لامعة كيميائية |
| chemoluminiscent | إشعاع كيميائي |
| chemotactic factor | عامل انجذاب كيميائي |
| chemotaxis | التجاذب والتدافع الكيمياءيان |
| cherry | كرز |
| chert | الشيرت (حجر الصوان) |
| chicago board of exchange option-pricing model | نموذج تسعير خيارات الأسهم لدى بورصة الخيارات في شيكاجو |

| | |
|---|---|
| chicory | شيكوريا (سريس) |
| chief advertising officer | كبير مدراء الدعاية |
| chief district attorney | رئيس نيابة |
| chief idea officer | كبير مدراء الأفكار |
| chief industrial officer | كبير المدراء الصناعيين |
| chief information officer | كبير مدراء المعلومات |
| chief information security officer | كبير مدراء أمن المعلومات |
| chief innovation officer | كبير مدراء الابتكارات |
| chief intellectual property officer | كبير مدراء الملكية الفكرية |
| chief internet officer | كبير مدراء الشبكة البينية |
| chief knowledge officer | كبير مدراء المعرفة |
| chief learning officer | كبير مدراء التعلم |
| chief legal officer | كبير المدراء القانونيين |
| chief licensing officer | كبير مدراء التراخيص |
| chief marketing officer | كبير مدراء التسويق |
| chief media officer | كبير مدراء الإعلام |
| chief of operations | رئيس العمليات |
| chief of staff | رئيس الأركان |
| chief patent counsel | كبير مستشاري (محاميي) البراءات |
| chief patent officer | كبير مدراء البراءات |
| chief privacy officer | كبير مدراء الخصوصية |
| chief science officer | كبير المدراء العلميين |
| chief technologist | كبير التقنيين |
| chief technology officer | كبير التقنيين |
| chief technology officer | كبير مدراء التقنية |
| chief visionary officer | كبير مدراء السياسات المستقبلية |
| child abuse | إيذاء الأطفال؛ الإساءة للأطفال |
| child care provider | المتكفل برعاية الطفل |
| child custody mediation | وساطة بشأن حضانة الطفل |
| child directory | مجلد فرعي |
| child restraint | أدوات وأحزمة تأمين سلامة الأطفال |
| chilled microfluidizer | مميع دقيق مبرد |
| chiller | مبرد |
| chiller train | سلسلة مبرِّد |
| chilling | تبريد (مفاجئ) |
| chimera | خيمر |
| chimeric | خيمري |
| chimeric contructs | أجزاء منشأة خيمرية |
| chinook helicopter | طائرة شينوك |
| chip | شريحة |
| chip, intent | المثقل بسخطه، الشاهر سيفه |
| chipping hammer | مطرقة كشط |
| chips | شرائح |
| chiral | كيرالي |
| chiral dichlorobenzyl intermediate (23) | المركب الوسيط عديم التماثل داي كلورو بنزيل ذو الصيغة 23 |
| chiral intermediate | مركب وسيط كيرالي |
| chiral seperation | الفصل الكيرالي |
| chlordiazepoxide | كلور ديازيبوكسيد |
| chloriding agent | عامل إضافة كلوريد؛ عامل معالجة بالكلوريد |
| chlorinated | معالج بالكلور |
| chlorinated hydrocarbons | هيدروكربونات معالجة بالكلور |
| chlorination process | عملية الكلورة |
| chlorine | كلور |
| chlorite | كلورايت |
| chloro substrate | ركيزة محتوية على الكلور |
| cho expression vectors | نواقل التعبير الوراثي عن خلايا CHO |
| choice of law clause | بند اختيار القانون. بند تعاقدي يبين القانون الذي سيتم الاحتكام إليه في حالة حصول نزاع |
| choke position | وضع الاختناق |
| choked position | وضع الاختناق |
| choked position; choke position | وضع الاختناق |
| cholangitis | التهاب قناة الصفراء |
| cholecystitis | التهاب المرارة |
| cholesterol | كوليستيرول |
| chondrocyte | خلية غضروفية |
| chondrosarcoma | الورم السرطاني الغضروفي |
| chord | وتر |
| chorion carcinoma | الورم السرطاني بالمشيمة |
| choroidal neovascularisation | حدوث تولد أوعية جديدة بالمشيمة |
| choroidea melanoma | الورم الميلانيني بالمشيمية |
| christmas tree= xmas tree | شجرة الصمامات |
| chromatograph | ينقي باستخدام كروماتوجراف |
| chromatography | كروموتوجراف |
| chromiferous | متعلق بالكروم والحديد |
| chromium | كروم |
| chromosome ten | الكروموسوم العاشر |
| chromotography | فصل (تنقية) كروموتوجرافي |
| chronic | مزمن |
| chronic ischemic cardiomyopathy (icmp) | داء عضلة القلب الناتج عن قصور الدم الموضعي المزمن (ICMP) |
| chronic lymphatic leukemia (cll) | سرطان الدم الليمفاوي المزمن |
| chronic myeloid leukemia (cml) | سرطان الدم شبه النخاعي المزمن |
| chronic obstructive pulmonary disease (copd) | مرض الانسداد الرئوي المزمن (COPD) |
| chronic pelvic pain | الألم الحوضي المزمن |
| chronic pulmonary inflammation | الالتهاب التنفسي المزمن |
| chronic renal failure (crf) | فشل كلوي مزمن |
| chronic venous abnormalities | التشوهات الوريدية المزمنة |
| chronoamperometry | قياس شدة التيار على فترات وجيزة |
| chronopotentiometry | قياس الجهد على فترات وجيزة |
| chuchotage | ترجمة فورية هامسة |
| chute | أنبوب |
| chylothorax | تكيلس الصدر |
| ci | بند التهيئة؛ كوري |
| cia world factbook | كتاب الحقائق العالمية |
| cib | أساس صورة التحكم |
| cider | عصير تفاح |
| cinema frame | لقطة سينمائية |
| cinema scope (wide-screen) | أفلام سينمائية سكوب، ذات مدى عريض |
| cinemagoer ; moviegoer | مرتاد دور السينما |
| cipher | شفرة |

| | |
|---|---|
| circuit | دائرة كهربائية |
| circuit | دائرة |
| circuit board | لوحة دوائر كهربائية |
| circuit board | لوحة دائرة |
| circuit switching network | شبكة تحويل بدائرة؛ شبكة تبديل الدوائر |
| circuit-breaker | قاطع دائرة كهربائية؛ قاطع الدارة؛ قاطع التيار |
| circuits | دوائر |
| circuit-switched network | شبكة تبديل الدوائر |
| circular thread | سن ملولب دائري |
| circulating gas capacitance | مواسع غازي دائر |
| circulating peripheral lymphocytes | خلايا لمفية في الجهاز الدوري الطرفي |
| circulation ; distribution | توزيع الصحف |
| circulatory shock | صدمة دموية |
| circumferential | محيطي |
| cirrhosis | تليف الكبد |
| cis; communication and information systems | نظام الاتصالات والمعلومات |
| cis-configuration | الهيئة سيس |
| cis-isomers | أيزومرات سيس |
| cisplatinium | سيسبلاتين |
| cisterna magna na | الصهريج الكبير |
| cited publications | المؤلفات (أو المطبوعات) المشار إليها (المذكورة) |
| cited reference | مرجع مقتبَس |
| citrate | سترات |
| civil code | القانون المدني |
| civil defence | الدفاع المدني |
| civil responsibility | مسئوليه مدنيه |
| cl | قائمة التطابق |
| claim | يدعي، دعوى، ادعاء |
| claim (sth to be) | يثبت؛ يتأكد |
| claim liability for | يعلن مسئوليته عن |
| claim validity | سلامة الادعاء |
| claimant's appointed arbitrator | المحكم المعين من قبل المُحتكِم |
| claimed | (1) الواردة؛ المذكورة (2) المطلوب حمايتها |
| claims | عناصر الحماية؛ دعاوى |
| clamp | مشبك |
| clamping of the membrane potential | تثبيت جهد الغشاء بمشبك |
| clandstine party | حزب سري |
| clarate | ناتج الترويق |
| clarifier | وحدة ترويق |
| class action | دعوى جماعية |
| class i pi3 kinases | إنزيمات PI3 كيناز من الفئة I |
| classified display advertising | إعلانات مبوبة ومصورة |
| classified invention | اختراع سري |
| classified material | وثائق سرية |
| classroom | الفصل (المدرسي)؛ غرفة الدراسة |
| clastic material | مواد فتاتية |
| clathrate | مركب احتباسي |

| | |
|---|---|
| clause | بند |
| clay bounding | قوة الارتباط الطيني |
| clay minerals | معادن طينية |
| clays | طفلات |
| claystone | حجر الوحل |
| clean edge | حافة ملساء |
| clean energy patent | براءة طاقة نظيفة |
| clean energy patent growth index | مؤشر براءات الطاقة النظيفة |
| clean hands doctrine | مبدأ اليد النظيفة. مبدأ مفاده أن إصدار حكم وقتي بشأن مطالبة متصلة بانتهاك براءة يمنح فقط لمن تصرف بحسن نية |
| clean technology | تقنية نظيفة |
| cleaning robot | روبوت منظف |
| clear bottom plates; cleaer-bottom | ذات قعر واضح |
| clear glass | الزجاج الصافي |
| clear or opaque protective coating | طبقة تغليف حامية شفافة أو غير شفافة |
| clear solution | محلول صافي |
| clear spin | تدويم نظيف |
| clearance | خلوص؛ تفاوت؛ فرجة |
| clearance | تصفية، استصفاء: قياس قدرة الجسم على التخلص من عقار |
| clearance | التصفية : قياس قدرة الجسم على التخلص من عقار |
| clearinghouse for networked information discovery and retrieval (cnidr) | دار المقاصة للتعرف على المعلومات الشبكية واسترجاعها |
| cleavable in vivo | قابل للانقسام داخل الجسم الحي |
| cleavage | انشطار؛ انقسام |
| cleaved amplified polymorphic sequence (caps) markers | واسمات متوالية متعددة الشكل مكبرة مقسومة |
| cleft | فلح - شق |
| click | ينقر؛ يضغط فوق |
| click rate | نسبة النقر |
| client | جهاز تابع (كمبيوتر)؛ عميل |
| client/server | عميل / خادم |
| client-patent advisor relationship | علاقة العميل بمستشار البراءات |
| client-solicitor privilege | خصوصية العلاقة بين المحامي وموكله |
| climate change mitigation | تقليص التغيرات المناخية |
| climb | صعود؛ تسلق |
| clinic | عيادة |
| clinic stage | مرحلة العيادة |
| clinical | إكلينيكي؛ سريري |
| clinical chemistry | كيمياء عيادتية |
| clinical laboratory abnormalities | الأخطاء المختبرية الإكلينيكية |
| clinically | من الناحية الإكلينيكية |
| clinician | طبيب سريري |
| clinician global impression | الانطباع العام للطبيب الإكلينيكي |
| clinicians | أطباء سريريون |
| clinostat | منظم للجاذبية |
| clinostat | مزيل للجاذبية |

| | |
|---|---|
| clip art | صورة جاهزة |
| clipper chip | شريحة مشفرة |
| clobber | يحذف؛ يلغي؛ يمسح |
| clone | نسيلة |
| clone into | يستنسخ إلى؛ ينشئ نسيلة إلى |
| clone to | يستنسخ إلى؛ ينشئ نسيلة إلى |
| closded position | موضع إغلاق |
| close | يغلق |
| close prior art | فن سابق قريب |
| close support fire | نيران المعاونة |
| closed circuit television | تلفزة مرتبطة بدائرة مغلقة. مجموعة كاميرات مراقبة مرتبطة بجهاز تسجيل للصور الملتقطة يستطيع من خلاله المراقب أن يراقب مايجري في أرجاء المنشأة وأن يحتفظ بمخزون صور يمكنه استرجاعها عندما يشاء لفحص حركة الأشخاص المرغوب التعرف عليهم |
| closed conformation multispecific antibody | جسم مضاد متعدد النوعية ذي هيئة مغلقة |
| closed cycle heat pump loop | مضخة حرارية للدائرة المغلقة |
| closed cycle refrigerator | مبرد عميق ذو دائرة مغلقة |
| closed head injury | إصابة الرأس المغلقة |
| closedown | الختام |
| close-quarters fighting | الحروب داخل المدن؛ حروب الشوارع |
| closest prior art | الفن السابق الأقرب |
| closest prior art reference | أقرب مراجع الفن السابق |
| close-up | لقطة أو صورة عن قرب |
| close-up | لقطة مقربة |
| closing and opening positions | لفتح وإغلاق الملامسين |
| closing device | وسيلة إغلاق |
| clostridium histolyticum | المجزآت الغزلية الحالة للنسج |
| clothing item | قطعة قماش |
| cloud point | نقطة التغيُّم |
| cloudy | مغيم |
| cloudy | غير صاف |
| cloudy mixture | خليط ضبابي |
| clpd | بالاديوم على كربون |
| clr | نسبة فقد الخلية |
| clue | دالة؛ إشارة دالة؛ علامة دالة؛ طرف خيط |
| clueless newbie | مبتدئ ساذج |
| cluster | تكتل |
| cluster indexes | فهارس مجموعات |
| cluster key | مفتاح مجموعة الجداول |
| cluster patent | براءة تكتلية. براءة مسجلة بحسبانها واحدة من تكتل براءات يراد منه حماية براءة مهمة من خلال منع منافس من تصميم براءة مشابهة لبراءة مهمة |
| cluster server | خادم تجمع |
| cm | إدارة التهيئة |
| cm | سنتيمتر |
| cm | سنتي مورجان |
| cm/hr | سنتيمتر في ساعة |
| cmm | معدل رجل شهر معتمد |
| cmp | خطة إدارة التهيئة |
| cmt | أدوات إدارة التهيئة |
| cng | غاز طبيعي مضغوط |
| cnn | شبكة أخبار كبلية |
| cns | الجهاز العصبي المركزي |
| co2 incubator | حاضن ثاني أكسيد الكربون: يستخدم لتحضين الخلايا والأنسجة حية عند درجات حرارة مناسبة ونسبة مناسبة من ثاني أكسيد الكربون. |
| coacervation | فصل المواد الغروية عن الماء |
| co-administered | إعطاء مشترك؛ توليفة من الإعطاء؛ إعطاء في توليفة |
| coagulable | متخثر |
| coagulase | إنزيم التجلط |
| coal bed | طبقة فحم حجري |
| coal gas | غاز الفحم |
| coal tar | قطران الفحم |
| coalescence | اندماج؛ التحام أو دمج؛ لحام |
| coalition for networked information (cni) | ائتلاف المعلومات الشبكية |
| coarse grained clastic rocks | الصخور الفتاتية كبيرة الحبيبات |
| coastline | خط الساحل |
| coat | يكسو، يغطي، سترة، غلاف |
| coat protein | غلاف بروتيني؛ بروتين ردائي؛ بروتين غلافي: الغلاف البروتيني لفيروس ويسمى أيضا capsid |
| coated | مصقول، مشمع، مطلي |
| coated glass | زجاج مطلي: زجاج قد تعرض للطلاء المرغوب، مثال ذلك طبقة رقيقة صلبة أو أكثر من مواد غير عضوية بهدف تعديل خاصية أو أكثر من خواصه |
| coated metal composition | تركيبة المعدن المطلي |
| coated paper | ورقة بطبقة خارجية |
| coated proppant | عامل حشو دعمي مغلف |
| coatee | سترة قصيرة |
| coating | تغليف (كيمياء) |
| coating | طبقة تغليف |
| coating | طلاء؛ مادة طلاء |
| coating | غلاف، طبقة خارجية |
| coating metal | معدن طلاء |
| coating roll | اسطوانة تغليف |
| coating slips | شرائح تغليف؛ شرائح طلاء |
| coax | كبل متحد المحور |
| coaxial cable | كبل متحد المحور |
| cobalt hydroformylation catalyst | محفز كوبالت لإدخال مجموعة هيدرو فورميل |
| cobra | نظام التأمين الصحي الحكومي كوبرا |
| cocatalyst | محفز مشترك |
| cochlear implants | زراعات قوقعة الأذن |
| cockpit | مقصورة القيادة |
| cocktail | خليط؛ كوكتيل |
| cocomitant | مرافق |
| co-current | في اتجاه التيار |

| | |
|---|---|
| code | شفرة |
| code | رمز |
| code | لائحة؛ مجموعة القوانين |
| code | يرمز، رمز، ميثاق |
| code bits | بتات الرمز؛ أرقاماً ثنائية للرمز |
| code division multiple access | الوصول المتعدد بتقسيم الشفرة |
| code division multiple access (cdma) system | نظام الوصول المتعدد بتقسيم الشفرة CDMA |
| code division multiple access (cmda) | الوصول المتعدد لتقسيم الشفرة (CMDA): هو معيار يخص الهواتف المحمولة الرقمية المستخدمة في اليابان وبعض أجزاء جنوب شرق آسيا والولايات المتحدة الأمريكية. |
| code of business conduct | لائحة السلوك التجاري |
| code of conduct | لائحة السلوك |
| code of conduct | ميثاق سلوك |
| code of ethics | ميثاق أخلاقي |
| code of judicial conduct | ميثاق سلوك قضائي |
| code of legal conduct | ميثاق سلوك قانوني |
| code readability | قابلية الشيء لأن يُقرأ |
| code readability | إمكانية قراءة الشفرة |
| codebook | الكتاب المشفر |
| codebook index; codebook indice | مؤشر كتاب شفرات؛ مؤشرات كتب شفرات |
| codec | برنامج تشفير |
| codewords | كلمات مشفرة |
| coding | تشفير؛ ترميز |
| coding system | نظام تشفير |
| codon | رامز |
| coe | بيئة تشغيل عامة |
| coefficient | معامل |
| coefficient of variation | معامل التباين؛ معامل الاختلاف؛ معامل التغير: وهو من أدق مقاييس التشتت النسبية، |
| coeliac disease | اعتلال الجوف |
| coercoin; duress; by force | الإكراه؛ بالإكراه |
| co-existing amino groups | مجموعات أمينو مشتركة |
| cofactor | معامل |
| co-gelation | تكوّن جل مشترك |
| cogenerate | يولد سخونة أو كهرباء من طاقة الفضلات |
| cogeneration | توليد سخونة أو كهرباء |
| cognate | متشابه |
| cognestive heart failure (chf) | قصور القلب الاحتقاني |
| cognition | إدراك |
| cognitive activity | نشاط ذهني |
| cognitive capacity | طاقة ذهنية |
| cognitive creations | ابتكارات ذهنية |
| cognitive impairment | قصور إدراكي |
| cognitive robotics | روبوتية ذهنية. ذلك الحقل المعني بتصميم الروبوت على نحو يمكنه من إدراك ما حوله وبناء حالة ذهنية لتحقيق أهداف معقدة في بيئة معقدة |
| coherence values | قيم الترابط المنطقي |

| | |
|---|---|
| coherence volume | حجم ترابط منطقي |
| coherent electromagnetic radiation | إشعاع كهرومغناطيسي متجانس |
| coherent high pressure abrasive jet fluid | مائع متدفق بالاحتكاك على الضغط الأساسي |
| coherent rayleigh noise ("crn") | تشويش رايليه المتجانس |
| cohesive patent portfolio | محفظة براءات متماسكة |
| cohesive strength | قوة التماسك |
| cohort study | دراسة مجموعة |
| coi | معلومات تشغيل الاتصالات |
| coil | ملف |
| coil spring | نابض لولبي |
| coil tubing | أنابيب ملتفة |
| coil tubing unit | وحدة أنبوبية ملتفة |
| coiled coil region | منطقة حلزونية ملتفة |
| coin service | خدمة العمل بالعملة |
| coincident with | متطابق مع؛ متوافق مع |
| coke | فحم الكوك |
| coke machine | ماكينة المياه الغازية |
| coker | وحدة صنع الكوك؛ وحدة تكويك |
| coker naphtha | نفثا لوحدة صنع الكوك |
| coking | تحويل الفحم إلى كوك؛ تكويك؛ تكوّن الكوك |
| cola | مقتطعات نفقات المعيشة؛ حسميات نفقات المعيشة |
| cold boot | تشغيل بارد |
| cold solidification | التصليب البارد |
| cold start | بدء التبريد |
| co-linearity | التطابق الخطي؛ التخاطط المشترك |
| colision | تعارض |
| collaborate | يتعاون |
| collaboration | المعاونة |
| collaboration | تعاون |
| collaborator | متواطئ |
| collaborator | متعاون |
| collagen | كولاجين |
| collagen arthritis model | التهاب المفاصل في الفأر باستخدام الكولاجين |
| collagen diseases | أمراض الكولاجين |
| collapse and deformation | الطي والتشوه |
| collapse from extended to shrinked position | طيّ (أنبوب، عمود الحفر) من الوضع الممتد/المنبسط إلى الوضع المنكمش |
| collapse or dissolution breccia | رواهص الانهيار أو الإذابة |
| collapsible | قابل للطي |
| collar | حلقة؛ طوق |
| collect | يجمع |
| collection | تجميع |
| collective invention ethics | أخلاقيات الاختراع الجماعي |
| collective know-how | دراية للكيفية جماعية |
| collective ownership | الملكية الجماعية |
| collective property | ملك جماعي |
| collective tenure | حيازة جماعية |
| collector | جامع، مجمع، مُقتني |
| collide | يتصادم |

| | |
|---|---|
| collided | متصادم |
| collimated | مرتب على التوازي |
| collimator lens | العدسة المجمعة |
| collision | تصادم |
| colloid mill | طاحونة الغرويات |
| colloidal | غروية؛ شبه غروية |
| colonel (col) | عقيد؛ الكولونيل |
| colonoscopy | فحص منظاري للقولون؛ تنظير القولون |
| colony | مستعمرة |
| color nite | اللون الليلي |
| color of law | سيماء القانون - ظاهر القانون |
| color tinting | تدقيق الألوان |
| colorado alliance of research libraries | اتحاد كولورادو لمكتبات البحث |
| colorectal | قولوني مستقيمي |
| colorimeter | مقياس الألوان؛ كلرمتر |
| colour index | فهرس الألوان. هو قاعدة بيانات مرجعية وضعت باشتراك جمعية الصباغين والملونين |
| colour palette | لوحة ألوان |
| colourants | مكسبات اللون؛ ملونات |
| colourings | مكسبات اللون؛ ملونات |
| column chromatography | عمود كروماتوجراف |
| column of appropriate size of ceramic protein a | عمود بروتين A خزفي بحجم ملائم |
| comb foundations for beehives | قواعد لخلايا النحل |
| combat mission | مهمة قتالية |
| combat robot | روبوت قتالي |
| combat zone, security, efficiency | منطقة؛ تأمين؛ الكفاءة القتال |
| combinability | قابلية الشيء للمزج |
| combinable | قابل للمزج |
| combination | توليفة |
| combination electrode | إلكترود تجميعي |
| combination therapy | علاج مشترك؛ توليفة من العلاجات |
| combination unit | وحدة مدمجة |
| combinations (of the invention) | توليفات (من الاختراع) |
| combinatorial | اندماجي |
| combine | آلة حصاد ودرس؛ يجمع (في التجارب)؛ يدمج أو يربط |
| combined know-hows | درايات كيفية ممزوجة |
| combined operations | عمليات مشتركة |
| combined presence | الوجود المشترك |
| combined stream | تيار مشترك |
| combined technology | تقنية مختلطة |
| combined therapy | علاج مشترك |
| combust | يحرق، يحترق |
| combustibility | الاحتراقية، القابلية للاحتراق |
| combustible | قابل للاحتراق |
| combustible non polluting gas | غاز غير ملوث قابل للاحتراق |
| combustion | إحراق، احتراق، هياج عنيف |
| combustion chamber | غرفة الاحتراق |
| combustion deposition | ترسيب بالاحتراق |
| combustion gas | غاز احتراق |
| combustor | وحدة احتراق |
| comedian | ممثل كوميدي (هزلي) |
| comedienne | ممثلة كوميدية (هزلية) |
| comint | استخبارات الاتصالات |
| comm(s) | اتصال (اتصالات) |
| comma | فاصلة |
| command | يتحكم في |
| command light 6 x 1,000w light tower | برج إنارة من نوع "كومند" بقوة 6 في 1000 واط |
| command line | سطر الأوامر |
| command mode | وضع الأوامر |
| command sergeant major | رقيب أول قيادة |
| commander | رائد |
| commander (us navy only) | مقدم بحري (في البحرية الأمريكية فقط) |
| commander of the armed forces | قائد القوات المسلحة |
| commander-in-chief | القائد العام |
| commanders (commandants) | كبار القادة |
| commanders and staff college | كلية القادة والأركان |
| command-line interference | واجهة سطر الأوامر |
| commandos (rangers) | الصاعقة |
| commercial | تجاري |
| commercial access provider | مزود الوصول التجاري |
| commercial and martime law | القانون التجاري والبحري |
| commercial arbitration | تحكيم تجاري |
| commercial feasibility | جدوى تجارية |
| commercial internet exchange (cie or cix) | منظمة التبادل التجاري على الإنترنت |
| commercial mediation | وساطة تجارية |
| commercial packages of therapeutic products | العبوات التجارية للمنتجات العلاجية |
| commercial potentialities | إمكانيات تجارية |
| commercial tankage | سعة صهريج تجارية |
| commercial usage | استعمال تجاري |
| commercial value | قيمة تجارية |
| commercial viability | الجدوى التجارية |
| commercial viability of invention | جدوى الاختراع التجارية |
| commercializability | قابلية الشيء أن يكون ذا طبيعة تجارية |
| commercializable | قابل أن يكون ذا طبيعة تجارية |
| commercializable idea | فكرة قابلة لأن تكون موضعا لتطبيقات تجارية |
| commercialization | تسويق |
| commercialization | وضع الشيء موضع تطبيقات تجارية |
| commercialization of life | جعل الحياة منتجا تجاريا |
| commercialize | يجعل الشيء ذا طبيعة تجارية |
| commercially unfeasible invention | اختراع غير مجد تجاريا |
| commercially unfeasible technology | تقنية غير مجدية تجاريا |
| comminuting the compound to a suitable fine size | تفتيت إلى حجم دقيق مناسب |
| comminution | تفتيت، سحق، تهشيم |
| commission # | رقم التفويض |
| commission clause | البند الخاص بوجود عمولات |
| commitments | التزامات |
| committee | لجنة |
| committee chairman | رئيس لجنة |

| | |
|---|---|
| committee on wipo standards | لجنة مستويات وايبو القياسية. أسستها الدول الأعضاء خلال الجمعية العامة للوايبو المنعقدة عام 2009، وهي معنية بتنفيذ الهدف الخامس من أهداف الوايبو الإستراتيجية الخاص بالتنسيق وتطوير البنية التحتية العالمية للملكية الفكرية، وبمراجعة المستويات القياسية المتصلة بالملكية الصناعية |
| committee rapporteur | مقرر لجنة |
| commodities | سِلع |
| commodore | عميد بحري |
| common denominator | صفة مشتركة |
| common land | أرض مشاع |
| common network node | وحدة شبكة معتادة |
| common patent bar practice | ممارسة شائعة ضمن إطار نقابة خبراء البراءات |
| common rail system | نظام من وصلة واحدة |
| common to | التي تشترك فيها |
| common-rail | مكوّن من وصلة واحدة |
| communicatable | قابل للاتصال |
| communicatable robot | روبوت قابل للاتصال |
| communicate | يتصل، يتواصل |
| communicate in writing | يكتب أو يكاتب؛ يخاطب كتابيا؛ يراسل خطيا |
| communicate sth to sth | ينقل أو يسلّم كذا إلى كذا |
| communicated signals | إشارات منقولة: إشارات تم نقلها |
| communication | اتصال |
| communication device | جهاز اتصال |
| communication program | برنامج الاتصالات |
| communication receiver | متلقي الاتصال |
| communication revolution | ثورة اتصالات |
| communication security | أمن اتصال |
| communication terminal protocol (cterm) | بروتوكول المحطة الطرفية للاتصالات |
| communications technology | تقنية اتصالات |
| communications toolbox (ctb) | مربع أدوات الاتصالات |
| communicator | متصل، موصل |
| community order | النظام الاجتماعي؛ العقد الاجتماعي |
| community trademark | علامة الجماعة الأوروبية |
| commute the punishment | يخفف العقوبة |
| commz | منطقة اتصالات |
| comonomers; co-monomers | مونومرات مشتركة |
| compact energy source | مصدر طاقة مكتنز |
| compact means | وسيلة صغيرة الحجم |
| compaction | دمج؛ تجميع؛ جمع؛ تراص مضغوط |
| companion animal | حيوان أليف |
| company | شركة، رفقة |
| company (coy) | سرية مشاة |
| company's franchisability | قابلية الشركة لأن تقوم بمنح امتياز |
| company's patent policy | سياسة الشركة بالنسبة للبراءات |
| compare and merge | قارن وادمج |
| comparisions between pre-drug and post-drug | المقارنات قبل وبعد إعطاء العقار |
| comparitor | مقارِن؛ وسيلة مقارنة |
| compete (with sth for sth) | يتنافس (مع كذا للارتباط بـكذا) |
| competence | اختصاص (قانون) |
| competencies | (1) قدرات؛ كفاءات<br>(2) اختصاصات |
| competition binding assay ; competitive binding assay ; competitive assay ; competition assay | اختبار قوة ارتباط |
| competition clause | بند المنافسة |
| competition radioligand binding assay | اختبار قوة ارتباط جزيء الربط المشع |
| competitive | تنافسي |
| competitiveness | تنافسية |
| complacency air conditioning | تكييف هواء مكمل |
| complaints board | لجنة تظلمات |
| complement | مكمل |
| complementarity | مدى الاستكمال |
| complementarity | تكامل |
| complementarity determining regions or complementary determining region ("cdrs") | مناطق محدِّدة لمدى الاستكمال ("CDRs") |
| complementary | مكمِّل؛ متمِّم |
| complementary innovations | ابتكارات متكاملة |
| complementary inventions | اختراعات متكاملة |
| complementary know-how | دراية للكيفية مكملة |
| complement-binding ; complement binding | ربط مكمل |
| complement-dependent cytotoxicity (cdc) | السمية الخلوية المتوقفة على المكمل |
| complete agreement clause | البند الخاص بكاملية الاتفاق. بند تعاقدي نمطي ينص على أن الاتفاق الذي ينظمه العقد اتفاقا كاملا وأنه لا توجد عقود أو اتفاقات أو تفاهمات شفهية أم مكتوبة أخرى بجانب الاتفاق الذي يرد البند المذكور فيه. |
| completed well | بئر منجزة؛ بئر مكتملة |
| complex | معقد |
| complex | معقد، مجمع |
| complex brain activity | نشاط مخي معقد |
| complex equalizer | معادل مركب |
| complex of variable stoichiometry | معقد من كميات متكافئة متغيرة |
| complex plane | مستوى مركب |
| complex quantity | كمية مركبة |
| complex value | قيمة مركبة |
| complexity | تعقيد |
| complex-valued chips | شرائح ذات قيم معقدة |
| compliance mandates | متطلبات الإذعان |
| complications | مضاعفات |
| component | مكون |
| components of a hydrocarbon gas mixture | مكونات خليط غاز هيدروكربوني |
| compose of | يتكون من كذا |
| compose with | يتكون بكذا |

| | |
|---|---|
| composing | جمع الحروف؛ تنضيد الحروف (في الطباعة) |
| composite | مركّب |
| composite | مادة مركبة؛ تركيبة |
| composite vessels and interconnecting hoses | أوعية مركبة؛ وخراطيم توصيل بيني |
| compound iii | المركب ذو الصيغة III |
| compound of formula x | مركب له الصيغة X |
| compound represented by the above formula (i) | مركب له الصيغة (I) أعلاه |
| compound represented by the formula x | مركب له الصيغة X |
| compounds (i) and (ii) | مركبان لهما الصيغة I وII |
| compounds according to the invention | مركبات وفقا للاختراع |
| compounds of refernce | مركبات المراجع ذات الصلة |
| compounds of the invention | مركبات الاختراع |
| compresive stress | إجهاد الانضغاط |
| compress | يضغط |
| compress | يضغط |
| compressed | مضغوط |
| compressed air | هواء مضغوط |
| compressed air energy storage | مخزن طاقة للهواء المضغوط |
| compressed air engine | محرك هواء مضغوط |
| compressed air vehicle | مركبة تسير بالهواء الضغوط |
| compressed volume ratio | نسبة الحجم المضغوط |
| compression | ضغط |
| compression aid | عامل مساعد للانضغاط |
| compression chamber | حجرة انضغاط |
| compression fit | مواءمة بالانضغاط |
| compression pressure | قوة ضغط |
| compression spring | نابض انضغاطي |
| compression strength | مقاومة الانضغاط |
| compression waves | موجات تضاغط |
| compressional wave | موجة تضاغطية |
| compressional wave velocity | سرعة الموجة التضاغطية |
| compressive force | قوة ضاغطة |
| compressive strength | مقاومة الانضغاط |
| compressor | ضاغط |
| compressor | ضاغط |
| comprise (in) | يتمثل (في) |
| compromise | يقضي على؛ يتخلص من |
| compromise | حالة وسطية |
| compromise drills | تدريبات لمواجهة الإفشاء عن معلومات سرية |
| compulsory alienation | النقل الإجباري للملكية |
| compulsory arbitration | تحكيم إجباري |
| compulsory license clause | بند الترخيص الإجباري |
| compulsory service | خدمة إلزامية؛ جبرية؛ قهرية |
| computation | حساب: القيام بالحساب أو العملية الحسابية |
| computational | حسابي؛ مرتبط بالعملية الحسابية |
| computational physics | فيزياء حاسوبية |
| computed tomography | تصوير مقطعي بالكمبيوتر |
| computed tomography | التصوير المقطعي المحوسب |
| computer | حاسوب |
| computer + science network (csnet) | شبكة العلم والكبيوتر |

| | |
|---|---|
| computer aided manufacturing | تصنيع يتم بمعونة الحاسب |
| computer emergency response team (cert) | فريق الطوارئ على الكمبيوتر |
| computer facilities, | أدوات كمبيوتر مساعدة |
| computer geek | عاشق الكمبيوتر |
| computer hacking software | برنامج لاقتحام الحواسيب |
| computer implementable invention | اختراع يمكن تطبيقه بواسطة حاسوب |
| computer professionals for social responsibility | منظمة محترفي الكمبيوتر للمسؤليات الاجتماعية |
| computer readable material | مادة حاسبية يمكن قراءتها |
| computer recycling | إعادة تدوير حاسوبي |
| computer security | أمن الحاسوب، نظام حماية الحاسوب من العبث والإفشاء الغير المرغوب للمعلومات |
| computer simulations | عمليات المحاكاة بالكمبيوتر |
| computer translatable material | مادة حاسبية يمكن ترجمتها |
| computer whiz | عبقري كمبيوتر |
| computer-implementable invention | اختراع ذو تطبيقات حاسبية |
| computer-implemented invention | اختراع مطبق حاسبيا |
| computer-mediated communication | اتصال عبر الكمبيوتر |
| computers | حاسوبيات |
| computing | حساب بالكمبيوتر؛ حوسبة |
| computing | احتساب |
| computing deviec | وسيلة كمبيوتر؛ وسيلة كمبيوترية |
| computing infrastructure | البنية التحتية للحوسبة |
| comsec | أمن الاتصالات |
| concave - convex contact | اتصال مقعر ـ محدب |
| conceal | يخفي |
| concealed prior art | فن سابق مَخفي |
| concealment | إخفاء |
| concealment of prior art | إخفاء فن سابق |
| conceivability | قابلية الشيء للتخيل |
| conceivable | قابل للتخيل |
| conceivable invention | اختراع قابل للتصور |
| conceive | يتخيل |
| conceived | متخيل |
| conceived invention | اختراع متصور |
| conceiver | متخيل |
| concentrate | ناتج التركيز |
| concentrated to give a free base of the title compound | تم تركيزه للحصول على قاعدة حرة للمركب المذكور في العنوان |
| concentrating the solution by co-evaporating with isopropanol | تركيز المحلول بالتبخير المشترك مع كذا |
| concentration camp | معسكر اعتقال |
| concentration gradient | تدرج التركيز |
| concentric rings | حلقات متحدة المركز |
| concept | مفهوم |
| concept idea | الفكرة المفهومية. فهم المخترع الفكري لاختراعه فهما تجريديا، وهو ما يعد أحد الخطوات المبكرة في إنجاز الاختراع |

| | |
|---|---|
| conception | مفهوم |
| conceptual | مفهومي |
| conceptual innovators | مبتكرون مختصون بالمفاهيم |
| conceptualizable invention | اختراع يمكن تحديد مفهومه |
| conceptualization | بناء مفهوم |
| conceptualization of invention | البناء المفهومي للاختراع |
| conceptualize | يبني مفهوما |
| conchoidal fracture | صدع محاري الشكل |
| concieved discovery | اكتشاف متصور |
| conciliation | المصالحة |
| concrete | خرساني |
| concrete | خرسانة |
| concrete blocks | أحجار خرسانية |
| concurrent invention | اختراع متزامن |
| concurrent licensing | ترخيص متزامن. |
| concurrent patent infringements | انتهاكات متزامنة لبراءة |
| concurrent patenting | إصدار أكثر براءة على نحو متزامن |
| concurrent patenting litigation | تقاض بشأن إصدار أكثر من براءة على نحو متزامن |
| concurrent work | عمل متزامن |
| concurrently | بشكل متزامن |
| concurring opinion | رأي موافق. رأي لقاضٍ عضوٍ في هيئة قضائية للنظر في قضية موافق لرأي أغلبية القضاة. |
| concussion | ارتجاج مخي |
| condensate | ناتج التكثيف |
| condensate drain | مصرف لنواتج التكثيف |
| condensate liquids | مواد سائلة مكثفة |
| condense | يكثف |
| condensed light | ضوء مكثف |
| condensed matter physics | فيزياء المادة المكثفة |
| condenser | مكثف |
| condenser | مكثف |
| condenser lens | عدسة مكثفة |
| condition | يهيء، تهيئة، حالة |
| conditionability | قابلية الشيء للتهيئة |
| conditionable | قابل للتهيئة |
| conditioned | مهيأ |
| conditioned | مهيأ |
| conditioned media | أوساط مهيأة |
| conditioner | منسق |
| conditioner machine | آلة تهيئة |
| conditions (medical) | ظروف |
| condominium conversion portfolio | محفظة تحويل الملكيات العقارية المشتركة |
| conducted signals | إشارات موصلة: إشارات تم توصيلها |
| conduction heating | تسخين توصيلي |
| conductivity | موصلية: تُقاس بالسيمنز |
| conductivity | مُوصليّة: وتقاس قيمتها بالميكرو سيمنز |
| conductivity cell | خلية توصيل |
| conductor | موصل |
| conduit | قناة توصيل؛ قناة؛ مجرى؛ ماسورة توصيل |
| cone voltage | جهد المخروط |
| conferencing | عقد مؤتمرات |
| confidence intervals | فترات الثقة |

| | |
|---|---|
| confidential information clause | البند الخاص بسرية المعلومات |
| confidential invention | اختراع تتوجب المحافظة على سريته |
| confidential know-how | دراية للكيفية سرية |
| configurable material | مادة قابلة للتشكيل |
| configuration | هيئة؛ صورة؛ شكل |
| configuration | تصميم (ميكانيكا) |
| confirm or repeal the judgement | يؤيد أو ينقض الحكم |
| confirm selection | تأكيد التحديد |
| confirmed infringer | منتهك مؤكد |
| confirmed patent eligibility | أهلية مؤكدة لاستصدار براءة |
| confiscation | المصادرة |
| conflict of interest | تضارب المصالح؛ تعارض المصالح؛ تضاد المصالح |
| confluence | نسبة تشابك النسيج الخلوي |
| confluence | نسبة تجمع؛ نقطة تجمع؛ نقطة الالتقاء |
| confluency | نسبة تشابك النسيج الخلوي |
| confluency | نسبة تجمع؛ نقطة تجمع؛ نقطة الالتقاء |
| confluent | متشابك النسيج الخلوي |
| confluent | متجمع |
| confocal | ذو بؤرة واحدة |
| conformation (of a protein, etc.) | هيئة - بنية (بروتين، إلخ) |
| conformational | بنائي؛ بنيوي |
| congestive heart failure | قصور القلب الاحتقاني |
| conglomerate | المدملكات ( الكونجلوميرات) |
| conglomerate | كتلة مختلطة؛ كتلة مركبة |
| conglomerates based on composition | مدملكات مبنية على التركيب |
| conglomerates based on origin | مدملكات أصلية المنشأ |
| conglomerates based on texture | مدملكات مبنية على النسيج |
| conjugate | مقترن؛ متقارن |
| conjugate | مترافق |
| conjunctivitis | رمد |
| conjunctivitis | التهاب الملتحمة |
| connate | حبيس أو كامن: مائع..إلخ حبيس في التكوين أو كامن فيه |
| connate fluid | المائع الحبيس: مائع حبيس في التكوين |
| connate water | ماء حبيس |
| connect | يربط أو يرتبط (ب) |
| connect | يصل أو يتصل (ب) |
| connect control language (ccl) | لغة التحكم في الاتصال |
| connect time | زمن الاتصال |
| connected to | متصل بـ |
| connecting devices | وسائل توصيل |
| connecting to a vcr | توصيل الكاميرا بالفيديو |
| connection | اتصال |
| connection closed by foreign host | انهاء الاتصال بواسطة المضيف الأجنبي |
| connection logic | منطق الاتصال |
| connection sub | وصلة |
| connectionless communication | اتصال متقطع |
| connection-oriented communication | اتصال غير متقطع |

| | |
|---|---|
| connector boards | ألواح توصيل أو موصلة أو واصلة |
| conradson carbonaceous residue | المادة الكربونية المتبقية لكونرادسون |
| conscript | مجند |
| conscription | تجنيد |
| consensus | توافقي: متفق عليه؛ عمومي؛ إجماعي |
| consensus sequence | متوالية توافقية. انظر consensus |
| conservation | حفظ |
| conservation technology | تقنية محافظة، تقنية ترشيد |
| conservative | محافظ؛ تحفظي: مقاوِم للتغيير |
| conservative amino acids | أحماض أمينية محافظة |
| conservative substitution | استبدال محافظ |
| conservatory | مستنبت زجاجي |
| conserve | يحفظ |
| conserver | حافظ أو واقي |
| consist (in) | يتمثل (في) |
| consistory clause | بند الفحوى. بند يتضمنه طلب تسجيل البراءة يشير إلى فحوى الاختراع، إذ يبدأ البند بعبارة the invention consists of يشيع ظهوره في الطلبات المقدمة في المملكة المتحدة |
| consolidated | متماسك |
| consolidated patent landscape | تعبير يطلق على حالة توحيد البراءات التي يفترض أن تكون مرتبطة ببعضها توحيدها |
| consolidated patents | براءات موحدة |
| consolidated patents genetic database | قاعدة بيانات موحدة لبراءات جينية |
| consolidation | توحيد |
| consortium for school networking (cosn) | منتدى الشبكة المدرسية |
| constant | ثابت |
| constant | ثابت؛ قيمة ثابتة |
| constellation | مجموعة |
| constituency | دائرة انتخابية |
| constituent assembly | جمعية تأسيسية |
| constituents | مكونات |
| constrained | مقيدة |
| constraint inequalities | متباينات القيود |
| constraints | ضوابط |
| constraints | قيود |
| constriction | جزء تضيّق |
| construct | جزء منشأ: بنية منشأة قام بتحضيرها الباحث ليبدأ أو ينشئ عليها تجارب |
| construction | بناء |
| constructivism | الاستنتاجية |
| consular access | الاتصال بالقنصلية |
| consumer driven innovation | ابتكار يقوده وضع المستهلك. جهد ابتكاري يسير على هدى من موقف الجمهور وحاجاته وإفاداته |
| consumer durable technology driven innovation | ابتكار استهلاكي معمر تقوده التقنية |
| consumer gadgets | أدوات استهلاكية |
| consumer goods industries | صناعات استهلاكية |
| consumer needs-driven innovation | ابتكار تسوقه قاطرة حاجات المستهلك |
| consumption" | استهلاك طاقة منخفض |
| contact | (1) تلامس [مصدر]؛ (2) ملامس: طرف تلامس |
| contact area | منطقة تلامس |
| contact dermatitis | التهاب الجلد التلامسي |
| contact product | منتج ناجم عن تلامس |
| contact product | منتج ناتج عن تلامس |
| contact, electrical | ملامس كهربائي |
| container | حاوية؛ إناء؛ وعاء |
| container | حاوية |
| container premium | التغليف الترويجي؛ التعليب الترويجي؛ قيمة التعليب الترويجية؛ قيمة التعليب للمستهلك؛ قيمة التعليب |
| containment | احتواء / حاوية |
| contaminated material | مادة ملوثة |
| contaminated water | ماء ملوث |
| contemplate | يراعي |
| contemporaneously | بالتزامن؛ في نفس الوقت |
| content detection | الكشف عن المحتوى |
| content management system | نظام إدارة محتوى |
| contention | تعارض |
| contentious patent | براءة مثيرة للنزاع |
| content-sharing network | شبكة تبادل محتوى. شبكة مقفلة على الشبكة يتبادل أعضاؤها المحتوى |
| contested right to a patent | حق متنازع عليه في براءة |
| contiguous markers | الواسمات المتجاورات |
| continuation-in-part (cip) application ; continuation in part (cip) application | طلب تكميلي |
| continuity solutions | حلول للاستمرار. حلول لضمان استمرار الأعمال وعد تعرضها للأعطال |
| continuous | متواصل العمل |
| continuous shooting | التصوير المستمر |
| continuous shots | اللقطات المستمرة |
| continuous time interval | فترة زمنية متصلة |
| continuously stirred reactor (cstr). | مفاعل تقليب مستمر (CSTR) |
| contour lines | خطوط محيطية؛ خطوط كفافية |
| contours | كونتورات |
| contract to borrow bank instruments | عقد إقتراض ادوات مصرفية |
| contractors clause | البند الخاص بالمتعاقدين |
| contractual liability | المسئولية التعاقدية |
| contracture | تقبض |
| contra-lateral limb | الطرف بالجانب المضاد |
| contrast agent | عامل تباين |
| contravention | مخالفة |
| contributory negligence | إهمال إسهامي |
| contributory patent infringement | انتهاك براءة إسهامي |
| control | عينة عيارية؛ عينة مقارنة؛ عينة تحكم في التجربة |

| | |
|---|---|
| control | تحكم |
| control | يتحكم، تحكم |
| control animals | حيوانات التجارب |
| control bus | ناقل التحكم |
| control channel | قناة التحكم |
| control character | حرف التحكم |
| control device | جهاز تحكم |
| control device for an electrical apparatus | وسيلة تحكم في جهاز كهربائي |
| control experiment | تجربة عيارية؛ تجربة مقارنة (للتأكد من صحة تجارب أخرى) |
| control key | مفتاح التحكم |
| control refolding | إعادة طي عينة عيارية |
| control sample | عينة المقارنة؛ العينة العيارية: عينة التحكم في التجربة |
| control solutions | حلول تحكم |
| control surface | سطح تحكم |
| control system | نظام تحكم |
| controllable | يمكن التحكم فيه |
| controlled release dosage form | صورة جرعة ذات إطلاق مقنَّن |
| controlled release matrix formualtion | صيغة لقالب ذات إطلاق مقنن |
| controlled release means | وسائل انبعاث مقننة |
| controlled-release or sustained-release | إطلاق مقنَّن أو إطلاق مستمر |
| controller | أداة تحكم |
| controller | مُتحكم |
| controllers, micro-controllers, microprocessors | وأدوات التحكم، أو أدوات التحكم الدقيقة، أو المعالجات الدقيقة، أو الوحدات الإلكترونية الأخرى |
| conus medullaris syndrome | متلازمة المخروط النخاعي |
| convection | حمل حراري |
| convection curing devices | وسائل المعالجة بالحمل الحراري |
| convection mixing process | عملية خلط بالحمل الحراري |
| convention arbitral award | حكم تحكيم صادر |
| conventional 4-chain antibodies | للأجسام المضادة رباعية السلسلة التقليدية |
| conventional irrigation | الري التقليدي |
| conventional tabletting machine | آلة تصنيع أقراص تقليدية |
| conventional wisdome | الفكرة العامة |
| convergent routes to | المسارات الموصلة إلى |
| converging-diverging nozzle section | قسم (أو مقطع) فوهة تقارب-تباعد |
| conversely | بالمقابل |
| conversion | تحويل |
| conversion device | جهاز تحويل |
| convert | يحول |
| converter | محول |
| convertibility | قابلية الشئ للتحويل |
| convertible | قابل للتحويل |
| convex | محدب |
| conveyance of land | نقل ملكية الأرض |
| conveying gas | غاز ناقل |
| conveying system | نظام نقل |
| conveyor belt | سير ناقل؛ سير نقال |
| conveyor belt | سير ناقل |
| convict | المدان؛ المحكوم عليه |
| convict infringer | منتهك حاصل على حكم إدانة |
| convict patent infringer | منتهك براءة حاصل على حكم إدانة |
| convicted patent infringer | منتهك براءة مدان، منتهك براءة حاصل على حكم إدانة |
| convolute bedding | التطبق المطوي |
| convolutional encoder | وحدة تشفير إفرادية؛ مرمِّز إفرادي |
| convolve with | يدور بـ |
| cook books | يسلق الكتب |
| cook laws | يسلق القوانين |
| cool | يبرد |
| coolant | مادة تبريد |
| cooled | مبرَّد |
| cooled nitrogen refrigerant gas | غاز النتيروجين المُبرَّد المستخدم في التبريد |
| cooled water | ماء مبرد |
| cooler | مبرد |
| cooling | تبريد |
| cooling industry | صناعة التبريد |
| cooling vents | فتحات تبريد |
| cooling water | ماء تبريد |
| coomassie brilliant blue | صبغ أزرق ساطع كوماسي |
| cooperative alignment | التعلُّم التعاوني |
| cooperative unfolding unit of protein | وحدة فك طي تعاونية لبروتين |
| coordinate (wit) | يتناسق (مع) |
| coordinate covalent bond | رابطٌ تَساهُمِيٌّ تَسانُدِيّ |
| coordinate system | نظام إحداثيات |
| coordinated structure | بنية متناسقة |
| coordinates | إحداثيات |
| coordination compound | مركب تناسقي الترابط |
| coordinator | منسق |
| co-pending ; copending | لم يتم البت فيه بعد |
| co-pending patent application | طلب براءة منظور مُوازٍ |
| coplanar | تقعان في نفس المستوى |
| copolymerization | بلمرة مشتركة |
| copolymerize | تتبلمر بالاشتراك |
| copolymerized fatty acid acrylate or methacrylate | أكريلات أو ميث أكريلات حمض دهني مبلمر بصورة مشتركة |
| copolymers | بوليمرات مشتركة |
| copper (i) | النحاس (I) |
| copper (i) bromide dimethyl sulphide complex | معقد كبريتيد داي ميثيل بروميد النحاس (I) |
| copper (ic and ous) | نحاسيك ونحاسوز |
| co-precipitation | تراسب مشترك |
| copy | نسخة |
| copy on write | النسخ على الكتابة |
| copying music files from a pc | نسخ ملفات الموسيقى من الكمبيوتر |
| copyright clause | بند حق المؤلف |
| copyright crime | جريمة متصلة بحق النشر |
| coquina | الحجر الجيري العضوي (كوكينا |
| coralline algae | الطحالب المرجانية |
| cord blood | دم الحبل السري |

| | |
|---|---|
| core | أساسي؛ قلبي |
| core | الجزء المركزي من الجزيء |
| core | قلب؛ جزء رئيسي؛ جزء مركزي |
| core | لب |
| core competencies | اختصاصات أساسية |
| core competencies | المجالات التنافسية الأساسية |
| core plug displacement tests | اختبارات الإزاحة خلال قلب السدادة |
| core region | منطقة الجزء الرئيسي (مركز داخلي) |
| core tablet | قلب القرص |
| core technology | تقنية لبية، تقنية مركزية |
| core temperature | درجة الحرارة الداخلية |
| core-shell copolymers | بوليمرات مشتركة مكونة من قلب وغلاف |
| core-shell graft copolymers; core-shell type graft copolymers | بوليمرات مشتركة مطعمة من النوع ذي القلب والغلاف |
| coring | أخذ عينة قلبية (من تكوين؛ حفرة بئر إلخ) |
| cork stopper | سداد فليني |
| corn starch | نشا الذرة |
| corneal | قرني |
| corner kick | ضربة ركنية |
| cornerstone technology | تقنية ارتكازية |
| cornus kousa | القرانيا اليابانية المزهرة |
| corona | هالة |
| coronary arterial bypass grafting (cabg) surgery | جراحة الترقيع مع تحويل الشريان التاجي |
| coronary circulation | دورة تاجية |
| coronary heart disease | مرض القلب التاجي |
| coronavirus | فيروس الهالة |
| co-rotating extruders | ماكينات بثق بمسمارين ملولبين يدوران معا |
| corporal (cpl) | عريف |
| corporate debt | ديون الشركات |
| corporate disclosure statement | بيان (تقرير) بأنشطة المؤسسة |
| corporate governance | حوكمة الشركات |
| corporate ict infrastructure | البنية التحتية الخاصة بتقنية المعلوماتية والاتصالات |
| corporate negligence | إهمال مؤسسي ـ إهمال ضمن إطار الشركة |
| corporate patent | براءة خاصة بشركة. براءة مملوكة لشركة لا لأفراد |
| corporate patent strategist | إستراتيجي براءات مرتبط بمؤسسة |
| corporate responsibility | مسئوليه مشتركه |
| corporate self-evaluation | تقييم الشركة لنفسها |
| corporate visionary officer | مسئول السياسات المستقبلية |
| correct | يصحح، صحيح |
| corrected drawings | رسومات مصححة |
| correction | تصحيح |
| corrector | مصحح |
| correlate | يرتبط بـ أو يربط |
| correlation | ارتباط |
| correlations | ارتباطات |
| correspond | يناظر |
| corresponding | مناظر |

| | |
|---|---|
| corrigent | معدل؛ مصلح |
| corrode | يتأكل |
| corrosion | تأكل |
| corrosion engineering | هندسة التصادم |
| corrosive | مسبب للتآكل |
| corrosive agent | مادة أكالة |
| corrosive chemicals | المواد الكيماوية المسببة للتآكل |
| corrugated | مموجة؛ مغضنة |
| corrupted password recovery | استعادة كلمة مرور معطوبة |
| corrupted upgrade file | ملف ترقية تالف |
| corseta units (cu) | وحدات كورسيتا |
| corticosteroid | كورتيكوستيرويد؛ ستيرويد قشري |
| cortisone | كورتيزون |
| cosmids | كوزميدات |
| cost account | حساب التكاليف |
| cost effectively | بطريقة اقتصادية |
| cost-adjusted spending | نفقات معدلة التكلفة |
| co-star | نجم يتقاسم البطولة |
| cost-effective | اقتصادي؛ غير مكلف اقتصاديا |
| cost-effective hardware solutions | حلول أدوات معدنية ذات فعالية على مستوى الكلفة |
| costimulatory signal | إشارة استثارية مشتركة |
| costs | مصاريف وأتعاب |
| costume designer | مصمم ملابس |
| costume jewellery | مجوهرات الزينة؛ المجوهرات الزائفة |
| cot | شهادة الاختبار |
| cots | معدات تجارية جاهزة للاستخدام |
| cotton bale | بالة قطن (رزمة قطن ضخمة) |
| cotton boll ; boll weevil | لوزة القطن؛ دودة لوزة القطن؛ |
| cotton extra blank, cotton fiber | قطن ناصع البياض، ليفة أو شعيرة قطن |
| cotton gin | محلج قطن |
| cotton seed, flax-seed oil, millet-oil, palm-oil | بذرة القطن،زيت بذرة الكتان، زيت الذرة، زيت النخيل |
| cotton waste | عوادم القطن |
| cotton worm | دودة القطن |
| cotyledon | فلقة |
| coumarone resin | راتنج الكومارون |
| council for mutual economic assistance | مجلس المعونة الاقتصادية المتبادلة |
| council tax | ضريبة البلدية |
| councilman court | محكمة كاونسلمان |
| counsel | مستشار، محام |
| counsel of record | الوكيل الرسمي |
| counsel's opinion | رأي مستشار |
| count bottle | زجاجة عدّ |
| count bottles | زجاجات عدّ |
| count rate | معدل العد |
| countable income | الدخل المعتبَر |
| counter current | تيار معاكس |
| counter electrode; counter-electrode | إلكترود مقابل |
| counter wrap knitting status | وضع حياكة باللف مقابل |
| counteract | يُضاد |
| countercurrent cascade | تتالي التيار المعاكس؛ شلال التيار المعاكس |
| counter-current imbibition | تشرب عكسي |

| | |
|---|---|
| countercurrent instead of cocurrent heat exchange | التبادل الحراري عكس الاتجاه بدلاً من التبادل الحراري في نفس الاتجاه |
| counter-current to | عكس اتجاه |
| counter-espionage | مكافحة الجاسوسية |
| counterion | أيون مضاد |
| counterion ; counter-ion ; counter ion | أيون معاكس |
| counterparts clause | بند نسخ الاتفاق. بند تعاقدي يبين عدد النسخ التي تم أو سيتم تحرير العقد فيها |
| counter-rotating extruders ..comprising two screws | ماكينات بثق بمسمارين ملولبين يدوران عكس بعضهما |
| counter-rotating screws | مسامير ملولبة تدور عكس بعضها البعض |
| countersunk head | رأس غاطس |
| countries | بلدان |
| country | بلد |
| country manager | المدير القُطري |
| country of incorporation | بلد تأسيس الكيان القانوني. البلد الذي تم فيه تأسيس الكيان القانوني الذي يتم طلب تسجيل البراءةباسمه، وهو ما يعد متطلبا من متطلبات تسجيل البراءة في بعض البلدان. |
| counts | عدّات |
| coupe | كوبيه |
| couple | يقرن |
| couple | يوصل [كهرباء] |
| coupling | إقران |
| courgette (baby marrow) | كوسة |
| course | مقرر دراسي |
| course | الإجراء المتخذ |
| court of administrative jurisdiction | محكمة القضاء الإداري |
| court of personal status | محكمة المواد الشخصية |
| court of record | محكمة سجل |
| court president | رئيس محكمة |
| court-appointed arbitrator | محكم معين من قبل المحكمة |
| court-martial | يحاكم عسكريا |
| covalently | تساهميًا |
| covalently bound | مرتبطة تساهميا |
| co-venturer's interest | مكاسب /مصالح المضارب المشارك |
| cover letter | خطاب تغطية |
| cover position | موقع غلافي |
| cover story | قصة مُختلقة |
| coverage | منطقة التغطية: المنطقة التي يستطيع خلالها الهاتف المحمول إستقبال وإرسال المكالمات. وعادة ما يعبر المختصين في مجال الشبكات عن التغطية على إنها النسبة المئوية للسكان المقيمين الذين يستطيعون إستخدام هواتفهم المحمولة خارج منازلهم. |
| coveralls | مئزر (ثوب عمل له كمين) |
| covered tube | أنبوب مغلف |
| coverslip / cover slip = cover glass | شريحة تغطية |
| covert listening device | جهاز سمع خفي |
| cow in milk | بقرة حلوب |
| cowboy | أفلام الكاوبوي |
| cow-in-calf | بقرة حامل |
| cp | سنتي بواز |
| cpa | محاسب عام معتمد |
| cpdms | نظام التهيئة وإدارة بيانات المنتج |
| cpi | خلية في البوصة |
| cps | سنتي بواز: لحساب اللزوجة |
| cps | عدة في الثانية: لحساب الشدة |
| cpsl | مكتبة إسناد برامج الحاسب |
| cpu | وحدة معالجة بالحاسب |
| cpvc | أقل من تركيز حجم الصبغ الحرج |
| crack ; cracks | شق؛ شقوق أو تشققات |
| cracking force | قوة تكسير |
| cracking force of at least about 110 n | قوة تكسير تبلغ 110 نيوتن. |
| cracking strength | مقاومة التكسير |
| craf | الأسطول الجوي الاحتياطي المدني؛ أسطول الطيران الاحتياطي المدني |
| crafts, craft | الحرف؛ حرفة |
| cramp | تقلص؛ شد |
| cramp | مشبك |
| crane | رافعة |
| crane | ونش؛ مرفاع |
| crane (winch) | رافعة (ونش) |
| craniopharyngeoma | الورم البلعومي الجمجمي |
| crash test | اختبار سريع |
| crawler | زاحف |
| crawler tractor | بلدوزر |
| crazing | الاحتكاك |
| creadit | اعتماد؛ ائتمان |
| cream | كريم |
| creamed cheese | جبن بالقشدة |
| crease, anti-crease, anti-creased, | الكرمشة، مقاومة الكرمشة، غير قابل للكرمشة، |
| cretonne | كريتون |
| creatable software | برنامج قابل للابتكار |
| create | يبتكر ابتكارا خلاقا، يخلق |
| creatine | كرياتين |
| creation | ابتكار، ابتكار خلاق |
| creations | ابتكارات خلاقة |
| creations of the mind | ابتكارات الذهن الخلاقة |
| creative | خلاق، ابتكاري |
| creative commons license | ترخيص العموم المبدع. ترخيص يقوم صاحب العمل الفكري بمنحه للغير لاستعمال العمل الفكري وفق نماذج تراخيص منظمة العموم المبدع تتسم بكونها تراخيص مرنة واسعة النطاق تستلهم فكرة تعزيز سلاسة تبادل المعرفة وحركة الفكر ومواجهة التقييدات المبالغ فيها التي ينطوي عليها نظام الملكية الفكرية التقليدي حسبما ترى المنظمة |
| creative environment | بيئة إبداعية |
| creative gap | فجوة إبداعية. من أبرز أمثلته التفاوت الإبداعي بين بعض شعوب الأرض وشعوب أخرى |
| creative genius | عبقرية خلاقة، عبقرية ابتكارية |

| | |
|---|---|
| creative heritage project | المشروع الخاص بالتراث الإبداعي. مشروع دشنته منظمة الملكية الفكرية العالمية لإنتاج حزمة إرشادات وممارسات مثلى فيما يتصل بإدارة الأمور ذات العلاقة بالملكية الفكرية عند تسجيل ورقم التراث الثقافي غير الملموس الخاص بالمجتمعات التقليدية |
| creative thinking | تفكير إبداعي |
| creativeless | غير خلاق |
| creativeness | ابتكارية |
| creativity | ابتكارية، إبداع |
| creativity enabler | مُمَكن للابتكار الخلاق |
| creativity evaluation | تقييم الابتكار |
| creativity growth | نمو الإبداع |
| creativity-friendly environment | بيئة مواتية للإبداع |
| creativity-oriented worker | عامل صاحب توجهات ابتكارية خلاقة |
| creator | وسيلة تكوين |
| credibility | مصداقية |
| credible | ذو مصداقية |
| credit | اعتماد |
| credit | ائتمان؛ اعتماد |
| credit offtake | الاقتراض |
| credit union | اتحاد ائتمان تعاوني؛ مصرف تعاوني؛ جمعية مصرفية |
| crest syndrome | متلازمة CREST |
| creutzfeld-jacob | داء جاكوب كروتزفيلد |
| crime | جريمة |
| criminal investigation department | المباحث العامة |
| criminal lab | المعمل الجنائي |
| criminal liability | المسئولية الجنائية |
| criminal negligence | إهمال إجرامي |
| criminal responsibility | مسئولية جنائية |
| crimping with valve | تركيب صمامات فيه |
| crisis | أزمة |
| crisis recovery | العودة من حالة الأزمة |
| criteria | معايير |
| criterion | معيار |
| critical velocity | سرعة حرجة |
| critique | تقييم -تُقَيم |
| crohn's disease | داء كرون |
| cron | خاصية الكرون cron |
| cron jobs | مهام مجدولة |
| crontabs/cronjobs | نظام محترف لتشغيل البرامج المجدولة ضمن نظام التشغيل الأساسي |
| crookneck | قرع معقوف |
| crop dusting | رش المحاصيل بالمبيدات |
| crop formation | التركيب المحصولي |
| crop rotation | دورة زراعية أو دورة محصولية |
| crops | المحاصيل |
| croscarmellose sodium type a | كروس كارميلوز الصوديوم من النوع أ |
| cross compete | تنافس تبادليً |
| cross examination | مناقشة الشاهد؛ بواسطة الطرف الآخر |

| | |
|---|---|
| cross flow | دفق معترض |
| cross linked | ذات روابط تشابكية |
| cross media effects: | تأثيرات عبر الأوساط: التحول المحتمل للتأثيرات البيئية من وسط بيئي إلى آخر |
| cross reference ; cross-reference | الإسناد المرجعي |
| cross reference to related applications | الإسناد المرجعي إلى الطلبات ذات الصلة |
| cross search | بحث متداخل |
| cross section | مقطع مستعرض؛ عرضي |
| cross sectional area (for) | مساحة المقطع العرضي (لكذا) |
| cross sth with sth | يهجن كذا بكذا |
| cross-bedding | التطبق المتقطع |
| crossbred ; cross-bred | مهجن تبادلياً |
| cross-compete (for) | ينافس تبادليا؛ ينافس تشابكيا |
| crosscorrelation ; cross-correlation ; cross correlation | ارتباط متقاطع؛ تقاطع |
| crosscorrelation values | القيم التقاطعية؛ قيم الارتباط المتقاطع |
| cross-coupling | اقتران تبادلي |
| crosscurrent; cross-current | في اتجاه عرضي؛ في اتجاه مستعرض |
| crosses | تهجينات |
| crossing | تهجين (زراعة) |
| cross-licensing agreement | اتفاق ترخيص متبادل. اتفاق يقوم بموجبه كل من طرفيه بترخيص حق فكري للطرف الآخر |
| crosslink | ارتباط تشابكي |
| crosslink | يربط تشابكيا؛ يربط بروابط تشابكية |
| cross-linkable | قابل للارتباط التبادلي |
| cross-linked | متشابك |
| cross-linked groups | مجموعات مرتبطة بروابط شبكية |
| crosslinked mercaptanized unsaturated ester composition | تركيبة إستر غير مشبعة مرتبطة تشابكيا معالجة بالمركبتان |
| cross-linked or amphipathic block copolymers of hydrogels | بوليمر مشترك تكتلي مرتبط تشابكيا أو مزدوج الألفة للمواد الهلامية المائية |
| cross-linked thiol esters | إسترات ثيول مرتبطة تشابكيا |
| cross-linker | مادة ربط تشابكي |
| crosslinking ; cross-linking | ربط تشابكي |
| crosslinking agent | عامل ربط تشابكي |
| cross-over design ; crossover design | تصميم متقاطع مقابل |
| cross-plot | مخطط متقاطع |
| cross-react | يتفاعل تبادليًا |
| cross-reactive | متفاعلة تبادليا؛ متبادلة التفاعل |
| cross-reactivity | تفاعلية متبادلة |
| cross-resist | يقاوم تبادليًا |
| cross-resistance | مقاومة متبادلة |
| cross-section | مقطع عرضي |
| cross-sectional; cross sectional | مقطعي عَرَضي |
| cross-sectional data | بيانات بالمقاطع العرضية |
| cross-sectional view | منظر مقطعي عرضي |
| cross-species | متعدي النوع |
| cross-well surveys | عمليات المسح العرضي للبئر |
| crosswise direction | اِتِّجَاهٌ مُسْتَعْرَضٌ |
| croupous | خناقي |

crowbar عتلة
crp خبير مخاطر معتمد
crt أنبوب أشعة الكاثود
cruciform صليبي الشكل
crude feed تيار تغذية خام ( وأيضا تيار التغذية بالخام)
crude oil pre-heat للتسخين المسبق للنفط الخام أو تسخين أولي
crude residue المادة المتبقية الخام
cruise طيران مطرد؛ تطواف
cruiser طراد
crumble يتفتت
crusher كسارة
crusher مطحنة
crushing strength مقاومة سحق
crust shovel جاروف لإزالة القشرة
cryogenic عند درجات حرارة منخفضة؛ مخفِّض الحرارة.
cryptography علم التشفير؛ علم الشفرة
crystal hardening powder مسحوق تماسك متبلر
crystal x-ray analysis التحليل البلوري بأشعة x
crystalisation germs بذور البلورة أو نوى البلورة. انظر crystalization seeds
crystalisation seeds نوى البلورة أو بذور البلورة. انظر crystalisation germs
crystalization germs بذور البلورة أو نوى البلورة. انظر crystalization seeds
crystalization seeds نوى البلورة أو بذور البلورة. انظر crystalization germs
crystalline بلوري
crystalline lattice شبكة متبلرة
crystalline state الحالة المتبلرة
crystalline texture النسيج البلوري
crystallinity درجة تبلور
crystallise يتبلر
crystallite حبيبة بلورية
crystallization التبلور
crystallization point (tc) نقطة التبلر: درجة الحرارة التي تتشكل فيها جزيئات المادة على شكل بلورات
crystallizers أوعية تبلور
crystallizing conveyor = crystallizing conveyor system نظام نقل خاص بالبلورة
crystallizing shaker هزاز بلورة
crystallography تصوير البلورات
csa حمض كامفور سلفونيك
csci(s) بنود تهيئة برامج الحاسب
csma/cd اكتشاف تضارب الوصول المتعدد بإحساس الموجة الناقلة
cst سنتي ستوك (مقياس اللزوجة، إلخ)
c-terminal الطرف C
c-terminal mature myostatin المايوستاتين الناضج الموجود في الطرف C
c-terminus الطرف C
cu وحدات كوريستا (لقياس الإنفاذية)
cubic feet قدم مكعب
cubit ذراع
cucumber mosaic تبرقش الخيار
cucurbita ; squash قرع
cucurbita maxima قرع كبير
cucurbita moschata قرع مسكي
cue إشارة بدء
cultivar صنف مزروع
cultivator مزارع
cultural creations ابتكارات خلاقة ثقافية
cultural creativity إبداع ثقافي
cultural heritage knowledge معرفة تراثية ثقافية
cultural knowledge معرفة ثقافية. مجمل العلوم والمعارف المتعلقة بثقافة المجتمع.
culture مزرعة؛ مستنبت
culture ثقافة
culture carrier flow loop حلقة تدفق حامل مزرعة
culture chamber غرفة استزراع
culture of creativity ثقافة إبداع
culture of invention ثقافة اختراع
culture of piracy ثقافة قرصنة. شيوع فكرة قرصنة الأعمال الفكرية وشيوع مسوغات لها في المجتمع
culturing استزراع (عمل مزرعة)؛ استنبات
cumulative audience (cume) الجمهور التراكمي؛ الحجم التراكمي للجمهور؛ النسبة التراكمية لحجم الجمهور
cumulative curve المنحنى التجمعي ( أو التراكمي)
cumulative innovation ابتكار تراكمي
cumulative innovation ابتكارات تراكميه
cuprous نحاسي
cups أكواب
curd خثارة اللبن
cure يعالج
cure يصلّب أو يتصلب [طبقة ملاط إلخ]
cure يعالج، علاج
cure notice إخطار بشأن الإصلاح. إطار يخطره متعاقد مع متعاقد أخل بأي من التزاماته التعاقدية ينذره بموجبه بوجوب قيامه بإصلاح الخلل الذي أحدثه
curer معالج
curing تصلب
curing معالجة
curing a formulation, tablet, etc. معالجة
curing device وسيلة المعالجة
curing the prepolymer composition معالجة تركيبة البوليمر الأولي
curing the said extended release formulation معالجة الصيغة ذات الإطلاق الممتد
current density كثافة تيار
current display indicator مؤشر العرض الحالي
current intensity شدة تيار عالية
current operating liabilities الالتزامات التشغيلية المتداولة
current strength شدة تيار
curriculum منهج دراسي
curriculum audit مراجعه المنهج
curriculum maps خرائط المنهج
curtain تدفق مستمر
curtain gas ستارة غاز
curvature انحناء؛ تقوس

| | |
|---|---|
| curve fitting techniques or algorithm | أساليب أو الطرق الحسابية بالرسم بالمنحنيات (التسوية الإحصائية) |
| curvilinear | منحني |
| curvilinear | مقوس |
| cushioning pad | وسادة تبطين |
| cusotmization of ict solution | تجهيز حل تقنية المعلومات والاتصالات حسب الطلب |
| custom wb | موازنة الأبيض المخصصة |
| customary arbitration | تحكيم عرفي |
| customary knowledge | معرفة عرفية. معرفة تناقلتها الأجيال بعد أن اتخذت قالب العرف المتبع |
| custom-built | مصنوع حسب الطلب |
| customizability | القابلية للتجهيز وفقا لطلب الزبون |
| customizable | قابل أن يتم تجهيزه حسب الطلب |
| customizable error pages | إمكانية تخصيص صفحات مصممة بشكل خاص لعرض رسائل الأخطاء بشكل أفضل |
| customizable solutions | حلول تصنع وفق الطلب |
| customization | التجهيزه حسب الطلب |
| customize | يجهز حسب الطلب |
| customized design | تصميم معد إعداد خاصا |
| customized solutions | حلول مصنعة وفق الطلب |
| cut | قطفة (كيمياء) |
| cut away view | منظر مقتطع؛ منظر مقطوع |
| cut into | يقطع إلى |
| cut pile | لفة خيط مقطوعة |
| cut-away view | منظر مقتطع؛ منظر مقطوع |
| cutoff | قطفة |
| cut-off time | فاصل |
| cut-off value | قيمة فصل |
| cutout ; cut-out | قِطع أو قاطع |
| cutter | قطاعه؛ أداة قطع: يعرف لدى المهندسين والفنيين باسم (قطر) |
| cutters | وسائل تقطيع |
| cutting | شتلة نبات |
| cutting edge | حد قاطع |
| cutting edge invention | اختراع مؤثر |
| cutting unit | وحدة قطع |
| cutting-room | غرفة المونتاج |
| cuttings | مفتتات |
| cuttings | قِطَع؛ قطوع |
| cv | (عدد) مرة قدر حجم العمود |
| cw | ضمانة العقد |
| cwbs | هيكل تفاصيل أعمال العقد |
| cyanate | سيانات |
| cyanogen | سيانوجين |
| cyanosis | زراق |
| cyanylating agent | عامل إدخال السيانيل |
| cyber | تخيلي؛ افتراضي: على شبكة الإنترنت |
| cyber age | عصر الحواسيب المرتبطة شبكيا |
| cyber-crime | جريمة متصلة بعالم الحواسيب المرتبطة شبكيا |
| cyberspace | فضاء تخيلي |
| cyber-warfare | حرب البريد الإلكتروني؛ حرب الأنترنت |
| cycle | يدور، دائرة، مدار، دراجة |
| cycle gas oil | زيت الغاز المعاد تدويره |
| cyclic or heterocyclic ring | حلقة أو حلقة غير متجانسة |
| cyclic prefix generator | مولد بادئ دوري |
| cyclic redundancy check (crc) | فحص الأخطاء الدوري |
| cyclic voltammetric analyzer | جهاز تحليل دوري بقياس الجهد |
| cyclisation | تحويل إلى مركب حلقي |
| cyclisation reaction | تفاعل تكوين الحلقات؛ تفاعل التحويل إلى مركب حلقي |
| cyclising | تحويل إلى الصورة الحلقية |
| cyclization | تحويل إلى مركب حلقي |
| cyclize the peptide | تحويل الببتيد إلى مركب حلقي |
| cyclized compound | المركب الذي تم تحويله إلى الصورة الحلقية |
| cycloaddition | إضافة حلقة |
| cyclone | فرازة دوامية |
| cyclone separator | وحدة فصل دوامي؛ فاصل دوامي |
| cyclonic fluid separator | وحدة فصل دوامية لمائع |
| cyclo-oxygenase inhibiting nitric oxide donors (cinods) | سيكلو - أوكسيجيناز مثبط لمانحات أوكسيد النيتريك (CINODs) |
| cyclooxygenase-inhibitory non-steroidal anti-inflammatory drug | عقار غير ستيرويدي مضاد للالتهاب مثبط لإنزيم سيكلو أوكسيجيناز |
| cyclo-paraffins | بارافينات حلقية |
| cyclopropanation | تكوين سيكلو بروبان |
| cyclopropane sufonylchloride | كلوريد سيكلو بروبان سلفونيل |
| cyclotron | سيكلوترون؛ جهاز تحطيم الذرة |
| cyclotron frequency | تردد جهاز لتحطيم نوى الذرات |
| cyclyl | سيكليل |
| cylinder diesel engine | محرك سلندر ديزل |
| cylinder of revolution | اسطوانة الدوران |
| cynomolgus | الرُبَّاح (جنس من النسانيس) |
| cyperspace, cyper space | عالم الإنترنت-الفضاء المعلوماتي |
| cypher | شفرة |
| cysteine | سيستين |
| cysteine engineered antibodies | أجسام مضادة معدلة وراثيا بالسيستيين |
| cysteinylation | إضافة سيستيين أو معالجة بالسيستيين |
| cystic | مثانة |
| cystic fibrosis | تليف كيسي؛ تليف البنكرياس الكيسي: مرض وراثي يتميز بوجود خلل وظيفي في الغدد خارجية الإفراز مثل البنكرياس وبخاصة تلك التي تفرز مخاطا. |
| cystine | سيستين |
| cytochemistry | فحوصات خلوية كيميائية |
| cytochrome | سيتوكروم |
| cytochrome p450 induction | حثّ (أو تنشيط) إنزيم السيتوكروم P450 |
| cytokines | سيتوكينات: بروتينات السيتوكين |
| cytomegalovirus | فيروسات مضخمة للخلايا |
| cytometry | عد الخلايا |
| Cytoprotective | حامي للخلية |
| cytosine | سيتوزين |
| cytosol | عصارة خلوية |
| cytosolic extracts | خلاصات عصارة خلوية |
| cytostatic | كابت للخلايا |

| | |
|---|---|
| cytotoxic factors | عوامل سامة للخلية |
| cytotoxicity | تسمم خلوي |
| cytotox-one homogeneous membrane integrity assay proceduretm technique | تقنية اختبار تكامل الغشاء المتجانس السام |

# D

| | |
|---|---|
| dac | اتصال تبادلي للوصول الرقمي |
| daffodils | النرجس البري كبير الزهر |
| dag | ديكا جرام |
| daggers | الخناجر |
| daily lighting cycle | بدورة إضاءة يومية |
| dairy | معمل الألبان |
| dairy farm | مزرعة ألبان |
| dairy machines | ماكينات الألبان |
| dairy products | منتجات الألبان |
| dal | قائمة الإضافة للبيانات |
| dama | وصول متعدد لطلب مخصص |
| damage | يضر بـ ، يضير، تعويض |
| damage infringement proceedings | إجراءات تتصل بانتهاك براءات |
| damage of liver | تلف الكبد |
| damaged file recovery | استعادة ملف مصاب |
| damaged neural tissues | أنسجة عصبية مدمرة |
| damages | تعويضان |
| damages | أضرار، تعويضات |
| damask | قماش دمشقي |
| damp | رطوبة |
| damp proofing preparations, except paints, for masonry | مستحضرات مقاومة للرطوبة، فيما عدا الدهانات، للاستخدام في البناء |
| dampers [heating] | منظمات خانقة [للتسخين] |
| dampers for musical instruments | أدوات لتوهين الذبذبات للاستخدام في الآلات الموسيقية |
| dancing robot | روبوت راقص |
| dandruff (pharmaceutical preparations for treating -) | قشرة الرأس (مستحضرات صيدلانية لمعالجة قشرة الرأس) |
| dao | نفط منزوع الأسفلت |
| darkroom lamps [photography] | مصابيح الحجرات المظلمة [التصوير الفوتوغرافي] |
| darkrooms [photography] | الحجرات المظلمة [التصوير الفوتوغرافي] |
| darning lasts | قوالب الرفو |
| darning machines | ماكينات الرفو |
| darning needles | إبر الرفو |
| darning thread and yarn | خيط وغزل الرفو |
| dart in and out of cover | يختفي ويظهر (من خلف الحجب) |
| darts | الأسهم ذات الريش |
| dash(ed) line | خط مقطع |
| dashed | متقطع |
| dashpot plungers [parts of machines] | مكابس أوعية التوهين [أجزاء من الماكينات] |
| dat | شريط صوتي رقمي |
| data acquisition tools | أدوات رصد بيانات |
| data archiving optimization | رفع كفاءة أرشفة البيانات إلى المستويات القصوى |
| data back-up software | برنامج حماية بيانات |
| data dictionary table | جدول قواميس البيانات |
| data eyeglasses | نظارات تمد الناظر ببيانات حول المنظورات |
| data eyeglasses | نظارات بياناتية |
| data media (magnetic -) | وسائل تخزين البيانات (وسائل مغناطيسية لتخزين البيانات) |
| data normalization | تشكيل البيانات هي مجموعة من الخطوات لإعادة تشكيل الجداول بطريقة صحيحة حتى لا يحدث بين البيانات تعارض داخل الجداول |
| data output | مخرجات البيانات |
| data processing apparatus | جهاز معالجة البيانات |
| data protection | حماية البيانات |
| data received | بيانات مستقبلة |
| data recovery software | برنامج لاستعادة البيانات |
| data retrieval | استرداد بيانات |
| data security | أمن البيانات |
| data sets | مجموعات البيانات |
| data signal | إشارة بيانات |
| data sink | مجمع بيانات |
| data spikes | الحدود أو القيم القصوى والدنيا |
| data storage | مخزن بيانات |
| data storage device | جهاز تخزين بيانات |
| data structure | هيكل بيانات |
| data transmission | إرسال بيانات |
| data verifying device | جهاز للتحقق من البيانات |
| database | قاعدة بيانات |
| database shutdown | إيقاف قاعدة البيانات |
| database startup | تشغيل قاعدة البيانات |
| data-leak prevention software | برنامج لمنع تسرب المعلومات |
| data-loss prevention software | برنامج منع فقدان البيانات |
| date / time indicator | مؤشر التاريخ / الوقت |
| date/time | الوقت/التاريخ |
| dates | البلح |
| daughter plates | أطباق مزدوجة |
| davits for boats | الداوودي (عواميد حديدية أو خشبية تساعد لرفع أو خفض القوارب أو حمولتها) |
| db | ديسيبل |
| dba | مدير قاعدة البيانات |
| dbdd | وصف تصميم قاعدة البيانات |
| dbms | نظام إدارة قاعدة البيانات |
| dbr | معدل بتات حتمي |
| dc | تيار مباشر؛ خلية شجرية |
| dc in 15v | دخول تيار مستمر 15 فولت |
| dc in socket | منفذ دخول التيار المستمر |
| dc-dc power converters | محول طاقة تيار مستمر-تيار مستمر |
| dce | معدة اتصالات البيانات؛ معدة إنهاء دائرة البيانات |
| dcg | التحكم بكسب الأعماق؛ تقنية للتحكم في مقدار الكسب من الأعماق ولتوفير صورة دقيقة للأعماق الوعرة |

| | |
|---|---|
| dc-in | دخول تيار مستمر |
| dcm | داي كلورو ميثان |
| dco(s) | اتصال بالمكتب المركزي (المكاتب) |
| dcom | نموذج كائن المكون الموزع |
| dcw | الخرائط الرقمية للعالم |
| dd | ثنائي الازدواج؛ ثنائي الثنائيات |
| dd/mo/yy | اليوم / الشهر / السنة |
| dda audit | تدقيق حسابات الإيداع تحت الطلب |
| ddbms | نظام إدارة قاعدة البيانات الموزعة |
| ddd | وصف تصميم قاعدة البيانات |
| deactivator | مخمد؛ معطل الفاعلية |
| dead box: | صندوق البداية، حيث يبدأ دخول اللب إلى ماكينة صنع الورق من هذه النقطة |
| dead patent | براءة ميتة. تعبير يطلق على البراءة المتروكة و/أو التي لا يمكن استعادتها |
| dead weight | حمولة ساكنة |
| deaerator | جهاز طارد للهواء |
| de-aerators for feedwater | أجهزة نزع الهواء من ماء التغذية |
| deafness (apparatus for the treatment of -) | الصمم (جهاز لمعالجة الصمم) |
| deal | يبرم صفقة، صفقة |
| deal flow | تدفق العروض |
| deal with the intruding aircrafts | يتعامل مع الطائرات الدخيلة |
| dealer imprint | ختم الوكيل |
| de-alumination | نزع الألومنيوم |
| deamidation | نزع الأميد |
| deaminase | إنزيم نازعة الأمين |
| dear sirs | السادة الأعزاء |
| deasphalted oil (dao) | زيت منزوع الأسفلت |
| deasphalting area (sda) | منطقة نزع أسفلت |
| death by hanging | الإعدام شنقا |
| death by injection | الإعدام بالحقن |
| death by shooting | الإعدام بالرصاص؛ رميا بالرصاص |
| death in the gas chamber | الإعدام بالغاز |
| debit card | بطاقة الصرافة الفورية؛ بطاقة السحب |
| debit card | بطاقة الرصيد الدائن |
| deblock | إزالة حجب |
| debottlenecking of existing plants | لإزالة الاختناقات في الوحدات الموجودة |
| debug | ينقح |
| debugger | مُنقح |
| debugging | تنقيح |
| dec | تحلل |
| dec. | تحلل |
| decalcified | مجرد من الكلس |
| decalcomanias | الرسومات الانطباعية |
| decalitre | ديكا لتر: وحدة تساوي 10 لتر |
| decametre | ديكا متر: 10 أمتار |
| decant off | فصل بالترويق |
| decant off | يروق (أو يصفق أو يفصل) بالترشيح |
| decant oil | نفط مروق |
| decantation | ترويق؛ صفق؛ إبانة: فصل بالترشيح |
| decanters | أواني الشرب |
| decanting liquids (implements for -) [hand tools] | سوائل التصفية (أدوات لسوائل التصفية) [عُدد يدوية] |
| decarbonising engines (chemical preparations for) | محركات نزع الكربون (مستحضرات كيميائية لنزع الكربون) |
| decay | ينحل؛ يتحلل؛ انحلال |
| decay factor | عامل الخمود؛ عامل الانطفاء التدريجي؛ عامل الوهن؛ عامل ضمور التأثير |
| decaying exponential | أس مضمحل |
| decentralized storage | مخزن بيانات لامركزي |
| decentralized storage system | نظام تخزين لامركزي |
| deceptive similarity requirement | مُتطلب التشابه الخادع. وجوب أن ينطوي العمل الفكري على مشابهة خادعة لعمل آخر حتى يقال إن هناك حالة انتهاك |
| decipher | يفك شفرة |
| decision making | صناعة القرار |
| decision support system | نظم دعم القرار |
| decision tree | شجرة الاختيارات |
| deck | منصة |
| deck boards ; deckboards | ألواح سطحية |
| deck chairs | كراسي طويلة قابلة للطي |
| deck hatch | فتحة الأرضية |
| declare | يعلن |
| decoctions for pharmaceutical purposes | مواد مستخلصة بالغلي للاستخدام في الأغراض الصيدلانية |
| decode | يفك الرموز |
| decode | يشفر |
| decoded data block | كتلة بيانات تم فك تشفيرها |
| decoder | وحدة فك تشفير؛ مشفر |
| decoding | تشفير |
| decoding broadcast signals | تشفير إشارات البث |
| decoding error | خطأ في فك التشفير |
| decolorants | مزيلات اللون |
| decomp. | تحلل |
| decomposable | قابل للتفكيك |
| decomposable | مركب قابل إلى أن يُفكك إلى عناصره الرئيسية أو إلى مركبات أبسط |
| decompose | يحل أو يفك؛ ينحل أو ينفك |
| decompose | يفكك مركباً إلى عناصره الرئيسية أو إلى مركبات أبسط |
| decomposer | مفكك |
| decomposing | تفكيك |
| decomposition | تحلل |
| decompression chambers | غرف تخفيف الضغط |
| decon | إزالة التلوث |
| deconstruct | يفكك، يهدم |
| deconstruction | تفكيك، هدم |
| deconvoluted | عديم الالتفاف؛ أو غير الملتف |
| deconvoluted mass spectra of peaks | الأطياف الكتلية عديمة الالتفاف (أو غير الملتفة) |
| deconvolution microscope | مجهر إزالة لفات |
| decoration of textile | زخرفة منتجات القماش (رقع |

| | |
|---|---|
| articles (heat adhesive patches for - ) [haberdashery] | اللصق الحراري لزخرفة منتجات القماش) [الخردوات] |
| decorations for cakes (edible -) | زخارف للكعك (زخارف للكعك قابلة للأكل) |
| decorations of plastic for foodstuffs | زخارف من البلاستيك للأطعمة |
| decoupage ; cut-outs | عملية تفريغ الصورة |
| decoys | شراك لـ |
| decoys for hunting or fishing | الطعم للصيد أو صيد الأسماك |
| decypher | يفك الشفرة |
| deduced sequence | متوالية مستنتجة |
| dedusted | منزوع الأتربة |
| deed of assignment | سند تنازل |
| deed poll certificate | سند تعهد فردي |
| deep brain stimulation | حث (تحفيز) عميق للمخ/للدماغ |
| deep fryers, electric | مقلاة كهربائية عميقة |
| deep fryers, non-electric | مقلاة غير كهربائية عميقة |
| defaoming agent | عامل لمنع تكون الرغوة |
| defatted milk | لبن منزوع الدهن |
| default | وضع افتراض؛ يخل، يهمل، إخلال، تخلف عن أمر، تخلف عن سداد التزام مالي |
| defective virus | فيروس معيب |
| defects in material or workmanship | عيوب في المواد أو الصناعة؛ عيوب في المواد أو التصنيع |
| defence council | هيئة الدفاع |
| defendant | مدعَى عليه |
| defendant ; respondent | مدعى عليه |
| defense base act | قانون القاعدة الدفاعية |
| defense reaction | تفاعل نفسي دماغي للدفاع |
| defensive licensing | ترخيص دفاعي |
| defibrillator | جهاز تخفيف الانقباض العضلي |
| deficits | عيوب |
| definable mime types | إمكانية تخصيص أنواع الملفات ضمن النظام بشكل مستقل لكل موقع داخل الشبكة |
| define | يعرف؛ يحدد |
| definitions clause | بند التعريفات. بند تعاقدي يتضمن تعريف المصطلحات المهمة التي يحويها العقد |
| deflect | يحرف، ينحرف |
| deflection | انحراف |
| deflection angle | زاوية انحراف |
| deflector | حارف |
| defoliants | سوائل كيميائية لتجريد الأشجار من الورق |
| deformable | قابل للتشكيل |
| deforming | (1) تشويه (2) تشكيل (تغيير شكل) |
| defroster | جهاز إزالة الصقيع |
| defrosting windows of vehicles (heating apparatus for -) | نوافذ إزالة الصقيع في المركبات (أجهزة تسخين نوافذ إزالة الصقيع في المركبات) |
| defucosylated | منزوع الفيوكوز |
| degenerate | ينحل، يتدهور |
| degeneration | إنحلال، تدهور |
| degenerative | انحلالي |
| degenerative | إنحلالي |
| degenerative motor diseases | الأمراض التنكسية للحركة |
| degenerative origin | أصل ضموري |
| de-glycosylated | غير مرتبط بالجليكوزيل |
| degradation | تحلل |
| degradation product ; degradation output | ناتج تحلل |
| degradation reactions | تفاعلات تحلل |
| degradative diseases | الأمراض المسببة للانحلال |
| degrade | يحلل {كيمياء} |
| degrade | يحتّ |
| degrade | تنخفض كفاءته |
| degreasers [machines] | مزيلات الشحم [ماكينات] |
| degreasers other than for use in manufacturing processes | مزيلات الشحم بخلاف الاستخدام في عمليات التصنيع |
| degreasing | إزالة الشحم |
| degreasing preparations for use in manufacturing processes | مستحضرات إزالة الشحم للاستخدام في عمليات التصنيع |
| degree of crystallinity | درجة التبلور؛ درجة البلورية |
| degumming preparations | مستحضرات إزالة المواد الصمغية |
| dehulled | منزوع القشر |
| dehydrate | ينزع الماء؛ يفقد الماء |
| dehydrating (apparatus for -) foodstuffs organic materials | مواد عضوية لنزع الماء من الأطعمة (أجهزة لنزع الماء) |
| dehydrating preparations | مستحضرات نزع الماء |
| dehydration | نزع الماء |
| dehydrochlorination | نزع كلوريد الهيدروجين |
| dehydrocyclization | نزع الصورة الحلقية |
| dehydrogenation | نزع الهيدرو جين |
| deimmunize | ينزع المناعة |
| deinking | إزالة الأحبار: عملية التخلص من الأحبار من الورق المطبوع المعاد استخدامه، ولكنها تشمل أيضا التخلص من المواد غير المرغوب فيها بصفة عامة |
| deionized | منزوع الأيون |
| deionized water | ماء مزال الأيونات |
| deionized water | ماء منزوع الأيونات |
| delamination | نزع صفائح |
| delay relay door control over secudity switch | تأخير موصّل التحكم بالباب عبر مفتاح الأمان |
| delayed release | متأخرة المفعول |
| delaying tactics | أسلوب القتال التعطيلي |
| delete | يحذف |
| deleting photo files | حذف ملفات الصور |
| deletion | حذف |
| deliberate infringement | انتهاك عمدي |
| deliberation | المداولة |
| delicate industries | الصناعة الدقيقة؛ مجمع صناعي |
| deliquore | ينزع الماء |
| delirium | هذيان |
| deliver | يوصل؛ ينقل؛ يسلم: يوصل مركب إلى العضو أو الموضع المرغوب فيه بالجسم |

| | |
|---|---|
| delivery | توصيل؛ إعطاء |
| delivery platforms | صور توصيل: صور توصيل العقاقير عبر الجلد أو الأنف إلخ |
| delivery pressure | ضغط تصريف |
| delivery tricycles | دراجات ثلاثية العجلات لتوصيل الطلبات |
| delocalized electrons | إلكترونات غير متمركزة |
| delta absorbance | فرق امتصاص |
| demagnetizing apparatus for magnetic tapes | جهاز نزع مغنطة الشرائط المغنطة |
| demand acquittal | يطالب بالبراءة |
| demand maximum punishment | يطالب بأقصى العقوبة |
| demeanor | السلوك الخارجي |
| dementia | عته |
| demesne | عقارات -عقار زراعي: أرض أو أرض عليها مبان ملك شخص |
| demethanizer | وحدة نزع الميثان |
| demethanizer operating pressure | ضغط تشغيل وحدة نزع الميثان |
| demethylation reaction | نزع تفاعل الميثيل |
| demijohns | دامجانات [زجاجات ضخمة مكسوة بالقش] |
| demilitarised zone | منطقة منزوعة السلاح |
| demineralization | زوال أو فقد أملاح الجسم المعدنية |
| deming quality cycle | دوره " دمنج" للجوده |
| demo | عرض توضيحي |
| demobilise | يسرح |
| demodulator | مزيل التضمين |
| demographics | الاحصائيات السـكانية |
| demonstration | عرض توضيحي |
| demulcent | ملين أو ملطف للجلد |
| demulsification | تفكك المستحلب |
| demulsifiers | عوامل تكسير للمستحلب |
| demultiplexer | مفكك إشارات |
| demux | إلغاء الإرسال المتعدد |
| demyelinating | مسببة لنزع النخاع |
| demyelinating disease | مرض مزيل للميالين |
| denaturants | مواد ممسخة |
| denaturation | تمسخ: تغيير الخواص الطبيعية |
| denaturing agents | عوامل التمسخ |
| dendrimeric | شجري؛ متفرعة |
| dendritic cell (dc) differentiation | تمايز الخلايا الشجرية |
| denervated | مجرد من العصب |
| dengue | حمى الدنج |
| denitrifying microorganism | كائنات حية دقيقة مزيلة للنترات |
| dense phase or dilute phase convey system | نظام نقل في الطور الكثيف أو الطور المخفف |
| densimeter | جهاز قياس الكثافة |
| densitometer | مقياس الكثافة |
| densitometer | جهاز قياس الكثافة البصرية |
| density gradient | متدرج الكثافة |
| density of a core tablet | كثافة قلب القرص |
| dental abrasives | أدوات كشط الأسنان |
| dental amalgams | ملغم للأسنان |
| dental apparatus | جهاز للأسنان |
| dental bridge | جسر أسنان |
| dental cements | ملاط الأسنان |
| dental crown | تاج أسنان |
| dental impression materials | مواد طبع الأسنان |
| dental lacquer | ورنيش لاكية للأسنان |
| dental mastics | صمغ المصطكا للأسنان |
| dental ovens | أفران الأسنان |
| dental prosthesis | تركيبة أسنان |
| dentifrices | مستحضرات لتنظيف الأسنان |
| dentists' armchairs | مقاعد ذات ذراعين لاستخدام أطباء الأسنان |
| denture polishes | مواد صقل أطقم الأسنان |
| dentures | أطقم الأسنان |
| deodorant soap | صابون إزالة الروائح الكريهة |
| deodorants for personal use | مزيلات الروائح الكريهة للاستعمال الشخصي |
| deodorants, other than for personal use | مزيلات الروائح الكريهة بخلاف الاستخدام في الاستعمال الشخصي |
| deodorising apparatus for personal use | معدات إزالة الروائح الكريهة للاستعمال الشخصي |
| deodorising apparatus, not for personal use | معدات إزالة الروائح الكريهة بخلاف الاستخدام في الاستعمال الشخصي |
| deoxidation | اختزال |
| department of commerce | وزارة التجارة |
| department of inspections and appeals | إدارة المعاينة والاستئناف |
| department of state | وزارة الخارجية الأمريكية |
| dependent claim | ادعاء تابع |
| dependent claims | عناصر الحماية التابعة |
| dependent claims | دعاوى تابعة |
| dependent industry | صناعة معمدة على عامل آخر |
| dependent variable | متغير تابع |
| depilation appliances, electric and non-electric | أجهزة إزالة الشعر؛ كهربائية وغير كهربائية |
| depilatories | مزيلات الشعر |
| depilatory preparations | مستحضرات إزالة الشعر |
| depleted flow | مستنفَد |
| depleted flow | تدفق مستنفد؛ تدفق مستهلك |
| deploy | ينشر وسيلة إلخ |
| deploy | ينشر قوات، أسحلة إلخ |
| deployment diagram | مخطط النشر؛ مخطط التجهيز |
| depolarization | منع استقطاب |
| depolymerization of fluoropolymers | إزالة بلمرة البوليمرات المحتوية على الفلور |
| deposit | راسب |
| deposite on | يرسب على أو يترسب على |
| deposition | ترسيب |
| depositional basin | الحوض الترسيبي |
| depot | مختزن؛ مخزَّن؛ مدَّخر |
| depot injectable formulations | الصيغ المخزَّنة (المدَّخرة) القابلة للحقن |
| depot injectable formulations | الصيغ المدخرة القابلة للحقن |
| deprotection | نـزع الحماية؛ نزع مجموعة الحماية (عن المركب) |
| dept | إدارة |
| depuratives | مطهرات |
| deputy attorney general | نَائِب اَلْمُدَّعِي اَلْعَامّ |
| deputy undersecretary of defense | نائب وكيل وزارة الدفاع |
| derivative trading | تداول المشتقات |

| | |
|---|---|
| dermal patche | لصقة جلدية |
| dermatitis | التهاب الجلد |
| dermatology | علم الجلد وأمراضه |
| dermatomyositis | التهاب الجلد والعضل |
| dermatosis | مرض جلدي |
| derrick assembly | تجميعة البرج؛ تجميعة برجية |
| derricks | أبراج الحفر |
| desalinate | تحلية |
| desalination | إزالة الملوحة، تحلية المياه |
| desalination plants | وحدات إزالة الملوحة |
| desalination process | عملية إزالة الملوحة |
| desalinator | محلِ للمياه |
| descale; de-scale | إزالة القشر عن (وفي وحدات تحلية المياه المالحة: إزالة الملح عن أغشية خلايا التشغيل) |
| descent | نزول |
| describability | قابلية الشيء للوصف |
| describable | قابل للوصف |
| describe | يصف |
| describe, described | يصف |
| description | وصف |
| description of the related art | الخلفية التقنية |
| desensitization | إبطال الحساسية أو نزعها |
| desiccating apparatus | جهاز تجفيف |
| design | تصميم؛ نموذج |
| design lacunae | ثغرة تصميمة |
| designability | قبالية الشئ للتصميم |
| designable | قابل للتصميم |
| designable invention | اختراع قابل للتصميم |
| designate (to) | يعبر عن؛ يمثل كذا |
| designated as = designated with | يشار إليه بـ |
| designer | مصمم |
| desilter | جهاز إزالة الطمي |
| desired block error rate (bler) | معدل أخطاء الكتل المطلوب |
| desired work | العمل المطلوب |
| desks [furniture] | مكاتب [أثاث] |
| desmoplastic carcinoma | كارسينوما صلبة |
| desolvation of a solvate | إزالة المذيب من ذوابة |
| desolvation temprature | درجة حرارة التذويب |
| desolvation temprature | درجة حرارة إزالة المذيب |
| desorb | مج؛ انتز |
| desorption | مج؛ انتزاز |
| destabilizing agent | العوامل غير المساعدة على التثبيت |
| destroyer | مدمرة: نوع من السفن الحربية |
| destructing apparatus for plant parasites | جهاز إتلاف طفيليات النبات |
| destruction | تلف - إتلاف (أكثر من تدمير) |
| destruction | تدمير |
| desulfurization | نزع الكبريت |
| desulphurisation of gases | نزع الكبريت من الغازات |
| desulphurisation of liquid hydrocarbon mixtures | نزع الكبريت من الخلائط الكربونية السائلة |
| desulphurized | منزوع الكبريت |
| desuperheater | جهاز إزالة الإحماء |
| detach | يحل، يفصل شيء عن آخر |
| detachable | قابل للحل |
| detachable collars | ياقات قابلة للنزع |

| | |
|---|---|
| detachable pad | وسادة يمكن انتزاعها |
| detacher | مُحل |
| detail-oriented mind | ذهن معنيٌّ بالتفاصيل |
| detect | يكشف عن، يكشف |
| detectability | قابلية الشيء للكشف |
| detectable | قابل للكشف |
| detection | كشف |
| detection software | برنامج رصد، برنامج اكتشاف |
| detection system | نظام اكتشاف |
| detection technology | تقنية الاكتشاف |
| detective | مستقص |
| detector | كاشف، جهاز كشف |
| detectors (metal -) for industrial or military purposes | أجهزة الكشف (أجهزة الكشف المعدنية) للاستخدام في الأغراض الصناعية أو العسكرية |
| detectors (smoke -) | أجهزة الكشف (أجهزة الكشف عن الدخان) |
| detent | حابسة |
| detention camp | المعتقل؛ |
| detergent | منظف |
| detergent additives to petrol [gasoline] | إضافات منظفة للبنزين [جازولين] |
| detergent dissolving device | جهاز محلل منظف |
| detergent surfactants | مواد منظفة خافضة للتوتر السطحي |
| detergents | مواد منظفة |
| detergents | منظف |
| determinant | محدِّد |
| determinants of innovation | محددات الابتكار |
| determinants of patent grant lag | محددات الفترة التي يستغرقها صدور قرار منح البراءة |
| determinants of patent length | محددات طول عمر البراءة |
| determinants of patent litigation | محددات النزاع القضائي المتصل ببراءات |
| determinants of patent opposition | محددات معارضة البراءة |
| determinants of patent quality | محددات جودة البراءة |
| determination | تحديد |
| determine | يحدد |
| deterrence | ردع |
| deterrent | رادع |
| detonating caps [toys] | كبسولات التفجير [ألعاب] |
| detonating fuses for explosives | صمامات صاعقة للمتفجرات |
| detonating plugs | شموع الإشعال للمتفجرات |
| detonators | مفجرات |
| detrital grains | حبيبات فتاتية أو حتاتية |
| detritus | فتات الصخور؛ الحتات؛ نفايات |
| deuterated | معالج بالديوتيريوم |
| deuterium labelled proteins | بروتينات مرقمة بالديوتيريوم |
| devastate | يكتسح؛ اكتساح |
| devastating invention | اختراع مدمر |
| develop | يستنبط |
| developed countries | بلدان نامية |
| developed idea | فكرة مُطورة |

| | |
|---|---|
| developers (photographic-) | مظهرات (مظهرات فوتوغرافية) |
| developing countries | بلدان في طور النمو |
| development awareness | وعي التنمية |
| development enabler | مُمَكن للتنمية |
| development stage | مرحلة التطوير |
| developmental cell | خلية |
| developmental robotics | روبوتية نامية |
| deveolp | يُصاب بـ (مرض إلخ) |
| deviated well | بئر مائلة؛ بئر منحرفة للحفر |
| device | جهاز؛ وسيلة |
| device failure | تعطُّل جهاز |
| device for trapping subsea fresh water resurgences | جهاز لاحتجاز انبعاثات الماء النقي تحت سطح البحر |
| device's wearability | قابلية الجهاز للارتداء |
| devolatization | نزع المواد المتطايرة |
| dew point | نقطة التكاثف |
| dexoxidize | يسحب الأكسجين |
| dextrine size | معجون الدكسترين الغروي |
| dfad | بيانات تحليل الخاصية الرقمية |
| dfd | مخطط تدفق البيانات |
| dg | ديسي جرام |
| diabetes | داء السكر |
| diabetes mellitus | بول سكري |
| diabetic bread | خبز لمرضى السكري |
| diabetic cataract | المياه البيضاء سكريّة المنشأ؛ المياه البيضاء لدى مرضى السكر |
| diabetic complication of neuropathy | تفاقم الداء السكري المتعلق بالعصاب |
| diabetic neuropathy | الاعتلال العصبي الناتج عن مرض السكر |
| diabodies (bivalent or bispecific) | أجسام مضادة ثنائية التكافؤ (ثنائية التكافؤ أو مزدوجة النوعية) |
| diabody | جسم مضاد ثنائي التكافؤ |
| diagenesis | عمليات التحور |
| diagnosis of pregnancy (chemical preparations for the -) | تشخيص الحمل (مستحضرات كيميائية لتشخيص الحمل) |
| diagnostic apparatus | جهاز تشخيص |
| diagnostic imaging | تصوير تشخيصي |
| diagnostic preparations | مستحضرات للتشخيص |
| diagonalize | يجعل شيء في اتجاه القطر |
| diagram | مخطط؛ رسم بياني؛ رسم تخطيطي |
| diagrammatic representation | تمثيل تخطيطي |
| dial-in temperature | درجة حرارة التشغيل |
| dialkylated | ثنائي الألكيل |
| dials (sun -) | أقراص مدرجة (أقراص شمسية مدرجة) |
| dials [clock- and watchmaking] | أقراص مدرجة [صناعة ساعات الحائط وساعات اليد] |
| dialysis | ديلزة-الفصل الغشائي-إنفاذ |
| dialytic stack | مجموعة فصل غشائي (في محطات تحلية المياه المالحة) |
| dialyzer | جهاز ديلزة |
| diamantine [abrasive] | ديامنتين [مادة كشط] |
| diameter | قطر |
| diamine | أمينات ثنائية |
| diamond burr | مثقب ماسي |
| diamonds (glaziers' -) | الماس (ماس الزّجاج) [أجزاء من |

| | |
|---|---|
| [parts of hand tools] | معدات يدوية] |
| diaper | حفاضة |
| diapered linen | نسيج مضلّع |
| diaphragm | حجاب حاجز |
| diaphragm pump | مضخة ذات غشاء مطاطي |
| diaphragms (pump -) | أغشية رقية (أغشية رقية للمضخات) |
| diaphragms [acoustics] | أقراص متذبذبة [علم الصوتيات] |
| diaphragms [photography] | الحدقة |
| diaphragms for scientific apparatus | أغشية للاستخدام في الأجهزة العلمية |
| diaphragms, shutters and flaps | حاجز؛ ومغلاق؛ وصمام قلاب |
| diastase | الدياستاز [خميرة نباتية] |
| diastereoisomers | مزدوجات تجاسم |
| diastereomeric | متعلق بمزدوجات التجاسم |
| diastereomers | مزدوجات التجاسم؛ الأيزومرات الفراقية |
| diatomaceous earth | تراب دياتومي |
| diaza | داي آزا |
| diazabicyclo | داي أزا باي سيكلو |
| diazo paper | ورق الديازو |
| diazonium salt | ملح الديازونيوم |
| dibasic sodium phosphate | فوسفات صوديوم ثنائي القاعدة |
| dibutyl tin dilaurate | داي بيوتيل قصدير ثنائي لورات |
| dicarboxylic | ثنائي الكربوكسيل |
| dice | النرد؛ لقمة |
| dichloridate solution | محلول داي كلوريدات |
| dichroic glass | زجاج مزدوج اللون |
| dichroscope | المجهر ثنائي اللون |
| diclosure of a conceived invention | إفصاح عن اختراع مُتصور |
| dictating machines | الدكتافون [مملاة] |
| did | وصف بند البيانات |
| die | قالب تشكيل |
| die face cutters | وسائل تقطيع وجه القالب |
| die face pellet cutters | وسائل تقطيع وجه القوالب للكريات |
| die plate | لَوْحُ القَالَبِ |
| die set | ضابطة القالب |
| diea | داي أيزو بروبيل إيثيل أمين |
| die-cutting and tapping machines | ماكينات قطع القوالب ودقها |
| dielectric | عازل؛ مادة عازلة |
| dielectric constant | ثابت عزل |
| dielectric wire | سلك عازل |
| diene (suffix, -diene) | داين (لاحقة للدَلاَلَةِ عَلَى وُجودِ رِباطَيْنِ مُضاعَفَيْنِ فِي المُرَكَّبِ). |
| dienyl ; -dienyl | دايينيل |
| dies [hand tools] | لقم اللولبة [عُدد يدوية] |
| diesel fuel treatment | معالجة وقود الديزل |
| diesel oil | زيت الديزل |
| diesel or an electric drive | محرك ديزل أو محرك كهربائي |
| diesel-operated | مشغَّلة بواسطة محرك ديزل |
| die-stamping machines | ماكينات سك القوالب |
| diet cola | كولا للحمية؛ دايت كولا؛ كولا محلاة ببدائل السكر |
| dietetic | غذائي |
| dietetic beverages | مشروبات مغذية |
| dietetic foods | أطعمة مغذية |

| | |
|---|---|
| dietetic substances | مواد مغذية |
| diethyl | داي إيثيل؛ ثنائي الإيثيل |
| diethyl ether | إيثر داي إيثيل |
| diethylene glycol ether | إيثر داي إيثيلين جليكول |
| diethylene glycol monoethyl ether | إيثر داي إيثيلين جليكول مونو إيثيل |
| differential effect | التأثير المتفاوت |
| differential fault | عطل تفاضلي |
| differential pressure separation device | وسيلة فصل بالضغط التفاضلي |
| differential scanning calerimetry (dsc) | القياس الحراري بالمسح التفاضلي؛ القياس الحراري الماسح التفاضلي |
| differential scanning calorimeter | المقياس الحراري بالمسح التفاضلي؛ المقياس الحراري الماسح التفاضلي |
| differential thermogravimetric analysis | التحليل الوزني الحراري التفاضلي |
| differential wall sticking | الالتصاقات المختلفة بالجدار |
| differentials | فروق |
| differentiated instruction | التعليم المميز |
| differentiating the immature dcs to mature dcs | تمايز الخلايا الشجرية غير الناضجة عن الخلايا الشجرية الناضجة |
| diffraction | حيود؛ انعراج |
| diffractogram | مخطط الحيود |
| diffractometer | مقياس حيود |
| diffuser | وسيلة تشتيت؛ مشتت |
| diffusion rate | معدل التشتيت |
| difiltration | ترشيح فائق |
| dig | وكزة، ملاحظة ساخرة، تنقيب، يحفر، يكد، يجتهد، مسهب، يستخرج بالحفر |
| digest | ينظم، يصنف، يستوعب، يهضم |
| digest magazine | مجلة الملخصات |
| digestant | هاضوم، مادة مساعدة على الهضم |
| digester | مهتضمة. قدر محكمة القفل تغلى فيها المواد تحت الضغط مع سائل آخرلكي تخل أو تلين أو يستخرج منها شيء |
| digesters [liqueurs and spirits] | مواد مساعدة على الهضم [مشروبات كحولية وخمور] |
| digestibility | الانهضامية، القابلية للهضم |
| digestible | منهضم، قابل للهضم |
| digestion | هضم (الطعام إلخ) |
| digestion | اهتضام (بواسطة الإنزيمات إلخ) |
| digestion | استخلاص |
| digestion | تصنيف، هضم |
| digestive | هضمي، مساعد على الهضم |
| digestives | العقاقير الهاضمة |
| digger | حفارة، مُنقب |
| diggers [hand tools] | الحفارات [معدات يدوية] |
| diggers [machines] | الحفارات [ماكينات] |
| digital | رقمي |
| digital | إصبعي |
| digital age | العصر الرقمي |
| digital- american mobile phone system | النظام الرقمي الأمريكي للهواتف المحمولة |
| digital audio player | مشغل صوت رقمي؛ مشغل سمعي رقمي |
| digital audio streamer | مشغل سمعي رقمي |
| digital audio/video player | مشغل فيديو/صوت رقمي |
| digital camcorder | كاميرا فيديو رقمية؛ كاميرا تسجيل رقمية |
| digital circuit | دائرة رقمية |
| digital data storage | مخزن بيانات رقمية |
| digital document | مستند رقمي |
| digital effect | مؤثر رقمي |
| digital hdtv | أجهزة التلفزيون الرقمي واضح الصورة |
| digital imaging technology | تقنية تصوير رقمي |
| digital light processing | معالجة ضوء رقمي |
| digital or analog electrical circuitry | مجموعة دوائر كهربائية رقمية أو تناظرية |
| digital representations of audiovisual works | عمليات التصوير الرقمية للأعمال السمعية البصرية |
| digital revolution | ثورة رقمية |
| digital signal processing devices (dspds) | أجهزة معالجة الإشارات الرقمية DSPDs |
| digital signal processors (dsps) | معالجات الإشارات الرقمية |
| digital slr camera | كاميرا رقمية بعدسة أحادية؛ كاميرا SLR الرقمية |
| digital television | تلفزة رقمية |
| digital tv frequency | تردد تلفزي رقمي |
| digital zoom | تكبير رقمي |
| digital zoom indicator | مؤشر التكبير الرقمي |
| digitalin | ديجتالين [منبه للقلب] |
| digitization | إدخال التكنولوجيا الرقمية |
| digitize | يرقم؛ يبرمج رقميا |
| digitized | مبرمَج: مزود ببرمجة رقمية أو تكنولوجيا رقمية |
| digoxin | ديجيوكسين |
| dihaploid ; diploid | ثنائي المجموعة الكروموسومية |
| di-hcl salt | ملح داي HCl |
| dihydrate | هيدرات ثنائية |
| dihydrofotate reductase (prfr)-deficient mutant cell line | سلالة الخلية الطافرة الناقصة في إنزيم داي هيدرو فولات ريدوكتاز (DHFR) |
| dii | البنية التحتية لمعلومات الدفاع |
| dilatative cardiomyopathy (dcm) | داء عضلة القلب الممتد (DCM) |
| dilation angle | زاوية تمدد: وزاوية التمدد هي مقياس لميل مادة صلبة نحو زيادة حجمها عند تعريضها للقص |
| diligence | عناية |
| diligent | كادّ، مجتهد، متقن، دال على جهد وعناية |
| dill oil for medical purposes | زيت الشبت للاستخدام في الأغراض الطبية |
| diluent | مادة مخفِّفة |
| diluents and carriers | المواد المخففة والمواد الحاملة |
| dilute | يضعف، مضعف، مخفف |
| dilute the enzyme (truncated form) | تخفيف الإنزيم (صورة مقتضبة) |
| dilution | إضعاف، محلول مخفف |
| dilutive | إضعافي |

| | |
|---|---|
| dimension | بُعد |
| dimensional stability | استقرار بعدي |
| dimensione | يزود بأبعاد |
| dimer | دايمر: وحدة بنائية ثنائية |
| dimeric | دايمري |
| dimeric compound | مركب دايمري |
| dimerization | دايمرة: التحويل إلى دايمر |
| dimerize | يحول إلى دايمر |
| dimethyl sulfoxide (dmso) | داي ميثيل سلفوكسيد |
| diminish | يتناقص |
| diminishability | قابلية الشيء للتناقص |
| diminishable | قابل للتناقص |
| diminished | منقوص |
| diminished responsibility | مسئولية متناقصة |
| diminishor | مسبب للتناقص |
| dimity | البفتة الهندية |
| dimmers [regulators] (light-) [electric] | أجهزة تعتيم [المنظمات] (أجهزة تعتيم الضوء) [كهربائية] |
| dimonomer | ثنائي الوحدات |
| dimples | نُقر |
| dining cars | عربات الطعام |
| dining cars [carriages] | عربات الطعام [عربات حمل الطعام] |
| dinner wagons [carriages] | عربات الطعام [مركبات] |
| dinner wagons [furniture] | عربات الطعام [أثاث] |
| diode detector | جهاز كشف بصمام ثنائي |
| diol | دايول |
| dione | داي أون |
| dioptric adjustment lever | زر ضبط مستوى انكسار الضوء |
| dioxalate (potassium -) | داي أوكسالات (داي أوكسالات البوتاسيوم) |
| dioxane | داي أوكسان |
| dioxide (titanium -) | ثاني أكسيد (ثاني أكسيد التيتانيوم) |
| dioxide (titanium -) [pigment] | ثاني أكسيد (ثاني أكسيد التيتانيوم) [خضاب] |
| dioxide of hydrogen | ثاني أكسيد الهيدروجين |
| dioxolane | داي أوكسولان |
| dip | ميل |
| dip tube | أنبوب غمس |
| di-pegylated | مضاف إليه ثنائي بولي إيثيلين جليكول |
| diphtheria | دفتيريا |
| diploid | ثنائي المجموعة الكروموسومية؛ ثنائي الصيغة الصبغية |
| diplomatic immunity | حصانة دبلوماسية |
| diplopia | ازدواج البصر |
| dipole moment | عزم ذو قطبين |
| diradical | ثنائي الشق |
| direct current (=dc electrical current) | تيار مستمر |
| direct disclosure | الكشف المباشر |
| direct fire weapons | أسلحة الضرب المباشر |
| direct inlet probe (dip) interface | وصلة بينية لمجس دخول مباشر (DIP) |
| direct ion-beam deposition | ترسيب بالحزم الأيونية المباشرة. قائمة النتائج |
| direct licensing | ترخيص مباشر |
| direct orthogonal | نظام إحداثيات متعامدة مباشر |
| coordinate system | |
| direct patent infringement | انتهاك براءة مباشر |
| direct response television (drtv) | تسويق تلفزيوني مباشر |
| direct sequence | متوالية مباشرة |
| direct transfer | النقل المباشر |
| direct transfer function | وظيفة النقل المباشر |
| direction indicators for bicycles, cycles, etc. | مؤشرات الاتجاه للاستخدام في الدراجات |
| direction of terminals | اتجاه أطراف التوصيل |
| direction signals for vehicles | علامات الاتجاه للمركبات |
| directional drilling | الحفر الموجه |
| directive council | المجلس االتوجيهي |
| direct-load gel standard | معيار جل التحميل المباشر |
| director of the defense technology security administration | مدير إدارة أمن تكنولوجيا الدفاع |
| dirigible balloons [airships] | مناطيد موجهة [سفن هوائية] |
| disability robot | روبوت إعاقة. روبوت معد على نحو يمكنه من مساعدة أصحاب الاحتياجات الخاصة والإعاقات |
| disability robotics | روبوتية الإعاقة. حقل علمي غرضه تطوير روبوتات تساعد أصحاب الاحتياجات الخاصة |
| disability tax credit | تخفيض ضريبي للمعاقين أو المعوقين |
| disaccarides | سكريات ثنائية |
| disadvantaged crudes | الخامات غير الملائمة؛ غير المؤاتية؛ غير المواتية؛ غير المميزة؛ المعيبة؛ غير الجيدة |
| disaggregate | ينقسم؛ ينفصل |
| disarmament committee (dc) | لجنة نزع الأسلحة |
| disassemble | يفك |
| disassembling | القيام بالفك |
| disassembly | فك |
| disaster recover | مواجهة الكوارث؛ الشفاء من الكوارث |
| disaster recovery | العودة من الكوارث |
| disaster recovery software | برنامج لإصلاح عطب الكوارث |
| disc finalizing | إنهاء القرص |
| disc formatting | تهيئة القرص |
| disc info | معلومات القرص |
| disc loading | تحميل القرص |
| disc operations | العمليات المتعلقة بالقرص |
| disc protection | حماية القرص |
| disc storage | تخزين قرصي |
| disc unfinalizing | عدم إنهاء القرص |
| discern | يميز، يُدرك |
| discernability | قابلية الشيء للإدراك |
| discernable | قابل للإدراك |
| discerned | مُدرك أو مُميز |
| discharge | تفريغ؛ تصريف؛ يفرغ، ينفث، ينحل، تفريغ، تدفق |
| discharge openings | فتحات تصريف |

| | |
|---|---|
| discharge tubes, electric, for lighting | صمامات تفريغ كهربائية للإضاءة |
| discharge tubes, electric, other than for lighting | صمامات تفريغ كهربائية؛ بخلاف الإضاءة |
| discharged | مفرغ، منفوث، مطلق |
| discharger | مفرغ |
| discharges | إفرازات |
| disciplinary referrals | إحالات تأديبية |
| disclaimer | إخلاء طرف ذاتي؛ براءة ذمة؛ النص المعتمد |
| disclose | يفصح |
| disclosed invention | اختراع مفصح عنه |
| disclosure | إفصاح |
| disclosure agreement | اتفاق إفصاح |
| disclosure of inventive concept | إفصاح عن مفهوم اختراعي |
| disclosure requirements | مُتطلبات كشف. هي الشروط المطلوب استيفاؤها للكشف عن اختراع أو براءة مسجلة واتخاذ أي إجراء بشأنها أو نحوها |
| disconnecting from | قطع الاتصال عن |
| disconnector unit ; disconnection unit | وحدة فصل |
| discontinue | يوقف |
| discontinued therapy | إيقاف العلاج |
| discoverer | مكتشف |
| discovery | اكتشاف |
| discrete units such as capsules or tablets | وحدات دقيقة أو منفصلة |
| discrete-time signals; discrete time signals | إشارات منفصلة في الزمن |
| discretionary portfolio management | الإدارة المصرفية للمحفظة الإستثمارية |
| discriminate | يميز |
| discrimination | تمييز |
| discs (compact -) [audio-video] | أقراص (أقراص مدمجة) [سمعية مرئية] |
| discs (compact -) [read-only memory] | أقراص (أقراص مدمجة) [ذاكرة للقراءة فقط] |
| discs (optical -) | أقراص (أقراص بصرية) |
| discuses for sports | أقراص الرمي للألعاب الرياضية |
| disease | مرض |
| disease incidence | حدوث مرض |
| disease modifying anti-rheumatic drug (dmard) | عقار مضاد للروماتيزم معدِّل لمرض (DMARD) |
| diseases | أمراض |
| disengaging gear for boats | تروس فصل التعشيق في القوارب |
| disgraceful act | عمل فاضح |
| dish covers | أغطية الأطباق |
| dishes (butter -) | أطباق (أطباق الزبد) |
| dishes for soap | أطباق الصابون |
| dishes of precious metal | أطباق من المعادن النفيسة |
| dishes, not of precious metal | أطباق ليست من المعادن النفيسة |
| dishonest operation | عملية غير أمينة |
| dishonest operation of a patent application | تسيير طلب براءة على نحو غير أمين |
| dishwashers | غسالات الأطباق |
| dishwashing brushes | فرش غسيل الأطباق |
| disincrustants | مزيلات القشور |
| disinfect | يطهر |
| disinfectant | مبيدات جراثيم؛ مطهرات؛ مطهر من الحشرات، مبيد حشري |
| disinfectant | مطهر |
| disinfectant apparatus | جهاز مطهر |
| disinfectant dispensers for toilets | وسائل توزيع مطهرة للمراحيض |
| disinfectant distributors for toilets | وسائل توزيع مطهرة للمراحيض |
| disinfectant soap | صابون مطهر |
| disinfectants | مطهرات |
| disinfectants for chemical toilets | مطهرات للمراحيض الكيميائية |
| disinfected | مطهر |
| disinfection | تطهير |
| disinfest | يطهر من الحشرات |
| disintegrants | مادة مفتتة؛ مفتتات |
| disintegrate | يحل، يفسخ، يحطم |
| disintegrating | مفكك -مفتت |
| disintegration agents | عوامل مفتتة |
| disintegrator | مفتت؛ جهاز تفتيت |
| disjoin | يفصل، ينفصل؛ يخلع، يفصل، يفكك |
| disjointed | مخلع، مفكك |
| disjunction | فصل، انفصال |
| disjunctive | فاصل، مفرق |
| disk drives [for computers] | مشغلات القرص [للحاسبات الآلية] |
| disk mirror | القرص المعكوس |
| diskette drive | محرك أقراص (مرنة) |
| disks [magnetic] | أقراص [مغناطيسية] |
| dislipidemia; dyslipidemia | خلل الدهون في الدم |
| dislodge | يزيح |
| dismantle ; disassemble | فكّ؛ يفكك |
| dismantling | تفكيك |
| dismiss from service | يصرف من الخدمة |
| dismissal | رفض، طرد |
| dismissal of a patent claim | رفض دفع (ادعاء) متعلق ببراءة |
| dismissal of a patent suit | رفض دعوى براءة |
| dismissed patent suit | دعوى براءة مرفوضة |
| d-isomer | أيزومر يميني الدوران |
| disorder | اضطراب، عدم اتزان، فوضى |
| dispensable powder | مسحوق قابل للتشتيت |
| dispense (medicines) | يركّب أو يحضّر (أدوية) |
| dispenser | وعاء |
| dispensers (adhesive tape-) [office requisites] | وسائل توزيع (وسائل توزيع الشرائط اللاصقة) [لوازم مكتبية] |
| dispensers (soap -) | أوعية توزيع (أوعية توزيع الصابون) |
| dispensers (towel -), not of metal, fixed | أوعية توزيع مثبتة ليست من المعدن (أوعية توزيع المناشف) |
| dispensing of the products | توزيع المنتجات |
| dispensing paper towels (metal boxes for -) | توزيع المناشف الورقية (صناديق معدنية لتوزيع المناشف الورقية) |
| disperging | البعثرة: المعالجة الميكانيكية لألياف الورق المعاد إستخدامه |

| | |
|---|---|
| | لبعثرة جسيمات الحبر |
| dispersant | عامل مشتّت |
| dispersants (oil -) | مواد مشتتة (مواد مشتتة للزيت) |
| dispersants (petroleum -) | مواد مشتتة (مواد مشتتة للنفط) |
| disperse | يشتت |
| disperse demonstrators peacfully | يفرق المظاهرات بسلام |
| disperser | مشتّت |
| dispersibility | إمكانية أو قابلية تشتيت |
| dispersing dyes | صبغات مشتتة |
| dispersion | تشتيت |
| dispersions | مشتتات |
| dispersions of plastics | مواد مشتتة من البلاستيك |
| dispersity | درجة التشتت الغروي |
| dispersive powder | مسحوق قابل للتشتت |
| display | عرض |
| display auto off | إيقاف تشغيل العرض تلقائياً |
| display boards | لوحات العرض |
| display device | جهاز عرض |
| display latch | مزلاج العرض |
| display priority | أفضلية العرض |
| display stands | قوائم العرض |
| display surface | سطح العرض |
| display unit | وحدة عرض |
| displayability | قابلية الشيء للعرض |
| displayable | قابل للعرض |
| displayer | عارض |
| disposability | قابلية الشيء للتخلص منه |
| disposable | يتم استخدامه مرة واحدة؛ أو يتم التخلص منه بعد الاستخدام |
| disposable | قابل للتخلص منه |
| disposable sterilization pouches | أكياس التعقيم التي يتم التخلص منها بعد استخدامها |
| disposals (garbage [waste]-) | أكياس يتم التخلص منها بعد استخدامها (أكياس القمامة [النفايات]) |
| dispose | يتخلص من |
| dispose (about, onto, on, at, etc.) | يضع (حول، على، عند، إلخ) |
| disposed | متخلص منه |
| disposer | متخلص، متصرف في |
| dispossession of owner | نزع الحيازة من المالك |
| dispute | ينازع، نزاع |
| dispute clause | البند الخاص بالمنازعات |
| dispute over water | نزاع حول المياه |
| dispute resolution clause | بند حل المنازعات. بند تعاقدي يحدد وسيلة حل النزاعات التي يمكن أن تنشأ عن العقد أو تنفيذه |
| dispute settlement clause | بند تسوية المنازعات. بند تعاقدي يتضمن تحديد وسيلة تسوية النزاعات التي يمكن أن تنشأ عن العقد أو تنفيذه |
| disrupt | (1) يمزق؛ يقسم. (2) يعطل (نشاط إلخ) |
| disruption | تمزيق؛ تمزق |
| disruption | اضطراب |
| disruptive technology | تقنية تشويشية |
| dissection | تشريح |
| dissenting opinion | رأي مفارق. رأي لقاضٍ عضوٍ في هيئة قضائية للنظر في قضية مخالف لرأي أغلبية القضاة. |
| dissociation constant | ثابت فصل |
| dissociation constant | ثابت فصل ارتباط |
| dissoluble | قابل للحل، قابل للذوبان |
| dissolute | حل، تذويب، انحلال |
| dissolution | الذوبان أو الإذابة |
| dissolution | حل، تذويب، انحلال |
| dissolvable | قابل للحل، قابل للذوبان |
| dissolvable material | مادة قابلة للانحلال |
| dissolve | يحلل، يفكك |
| dissolved | متحلل |
| dissolvent | مذيب، عامل مذيب |
| dissolver | محلل |
| dissolving | تحليل |
| dissolving device | جهاز محلل |
| dissonance | تنافر، تنافر الأصوات |
| dissonant | متنافر |
| dissymmetric | غير متجانس، غير متساوق |
| distal end | طرف بعيد |
| distal limp tail | ذيل مترهل عند الطرف |
| distance measuring apparatus | جهاز قياس المسافات |
| distance recording apparatus | جهاز تسجيل المسافات |
| distempers | دهانات مائية طباشيرية |
| distend | ينفخ، يضخم، يتضخم |
| distensible | قابل للنفخ، قابل للتضخيم |
| distension | نفخ، انتفاخ |
| distichous | ذو صفين، منقسم إلى فصين |
| distill | يستقطر، يجعله يتساقط، يرشح، يركز |
| distillate | ناتج التقطير |
| distillate | القطارة، النتاج المكثف لعملية التقطير |
| distillation | تقطير، القطارة |
| distillation apparatus | جهاز التقطير |
| distillation columns | أعمدة التقطير |
| distillation residue | المادة المتبقية من التقطير |
| distilled beverages | مشروبات مقطرة |
| distilled water | ماء مقطر |
| distiller | المقطر، جهاز التقطير |
| distillery | المقطر، معمل التقطير |
| distillery waste for animal consumption | بقايا التقطير للاستهلاك الحيواني |
| distinct invention | اختراع مميز |
| distinguish | يميز |
| distribution agency | وكالة توزيع الصحف |
| distribution boards [electricity] | ألواح التوزيع [كهرباء] |
| distribution boxes [electricity] | صناديق التوزيع [كهرباء] |
| distribution channel | قناة توزيع |
| distribution consoles [electricity] | نضد التحكم في التوزيع [كهرباء] |
| distribution machines, | ماكينات التوزيع الأتوماتيكية |

| | |
|---|---|
| Automatic | |
| distribution of student performance | توزع الأداء الطلابي |
| district | إقليمي؛ إقليم أو إقليم قضائي |
| disubstituted | مزدوج الاستبدال؛ به استبدال ثنائي |
| disubstituted bicyclic heterocycles | حلقات ثنائية غير متجانسة بها استبدال ثنائي |
| disuccinimidyl suberate | داي سكسين إيميديل سيوبيرات |
| disulfide | ثنائي كبريتيد |
| disulphide bridges | قناطر ثنائي الكبريتيد |
| ditchers [hand tools] | حفارات الخنادق [عدد يدوية] |
| ditchers [ploughs] | حفارات الخنادق [جرافات] |
| di-tert-butylazodicarboxylate | داي-t-بيوتيل أزو داي كربوكسيلات |
| diuresis | إدرار البول |
| diuretics | مدرات البول |
| divalent | ثنائي التكافؤ |
| divans | آرائك |
| dive | غوص؛ انقضاض |
| divergence | انفراج؛ تباعد |
| divers' apparatus | جهاز الغطاسين |
| divers' masks | أقنعة الغطاسين |
| diversified patent port | محفظة براءات مُنَوعة |
| diversity interleaving | توليف متنوع |
| diversity" | تنوَّع التضمين |
| diversomers | أيزومرات متنوعة |
| diverticulitis | التهاب الردب |
| divide (by) | يَقسِم (على) |
| divide (into) | يَقسِم (إلى) |
| divider | مقسم: وسيلة تقسيم |
| dividing machines | آلات القسمة |
| diving boards of metal | ألواح الغطس من المعدن |
| diving boards, not of metal | ألواح الغطس ليست من المعدن |
| diving lights | مصابيح الغطس |
| diving suits | حُلل الغطس |
| division | فرقة (عسكرية) |
| divisional headquarters | مقر قيادة الفرقة |
| divorce mediation | وساطة بشأن الطلاق |
| divot repair tools [golf accessories] | أدوات إصلاح عشب ملعب الجولف [محلقات الجولف] |
| diyl | داي يل |
| dizziness | دُوار؛ دوخة |
| dl | ديسي لتر |
| dl | ثنائي الطبقة |
| dl/g | ديسي لتر / جم |
| dlp | شريحة معالجة الضوء الرقيمة |
| dlrn | رقم المرجع برابطة البيانات |
| dmem | وسط إيجل المعدَّل لدولبيكو |
| dmm | ديسي مليمتر: وحدة قياس التغلغل |
| dmo | نفط منزوع المعدن |
| dmpi | متوسط نقطة الاصطدام المرغوبة |
| dmso | داي ميثيل سلفوكسيد |
| dna cassettes | مجموعة DNA؛ طقم DNA؛ أغلفة DNA |
| dna insert | وليجة (أو غريسة) حمض DNA |
| dna repair | تصحيح الحمض النووي DNA أو إصلاحه أو ترميمه |
| dns | خادم اسم المجال |
| dock | قفص الاتهام |
| docking program | برامج توجيه |
| docks of metal for mooring boats (floating -) | أرصفة من المعدن لرسو القوارب (أرصفة طائفة) |
| docks, not of metal, for mooring boats (floating -) | أرصفة ليست من المعدن لرسو القوارب (أرصفة طائفة) |
| doctrine | مبدأ |
| doctrine of claim differentiation | مبدأ تمايز الادعاء. مبدأ مفاده عدم إمكان تطابق نطاق طلبين بإزاء براءة واحدة |
| doctrine of implied license | مبدأ الترخيص الضمني |
| doctrine of inequitable conduct | مبدأ المسلك غير القائم على الإنصاف. مبدأ يسمح للمحكمة أن تبطل براءة في حالة ما إذا اكتشفت أن صاحب البراءة قد سلك مسلكا غير قانوني أو قائم على الغش في سبيل الحصول عليها |
| doctrine of intervening rights | مبدأ حقوق التدخل. مبدأ مفاده عدم محاسبة الغير على جهله بالتطورات التي آلت إلأيها براءة فيما يتصل بنطاقها أو غير ذلك عند عادة صدورها أو إحيائها، واعتماد الغير على آخر وضع كانت عليه البراءة، وذلك تأسيساً على استحالة علمه بتلك التطورات |
| document | يوثق، وثيقة، مستند |
| document clause | البند الخاص بالمستندات |
| document files [stationery] | ملفات حفظ الوثائق [قرطاسية] |
| document laminators for office use | أدوات تصفح الوثائق للاستخدام المكتبي |
| document management software | برنامج إدارة بيانات |
| document management software system | نظام برمجيات إدارة وثائق |
| document management system | نظام إدارة المستدات |
| document storage | مخزن مستندات |
| document workspaces | مساحات عمل المستند |
| documentary film | فيلم تسجيلي |
| documentation | توثيق |
| documentation | توثيق، إفراغ أمر في قالب مستندي |
| documents | وثائق، مستندات |
| dog biscuits | طعام الكلاب |
| dog collars | أطواق لعنق الكلاب |
| dog kennels | أكشاك تربية الكلاب |
| dog leg | ميل |
| dog lotions | غسول (لوسيون) لغسيل الكلاب |
| dog washes | غسول الكلاب |
| dog whistles | صفارات استدعاء الكلاب |
| dogfight | اشتباك جوي |
| dog-leg ; dogleg | مائل؛ مقوس (كالقدم الخلفية للكلب) |
| dogleg severity | شدة الميل |
| dogs (chains for -) | الكلاب (سلاسل للكلاب) |
| dogs (repellents for -) | الكلاب (مواد طاردة لحشرات الكلاب) |

| | |
|---|---|
| dol | لغة تصميم البيانات |
| dolls | دُمى |
| dolls' beds | أسرة الدمية (من اللعب) |
| dolls' clothes | ملابس الدمية (من اللعب) |
| dolls' feeding bottles | زجاجات لطعام الدمية (من اللعب) |
| dolls' houses | بيوت الدمى |
| dolls' rooms | غرف الدمية (من اللعب) |
| dolomite | دولوميت |
| dolomitization | بعملية الدلمتة أو التدلمت |
| domain | مجال (أو نطاق) |
| domain | نطاق (أو مجال) |
| domain name purchase agreement | اتفاق بشأن شراء اسم نطاق |
| domain officer | المسئول عن أسماء النطاقات |
| domain type | نوع المجال |
| domestic arbitral award | حكم تحكيم محلي |
| domestic grinders, non-electric | آلات جرش غير كهربائية للاستخدام المنزلي |
| domestic robot | روبوت منزل |
| domestic technology | تقنية منزل |
| dominoes | لعبة الدومينو |
| domotics | نظم إليكترونية منزلية |
| donor and acceptor fluorophore | حاملة تألق مانحة ومستقبلة |
| donor framework sequence | متوالية إطار لمانح |
| donor nucleic acid | حمض نووي مانح |
| door bells [non-electric] | أجراس الأبواب [غير كهربائية] |
| door bolts | مزاليج الباب |
| door cases of metal | أطر الأبواب من المعدن |
| door casings, not of metal | أطر الأبواب ليست من المعدن |
| door closers [non-electric] | آلات غلق الأبواب [غير كهربائية] |
| door closers, electric | آلات كهربائية لغلق الأبواب |
| door curtains | ستائر الأبواب |
| door fittings, not of metal | تجهيزات الأبواب غير مصنوعة من المعدن |
| door fittings, of metal | تجهيزات الأبواب مصنوعة من المعدن |
| door frames of metal | أطر الأبواب من المعدن |
| door frames, not of metal | أطر الأبواب ليست من المعدن |
| door handles of metal | مقابض الأبواب من المعدن |
| door knockers | وسائل الطرق على الأبواب |
| door mats | ممسحة الأرجل عند الأبواب |
| door openers and closers (hydraulic -) [parts of machines] | آلات غلق وفتح الأبواب (آلات هيدروليكية) [أجزاء من ماكينات] |
| door openers and closers (pneumatic -) [parts of machines] | آلات غلق وفتح الأبواب (آلات تعمل بالهواء المضغوط) [أجزاء من ماكينات] |
| door openers, electric | آلات كهربائية لفتح الأبواب |
| door openers, non-electric | آلات غير كهربائية لفتح الأبواب |
| door panels of metal | ألواح الأبواب المطوقة بإطار، من المعدن |
| door panels, not of metal | ألواح الأبواب المطوقة بإطار، ليست من المعدن |
| door scrapers | كاشطات الأحذية عند الأبواب |
| door springs [non-electric] | نوابض الأبواب [غير كهربائية] |
| door stops of metal | مصدات الأبواب من المعدن |

| | |
|---|---|
| door-handles of porcelain | مقابض الأبواب مصنوعة من البورسلين |
| door-opener | فاتحة؛ دعاية استدراجية؛ مادة جاذبة للاستماع |
| doors for furniture | الأبواب للاستخدام مع الأثاث |
| doors for vehicles | الأبواب للاستخدام في المركبات |
| doors of metal | الأبواب مصنوعة من المعدن |
| doors, not of metal | الأبواب، ليست من المعدن |
| dopamine (da) | دوبامين (DA) |
| dopant | عامل إشابة |
| dopantistry | كيمياء الإشابة؛ كيمياء التطعيم |
| doped (with) | مُشَاب (ب) |
| doped with | مشابَة بـ |
| doping | إشابة |
| dormant patent | براءة نائمة |
| dorsal | ظهري |
| dorsalis pedis | القدمي الظهري |
| dos | نظام تشغيل الأقراص |
| dosage dispenser | جهاز توزيع الجرعات |
| dose-normalized | مقاس عن طريق الجرعة |
| dose-response curve ; dose response curve | مُنْحَنَى الجرعة-الاستجابة؛ منحنى الجرعة مقابل الاستجابة |
| dosification | تنبيه |
| dosimeter | أجهزة قياس الجرعات |
| dotted line | خط متقطع |
| double basses | الطبل المزدوج |
| double block and bleed pipe | أنبوب الإغلاق والتسريب المزدوج |
| double check valve | صمام ذو فحص مزدوج |
| double cheese cream | جبن القشدة |
| double layer capacitance | مكثف مزدوج الطبقة |
| double multiplet | ثنائي الثلاثيات |
| double patenting | منح براءتين عن أكثر من اختراع لنفس الشخص |
| double salt | ملح مزدوج |
| double-beat valve | صمام ذو نبضتين |
| double-blind clinical trial; double blind clinical trial | تجربة إكلينيكية مجهولة للطرفين: أي العلاج فيها مجهول للمريض والقائمين عليها |
| double-blind treatment period | فترة العلاج المحجوب للطرفين |
| double-crossover study; double crossover study | دراسة تحويلية مجهولة للطرفين: دراسة لا يعلم عنها المريض والطبيب المعالج شيئاً ويتم فيها التحويل بين عقارين أو أكثر أثناء الجربة ومعرفة تأثير كل منها على المريض |
| doubled haploid technique | تقنية مضاعفة المجموعة الكروموسومية الأحادية؛ تقنية ازدواج المجموعة الكروموسومية |
| doublet of doublets | ثنائيات مزدوجة |
| doublet of doublets | ثنائي الثنائيات |
| doublet of triplets | ثلاثيات مزدوجة |
| doublet of triplets | ثنائي الثلاثيات |
| doubling time | زمن التضاعف |
| doubted originality | أصالة مشكوك فيها |
| doughnut | أنبوب حلقي |
| dowels, not of metal | مسامير ليست من المعدن |

| | |
|---|---|
| down [feathers] | وبر [ريش] |
| down an aircraft | يسقط طائرة |
| downconverter | محول خفض |
| downer | هابط؛ مفاعل هابط؛ مفاعل سفلي |
| downfield | أسفل المجال |
| down-flow cracking reactor | مفاعل تكسير (حفزي) ذي اتجاه سفلي |
| down-flow mode | وضع تدفق إلى أسفل |
| downhole | أسفل البئر |
| downhole interval control valves | صمامات تحكم فاصلة بقاع البئر |
| downhole toolstring | أدوات الحفرعمود أسفل البئر |
| downhole tubing pressure(dhp) | ضغط الأنابيب السفلية |
| downlink broadcast reference signal information | معلومات إشارة مرجعية لبث اتصال هابط |
| downlink, down-link | اتصال هابط أو (الوصلة الهابطة) |
| download | تحميل |
| download | تحميل؛ إنزال |
| downregulate ; down-regulate | يقلل بشكل متحكم فيه |
| downregulation | نقص متحكم فيه |
| downsampling | تخفيض عينات |
| downside | عجز |
| downstream | الاتجاه السفلي |
| downstream | بُعدي |
| downstream | بعد كذا |
| downstream of a bulk separator | بعد جهاز فصل حجمي |
| downstream targets | الأهداف البعدية |
| down-time | زمن توقف التشغيل؛ زمن التوقف عن العمل |
| downtime; down-time; down time | الزمن الأدنى |
| downward departure | استثناء تخفيفي |
| dpi | نقط كل بوصة |
| dpm | عمليات تفتيت في الدقيقة |
| dppdb | قاعدة بيانات تحديد موقع النقطة الرقمية |
| dr | مراجعة التصميم |
| dr(s) | مراجعة (مراجعات) التصميم |
| draff | مقدار السمك الذي تم صيده |
| draft | يسحب، يجر، يحرر مسودة، جاهز للسحب، مسودة، تيار هوائي |
| draft tube | أنبوب السحب |
| draftee | جندي مجند (من أجل حرب مثلا) |
| drafting | صياغة طلبات، تحرير أوراق |
| draftsman | المخطط، المصمم، واضع المخططات، صائغ الوثائق ومشروعات القوانين |
| draftsman fees | أتعاب القائم على الصياغة |
| drag | كبح؛ مقاومة هوائية |
| dragees | ملبسات؛ حبوب مسكرة |
| drain | مصرف: ماسورة الصرف الصحي: بالوعة |
| drain cocks | محابس الصرف |
| drain pipes of metal | مواسير الصرف من المعدن |
| drain traps | مجمعات المجارى |
| drain valve | صمام التصريف أو التفريغ |
| drainage | نظام صرف |

| | |
|---|---|
| drainage machines | آلات الصرف |
| drainage tubes | أنابيب تصريف |
| drainage waters | مياه المجاري |
| drained elastoplastic properties | خواص اللدونة المرنة الجافة |
| drainers for use in photography | المجففات للاستخدام في التصوير الفوتوغرافي |
| draining | الصرف |
| drains | مصارف |
| drains preparations (clearing blocked -) | مستحضرات التصريف (مستحضرات تصريف-) |
| dram | درام |
| draught excluder strips | شرائط منع النزح |
| draughtboards | ألواح لعبة الداما |
| draughtman's tables | مناضد الرسامين |
| draughts [games] | لعبة الداما [ألعاب] |
| draw | يرسم، تعادل |
| drawer liners of paper [perfumed or not] | بطانات للأدراج من الورق [معطرة أو غير معطرة] |
| drawers [clothing] | سراويل تحتية [ملابس] |
| drawing | رسم |
| drawing boards | لوحات الرسم |
| drawing instruments | أدوات الرسم |
| drawing knives | سكاكين للكشط والرسم |
| drawing materials | مواد الرسم |
| drawing pads | مساند الرسم |
| drawing pens | أقلام رسم |
| drawing pins | دبابيس الرسم |
| drawing sets | معدات الرسم |
| drawing squares | مساطر الرسم |
| drawing t-squares | مساطر تائية للرسم |
| drawing-off | سحب |
| drawings | رسومات البراءة. الرسومات التي تعكس الاختراع موضوع طلب البراءة والتي يجب أن تتوافر في الطلب. |
| drawings objections | اعتراضات على الرسومات. إعتراضات فاحص طلب البراءة على الرسومات المرفقة التي قد يكون من بين أسبابها عدم وضوحها |
| draw-sheets for sick beds | أغطية سحب للاستخدام في أسرة المرضى |
| dredgers [boats] | صنادل مجهزة بالكراءات [قوارب] |
| dress body fasteners | سحابات الملابس |
| dress fastenings | أربطة الثوب |
| dress guards for bicycles, cycles | وسائل لوقاية الثوب عند ركوب الدراجات |
| dress shields | لباد يُحشى به الثوب عُرضة للعرق |
| dressing | ضمادة؛ تضميد الجروح |
| dressing (apparatus for -) | التسوية (جهاز للتسوية) |
| dressing and finishing preparations for textiles | مستحضرات لتهذيب واستكمال الأقمشة |
| dressing chemicals (leather- -) | مواد كيميائية للتهذيب (مواد كيميائية لتهذيب الجلود) |
| dressing gowns | روب دوشامبر (مباذل) |
| dressing tables | مناضد الزينة |
| dressing, except oils, for | دباغة الجلود فيما عدا الزيوت |

| | |
|---|---|
| Skins | |
| dressings (surgical -) | ضمادات (ضمادات للاستخدام في الجراحة) |
| dressings [medical] | ضمادات [طبية] |
| dressings for salad | توابل للسلطة |
| dressmakers' dummies | تماثيل عرض الملابس لدى خياطي السيدات |
| dressmakers' measures | أدوات قياس خاصة بالخياطين |
| dried milk | تجفيف اللبن |
| driers (air -) | مجففات (مجففات هوائية) |
| driers (hair -) | مجففات (مجففات الشعر) |
| drill | تدريب المشاة |
| drill bit ; drilling bit | لقمة الحفر |
| drill chucks [parts of machines] | أظرف المثقاب [أجزاء من الماكينات] |
| drill collars | وصلات عمود الحفر (وصلات الحفر) |
| drill cutting | مفتتات الحفر |
| drill holders [hand tools] | أدوات ربط المثقاب [عدد يدوية] |
| drill mixer | خلاط الحفر |
| drill pipe | أنبوب الحفر |
| drill string | عمود الحفر؛ سلسلة أنابيب حفر |
| drilling fluid | مائع الحفر |
| drilling heads [parts of machines] | رؤوس الحفر [أجزاء من الماكينات] |
| drilling machines | ماكينات الحفر |
| drilling mud | طين حفر |
| drilling operation | عملية الحفر |
| drilling rig [floating or non-floating] | منصة الحفر [طافية أو غير طافية] |
| drilling spindle | عَمُودُ دَوَرَانِ المِثْقَبِ |
| drilling tool suspended by rig | أداة حفر متدلية من منصة |
| drills | أدوات للثقب |
| drills (electric hand -) | أدوات للثقب (أدوات للثقب كهربائية تدار باليد) |
| drinking flasks for travellers | قوارير الشرب للمسافرين |
| drinking glasses | أكواب الشرب |
| drinking straws | الشاروقة (شفاط) (أنبوبة ورقية يُمتص بها الشراب) |
| drinking troughs | أوعية الشرب |
| drinking vessels | آنية الشرب |
| drinking water (filters for-) | ماء الشرب (مرشحات لماء الشرب) |
| drinks (medicinal -) | مشروبات (مشروبات دوائية) |
| drip bag | حقيبة تقطير |
| drip irrigation emitters [irrigation fittings] | رشاشات الري بالتنقيط [تجهيزات للرى] |
| dripping irrigation | الري بالتنقيط |
| drivability | قابلية الشيء للقيادة |
| drive (by) | يشغل (بواسطة) |
| drive belt | السير ناقل الحركة |
| drive mechanism | آلية التدوير |
| drive shaft | عمود التدوير؛ عمود الإدارة؛ عمود التشغيل |
| drive train | وحدة تشغيل |
| drive-by shootings | عمليات إطلاق نار من المركبات |
| driven country | بلد ذو وجهة |

| | |
|---|---|
| driven growth | نمو ذاتي |
| driven industry | صناعة ذات وجهة |
| driven innovation | ابتكار ذو وجهة |
| driven society | مجتمع ذو توجه |
| driver | مشغِّل |
| driver software | برنامج تشغيل |
| drivers | العوامل التي تقود شيئا للأمام |
| drivers (disk -) [for computers] | مشغلات (مشغلات القرص) [في الحاسبات الآلية] |
| drives (pedal -) for sewing machines | مشغلات (بدالات) في ماكينات الخياطة |
| driving chains for land vehicles | سلاسل التدوير في المركبات الأرضية |
| driving chains other than for land vehicles | سلاسل التدوير بخلاف المستخدمة في المركبات الأرضية |
| driving compound | مركب دفع |
| driving device | جهاز تحريك |
| driving force | قوة دافعة |
| driving motors for land vehicles | موتورات التدوير في المركبات الأرضية |
| driving motors other than for land vehicles | موتورات التدوير لغير المركبات الأرضية |
| driving point in elevation | نقطة تحريك في اتجاه الرأس |
| drop point | نقطة التسيُّل |
| drop-down-menus | قوائم منسدلة |
| drop-in filters | المرشحات الدوارة |
| dropper bottles | زجاجات القطارة |
| droppers for medical purposes | القطارات للاستخدام في الأغراض الطبية |
| dropwise | بالتنقيط؛ قطرة قطرة |
| drosophila | ذبابة الفاكهة |
| droup-out rate | معدل التسرب: خروج المريض من الدراسة بسبب آثار جانبية أو غيرها من المضاعفات |
| drp | قطرات |
| drug | يتعاطى المخدرات، دواء، يخدر، مخدر |
| drug allergy | حساسية تجاه عقار معين |
| drug and cosmetic colors (d&c) | ملوّنات العقاقير ومستحضرات التجميل |
| drug discovery | اكتشاف الدواء. عملية اكتشاف و/أو صناعة الدواء |
| drug eluting stents | دعامات التخلص من العقار |
| drug holiday | إجازة من العقار: فترة يتم فيها إيقاف إعطاء العقار |
| drug patentability | قابلية الدواء لأن تصدر عنه براءة |
| drug resistance | مقاومة لعقار |
| drug screening | فحص العقار |
| drug trafficking | تجارة المخدرات |
| drug-carrier system | نظام العقار-المادة الحاملة |
| drugget | لباد |
| drugs | العقاقير |
| drum | طبلة |
| drum dryer | مجفف برميلي |
| drum light | لمبة اسطوانية |
| drum type | أسطواني؛ من نوع أسطواني |
| drumheads | جلدة الطبل |
| drums [musical | الطبل [آلات موسيقية] |

| | |
|---|---|
| instruments] | |
| drums [parts of machines] | أوعية أسطوانية [أجزاء من الماكينات] |
| drumsticks | عصى النقر على الطبل |
| drusy crystallization | عملية التبلور التنوئي |
| dry cough | سعال جاف |
| dry cow | بقرة لا تنتج الحليب؛ بقرة غير حلوب |
| dry end | النهاية الجافة: جزء من عملية صناعة الورق بعد تكون نسيج الورق |
| dry ice | جليد جاف |
| dry ice [carbon dioxide] | جليد جاف [ثاني أكسيد الكربون الجليدي] |
| dry over | يجفف باستخدام |
| dry rot fungus (preparations for destroying -) | فطر التعفن الجاف (مستحضرات للقضاء على فطر التعفن الجاف) |
| dry wall | جدار جاف |
| dry weight (dw) | الوزن الجاف |
| dry-cleaning preparations | مستحضرات التنظيف الجاف |
| dryers (air -) | مجففات (مجففات هوائية) |
| dryers (hair -) | مجففات (مجففات الشعر) |
| drying apparatus | جهاز تجفيف |
| drying apparatus and installations | أجهزة وتجهيزات للتجفيف |
| drying apparatus for fodder and forage | جهاز تجفيف العلف والكلأ |
| drying apparatus for photographic prints | جهاز تجفيف الصور الفوتوغرافية |
| drying machines | ماكينات التجفيف |
| drying racks [photography] | مناصب تجفيف |
| drying racks for washing | مناصب تجفيف للغسيل |
| dsl | قائمة ملخص الوثائق |
| dslam | ومضاعِف إرسال خط المشترِك الرقمي |
| dsp core | قلب DSP |
| dsss | الطيف الموزع عبر التتابع المباشر |
| dst | أداة إسناد الوثيقة |
| dt | ثنائي الثلاثيات (ثلاثي الازدواج) |
| dte | معدة بيانات طرفية |
| dted | بيانات رقمية عن طبيعة الأرض والارتفاعات |
| dtex | دسي تكس |
| dtg | مجموعة التاريخ - الوقت |
| dtm | تردد متعدد ثنائي النغمة |
| dtop | بيانات طبوغرافية رقمية |
| dtt | داي ثيو ثريوتول |
| dual band | الموجة المزدوجة: جميع الهواتف المستخدمة الآن هى من النوع مزدوج الموجة الذي يستطيع التحول من ترددات GSM 1800 إلى ترددات GSM 900. تستفيد كثير من الشركات من إمكانيات الموجة المزدوجة في بعض الدول وذلك بإستخدام عرض الموجة MHz 1800 لحل مشاكل السعة في شبكاتهم |
| dual band mobile phone | هاتف محمول بنطاق تردد ثنائي |
| dual mode (of mobile phone) | الوضع المزدوج (للهواتف المحمولة): أي أن الهاتف مجهز ليمكنه إستخدام طريقتين مختلفتين للتشغيل. تتوفر في أمريكا هواتف محمولة تستخدم النظام الرقمي digital والنظام التماثلي analogue للتشغيل وتوجد حاليا هواتف محمولة من الجيل الثالث ذات تشغيل مزدوج G/GSM 3. |
| dual role actor | ممثل يقوم بأداء دورين في نفس الفيلم |
| dual-robot system | نظام ثنائي الروبوتية |
| dub | يدبلج |
| dubbing # to dub | دوبلاج؛ يدبلج |
| duckboards of metal | مجموعة ألواح تستخدم في العبور مصنوعة من المعدن |
| duckboards, not of metal | مجموعة ألواح تستخدم في العبور غير مصنوعة من المعدن |
| duct | قناة |
| duct | مسلك؛ مجرى؛ قناة |
| duct network | شبكة مسالك |
| ductal | قنوي |
| ductility | قابلية السحب والطرق |
| ducts [electricity] | أنابيب [كهرباء] |
| ducts of metal for ventilating and air conditioning installations | قنوات من المعدن للاستخدام في التجهيزات الخاصة بالتهوية وتكييف الهواء |
| ducts of metal, for central heating installations | قنوات من المعدن للاستخدام في تجهيزات التدفئة المركزية |
| ducts, not of metal, for ventilating and air-conditioning installations | قنوات، غير مصنوعة من المعدن، للاستخدام في التجهيزات الخاصة بالتهوية وتكييف الهواء |
| due diligence | مراجعة واجبة، فحص الواجب. عملية تقييم وضع الشركة أو النشاط التجاري |
| due diligence clause | بند المراجعة الواجبة. بند تعاقدي يبين أن المتعاقد قد قام بالمراجعة الواجبة والفحص الواجب النافيين للجهالة |
| due-diligence reviews | تقارير الاجتهاد اللازم |
| duffel bags | حقائب من الدفيل (نسيج صوفي غليظ) |
| dumb-bells | الدمبل [كرتان حديديتان يربط بينهما قضيب تمرن بهما العضلات] |
| dummies [teats] for babies | لهايات (مصاصات الرضاعة) للأطفال الرضع |
| dummy variable | متغير اعتباطي |
| dump truck | قلاب |
| duodenum | الاثنا عشر |
| duplex | إشارة مضاعفة؛ إشارة مزدوجة |
| duplexer | دائرة إرسال واستقبال؛ جهاز مزدوج الدخل |
| duplicators | آلة نسخ |
| duplicators (inking sheets for -) | الناسخات (أوراق التحبير للاستخدام في الناسخات) |
| durability | قابلية الشيء للتحمل |
| durable | جيد التحمل |
| duration of action ; action duration | مدة تأثير؛ مدة فعل |
| during the +10mv step | خلال الخطوة +10 ملي فولت |
| durometer | مقياس التحمل |

| | |
|---|---|
| dust bin | صندوق القمامة |
| dust binding compositions for sweeping | تركيبات لصق الغبار للاستخدام في الكنس |
| dust exhausting installations for cleaning purposes | التجهيزات الخاصة بتفريغ الغبار للاستخدام في أغراض التنظيف |
| dust laying compositions | تركيبات ترقيد الغبار |
| dust removing installations for cleaning purposes | التجهيزات الخاصة بإزالة الغبار للاستخدام في أغراض التنظيف |
| dust removing preparations | مستحضرات إزالة الغبار |
| dustbins | صناديق النفايات |
| dusters (furniture -) | منافض (منافض الأثاث) |
| dusting apparatus, non-electric | معدات إزالة الغبار غير كهربائية |
| dusting cloths [rags] | قطع قماش لإزالة الغبار[خرق] |
| duty | واجب، ضريبة |
| duty remission | الإعفاء الجمركي؛ الإعفاء الضريبي |
| duty to disclose | واجب الإفصاح |
| dvc | عقد مؤتمر فيديو على سطح الحاسب |
| dvd writers | محركات الأقراص المضغوطة دي في دي القابلة للكتابة |
| dvd-rom drive | محرك أقراص دي في دي |
| dwarf of rice | تقزم الأرز |
| dwell time | زمن انتظار؛ توقف |
| dye | صبغ (م: أصباغ) |
| dyeing machines | ماكينات الصباغة |
| dyeing of cotton, penshing off cotton | صباغة القطن؛ تقليع القطن |
| dyes | أصباغ |
| dyes (cosmetic -) | أصباغ (أصباغ التجميل) |
| dyes (food -) | أصباغ (أصباغ الطعام) |
| dyestuffs | مواد الصباغة |
| dyestuffs (wood -) | مواد الصباغة (مواد لصباغة الأخشاب) |
| dye-test | اختبار الصبغة |
| dyewood | الخشب الصبغي |
| dyewood extracts | مستخلصات الخشب الصبغي |
| dying-off | الذبول |
| dyn. (dynamic) viscosity | لزوجة دينامية |
| dynamic | ديناميكي، ذو علاقة بالقوة أو الطاقة الطبيعية، فعال، نشط |
| dynamic poisson's ratio | نسبة بواسون الديناميكية |
| dynamics | ديناميكا، علم الحيل. فرع من الفيزياء يخصت ببحث أثر القوة في الأجسام المتحركة والساكنة، القوى المحركة |
| dynamite | الديناميت |
| dynamo belts | سيور المولد |
| dynamo brushes | فرش المولد |
| dynamometer | عداد قوة الشحن [جهاز قياس القوة] |
| dynamos | المولدات |
| dynias | حالات الألم |
| dys-, prefix | سابقة بمعنى اختلال |
| dysaesthesia | اضطراب الحس |
| dysembryoplastic | شُذُوْذُ التَّخَلُّق المُضْغِيّ |
| dyskinesia | ضعف الحركات الإرادية |
| dyslipidaemia | اختلال نسبة الدهون في الدم |
| dysmenorrhea | عسر الطمث |
| dysmyelinating | خلل تخلُّق النخاع |
| dyspepsia | عسر الهضم |
| dyspnea | ضيق النفس |
| dysprosium | الديسبروسيوم [عنصر فلزي] |
| dysthemia | الاكتئاب العصبي (ديسثيميا) |
| dystonia | ضعف القوة |
| dystrophy | سوء التغذية |

# E

| | |
|---|---|
| e.coli | بكتيريا إشيريشيا كولاي |
| e.coli inclusion bodies | أجسام تضمين E.coli |
| each catalyst sulfiding method | طريقة إدخال كبريتيد إلى كل محفز |
| each isogenic, recombinant virus | فيروس مماثل ناتج عن عودة الارتباط الجيني |
| ear duct; ear canal | قناة السمع |
| ear muffs | واقيات الأذن: فراء لتدفئة الأذن |
| ear picks | أدوات إزالة الشمع من الأذن |
| ear plugs | سدادات الأذن |
| ear plugs for divers | سدادات الأذن يستخدمها الغطاسون |
| ear trumpets | أدوات سمع على شكل بوق |
| earlier invention | اختراع أسبق، اختراع سابق |
| earlier inventor | مخترع أسبق |
| earlier patent | براءة أسبق، براءة سابقة |
| earlier patented invention | اختراع لاحق صادرة عنه براءة |
| early diagenitic dolomitization | الدلمتة المبكرة |
| early warning system | نظام للإنذار المبكر |
| earmark | علامة مميزة، يسم بعلامة مميزة |
| earmarked | موسوم بعلامة مميزة |
| earphone | سماعة |
| earpiece | سماعة |
| ear-piercing apparatus | معدات ثقب الأذن |
| earrings | الأقراط |
| earth | تراب؛ تربة |
| earth (diatomaceous -) | تراب (تراب طحلب الدياتوم) |
| earth (sienna -) | تراب (تراب صمغ الترسينة) |
| earth for bricks | طين الآجر |
| earth for growing | تراب للزراعة (تربة صناعية للزراعة) |
| earth metal | فلز أرضي |
| earth moving machines | ماكينات جرف التراب |
| earth rammers [hand tools] | مدكات الأرض [عُدد يدوية] |
| earth shaking invention | اختراع ذو أثر عظيم |
| earth's core | لب الأرض |
| earthenware | أواني خزفية |
| earth-friendly information technology operation | عملية تقنية معلومات مُنسجمة مع الأرض |
| earthquake belts | نطاقات الزلازل أو أحزمة |
| earths (metal -) | تراب (تراب المعادن) |
| earths (rare -) | عناصر أرضية (أكسيدات العناصر الأرضية النادرة) |
| earth-shaking technology | تعبير يطلق على التقنية شديدة التأثير |
| easels (painters' -) | مساند (مساند لوح الرسامين) |
| easily-infingible drug | دواء سهل الانتهاك |
| easter eggs (paper for dyeing -) | بيض الفصح (ورق لصبغ بيض الفصح) |
| easy chairs | مقاعد لينة |

| | |
|---|---|
| eau de cologne | ماء الكولونيا |
| ebit = earnings before interest and taxes | الأرباح قبل استقطاع الفائدة والضرائب |
| ebonite [vulcanite] | أبونيت [فلكنايت: مطاط مقسى بالكبريت] |
| ebonite [vulcanite] molds [moulds] | قوالب أبونيت [فلكنايت] |
| ebullated-bed reactors | مفاعلات ذات طبقة غليانية |
| ebullating bed reactor | مفاعلات الطبقة الفوارة |
| echocardiography | تخطيط القلب بصدى الصوت |
| echo-friendly patent | براءة صديقة للبيئة |
| ecl | مستوى معرفة اللغة الانجليزية |
| ecliptic | دائرة البروج في الفلك |
| eco-efficiency programs | برامج الكفاءة البيئية |
| eco-friendly car model | سيارة ملائمة للبيئة |
| eco-friendly green invention | اختراع أخضر صديق للبيئة |
| eco-friendly technology | تقنية صديقة للبيئة |
| eco-invention | اختراع بيئي |
| e-commerce communication technology | تقنية اتصال تجارة إلكترونية |
| economic and social council (esc) | المجلس الاقتصادي الاجتماعي |
| economic efficiency | الفعالية الاقتصادية |
| economic efficiency of labor | الفعالية الاقتصادية للعمالة |
| economic growth | نمو اقتصادي |
| economic priced drafting | صياغة مسعرة على نحو اقتصادي |
| economic value | قيمة اقتصادية |
| economic value of intellectual property | القيمة الاقتصادية للملكية الفكرية |
| economical use of an invention | استعمال اقتصادي لاختراع |
| economizer | وحدة توفير |
| economizers (fuel -) | معدات الاقتصاد (معدات الاقتصاد في الوقود) |
| economy | اقتصاد |
| eco-system | نظام بيئي |
| ecp(s) | عروض تغيير هندسة |
| ecthr | المحكمة الأوروبية لحقوق الإنسان |
| eczema | الإكزيما |
| edam | جبن فلمنك |
| eddy | تيار دوامي |
| edema | أوديما- استسقاء- ورم مائي |
| edema resulting from trauma associated with burns | الأوديما الناتج عن الرضوح المتعلقة بالحروق |
| edge | سرعات البيانات المعززة لتطور النظام العالمي للاتصالات المتنقلة |
| edge tools [hand tools] | عدة حدية [عدد يدوية] |
| edges of skis | حواف الزلاجات |
| edgings (lace for -) | حواشي (مخرمات للحواشي) |
| edgings for clothing | حواشي الملابس |
| edgings of plastic for furniture | حواش الأثاث من البلاستيك |
| edible birds' nests | أعشاش الطيور الصالحة للأكل |
| edible fats | دهون صالحة للأكل |
| edible foams or whips | مواد رغوية أو مخفوقات يمكن تناولها |

| | |
|---|---|
| edible oils | زيوت صالحة للأكل |
| edible pastes making machines | ماكينات صنع المعجنات القابلة للأكل |
| editing appliances for cinematographic films | أجهزة التحرير للاستخدام في الأفلام السينمائية |
| editing playlist | تحرير قائمة تشغيل |
| editing scenes on a computer | تحرير المشاهد على الكمبيوتر |
| editorial staff/team | فريق التحرير |
| edta | حمض إيثيلين داي أمين تترا أسيتيك |
| education | تعليم |
| education (system, policy, etc.) | التعليم (نظام، سياسة، إلخ) |
| education revolutionizing | تثوير التعليم. القيام بقفزات منهاجية ومضمونية فيما يتصل بأطر التعليم نتيجة توظيف تقنيات المعلومات والاتصالات |
| educational empowerment | تمكين تعليمي |
| educational leader | مسئول تربوي |
| educational robot | روبوت تعليمي |
| educational technology | تقنية تعليمية |
| educator | تربوي أو مربي |
| ee | زيادة تشاكلية |
| eec | المجموعة الاقتصادية الأوروبية |
| eec directive | وثيقة التوجيه الأوروبي |
| eefi | عناصر أساسية لمعلومات صديقة |
| eel | عناصر أساسية للمعلومات |
| efa | التعليم للجميع |
| effect | تأثير |
| effect indicator | مؤشر التأثير |
| effective patent | براءة سارية |
| effectiveness | فعالية |
| effector | مستجيب (للتأثير)؛ مؤثر |
| effector cells | خلايا مستجيبة (للتأثير) |
| effector memory | ذاكرة الإرسال العصبي |
| effervescent | فوار |
| effervescent mixtures | خلائط فوارة |
| effervescing beverages (pastilles for-) | مشروبات فوارة (أقراص محلاة للاستخدام في المشروبات الفوارة) |
| effervescing beverages (powders for-) | مشروبات فوارة (مساحيق للاستخدام في المشروبات الفوارة) |
| efficacious | فعالة |
| efficacy | كفاءة؛ فعالية |
| efficacy of the invention | فعالية الاختراع |
| efficiency | فعالية |
| efficiency - (school ~) | كفاءة |
| efficient | كفء؛ ذو كفاءة؛ فعال |
| efficient solutions | حلول فعالة |
| efficient technology | تقنية فعالة |
| effictive | فعال |
| effictiveness | فعالية |
| effluent | تدفق؛ تيار متدفق (منصرف). قارن influent |
| efflux | تدفق |
| e-filing | إيداع إلكتروني |
| e-filing of patent application | إيداع إلكتروني لطلب براءة |
| egg cups of precious metal | كؤوس البيض مصنوعة من المعادن النفيسة |
| egg cups, not of precious metal | كؤوس البيض غير مصنوعة من المعادن النفيسة |
| egg laying poultry (preparations for -) | دواجن بيّاضة (مستحضرات خاصة بالدواجن البيّاضة) |
| egg slicers [non-electric] | أدوات تقطيع البيض لشرائح [غير كهربائية] |
| egg timers [sandglasses] | الساعات الرملية لمراقبة غليان البيض [الساعات الرملية] |
| egg white lysozyme | ليزوزيم بياض البيضة [إنزيم] |
| egg-candlers | وحدات فحص تخصيب البيض |
| eggs | البيض |
| eggs (powdered -) | بيض (بيض على شكل مسحوق) |
| eggs (snail -) [for consumption] | بيض (بيض الحلزون) [للاستهلاك] |
| eggs for hatching [fertilised] | بيض للفقس [مخصب] |
| eggshell catalyst | محفز قشري رقيق |
| eggshell formation | تكوين على شكل قشرة بيض |
| egress | خروج |
| eiderdown | زغب البط |
| eiderdowns [down coverlets] | لحف محشوة بزغب البط [أغطية بزغب] |
| eis indicator | مؤشر EIS |
| eject | يخرج |
| eject button | زرار إخراج |
| ejectability | قابلية الشيء للإخراج |
| ejectable | قابل للإخراج |
| ejector | قاذف |
| ejector | مخرج |
| ejector seats [for aircraft] | مقاعد القاذف [للطائرات] |
| el nino | ظاهرة النينو |
| elan | شبكة محلية محاكاة |
| elapsed time /remaining time | الوقت المنقضي/الوقت المتبقي |
| elapsed time/full time | الوقت المنقضي/الوقت الكلي |
| elastic | مرن؛ مطاطي |
| elastic | شريط مطاطي |
| elastic bands for offices | الأشرطة المطاطية للاستخدام المكتبي |
| elastic compliance tensor | موتر مطاوعة مرن |
| elastic limit | حد المرونة |
| elastic rebound theory | نظرية الرجعة المرنة |
| elastic return means | وسائل ارتداد مرنة |
| elastic ribbons | الشرائط المطاطية |
| elastic stiffness tensor | موتر صلابة مرن |
| elastic stockings for surgical purposes | الجوارب الطويلة المطاطية للاستخدام في الأغراض الطبية |
| elastic thread and yarn for textile use | الخيوط والغزل المطاطي للاستخدام في النسيج |
| elastic threads, not for use in textiles | الخيوط المطاطية ليست للاستخدام في المنسوجات |
| elastic woven material | مادة منسوجة مطاطية |
| elastic yarns, not for use in textiles | الغزل المطاطي؛ ليس للاستخدام في المنسوجات |
| elasticity physics | فيزياء المرونة |
| elastin | إيلاستين؛ مرنين |

| | |
|---|---|
| elastomer | لدينة مرنة؛ مادة لدنة مرنة |
| elastomeric | لدن مرن؛ لدائني مرن |
| elastomeric diaphragm | حاجز لدن مرن |
| elastoplastic | لدِن مرِن |
| elastoplastic properties | خواص اللدونة المرنة |
| elastoplastic property | خاصية اللدونة المرنة |
| elbow guards [sports articles] | أدوات لوقاية المرفق [أدوات رياضية] |
| elbows of metal for pipes | التواء المواسير المرفقية مصنوعة من المعدن |
| elder law | قانون المسنين أو قانون الشيخوخة |
| e-learning | التعلم عن بعد: بواسطة الإنترنت عن طريق جهاز الكمبيوتر |
| electorate | مجموع الناخبين |
| electric | كهربائي |
| electric | كهربائي |
| electric acupuncture instruments | معدات كهربائية للعلاج بالإبر |
| electric appliances | أجهزة كهربائية |
| electric appliances for making yogurt | أجهزة كهربائية لصناعة لبن الزبادي |
| electric arc | قوس كهربائي |
| electric arc cutting apparatus | جهاز القطع بالقوس الكهربائي |
| electric arc welding apparatus | جهاز اللحام بالقوس الكهربائي |
| electric beaters | خلاطات كهربائية |
| electric blankets | بطانيات كهربائية (للاستخدام في الأغراض الطبية) |
| electric blenders for household purposes | الخلاطات الكهربائية للاستخدام في الأغراض المنزلية |
| electric coupling | وصلة إقران كهربائية |
| electric door bells | أجراس الباب الكهربائية |
| electric energy | طاقة كهربية |
| electric engine | محرك كهربي |
| electric fault | عطل كهربائي |
| electric hammers | مطارق كهربائية |
| electric installations for the remote control of industrial operations | تجهيزات كهربائية للتحكم عن بعد في العمليات الصناعية |
| electric lamps | مصابيح كهربائية |
| electric loss indicators | مؤشرات الفقد الكهربائية |
| electric mains (insulators for -) | المصادر الرئيسية للتيار الكهربائي (عوازل للمصادر الرئيسية للتيار الكهربائي) |
| electric potential | الجهد الكهربائي |
| electric screw driver | مَفَكّ كَهْرَبَائِيّ |
| electric terminals | وحدات طرفية كهربائية |
| electric vehicles | المركبات الكهربائية |
| electric welding apparatus | جهاز اللحام الكهربائي |
| electrical characteristics | خصائص كهربائية |
| electrical connection; electrical contact | توصيل كهربائي |
| electrical lead | سلك توصيل كهربائي |
| electrical measurements ac &dc | أجهزة قياس الخواص الكهربائية |
| electrical power supply network | شبكة للإمداد بطاقة كهربائية |
| electrical power supply source | مصدر للإمداد بطاقة كهربائية؛ مزود طاقة كهربائية |
| electrical power uptake of appliances | مقدار استهلاك الطاقة الكهربائية للأجهزة |
| electrical protection devices | وسائل الحماية الكهربائية |
| electrical transmission power lines | أسلاك نقل الطاقة الكهربائية |
| electrically heated carpets | السجاجيد المدفأة كهربائياً |
| electrically live parts | الأجزاء الموصلةكهربائيا - الأجزاء المتصلة بالكهرباء |
| electricity | كهرباء |
| electricity conduits | مواسير أسلاك وكوابل |
| electricity mains (material for -) [wires, cables] | المصادر الرئيسية للتيار الكهربائي (مادة للمصادر الرئيسية للتيار الكهربائي) [أسلاك وكبلات] |
| electricity physics | فيزياء الكهرباء |
| electrified fences | الحواجز المكهربة |
| electrified rails for mounting spot lights | قضبان مكهربة لتركيب الأضواء الكشافة |
| electroactive | نشط كهربائياً |
| electrocardiograph electrodes (chemical conductors for -) | الكترودات أجهزة تخطيط القلب الكهربائية (موصلات كيميائية لالكترودات أجهزة تخطيط القلب الكهربائي) |
| electrocardiograph paper | الورق الخاص بأجهزة تخطيط القلب الكهربائية |
| electrocardiographs | أجهزة تخطيط القلب الكهربائية |
| electro-chemical cell | خلية كهروكيميائية |
| electrochemical clarification | ترويق كهروكيميائي |
| electrochemical equipment | الجهاز الكهروكيميائي |
| electrochemiluminescence (ecl). | التألق الكهروكيميائي ECL. |
| electro-chemistry | كيمياء كهربية |
| electrocution | الإعدام بالكرسي الكهربائي |
| electrod | قطب |
| electrode | إلكترود |
| electrodeionization | نزع الأيونات كهربائيا |
| electrodes | إلكترودات |
| electrodes (chemical conductors for electrocardiograph -) | الكترودات (موصلات كيميائية لالكترودات أجهزة تخطيط القلب الكهربائية) |
| electrodes for medical use | الالكترودات للاستخدام الطبي |
| electro-dynamic apparatus for the remote control of railway points | أجهزة كهرو ديناميكية للتحكم عن بعد في محطات السكك الحديدية |
| electro-dynamic apparatus for the remote control of signals | أجهزة كهرو ديناميكية للتحكم عن بعد في الإشارات |
| electroluminescent display | شاشة عرض التوهج الإلكتروني |
| electrolyser | جهاز التحليل بالكهرباء |
| electrolysis | التحليل الكهربائي |
| electrolysis cell | خلية إلكتروليتية |
| electrolyte | إلكتروليت؛ محلول إلكتروليتي |
| electrolytic bath | مغطس إلكتروليتي |

| | |
|---|---|
| electrolytic cell | خلية إلكتروليتية |
| electrolytic cell | خلية |
| electro-magnetic | مغنطيسي كهربائي |
| electromagnetic coils | ملفات كهرومغناطيسية |
| electromagnetic relay | ناقل توصيل كهرومغناطيسي |
| electromagnetic resonator | مِرنان كهرومغناطيسي |
| electromagnetism | مغنطسة كهربائية |
| electromechanical machines for chemical industry | ماكينات كهروميكانيكية للاستخدام في الصناعات الكيميائية |
| electromotive force | قوة دافعة كهربائية |
| electron cryomicroscopy; cryo-em; cryo-electron microscopy | القياس المجهري الإلكتروني فاحص بالبرد |
| electron donor compound | مركب مانح للإلكترونات |
| electron impact ion source | مصدر أيونات بالصدم الإلكتروني (EI) |
| electron impact ionisation | التأين الصدمي للإكترون |
| electron spray ionization | تأين بالرش الإلكتروني |
| electron-donor ; electron donor | مانح للإلكترونات مركب مانح للإلكترونات |
| electronic | إلكتروني |
| electronic and chemical warfare | الحرب الإلكترونية والكيماوية |
| electronic circuit | دائرة إلكترونية |
| electronic controllers, recorders & thermowell | أدوات تحكم ومسجلات الكترونية وجيوب حرارية |
| electronic coordinator | منسق إلكتروني |
| electronic enabler | مُمَكن إلكتروني |
| electronic fuel injection | حاقن وقود إلكتروني |
| electronic musical instruments | الآلات الموسيقية الالكترونية |
| electronic notice boards | لوحات الإعلانات الإلكترونية |
| electronic optimization | رفع الكفاءة الإلكتروني إلى المستويات القصوى |
| electronic patent assignment system | نظام إلكتروني للتنازل عن البراءات |
| electronic pens [visual display units] | الأقلام الإلكترونية [وحدات للعرض المرئي] |
| electronic pocket translators | أجهزة الترجمة الإلكترونية المحمولة في الجيب |
| electronic publications [downloadable] | النشرات الإلكترونية[قابلة للتنزيل] |
| electronic reader | قارئ إلكتروني، مقرأة إلكترونية |
| electronic storage | مخزن إلكتروني |
| electronic storing of content | تخزين إلكتروني لمحتوى |
| electronic storing system | نظام تخزين إلكتروني |
| electronic tags for goods | بطاقات إلكترونية للسلع |
| electronic-commerce legal infrastructure | البنية التحتية القانونية للتجارة الإلكترونية |
| electronics | إلكترونيات |
| electrooptics | بصريات كهربية |
| electrophile | أليف الإلكترونات |
| electrophilic | أليف الإلكترونات |
| electrophoresed proteins | البروتينات التي تم تعريضها للإشراد الكهربائي |
| electrophoresis | إشراد كهربائي؛ استشراد كهربائي |
| electrophysiological recording | تسجيل فسيولوجي كهربائي |
| electrophysiology | الفيسيولوجيا الكهربائية |
| electroplating apparatus | جهاز الطلاء الكهربائي |
| electroporation | المسامية الكهربائية |
| electroporation | نقل كهربائي |
| electrospray | الرش الإلكتروني |
| electrospray ion source (es) | مصدر أيونات للرش الإلكتروني |
| electrospray positive ionisation | تأين موجب بالرش الإلكتروني |
| electrostatic spraying | رش كهروستاتي |
| electrosynthesis | تخليق كهربائي |
| electrotypes | صفائح حروف كهربائية |
| electuary | لعوق: عجينة من البودرة مخلوطة بالعسل يمكن تناولها عبر الفم. |
| elegant streetscapes | شوارع ذات أجواء أنيقة |
| element | عنصر |
| elemental analysis | التحليل العنصري |
| elemental forces | العوامل الطبيعية |
| elemental microanalysis | التحليل العنصري الدقيق |
| elements (heating -) | عناصر (عناصر التسخين) |
| elevating apparatus | معدات الرفع |
| elevating tailgates (am.) [parts of land vehicles] | الأبواب الخلفية الرافعة [أجزاء من مركبات أرضية] |
| elevation view | مسقط رأسي |
| elevational | متعلق بمسقط رأسي |
| elevator | مصعد، رافعة |
| elevator belts | سيور الرافعة |
| elevator chains [parts of machines] | سلاسل الرافعة [أجزاء من الماكينات] |
| elevator operating apparatus | جهاز تشغيل الرافعة |
| elevators [lifts] | المصاعد |
| eligibility | أهلية |
| eligibility assessment | تقييم الأهلية |
| eliminatability | قابلية الشيء للعزل |
| eliminatable material | مادة قابلة للعزل |
| elimination rate constant | ثابت معدل الإزالة |
| elisa | اختبار ELISA؛ الاختبار المناعي الإنزيمي ELISA: اختبار المادة الماصة المناعية المتصلة بالإنزيم المقارن |
| elisa plate reader | قارئ أطباق ELISA؛ قارئ أطباق الاختبار المناعي الإنزيمي ELISA: جهاز لقراءة درجة الامتصاص للمركبات في الشرائح متعددة الخلايا يستخدم في قياس درجة امتصاص المواد الناتجة من التفاعلات الحيوية والمناعية والانزيمات والتي يستخدم فيها الطبق ذي 96 عين. |
| elite forces | قوات ذات تدريب راق |
| elixirs | الإكسيرات؛ الأكاسير؛ الإلكسيرات [مستحضرات صيدلانية] |
| ellipsoidal | بيضاوي (الشكل)؛ إهليلجي |
| ellipticity | بيضاوية (الشكل)؛ إهليليجية |
| elongate | مطوّل؛ ممتد |

| | |
|---|---|
| elongate | يطوّل؛ يمد أو يستطيل؛ يمتد |
| elongation | استطالة؛ تطويل؛ تمديد |
| eluent | مادة تصفية تتابعية |
| elute | يصفي تتابعيا |
| eluting successively | تصفية متتابعة |
| eluting with a gradient of | التصفية المتتابعة باستخدام تدرج من |
| elution gradient | تدرج للتصفية التتابعية |
| em | كهروميكانيكي |
| e-mail ; email | البريد الإلكتروني |
| e-mail smtp server | خادم SMTP للبريد الإلكتروني: خادم بريد صادر مستقل وخاص لكل موقع متوفر لكم حصرياً في جميع الأوقات |
| embed | يطمر، يضمن |
| embed sth into sth | يدمج |
| embeddability | قابلية الشيء للطمر |
| embeddable | قابل لأن يُطمر، قابل لأن يضمن |
| embedded | مغمور (مجال البناء) |
| embedded | مدمج |
| embedded device | جهاز مطمور |
| embedded particles | جسيمات مطمورة |
| embezzle | يختلس |
| embezzlement | اختلاس |
| embodied | متجسد |
| embodiment | نموذج |
| embodiment | تجسد |
| embodiment variation | صورة بديلة للنموذج |
| embodiments | تجسيدات |
| embody | يتجسد |
| emboss | نقش |
| embossers [hand tools] | أدوات للزخرفة [عُدد يدوية] |
| embossing | إبراز |
| embossing machines | ماكينات الزخرفة |
| embrace | يعبر عن: يتضمن |
| embroidering crochet hooks | خطافات التطريز بالكروشيه |
| embroidery | تطريز |
| embroidery (thread of metal for -) | التطريز (خيط التطريز من المعدن) |
| embroidery (traced cloth for -) | التطريز (القماش المزخرف بالخطوط والأشكال المتشعبة للاستخدام في التطريز) |
| embroidery designs [patterns] | تصميمات التطريز [نماذج] |
| embroidery frames | إطارات التطريز |
| embroidery thread and yarn | خيوط وغزل التطريز |
| embryogenesis | تكوين الجنين |
| embryonic | جنيني |
| embryonic stem cell | خلية |
| embryonic stem cells | خلايا مدورية جنينية |
| emc | توافق كهرومغناطيسي |
| emcon | التحكم في الانبعاثات |
| emerge (from) | ينبثق (من) |
| emergency | طوارئ |
| emergency brake | مكبح اضطراري |

| | |
|---|---|
| emergency law | قانون الطوارئ |
| emergency power generators | مولدات القوى في حالات الطوارئ |
| emerging technology | تقنية ناشئة |
| emery | مسحوق صنفرة أو صقل |
| emery cloth | قماش الصنفرة |
| emery grinding wheels | عجلات جلخ للصنفرة |
| emery paper | ورق صنفرة |
| emesis | قيء |
| emi | تداخل كهرومغناطيسي |
| emi | التداخل الكهرومغناطيسي |
| emission | ابتعاث |
| emissions | ابتعاثات |
| emissions standards | مقاييس الانبعاث |
| emit | ينبعث |
| emitted | منبعث |
| emitted energy | طاقة منبعثة |
| emitter | باعث |
| emitting | انبعاث |
| emollient | ملطف |
| emp | نبضة كهرومغناطيسية |
| empennage | مجموعة الذيل |
| emphysema | انتفاخ الرئة (إمفزيما - ورم هوائي يحدث في الحويصلات الهوائية) |
| employee assigned invention | اختراع متنازل عنه من قبل موظف |
| employee invention | اختراع موظف |
| employee invention agreement | اتفاق بشأن اختراعات الموظف. اتفاق تبرمه بعض الشركات مع الموظفين الجدد لتنظيم حقوق الطرفين فيما يتصل بالحقوق المنبثقة عن الاختراعات التي قد يخترعونها خلال ارتباطهم الوظيفي بالشركة |
| employee inventions assignment agreement | اتفاق تنازل موظف عن اختراعاته |
| employee inventor | مخترع موظف |
| employee inventors rights | حقوق المخترعين الموظفين |
| employee owned invention | اختراع مملوك لموظفين |
| employee scheduling software | برنامج جدولة موظفين |
| employee scheduling system | نظام جدولة عمل موظفين |
| employee-driven innovation | ابتكار يأتي به الموظف |
| employer-employed inventor relationship | علاقة الموظف المخترع برب العمل |
| employer's responsibility | مسئولية رب العمل |
| employment tribunal | محكمة بشأن نزاع وظيفي |
| empower | يمكن |
| empowering | تمكين |
| empowering employee inventon | تمكين المخترع الموظف |
| empowering inventor | تمكين المخترع |
| empowering of indigenous people | تمكين السكان المحليين. مساعدة السكان المحليين بمختلف الأشكال |

| | |
|---|---|
| | المساعدة التي تصل بهم إلى ممارسة حقوقهم، ومن ذلك تمكينهم على مستوى الملكية الفكرية من خلال مساعدتهم لمعرفة حقوقهم الفكرية وصون ممتلكاتهم الفكرية ومواجهة سبل التعدي عليها |
| empowerment | تمكين، تفويض، تخويل |
| empty case | الظرف الفارغ |
| empty files (0 bits) | الملفات الفارغة (المساحة المتبقية تساوي صفر بت) |
| empyema | صديد بلوري |
| emt | علاج طبي طارئ |
| emulsifiers | مواد استحلاب أو مستحلبات |
| emulsifying | استحلاب |
| emulsion | مستحلَب |
| emulsion breakers | عوامل تكسير للمستحلب |
| emulsion copolymerized ethylenically unsaturated monomers | مستحلب مونومرات غير مشبعة مبلمرة بصورة مشتركة إيثيلينياً |
| emulsions | المستحلبات |
| emulsions (photographic-) | سوائل مستحلبة (سوائل مستحلبة للتصوير الفوتوغرافي) |
| emulsions (silver -) [pigments] | سوائل مستحلبة (سوائل مستحلبة فضية) [خضاب] |
| en block ; en bloc; en masse; all together; as a group | بالجملة؛ ككل؛ تماما |
| en% | طاقة% |
| enable | يمكن |
| enabled | مُمَكَّن |
| enablement | تمكين، دعم |
| enablement | تمكين |
| enablement requirement | متطلب التمكين |
| enablement test | اختبار التمكين |
| enabler | ممكن |
| enabler of carbon reduction | مُمَكن لخفض الكربون |
| enabler of competitiveness | ممكن للتنافسية. ينظر البعض للبراءات على أنها تعزز التنافسية وترسخها |
| enabler of development | ممكن للتنمية. ينظر البعض للبراءات على أنها تعزز التنمية وترسخها |
| enabler of sustainable development | مُمَكن للتنمية المستدامة |
| enabling | تمكين |
| enabling disclosure | إفصاح مُمَكن. إفصاح مقدِّم طلب البراءة عن تفاصيل الاختراع على نحو يمكن الغير من فهمه ويجنبه أي اختبار غير لازم |
| enamel (chemical preparations, except pigments, for the manufacture of -) | المينا (مستحضرات كيميائية، فيما عدا الخضاب، لتصنيع المينا) |
| enamel (opacifiers for -) | المينا (مركبات لا إنفاذية للمينا) |
| enamelled glass | زجاج مطلي بالمينا |
| enamels [varnishes] | المينا [ورنيش] |
| enamels for painting | المينا المستخدمة في الطلاء |
| enamel-staining chemicals | مواد كيميائية للصبغ بالمينا |
| enantioenriched | غني بالمتشاكلات |
| enantiomeric | تشاكلي |
| enantiomeric excess (ee) | الزيادة التشاكلية |
| enantiomers | المتشاكلات؛ الأيزومرات المرآتية |
| encapsulate | يغلف |
| encapsulated | مغلفة؛ مكبسلة |
| encapsulation | التغليف؛ الكبسلة |
| encapsulation | تغليف |
| encapsulator | مغلف |
| encapsules | كبسولات |
| encase | يغلف |
| encasing | القيام بعملية التغليف |
| encephalopathy | اعتلال دماغي |
| encipher | يشفر |
| encircle | يطوق |
| enclosure | غلاف |
| enclosure or housing | غلاف أو مبيت |
| encode | يشفر |
| encoded cards, magnetic | بطاقات مغناطيسية مشفرة |
| encoder | جهاز تشفير؛ جهاز ترميز |
| encoders (magnetic -) | أجهزة التشفير (أجهزة التشفير المغناطيسية) |
| encounter battle | معركة تصادمية |
| encroachment on the estate | التعدي على الملكية |
| encryptable | قابل للتشفير |
| encryption | تشفير |
| encumbered | مرهون أو مقيد أو محتجز |
| end | طرف |
| end business goals | أهداف العمل التجاري النهائية |
| end elevation | مسقط طرفي |
| end flash drum | اسطوانة تقطير ومضي طرفية |
| end flash system | نظام ومضي طرفي |
| end plate | ألواح طرفية |
| end point | النقطة النهائية |
| end point dilution titer | عيار التخفيف الحجمي لنقطة التعادل |
| end view | منظر طرفي |
| endarectomy | استئصال بطانة الشرايين |
| endless | متواصل |
| endless belt | حزام متصل |
| endocannabinoid | شبيه القنب الباطني |
| endocardium | بطانة القلب |
| endocrine diseases such as type-i diabetes | أمراض الغدد الصماء مثل داء السكر من النوع 1 |
| endocrine secretion | إفراز الغدد الصماء |
| endocytosis | الالتقام الخلوي؛ الابتلاع؛ الإدخال الخلوي: هي عملية إدخال المواد والجزيئات الكبيرة إلى داخل الخلية من خلال تشكل حويصلات كبيرة تقوم بابتلاع تلك المواد |
| endogenetic | داخلي النشأة |
| endogenous | داخلي النشأة |
| endometrial | متعلق ببطانة الرحم |
| ometriosis | الانتباذ البطاني الرحمي |
| endometrium carcinoma | الورم السرطاني ببطانة الرحم |
| end-on | اتجاه معامد للمحور |
| endonuclease | إندو نيوكلياز؛ إنزيم القيد (إنزيم نووي داخلي) |
| endothelial | بطاني؛ متعلق بالطبقة المبطنة |

| | |
|---|---|
| endothelium | الطبقة البطانية للأوعية |
| endothermic | ماصة للحرارة |
| endotoxemia | تسمم داخلي |
| endotoxic | متعلق بالتسمم الداخلي |
| end-point energy x-ray tube | أنبوب أشعة سينية بطاقة مفردة عند النقطة النهائية |
| end-product | ناتج نهائي |
| endurance | تحمُّل |
| enema | حقنة شرجية |
| energization | منح الطاقة |
| energize | يمنح الطاقة |
| energizer | مانح الطاقة |
| energy | طاقة |
| energy absorbing device | جهاز امتصاص الطاقة |
| energy capturer | ممسك بالطاقة، قابض على الطاقة |
| energy conservation technology | تقنية تحافظ على الطاقة |
| energy conservator | حفظ طاقة |
| energy conversion device | جهاز تحويل طاقة |
| energy converter | محول طاقة |
| energy convertibility | قابلية الطاقة للتحويل |
| energy efficiency | فعالية طاقة |
| energy efficient | موفر للطاقة |
| energy efficient products | منتجات فعالة على مستوى الطاقة |
| energy engineering | هندسة طاقة |
| energy management | إدارة الطاقة |
| energy management solutions | حلول إدارة الطاقة |
| energy patent | براءة طاقة |
| energy physics | فيزياء الطاقة |
| energy recovery | تعافٍ طاقتي |
| energy storage | مخزن طاقة |
| energy technology | تقنية طاقة |
| energy value | قيمة الطاقة؛ قيمة طاقية |
| energy-efficient invention | اختراع فعال على مستوى الطاقة |
| energy-filtered inelastic electron images | الصور الإلكترونية غير المرنة المرشَّحة بالطاقة |
| energy-saving behavior | سلوك مدخر للطاقة |
| energy-saving invention | اختراع موفر للطاقة |
| enforce | ينفذ |
| enforceability | القابلية للإنفاذ |
| enforceability opinion | الرأي بشأن الصلاحية. الرأي بشأن صلاحية البراءة |
| enforceable patent | براءة قابلة للإنفاذ |
| enforced patent | براءة مُنفذة |
| enforcement | إنفاذ |
| engage | يربط، يجذب، يشغل، يتعاطى عملا، يرتبط، يشارك |
| engage sth | يتعشق معه |
| engage with sth | يتعشق معه |
| engageability | قابلية الشيء للربط |
| engageable | يمكن ربطه، يمكن جذبه |
| engaged | مرتبط |
| engagement | ارتباط، التزام، خطبة |
| engaging teeth | أسنان تعشيق |
| engine | محرك |
| engine | محرك |
| engine (in vehicles) | آلة احتراق داخلي |
| engine coolants (anti-boil preparations for -) | مواد تبريد المحركات (مستحضرات مقاومة للغليان للاستخدام مع مواد تبريد المحركات) |
| engine drivability | قابلية المحرك للقيادة |
| engine optimization | رفع كفاء المحرك لأقصى مستوى ممكن |
| engine's balance shaft | عمود توازن المحرك |
| engined | مُزود بمحرك |
| engine-decarbonising chemicals | مواد كيميائية لإزالة الكربون المترسب في المحركات |
| engineer | يعدل وراثيا؛ يحول وراثيًا |
| engineer | مهندس |
| engineered into | بمعنى إدخال إلى |
| engineering | هندسة |
| engineering corps | سلاح المهندسين |
| engineering physics | فيزياء هندسية |
| engineering, electronic, metallurgical, pharmaceutical industries | الصناعات الهندسية؛ الإلكترونية؛ المعدنية؛ الدوائية |
| engines (coolants for vehicle -) | محركات (مواد تبريد للاستخدام في محركات المركبات) |
| engines (traction -) | قاطرات (قاطرات جر) |
| engines for boats | محركات القوارب |
| engines for land vehicles | محركات المركبات الأرضية |
| engines, other than for land vehicles | محركات بخلاف المستخدمة في المركبات الأرضية |
| engraftment | التطعّم: مرحلة التطعّم (Engraftment) وتحدث غالبا خلال أسبوعين إلى ستة أسابيع عقب الزرع |
| engraving ink | حبر النقش |
| engraving machines | ماكينات النقش |
| engraving needles | إبر النقش |
| engraving plates | ألواح النقش |
| engravings | النقش |
| enhance | يعزز؛ يحسن؛ يقوي؛ يدعم |
| enhance | يدعم |
| enhanceability | قابلية الشيء للتعزيز |
| enhanceable | قابل للتعزيز |
| enhanceable software | برنامج حاسبي قابل للتعزيز |
| enhanced messages system (ems) | خدمة الرسائل المطورة: نظام تطور من نظام الرسائل النصية القصيرة المبسطة؛ وهى خدمة تتيح إمكانية إرسال الرسوم البيانية الأساسية والنغمات إلى الهواتف المحمولة الأخرى المزودة بخدمة الرسائل المطورة إضافة إلى الرسائل النصية. |
| enhanced software | برنامج مُعزز |
| enhancement | دعم |
| enhancer | معززة |
| enhancer | مدعم |
| enhancer sequence | متوالية معززة |
| enhancing-effective amount | كمية فعالة محسِّنة؛ كمية فعالة معزِّزة |
| enlarging apparatus | جهاز تكبير |

| | |
|---|---|
| [photography] | |
| enmeshed resin | راتنج مشترك القياس |
| enrich a culture medium with | تغذية وسط استزراع (وسط مزرعة) |
| enriched milk | لبن مدعم (مخصب) |
| enriched with | غني ب؛ خصب بـ |
| enrichment treatment | معالجة تخصيب؛ معالجة إغناء |
| enrollment | تسجيل أسماء الأعضاء الجدد |
| enter parte examinations | إعادة فحص للبراءة. عملية إعادة فحص سلامة البراءة بناء على طلب مقدم من قبل الغير، ويتسم هذا النوع من إعادة الفحص بأن المراسلات التي تنبثق عن هذا الطلب تشمل غير مقدم الطلب من الصورة. |
| enteral | معوي |
| enteric | معوي |
| enteric coating | غلاف معوي |
| enterobacteria | بكتيريا معوية |
| enterococcus | مكورة معوية |
| enterocyte | خلية معوية |
| enteropathy | اعتلال معوي |
| enteroviruses | فيروسات معوية |
| enterposing carbon atom | ذرة كربون وسيطة |
| enterpreneurial idea | فكرة مضاربة |
| enterprise applications | برامج الأعمال؛ برامج المؤسسات |
| entertainment robot | روبوت ترفيه |
| enthalpy | المحتوى الحراري (الانثالبي): كمية الحرارة التي تحتويها مادة ما عند درجة حرارة وضغط معينين |
| enthalpy of fusion | حرارة الانصهار: هي كمية الطاقة الحرارية اللازمة لتحويل مول واحد من مادة ما من الحالة الصلبة إلى الحالة السائلة أو بالعكس. |
| enthalpy of vaporization | حرارة التبخر: هي الحرارة اللازمة لتبخير مول واحد من المادة عند نقطة غليانها تحت الضغط القياسي |
| entire agreement clause | البند الخاص بكاملية الاتفاق. بند تعاقدي يبين أن العقد اتفاق كامل وأنه لا توجد عقود أو اتفاقات أو تفاهمات شفهية أم مكتوبة أخرى بجانب الاتفاق الذي يرد البند المذكور فيه. بند الكلية والتعديل. بند تعاقدي مفاده أن العقد الماثل يعبر عن كامل الاتفاق المبرم بين الطرفين |
| entirely national arbitration award | حكم تحكيم محلي بالكلية |
| entirely novel invention | اختراع جديد كليا |
| entirety and modification clause | بند الكلية والتعديل. بند تعاقدي مفاده أن العقد الماثل يعبر عن كامل الاتفاق المبرم بين الطرفين، وأن أي تعديلات لاحقة على العقد لن تكون نافذة إلا إذا كانت بموافقة الطرفين ومكتوبة |
| entitlement | استحقاق |

| | |
|---|---|
| entitlements | استحقاقات |
| entrain | يحتجز |
| entrepreneur | مضارب |
| entrepreneurship | مضاربة، توجه نحو المضاربة |
| entrepreneurship in tourism | المشروعات الاستثمارية الصغيرة في مجال السياحة وإدارتها |
| entry into force clause | بند الدخول في حيز التنفيذ. بند تعاقدي نمطي ينظم موعد دخول العقد في مرحلة التنفيذ |
| entry location | موقع إدخال؛ موقع دخول |
| entry needle | مداخل إبر |
| envelop | يغلف؛ يلف |
| envelop | يلتف حول؛ يحاصر |
| envelope | غشاء |
| envelope sealing machines, for offices | آلات ختم الأظرف للاستخدام المكتبي |
| envelopes (bottle -) of straw | أغلفة (أغلفة الزجاجات) من القش |
| envelopes [stationery] | أظرف [القرطاسية] |
| envelopes, of leather, for packaging | أغلفة من الجلد للاستخدام في التغليف |
| envionable invention | اختراع قابل للتخيل |
| environment | بيئة |
| environmental industries | صناعات بيئية |
| environmental negligence | إهمال بيئي |
| environmental patent | براءة بيئية |
| environmental scanning electron microscopy (esem) | القياس المجهري الإلكتروني الماسح في الوسط المحيط |
| environmental technology | تقني بيئية |
| environmentally friendly invention | اختراع صديق للبيئة |
| environmentally friendly patent | براءة صديقة للبيئة |
| environmentally responsible patent | براءة مسئولة بيئيا |
| environmentally sound it infrastructure | بنية تحتية لتقنية المعلومات مقبولة بيئيا |
| enviro-tech | تعبير يعني التقنية البيئية |
| envision | يتخيل |
| envisionability | قابلية الشيء للتخيل |
| envisionable software system | نظام برمجيات يمكن تخيله |
| envisioned invention | اختراع مُتخيل |
| enzymatic digestion | الاهتضام الإنزيمي |
| enzyme linked immuno assay (elisa); enzyme-linked immuno-assay (elisa ) | الاختبار المناعي الإنزيمي |
| enzyme preparations | مستحضرات الإنزيم |
| enzyme" | إنزيم مؤيض للعقار من الطور الثاني |
| enzymes | إنزيمات |
| enzymes catalyze reversible reactions | تفاعلات |
| eoc | قدرة تشغيلية موسعة |
| eosb | مستحقات نهاية الخدمة |
| eosinophiles | اليوزينيات = الخلايا الآلفة للإيوزين |

| | |
|---|---|
| eosinophilia | ألفة اليوزين,فرط الألفة للإيوسين,, |
| eosinophilic | يوزيني |
| eosinophils | خلايا يوزينية,خلايا أليفة للأيوسين,, |
| e-patent strategy | إستراتيجية براءات إلكترونية |
| ependymoma | ورم الرداء الفوقاني |
| epergnes of precious metal | أواني المائدة المركبة مصنوعة من المعادن النفيسة |
| epergnes, not of precious metal | أواني المائدة المركبة ليست من المعادن النفيسة |
| ephys | الفيسيولوجيا الكهربائية |
| epicardium | ظهارة القلب |
| epicentral distance | المسافة المركزية الأرضية |
| epiclastic rocks | صخور مكانية النشأة |
| epidemiology | علم الأوبئة؛ الوبائيات |
| epidermal growth factor | عامل نمو البشرة |
| epidermal growth factor receptor | مستقبل عامل نمو البشرة |
| epidermolysis bullosa | انحلال البشرة الفقاعي |
| epidermolysis bullosa erythema multiforme major | انحلال البشرة الفقاعي الإحمراري متعدد الأشكال الرئيسي |
| epidiascopes | الخيالات [نوع من الفوانيس السحرية] |
| epifluorescence microscope | مجهر فوق فلوري |
| epifluorescence microscopy | الفحص المجهري فوق فلوري |
| epigastric distress | الألم شراسيفي |
| epigenetic robotics | روبوت متغير الصفات |
| epilepsy | صرع |
| epimer | متشاكل سكري |
| epimerisation ; epimerization | تشاكل سكري |
| epiorogenic movements | حركات أرضية خفيفة معظمها بانية للقارات |
| episode ; instalment | حلقة (في مسلسل) |
| episomal | جسيمي كروموسومي؛ جسيمية ملحقة بالكروموسومات |
| episome | جسم كروموسومي؛ يَصْبوغ؛ إبيسوم: جُسَيْم إضافي مرتبط بالكروموسومات خاص بالبكتيريا. |
| epithelial cells | خلية ظهارية |
| epithelialize | يغطي بالخلايا الظهارية أو يتحول إلى خلايا ظهارية |
| epitope | قمة لاصقة |
| epitope bin | جزء من القمة اللاصقة |
| epitope competition | اختبار قوة القمة اللاصقة |
| epitope imprinting | الآثر الذي تحدثه القمة اللاصقة - "أثر قمة لاصقة" |
| epo leads | بروتينات EPO القيادية |
| epo variants | صور EPO المتغيرة |
| epoxidation | إدخال مجموعة إيبوكسي |
| epoxy | إيبوكسي |
| epoxy resin | راتنج الإيبوكسي |
| epoxy resins, unprocessed | راتنجات إيبوكسي غير معالجة |
| eq | مكافئ |
| eqn. | معادلة |
| equalized pupil | طالب متكافئ |
| equidistant from | على مسافات متساوية من |
| equilibrium concentration | التركيز المتعادل؛ التركيز التوازني |
| equilibrium reaction | تفاعل متعادل |
| equimolar | متساوي المولية |
| equimolecular | متساوي الجزيئات |
| equity | عدالة |
| equivalent | مكافئ |
| erasers (writing board -) | المحاة (المحاة الخاصة بلوح الكتابة) |
| erasing products | منتجات المحو |
| erasing shields | واقيات المحو |
| erasure detection | الكشف عن المحو |
| erasure threshold | القيمة الحدية للمحو؛ عتبة المحو |
| erbium | الإربيوم [عنصر فلزي] |
| ergometers | إرجومترات [أجهزة قياس الشغل أو الطاقة] |
| ergonomic backpack | حقيبة الظهر الصحية |
| ergonomics | هندسة بيئة العمل |
| ergot | الإرجوت [مادة طبية تستعمل لوقف النزيف الدموي] |
| erosion | التعرية |
| erosion control | السيطرة على التعرية |
| erosion factors | عوامل التعرية |
| error : no ink | خطأ: لا يوجد حبر |
| error : no paper | خطأ: لا يوجد ورق |
| error bars | أعمدة الخطأ |
| error detection code | شفرة كشف الأخطاء |
| error function | دالة الخطأ |
| erythema | طفح وردي |
| erythrocytes | كريات دموية حمراء |
| erythropoesis | تكوين خلايا الدم الحمراء |
| escalators | سلالم صاعدة |
| escape | يتسرب؛ يلوذ بالفرار |
| escaping | تسرب |
| escrow | حساب الضمان -الحساب المحجوز عليه |
| esi | تأين بالرش الكهربائي |
| esophageal | بالمريء |
| esophageal dysmotility | قصور الحركة المريئية |
| esophageal reflux disease | مرض الارتداد المريئي |
| esophageal sphincter | فتحة المرئ |
| esophagitis | التهاب المريء |
| esophagus | المريء |
| esparto fabric | قماش الحلفاء (الفصيلة النخلية) |
| esparto grass | نجيل الحلفاء (الفصيلة النخلية) |
| esparto shoes or sandals | الأحذية أو الصنادل من الحلفاء (الفصيلة النخلية) |
| espionage system | نظام تجسس |
| essence clause | بند العقد الجوهري |
| essences (ethereal -) | العطور (العطور الأثيرية) |
| essences for foodstuffs [except etheric essences and essential oils] | مكسبات الرائحة المستخدمة في الأطعمة [بخلاف العطريات الأثيرية والزيوت العطرية] |
| essences for making beverages | مكسبات الرائحة لصناعة المشروبات |
| essential oil | زيت عطري |
| essential oils | الزيوت العطرية |
| essentials of crime | أركان الجريمة |

| | |
|---|---|
| establish | يؤسس، يثبت |
| establish a connection | إقامة اتصال؛ إعداد اتصال؛ تأسيس اتصال |
| establish the potency of each material | يحدد فعالية كل |
| established patentability | إمكانية صدور براءة ـ مثبتة ـ عن طلب أو اختراع |
| established unpatentability | عدم قابلية الاختراع ـ مُثبتة ـ أن يصدر عنها براءة |
| establishing | إثبات |
| establishing patentability | إثبات قابلية الطلب أو الاختراع أن يصدر عنه براءة |
| esterification | أسترة |
| esters | الإسترات |
| esthetic massage apparatus | جهاز التدليك للتجميل |
| estimator | وحدة تقدير؛ مقدِّر |
| estrogenic | إستروجيني |
| estuaries | المستنقعات الساحلية |
| et | إيثيل |
| eta-alumina | ألومينا إيتا |
| etac | محول من الإيثرنت إلى وضع التحويل غير المتزامن |
| etch | محلول كيميائي |
| etching | خدش |
| etching needles | إبر حفر للكليشيه |
| etching phosphate ore | تنميش خام الفوسفات |
| etching solutions | محاليل التنميش الأكالة |
| etchings | آلات حفر للكليشيه |
| eterocyclyloxy | سيكليل أوكسي غير متجانسة |
| ethan recovery configurations | تصميمات لاستخلاص الميثان |
| ethane | إيثان |
| ethanol | إيثانول |
| ethanol fuel | وقود إيثانول |
| ethanol fuel program | برنامج وقود إيثانول |
| ether | إيثر |
| ether (petroleum -) | الإيثر (إيثر بترولي؛ إيثر النفط) |
| ethereal | إيثري |
| ethereal essences | عطور من الإتير |
| ethereal oils | الزيوت من الإتير |
| ethical patent lobbying | استمالة أخلاقية فيما يتصل بسياسات البراءات |
| ethical subject matter | مادة أخلاقية |
| ethically questionable patent | براءة بعدها الأخلاقي موضع تساؤل |
| ethically questionable technology | تقنية بعدها الأخلاقي موضع تساؤل |
| ethics | أخلاق |
| ethoxy | إيثوكسي |
| ethoxylated isostearyl alcohols | كحولات أيزو ستياريل بها مجموعة إيثوكسيل |
| ethoxylation | معالجة بالإيثوكسي؛ إضافة مجموعة إيثوكسي؛ إدخال مجموعة إيثوكسي |
| ethyl | إيثيل |
| ethyl acetate | أسيتات إيثيل |
| ethyl alcohol | كحول الإيثيل |
| ethyl ether | إيثر الإيثيل |
| ethylbenamide | إيثيل بناميد |
| ethylbenzamide | إيثيل بنزاميد |
| ethylen | إيثيلين |
| ethylene | إيثيلين |
| ethylene copolymer | بوليمر إيثيلين مشترك |
| ethylenediaminetetraacetic acid (edta) | حمض إيثيلين داي أمين تترا أسيتيك EDTA |
| ethylenolysis | تحليل باستخدام الإيثيلين |
| ethylenolysis of 2- butene | تحليل 2- بيوتين باستخدام إيثيلين |
| etiology | علم الأسباب المرضية |
| etoac | أسيتات إيثيل |
| etoh | إيثانول |
| eu | وحدة أوروبية |
| eu/mg | وحدة أوروبية/مجم |
| eucalyptol for pharmaceutical purposes | سائل عطري [ إيكاليبتول] للاستخدام في الأغراض الصيدلانية |
| eucalyptus for pharmaceutical purposes | شجر الكافور للاستخدام في الأغراض الصيدلانية |
| euclidean distance | المسافة الإقليدية |
| eukaryote | حقيقي النواة |
| eukaryotes | الخلايا ذات الأنوية الحقيقية (الطبيعية) |
| eukaryotic | حقيقي النواة |
| eulas | اتفاقيات الترخيص للمستخدم النهائي |
| eurasian patent organization | المنظمة الأوروآسيوية للبراءات. منظمة إقليمية تأسست بموجب معاهدة البراءات الأوروآسيوية |
| euroclear and clearstream | شركتا يوروكلير وكليرستريم |
| eurofighter typhoon | طائرة يوروفايتر تايفون الحربية |
| european community, ec | السوق الأوربية المشتركة |
| european patent organization | منظمة البراءات الأوروبية. |
| europium | اليوروبيوم [عنصر فلزي] |
| euros | يورو |
| ev | إلكترون فولت |
| evacuants | أدوية مفرَّغة |
| evacuate | يفرغ |
| evacuate | يجلي |
| evade | ينفلت من، يتملص من، يهرب من |
| evaluate | يقيم |
| evaluation | تقييم |
| evaluation of concept idea | تقييم الفكرة المفهومية. قيام المخترع بتقييم فهمه الفكري لاختراعه فهما تجريديا، وهو ما يعد أحد الخطوات المبكرة في إنجاز الاختراع |
| evaluation of instruction | تقييم التعليم |
| evaluation of teaching | تقييم التدريس |
| evaluator | مقيم |
| evaporated in vacuo | تم تبخيرها في وسط مفرغ |
| evaporation systems | جهاز تبخير بالحرارة |
| evaporator | مبخر؛ جهاز تبخير |
| evaporator blowdown | وحدة تصريف خاصة بجهاز تبخير |
| evaporites | المتبخرات: صخور رسوبية كيميائية تبخرية |

| | |
|---|---|
| evenly spaced | يتم تباعد كذا على مسافات متساوية |
| event analysis | تحليل الحدث |
| event marketing | التسويق بالمناسبات |
| events | حالات، أحداث |
| ever-changing technology | تقنية متغيرة دائما |
| eviction of tenant | طرد المستأجر |
| evidence | دليل |
| evolution | نشوء وتطور |
| evolutionary | متطور؛ مرفق |
| evolutionary robotics | روبوت متطور |
| ewing sarcoma | الورم السرطاني ليوينغ |
| ex officio | بحُكم المنصب |
| ex parte | رِعَايَة قانونية فورية أو عناية فورية |
| ex parte reexaminations | إعادة فحص للبراءة. إعادة فحص لسلامة البراءة بناء على طلب الغير وهو ما يجعل المراسلات المنبثقة عنه تقتصر على صاحب البراءة والفاحص دون الغير مقدم الطلب |
| ex rel. | بناء على بلاغ من |
| ex: oxedase amine" | إنزيم كذا إنزيم أكسيداز أمين" |
| exact a heavy toll on | يوقع به خسائر جسيمة |
| examination | تحقيق النيابة |
| examination | فحص |
| examination report | تقرير الفحص |
| examiner | فاحص |
| examplary | تمثيلي (وعند المقارنات بين النماذج المختلفة: "مفضل") |
| example: ( a third heat-exchanger 62 is coupled/connected in series between the first heat-exchanger 32 and the first gas/liquid separator 36)" | على التوالي مثال: يتم إقران/اتصال المبادل الحراري الثالث 62 على التوالي بين المبادل الحراري الأول 32 وجهاز الفصل الأول لـ (الغاز/الحرارة) 36." |
| excavators | الحفارات الميكانيكية |
| excessive patenting | إصدار براءات كثيف. |
| exchange | يتبادل، تبادل |
| exchange rate | سعر تبادل العملات |
| exchanged for | استبدال كذا بكذا |
| exchangers (ion -) [chemicals] | المبادلات (المبادلات الأيونية) [مواد كيميائية] |
| excipient | سواغ |
| excipients | سواغات |
| excitatory postsynaptic potentials (epsp) | الجهود الاستثارية بعد المشبك |
| exclusion criteria | معايير الإقصاء |
| exclusive distributer | موزع وحيد |
| exclusive franchise agreement | اتفاق لمنح امتياز حصري |
| exclusive license | ترخيص حصري |
| exclusivity | حصرية |
| exclusivity clause | بند الحصرية: بند تعاقدي يبين أن الطرف المسند له بالعقد يتمتع بحق الحصرية فيما هو مسند إليه وأنه لا يحق للطرف المسند الإسناد للغير |

| | |
|---|---|
| executable foreign arbitral award | حكم تحكيمي أجنبي قابل للتنفيذ |
| execute | ينفذ |
| executive | تنفيذي |
| executive information system | نظام معلومات تنفيذية |
| executive officer | ضابط تنفيذي؛ قائد ثان؛ نائب أو مساعد القائد |
| executive regulation | لائحة تنفيذية |
| executive responsibility | مسئولية تنفيذية |
| executive support system | نظم الدعم التنفيذي |
| executives | تنفيذيون |
| exemplary embodiment | تجسد مثالي |
| exemplified embodiment | نموذج تمثيلي |
| exercisability | القدره على الممارسه |
| exercisability of right | قابلية الحق للممارسة، إمكانية ممارسة الحق |
| exercisable license | ترخيص للاستعمال |
| exercise | تمرين، ممارسه |
| exercise bicycles (rollers for stationary -) | دراجات التمرين (أسطوانات متدحرجة للاستخدام في دراجات التمرين الثابتة) |
| exercise bicycles (stationary -) | دراجات التمرين (دراجات التمرين الثابتة) |
| exercised license | ترخيص موضع تنفيذ |
| exercise-induced bronchoconstriction | الانقباض الشعبي الناتج عن مجهود |
| exercisers [expanders] | أدوات التمرين الرياضي [موسعات] |
| exert a certain force on | يسلط قوة معينة على |
| exfoliating bark | تقشير اللحاء |
| exfoliation | تقشر |
| exhaust | يرهق، عادم |
| exhaust emissions | ابتعاثات عادمية |
| exhaust gas | غاز عادم |
| exhaust stack | مدخنة العادم |
| exhauste from | يفرغ؛ يصرف (من) |
| exhauster | عادم |
| exhausting pressure; exhuast pressure | ضغط إجهاد؛ ضغط إنهاك؛ ضغط شديد |
| exhausts for motors and engines | أنابيب العادم في الموتورات والمحركات |
| exhibit a | المستند أ |
| exhibitionist | استعراضي |
| exist in tautomeric or enantiomeric forms | قد تتواجد في صور صنوية أو في صورة متشاكلات |
| exit location | موقع خروج |
| exo | إكسو |
| exo and endo double bonds | الروابط المزدوجة الخارجية والداخلية |
| exocrine | خارجي الإفراز |
| exogenetic | خارجي النشأة |
| exon | أكسون |
| exothermic | طارد للحرارة |
| expander | موسّع |
| expanders | وسائل تمديد |
| expanders [hand tools] | الموسعات [عُدد يدوية] |

| | |
|---|---|
| expanding bands for holding sleeves | أربطة يمكن توسيعها لتثبيت الأكمام |
| expansion | تمدد (كيمياء) |
| expansion joint | وصلة تمدد |
| expansion joint filler | حشو وصلة التمدد |
| expansion of the gas mixutre | تمديد؛ تمدد |
| expansion tanks [parts of machines] | صهاريج التمدد [أجزاء من الماكينات] |
| expansion tanks for central heating installations | صهاريج التمدد للاستخدام في تجهيزات التدفئة المركزية |
| expectorant | طارد للبلغم |
| expel reservoir is fluidly connectable to .... | يكون خزان الطرد الأول متصلاً عن طريق المائع ... |
| expenses clause | بند النفقات: بند تعاقدي يبين طريقة تحمل النفقات الناشئة عن تنفيذ العقد |
| experiment | يختبر، اختبار |
| experimental | تجريبي؛ متعلق بالطرق التجريبية المعملية |
| experimental % | النسبة التجريبية |
| experimental design | تصميم التجربة |
| experimental innovators | مبتكرون يعتمدون منهاج الاختبار |
| experimental variability | التغير الحادث في التجربة |
| experimentation | اختبار |
| expert | خبير |
| expert determination clause | بند تقرير الخبير. بند ينظم عملية الفصل في النزاع بين المتعاقدين من خلال اللجوء إلى خبير يقوم بإصدار تحديد. ويعد من البنود النمطية العامة التي تتضمنها عقود الملكية الفكرية |
| expert opinion | رأي الخبير |
| expert system | نظام خبير |
| expertise | خبرة |
| expert's opinion | رأي خبير. من أمثلته الرأي الذي يبديه الخبير القضائي في قضية ما. |
| expiration | انقضاء أجل |
| expiration of lease | إنتهاء مدة الإيجار |
| expire | ينقضي أجله |
| expired patent | براءة منتهية الصلاحية |
| expiry | انقضاء صلاحية |
| explant | زريعة: نسيج فحص مفصول |
| explants | زريعات: أنسجة الفحص المفصولة |
| exploded perspective view of | رسم منظوري مفكك |
| exploded view | منظر مفكك |
| exploitability assessment | تقييم إمكانية الاستغلال |
| exploited patent | براءة مستغلة |
| explosive bonbons [christmas crackers] | حلويات مفرقعة [مفرقعات تشتمل على قطع حلوى خاصة بأعياد الميلاد] |
| explosive cartridges | الخراطيش المتفجرة |
| explosive charges | عبوات متفجرة |
| explosive device | وسيلة تفجير |
| explosive powders | مساحيق متفجرة |
| explosive units | وحدات متفجرة |
| explosives | متفجرات؛ مواد متفجرة |
| export control enforcement program | برنامج تطبيق الرقابة على الصادرات |
| exporting as a screen saver | تصدير كشاشة توقف |
| exporting as a wallpaper | تصدير كخلفية شاشة |
| exporting shooting properties | تصدير خصائص الالتقاط |
| exporting still images | تصدير الصور الثابتة |
| exposure adjustment | ضبط درجة الإضاءة |
| exposure bracketing | مضاهاة شدة الإضاءة تلقائيًا |
| exposure compensation | تعويض درجة الإضاءة |
| exposure level | مستوى درجة الإضاءة |
| exposure meters [light meters] | أجهزة قياس التعريض [أجهزة قياس الضوء] |
| exposure therapy | العلاج بالتعرض |
| express | يعبر وراثيًا عن |
| express | يعبر، سريع، واضح، راسلة عاجلة، يظهر، يجسد، يعصر |
| express mail | بريد سريع |
| expression | تعبير، أسلوب التعبير |
| expression (of) | تعبير وراثي (عن) |
| expression vector | ناقل تعبير (وراثي) |
| expressive | معبر، تعبيري |
| expressiveness | تعبيرية |
| expressivity | كون الشيء معبرا |
| expropriate | يجرد من الملكية، يصادر |
| expropriated | مُصادَر |
| expropriated patent | براءة مُصادرة |
| expropriation | تجريد من الملكية، مصادرة |
| expropriation (in the public interest) | نزع الملكية (للمنفعة العامة) |
| expropriation of patent | مصادرة براءة |
| expropriation of patent right | مصادرة الحق في براءة |
| exsanguination | استنزاف |
| extended-dwell tenecteplase | تينيكتيبلاز ممتد الثبات |
| extender pigments | خضابات باسطة |
| extenders | مواد باسطة |
| extension | امتداد |
| extension pieces for braces for screwtaps | وصلات التمديد لملفات ذكر اللولبة |
| extensive expansion | التوسع الزراعي الأفقي |
| extensive proteolysis | التحلل البروتيني الشامل |
| extensometer | مقياس امتداد؛ مقياس استطالة |
| extent of polymeric object | امتداد جسم البوليمر |
| external connections | التوصيلات الخارجية |
| external debt | الدين الخارجي |
| external drug and cosmetic colors (ext. d&c) | ملوّنات العقاقير الخارجية ومستحضرات التجميل (C&Ext. D) |
| external monitor | جهاز عرض خارجي |
| external monitor port | منفذ شاشة خارجية |
| extinction coefficient | معامل الاندثار |
| extinguishers | عدة الإطفاء |
| extinguishing compositions (fire -) | تركيبات الإطفاء (تركيبات إطفاء النيران) |
| extrabasinal | خارج الحوض |
| extracellular | خارج الخلية |
| extra-cellular | خارج الخلية |

| | |
|---|---|
| extract | يستخلص |
| extract | يستخرج؛ يستخلص |
| extract | يستخلص، مُستخلَص |
| extractability | قابلية الشيء للاستخلاص |
| extracted vapor | بخار مستخلص |
| extractible | قابل للاستخلاص |
| extracting | استخلاص |
| extraction site | موقع الاستخلاص موقع الاستخراج |
| extractor | مُستخلِص |
| extractor hoods for kitchens | أغطية أجهزة الاستخلاص للاستخدام في المطابخ |
| extractors (nail -) | كماشات [كلابات مسامير] |
| extractors for mines | أجهزة الاستخلاص للاستخدام في المناجم |
| extracts | نواتج استخلاص؛ مستخلصات |
| extracts of flowers [perfumes] | مستخلصات من الزهور [عطور] |
| extradite | يسلم مجرم (ليد دولة أخرى) |
| extradition accord | اتفاقية لتسليم وتبادل المجرمين |
| extrapolate | يستنتج |
| extrapyramidal side effects | الآثار الجانبية خارج السبيل الهرمي |
| extrasystole (es) | انقباض خارجي |
| extraterritoriality | تطبيق القانون خارج الحدود |
| extravasation ; extravazation | تسرب الموائع إلى النسيج |
| extreme pressure | ضغط أقصى |
| extreme ultraviolet lithography | الطباعة الصلبة بالأشعة الفوق بنفسجية المكثفة |
| extrudable | قابل للبثق |
| extrudates | مواد بثق |
| extruded aluminium | ألومنيوم مشكل بالبثق |
| extruded polyester strands | الجدائل المشكَّلة بالبثق |
| extrusion process | عملية تشكيل بالبثق |
| exudtaes | موائع الجسم |
| exuivalence queries | استعلامات التكافؤ |
| eye bolts | مسامير ذات عروة |
| eye implants | زراعات العين |
| eye lens | العدسة العينية |
| eye witnesses | شهود العيان |
| eyebrow brushes | فرش الحواجب |
| eyebrow cosmetics | مستحضرات تجميل الحواجب |
| eyebrow pencils | أقلام الحواجب |
| eyeglass cases | علب النظارات |
| eyeglass chains | سلاسل النظارات |
| eyeglass cords | أشرطة النظارات |
| eyeglass frames | أطر النظارات |
| eyeglasses | النظارات |
| eyeglasses | نظارات |
| eyelash curlers | أدوات عقص الأهداب |
| eyelashes (adhesives for affixing false -) | الأهداب (مواد لاصقة لتثبيت الأهداب الصناعية) |
| eyelashes (cosmetic preparations for -) | الأهداب (مستحضرات تجميل للأهداب) |
| eyelashes (false -) | الأهداب (الأهداب الصناعية) |
| eyelets (shoe -) | فتحات عينية (للحذاء) |
| eyelets for clothing | فتحات عينية [ثقوب صغيرة في طرف ثوب يُدخل فيها الشريط] في الملابس |
| eyepatches for medical purposes | رقع للعين للاستخدام في الأغراض الطبية |
| eyepieces | عدسات المجهر |
| eyepieces (instruments containing -) | عدسات المجهر (معدات تحتوى على عدسات المجهر) |
| eyes (artificial -) | العيون (العيون الصناعية) |
| eyeshades | ظلال العين |
| eye-wash | غسول العين |

# F

| | |
|---|---|
| fabric | قماش |
| fabric for boots and shoes | قماش للأحذية عالية الرقبة والأحذية العادية |
| fabric of imitation animal skins | قماش مقلد لجلود الحيوانات |
| fabric softeners [for laundry use] | مواد لتنعيم القماش [للاستخدام في الغسيل] |
| fabric, impervious to gases, for aeronautical balloons | قماش غير منفذ للغازات للاستخدام في مناطيد الطيران |
| fabrics (asbestos -) | أقمشة (أقمشة الأسبستوس) |
| fabrics (buckets made of woven -) | أقمشة (دلاء مصنوعة من الأقمشة المغزولة) |
| fabrics (fiberglass [fibreglass] -), for insulation | أقمشة العزل(أقمشة من الزجاج الليفي) |
| fabrics (insulating -) | أقمشة (أقمشة عازلة) |
| fabrics (stain-preventing chemicals for use on -) | أقمشة (مواد كيميائية مضادة للبقع للاستخدام على الأقمشة) |
| fabrics for bookbinding | أقمشة لتجليد الكتب |
| fabrics for textile use | أقمشة للاستخدام في المنسوجات |
| façade | واجهة |
| face region of magnet | المنطقة السطحية للمغناطيس؛ سطح المغناطيس |
| face towels of paper | مناشف الوجه من الورق |
| face towels of textile | مناشف الوجه من القماش |
| face-shields (workmen's protective -) | حواجز للوجه (حواجز لحماية وجوه العمال) |
| facet | سطح صغير |
| facial | وجهي |
| facial angel | الزاوية لوجهية |
| facial recognition | التعرف إلى الوجه. تعرف الآلة على ملامح وجه الإنسان |
| facilitative business environment | بيئة تجارية مُيسرة |
| facility | أداة مساعدة |
| facing | وجهة الإعلان |
| facing end surfaces | له سطحين طرفين متقابلين |
| facings | مواد الواجهة؛ مادة طلاء |
| facings, not of metal, for building | مواد لكساء واجهات الأبنية ليست من المعدن |
| facsimile machines | آلات الفاكس |
| fact-finding committee | لجنة تقصي الحقائق |
| factor = index | معامل |
| factory chimney | مداخن المصانع |
| faculties | قدرات |
| faculty | قدرة، قوة، وظيفة جسدية |
| faculty members | أعضاء الكلية |
| fade | يتلاشى ،يتضاءل تدريجا صوتان أو وضوحا |
| fade in | يظهر تدريجيا |
| fade in | يظهر |
| fade out | يختفي؛ يتلاشى |
| fade out | يختفي تدريجيا |
| fadeless | غير قابل للتلاشي |
| fading | خفوت في الإرسال |
| failed invention | اختراع فاشل |
| fail-safe | آمن عند الفشل؛ آمن عند التعطل |
| failure | فشل، إخفاق |
| failure ; failures | انهيار (في مجال الكهرباء)، مثل انهيار العَزْل، إلخ |
| failure detection system | نظام اكتشاف الإخفاق |
| failure recovery | استعادة التشغيل بعد العطل |
| fair credit reporting act | قانون إبلاغ الائتمان المباشر |
| fair huts | أكواخ المعارض |
| fairground ride apparatus | جهاز الركوب في أرض المعرض |
| fairy lights for festive decoration | الأنوار الخافتة للاستخدام في زينة الاحتفالات |
| fall detection | اكتشاف السقطات. اكتشاف حالات الوقوع التي يعانيها البشر لاسيما كبار السن وأصحاب الاحتياجات الخاصة والإعاقات، إذ يعقب الاكتشاف إرسال رسالة إلى جهة يمكنها تقديم يد العون بسرعة |
| fall into police hands | يسقط في يد البوليس |
| falling address | عنوان متلاشي |
| falling weight deflectometer (fwd) | اختبار الهبوط تحت تاثير الوزن الساقط |
| falling weight impact test | اختبار الصدمات تحت تأثير الوزن الساقط |
| falling-film evaporator | جهاز تبخير ذي طبقة رقيقة هابطة |
| fallow land | الأرض المراحة: أرض تحرث ثم تترك موسم كامل للراحة |
| false beard | لحى صناعية |
| false beards | اللحى الصناعية |
| false coin detector | جهاز الكشف عن العملات الزائفة |
| false eyelashes | الأهداب الصناعية |
| false hair | الشعر المستعار |
| false hair (adhesives for affixing -) | الشعر المستعار (مواد لاصقة لتثبيت الشعر المستعار) |
| false hems | الحواشي الصناعية |
| false moustaches | الشوارب المستعارة |
| false nails | الأظافر الصناعية |
| false report | بلاغ كاذب |
| false testimony | شهود الزور |
| familiary adenomatous polyposis carcinoma | الورم السرطاني للبوليب المتعلق بالورم الغدي العائلي |
| family | عائلة؛ أسرة |
| family | مجموعة؛ طقم |
| family | فصيلة (في تصنيف الأحياء) |
| family | سلالة (للفيروسات التي تصيب الكمبيوتر، إلخ) |
| family | عائلة |
| family medicine | طب الأسرة |
| family member | أفراد الأسرة |
| fan | مروحة |
| fan | يذري، ينفخ على، يثير، مذراة، مروحة |

| | |
|---|---|
| fan belts for motors and engines | سيور المروحة في الموتورات والمحركات |
| fancy goods [embroidery] | منتجات للزينة [زخارف] |
| fang | ناب، شوكة |
| fanner | المروح، حامل المروحة |
| fanny packs (waist packs) | حقائب تلف حول الوسط وتحمل على الظهر |
| fans (electric -) for personal use | مراوح (مراوح كهربائية) للاستخدام الشخصي |
| fans ; buffs | محبي السينما؛ جمهور ها |
| fans [air-conditioning] | مراوح [تكييف الهواء] |
| fans [parts of air conditioning installations] | مراوح [أجزاء من تجهيزات تكييف الهواء] |
| fans for motors and engines | المراوح للاستخدام في الموتورات والمحركات |
| fans for personal use [non-electric] | المراوح للاستخدام الشخصي [غير كهربائية] |
| fans for the compression, sucking and carrying of grain | مراوح ضغط الحبوب وسحبها وحملها |
| faqs | الأسئلة المتكررة (للمستخدمين) |
| farad | وحدة السعة الكهربائية |
| faraday | وحدة الكمية الكهربائية |
| faradic | حاث أو مستحث |
| faradism | الفارادية، المفاردة. استخدام التيار الكهربائي المستحث |
| faradize | يفارد. يعالج بالتيار الكهربائي المستحث |
| farinaceous food pastes | عجين الأطعمة النشوية |
| farinaceous foods | الأطعمة النشوية |
| farm lease act | قانون الإيجارات الزراعية |
| farmer | مزارع |
| farmer's lungs | التهاب الحويصلات الرئوية؛ مرض رئة الفلاح؛ داء الفلاحين |
| farmer's disease | التهاب الحويصلات الرئوية؛ مرض رئة الفلاح؛ داء الفلاحين |
| farriers' knives | سكاكين الطبيب البيطري |
| far-uv circular dichroism; far-uv cd | ثنائي اللون الدائري بالأشعة فوق البنفسجية البعيدة |
| fas chromatograph (gc) | جهاز كروماتوجراف الغاز (GC) |
| fascia | النسيج تحت الجلدي |
| fascicle | عنقود، حزمة |
| fast and localized computations | بإجراء حسابات سريعة وموضعية |
| fast forward playback | تشغيل التقديم السريع |
| fast moving subjects | الأهداف سريعة الحركة |
| fast reverse playback | تشغيل الترجيع السريع |
| fasted state ; fasting state | في حالة صيام |
| fasten | يحكم |
| fastened | محكم |
| fastener | محكم |
| fasteners (shoe -) | أدوات ربط (إبزيم الحذاء) |
| fasteners (slide -) [zippers] | أدوات ربط (السحابات) |
| fastening means | وسيلة تثبيت |
| fastening pipes (collars of metal for - ) | تثبيت الأنابيب (طوق من المعدن لتثبيت الأنابيب) |
| fastening the grip belt | تثبيت حزام الإمساك بالكاميرا |
| fastenings for clothing | أدوات ربط الملابس |
| fastenings for saddles | أدوات ربط السروج |
| fastenings for suspenders | أدوات ربط الحمالات |
| fasting blood glucose | تحليل سكر الصائم |
| fasting plasma glucose test | مستوى السكر في الدم صائماً |
| fat | اختبار القبول بالمصنع |
| fat (coconut -) | الدهون (دهون جوز هند) |
| fat tissues | الأنسجة الدهنية |
| fat-bleaching chemicals | مواد كيميائية لتقصير الدهون |
| fat-containing mixtures for bread slices | خلائط تحتوى على الدهون لشرائح الخبز |
| fatless cream | جبن خالي من الدهن |
| fattening preparations (animal -) | مستحضرات تسمين (مستحضرات تسمين الحيوانات) |
| fatty acids | الأحماض الدهنية |
| fatty substances for the manufacture of edible fats | مواد دهنية لتصنيع الدهون الصالحة للأكل |
| faucets for pipes (am.) | صنابير المواسير |
| faujasite | فوخاسيت |
| fault | خطأ؛ عطل |
| fault breccia | رواهص الصدوع |
| fault detection means | وسيلة كشف الأعطال |
| fault fragment | جزء صدعي |
| fault interpretation | تفسير الصدوع |
| fault surface | سطح صدعي |
| fault-bounded intracratonic basins | الأحواض الصدعية |
| fawn | بني يميل إلى الرمادي الفاتح |
| fax | فاكس |
| fbp | نقطة غليان نهائية |
| fbre plants | النباتات الليفية |
| fc region of an antibody | منطقة Fc من جسم مضاد |
| fcc | التكسير الحفزي في وجود طبقة متميعة |
| fcc | لجنة الاتصالات الفيدرالية (الولايات المتحدة الأمريكية) |
| fci | بند تهيئة تشغيلي |
| fddi | واجهة بيانات موزعة بالألياف الضوئية |
| fdma | الوصول المتعدد بتقسيم التردد |
| feasibility | جدوى |
| feasible | امتياز غير مجدٍ |
| feather key | خابور غاطس |
| feather-dusters | منافض الريش |
| feathers [clothing accessories] | الريش [إكسسوارات الملابس] |
| feathers for bedding | ريش للأسِرّة |
| feathers for stuffing upholstery | ريش لحشو التنجيد |
| feature | خاصية |
| feature film | فيلم روائي طويل |
| features and specifications | الخصائص والمواصفات |
| febrifuges | عقاقير مضادة للحمى |
| feces | روث |
| fecralloy | سبيكة حديد وكروم |
| fed sponsored | تحت إشراف فيدرالي |
| federal & state government properties. | ممتلكات الحكومة الاتحادية (الفدرالية) وحكومات الولايات |
| federal acquisition regulation | نظام المشتريات الاتحادي |
| federal consumer credit | القانون الفدرالي لحماية ائتمان |

| | |
|---|---|
| protection act | المستهلك |
| federal highway administration | إدارة الطرق السريعة الفيدرالية |
| federal information exchange | تبادل المعلومات الفيدرالية |
| federal information processing standards (fips) | مقاييس معالجة المعلومات الفيدرالية |
| federal networking council (fnc) | مجلس الشبكات الفيدرالية |
| federally sponsered research or development | بحث أو تطوير تحت إشراف فيدرالي؛ بحث أو تطوير برعاية فيدرالية |
| federally-owned invention | اختراع مملوك للحكومة الفيدرالية |
| fee | رسم، أتعاب |
| fee processing | تقديم الرسوم |
| fee record sheet | بيان سجل الرسوم |
| fee simple | ملكية مطلقة |
| feed | تيار تغذية (feed stream)؛ مادة تغذية |
| feed | يغذي |
| feed gas | غاز التغذية؛ غاز تم التغذية به |
| feed hopper | قادوس تغذية |
| feed oil | زيت التغذية |
| feed pressure | ضغط التغذية |
| feed stream | تيار تغذية |
| feed temperature | درجة حرارة التغذية |
| feedback | ردود؛ رواجع؛ مُرتَدّات |
| feedback | تغذية مرتدة؛ تغذية عكسية؛ ملاحظات (المستخدمين الآخرين) |
| feedback loop | حلقة تغذية مرتدة |
| feeders (mechanized livestock -) | ماكينات تغذية (ماكينات مجهزة بالمعدات الميكانيكية لتغذية الماشية) |
| feeders [parts of machines] | أجزاء تغذية [أجزاء من ماكينات] |
| feeding a first gas flow into a reforming reactor. | تغذية مفاعل إعادة تشكيل بتدفق تيار أول (أو التغذية بتدفق تيار أول إلى مفاعل إعادة تشكيل) |
| feeding apparatus for engine boilers | جهاز تغذية لغلايات المحرك |
| feeding apparatus for heating boilers | جهاز تغذية لغلايات التسخين |
| feeding bottle teats | حلمات زجاجات التغذية |
| feeding bottle valves | صمامات زجاجات التغذية |
| feeding bottles | زجاجات التغذية |
| feeding bottles (dolls' -) | زجاجات التغذية (زجاجات التغذية الخاصة بالعرائس) |
| feeding bottles (heaters for-), non-electric | زجاجات التغذية (سخانات زجاجات التغذية)؛ غير كهربائية |
| feeding bottles (heaters, electric, for - ) | زجاجات التغذية (سخانات كهربائية لزجاجات التغذية) |
| feeding industries | صناعات تغذي صناعات أخرى |
| feeding troughs | أوعية التغذية |
| feeding troughs for animals | أوعية تغذية الحيوانات |
| feedlot | مرعى، معلف |
| feedstock ; feed stock; feed-stock | خام تغذية |
| feedstocks | خامات تغذية |

| | |
|---|---|
| feedthrough; feed-through | تغذية نافذة |
| feedwater regulators | منظمات مياه التغذية |
| fees | رسوم، أتعاب |
| felon | جاني |
| felony | جناية |
| felt | يصنع من اللباد |
| felt | لباد |
| felt (asbestos -) | لباد (لباد الأسبستوس) |
| felt (insulating -) | لباد (لباد عازل) |
| felt for building | لباد البناء |
| felt-tip pen | قَلَم بِـسنّ لبَاديّ |
| female athymic nude mice | فئران منزوعة الشعر منزوعة الغدة الصعترية من الإناث |
| femoral | فخذي |
| femur | عظم الفخذ |
| fences (electrified -) | أسوار (أسوار مكهربة) |
| fences of metal | أسوار من المعدن |
| fences, not of metal | أسوار ليست من المعدن |
| fencing gauntlets | قفازات واقية للمبارزة بالسيف |
| fencing masks | أقنعة للاستخدام في المبارزة بالسيف |
| fencing weapons | أسلحة المبارزة بالسيف |
| fenders for ships | صدادات السفن |
| fennel for medical purposes | الشمار للاستخدام في الأغراض الطبية |
| fermentation | تخمر |
| fermentation (apparatus for -) [laboratory apparatus] | تخمر (أجهزة التخمر) [أجهزة معملية] |
| fermenting wine (chemicals used in - ) | تخمير الخمور (مواد كيميائية للاستخدام في تخمير الخمور) |
| ferments (milk -) for chemical purposes | خميرة (خميرة اللبن الحليب) للاستخدام في الأغراض الكيميائية |
| ferments for pastes | خميرة العجين |
| fermium | الفرميوم |
| ferric chloride | كلوريد الحديديك |
| ferris wheel | عجلة Ferris |
| ferrocyanides | فروسيانيد |
| ferromagnetic | ذو مغناطيسية حديدية |
| ferromagnetic material | مادة حديدية مغناطيسية |
| ferrotitanium | فروتيتانيوم [تيتانيوم الحديدوز] |
| ferrotype plates [photography] | ألواح الصور الموجبة ذات السطوح الداكنة |
| ferruginous sandstone | الحجر الرملي الحديدي |
| ferrules of metal | حلقات من المعدن |
| ferrules of metal for handles | حلقات من المعدن للمقابض |
| ferrules of metal for walking sticks | حلقات من المعدن لعصى السير |
| ferry boats | قوارب عبور |
| fertilizer | الأسمدة: |
| fertilizing preparations | مستحضرات تسميد |
| festoons [embroidery] | نقوش [تطريز جمالي] |
| fetal bovine serum | مصل جنين بقري |
| fetal bovine serum (fbs) | مصل جنيني بقري |
| fetch | يحضر |
| fev1 | الحجم الزفيري القسري في الثانية الأولى |
| few early purple orchids | القليل من باكورة زهور الأوركيدا الأرجوانية |

| | |
|---|---|
| ff | تقديم سريع |
| fg | فمتو جرام |
| fhss | الطيف الموزع عبر تغيير التردد |
| fiber | ليفي؛ ذو ألياف |
| fiber | ليفة |
| fiber | ليف، نبات أو نسيج عضلي |
| fiber (coconut -) | ألياف (ألياف جوز الهند) |
| fiber (vulcanized -) | ألياف (ألياف معالجة بالكبريت) |
| fiber bragg grating (fbg) | شبكة براج الليفية (شبكة براج بألياف) |
| fiber channel switched network | شبكة تبادل قنوات بألياف |
| fiber crops | محاصيل الألياف |
| fiber distributed data interface | واجهات البيانات الموزعة عبر الألياف |
| fiber optic cable | كبل ألياف ضوئية |
| fiber optic cable; fibre optic | كبل ألياف ضوئية |
| fiber optic terminations | نهايات للألياف الضوئية؛ النهايات الطرفية للالياف الضوئية |
| fiber optic tethers | مطاولات ألياف ضوئية |
| fiberboard | مادة تصنع بضغط ألياف الخشب وغيره إلى رقاقات قاسية |
| fiberform | ليفي الشكل |
| fiberglass fabrics for insulation | أقمشة من الزجاج الليفي للعزل |
| fiberglass fabrics, for textile use | أقمشة من الزجاج الليفي للاستخدام في المنسوجات |
| fiberglass for insulation | الزجاج الليفي للعزل |
| fiberglass other than for insulation or textile use | الزجاج الليفي بخلاف الاستخدام في العزل أو الاستخدام في المنسوجات |
| fiberglass thread for textile use | خيط الزجاج الليفي للاستخدام في المنسوجات |
| fiberglass thread, not for textile use | خيط الزجاج الليفي لغير الاستخدام في المنسوجات |
| fiber-optic cable | كبل ألياف ضوئية |
| fiber-optic-distributed-interferometeric tool | أداة قياس التداخل الموزعة ذات الليفة الضوئية |
| fibers (asbestos -) | ألياف (ألياف الأسبستوس) |
| fibers (edible plant -) [non-nutritive] | ألياف (ألياف نباتية صالحة للأكل) [ليس لها قيمة غذائية] |
| fibers (glass -), for insulation | ألياف (ألياف زجاجية) للعزل |
| fibers (plastic -), not for use in textiles | ألياف (ألياف بلاستيكية) ليست للاستخدام في المنسوجات |
| fibers (textile -) | ألياف (ألياف نسيجية) |
| fibre (coconut -) | ليف (ليف جوز الهند) |
| fibre (vulcanized -) | ليف (ليف معالج بالكبريت) |
| fibre [fiber (am.)] optic cables | كبلات بصرية من الليف |
| fibreglass | زجاج ليفي: ألياف زجاجية مضفرة |
| fibreglass fabrics for insulation | أقمشة من الزجاج الليفي للعزل |
| fibreglass fabrics for textile use | أقمشة من الزجاج الليفي للاستخدام في المنسوجات |
| fibreglass for insulation | الزجاج الليفي للعزل |
| fibreglass other than for insulation or textile use | الزجاج الليفي بخلاف الاستخدام في العزل أو في المنسوجات |
| fibreglass thread for textile use | خيط من الزجاج الليفي للاستخدام في المنسوجات |
| fibreglass thread, not for textile use | خيط من الزجاج الليفي لغير الاستخدام في المنسوجات |
| fibres (asbestos -) | ألياف (ألياف الأسبستوس) |
| fibres (edible plant -) [non-nutritive] | ألياف (ألياف نباتية صالحة للأكل) [ليس لها قيمة غذائية] |
| fibres (glass -), for insulation | ألياف (ألياف زجاجية) للعزل |
| fibres (plastic -), not for use in textiles | ألياف (ألياف بلاستيكية) لغير الاستخدام في المنسوجات |
| fibres (textile -) | ألياف (ألياف من القماش) |
| fibrillar extension | امتداد ليفي؛ امتداد التليف |
| fibrinolytic | محلل الليفين |
| fibroblast | خلية ليفية أولية غير ناضجة؛ خلية مولِّدة للألياف. |
| fibromyalgia | ألم العضلات الليفية |
| fibromyalgic syndrome | متلازمة الألم العضلي المزمن |
| fibronectin | فيرونيكتين (بروتين لاصق للخلايا) |
| fibrosarcoma | الورم السرطاني الليفي |
| fibrosis | تليف |
| fibrotic | متليف |
| fictitious drug | دواء زائف |
| fictitious innovator | مبتكر وهمي |
| fidonet | شبكة فيدونت |
| field | حقل |
| field | مجال |
| field army | جيش ميداني |
| field artillery | مدفعية الميدان |
| field crops | محاصيل حقلية |
| field engineering | هندسة الميدان؛ هندسة ميدانية |
| field marshal (marshal) | المشير |
| field programmable gate array (fpga) | مصفوفة بوابة قابلة لبرمجة مجال بعينه |
| field programmable gate arrays (fpgas) | مصفوفات البوابات المبرمجة حقليا FPGAs |
| field reactive electrodes | حقل إلكترودات متفعلة |
| fighter-bombers | مقاتلات قاذفة |
| fighters | مقاتلات؛ مقاتلاة |
| fighting robot | روبوت مقاتل |
| figurative device | جهاز تشكيل |
| figurines [statuettes] of common metal | التماثيل الصغيرة من المعادن غير النفيسة |
| figurines [statuettes] of papier mâché | التماثيل الصغيرة من الورق المعجن |
| figurines [statuettes] of porcelain, terra-cotta or glass | التماثيل الصغيرة من البورسلين أو الطين النضج أو الزجاج |
| figurines [statuettes] of precious metal | التماثيل الصغيرة من المعادن النفيسة |
| figurines [statuettes] of stone, concrete or marble | التماثيل الصغيرة من الحجر أو الخرسانة أو الرخام |
| figurines [statuettes] of wood, wax, plaster or plastic | التماثيل الصغيرة من الخشب، أو الشمع أو الجص أو البلاستيك |

| | |
|---|---|
| filable patent form | طلب براءة قابل (صالح) للإيداع |
| filament | خيط رفيع؛ فتيلة |
| filamentous | خيطية |
| filaments (magnesium -) for lighting | فتائل (فتائل الماغنسيوم) للإنارة |
| filaments for electric lamps | فتائل للمصابيح الكهربائية |
| filaments, electric (heating -) | الفتائل الكهربائية (فتائل التسخين) |
| filariasis | داء الخيطيات |
| fildom | صناعة السينما |
| file | يضبر، ملف، إضبارة، مجموعة أوراق، إيداع طلب، تقديم طلب |
| file (a patent) | يودع (براءة إلخ) |
| file [tools] | مبرد (والجمع: مبارد) [عدد] |
| file attach | إرفاق ملف |
| file infector (virus) | فيروس تلويث الملفات؛ فيروس إتلاف الملفات: هذه الفيروسات تلحق attach نفسها بملفات البرامج program files، وعادة تختار ملفات EXE أو COM، والبعض يمكن أن يصيب أي برنامج حيث يتطلب فيه ملف تنفيذ بما في ذلك ملفات.SYS و.OV و.PRG و.MNU . عندما يتم تحميل البرنامج فإ |
| file length | طول الملف |
| file list display | عرض قائمة الملفات |
| file locking | إقفال الملف |
| file name/file format | اسم الملف/تنسيق الملف |
| file no. | رقم الملف |
| file recovery | استعادة ملف |
| file recovery procedures | إجراءات استرداد الملفات |
| file request | طلب ملف |
| file server | خادم الملفات |
| file transfer | نقل الملفات |
| filed patent documents | مستندات براءة مودعة |
| files [office requisites] | ملفات [لوازم مكتبية] |
| filiform | خيطاني، شبيه بخيط |
| filing | تقديم طلب، إيداع |
| filing a patent application | إيداع طلب براءة |
| filing cabinets | خزائن الملفات |
| filing date | تاريخ الإيداع (لبراءة إلخ) |
| filing fees | رسوم الإيداع |
| filing power | قوة إيداعية. تعبير يطلق على البلدان التي تشهد إيداعا كبيرا للبراءات وهو ما يعد مؤشرا على قوة البلد |
| filings of metal | بُرادات المعدن |
| fill | يملأ، يصب، يحشو، يركب دواء، يطلي بالذهب، يمتلأ، ينسد، ينتفخ |
| filler | مادة ملء؛ حشوة |
| filler | حشوة |
| fillers (expansion joint -) | حشوات (حشوات وصلة التمدد) |
| fillers (tree cavity -) [forestry] | حشوات (حشوات تجويف الشجرة) [زراعة الغابات] |
| fillet | يربط بعصابة، يقطع إلى شرائح |
| fillets (fish -) | شرائح سمك منزوعة العظم |
| filling great power | قوة إيداعية عظيمة. تعبير يطلق على البلدان التي يكون عدد إيداعات البراءات كبيرا بالموازنة بالبلدان الأخرى |
| filling machines | آلات الحشو |
| film | طبقة رقيقة |
| film | يصنع عرضا سينمائيا، يصور، يتغشى، تعلوه غشاوة، غشاء، غطاء رقيق، طبقة رقيقة جدا |
| film (plastic -), not for wrapping | غشاء رقيق (غشاء رقيق بلاستيكي) ليس للاستخدام في التغليف |
| film (plastic cling -) extensible, for palletization | غشاء رقيق (غشاء رقيق بلاستيكي لاصق) قابل للتمدد للنقل على منصة |
| film cutting apparatus | جهاز قطع الفيلم |
| film is a thin layer | غشاء عبارة عن طبقة رقيقة |
| fimbriate | مهذب، مشرشر |
| films (editing appliances for cinematographic -) | أفلام (أجهزة لتنقيح الأفلام السينمائية) |
| films (sensitized -), unexposed | أفلام (أفلام حساسة) غير مكشوفة للضوء |
| films, exposed | أفلام مكشوفة للضوء |
| filmy | غشائي، رقيق، شفاف |
| filose | خيطي |
| fil's running time | مدة عرض الفيلم |
| filter | مرشح |
| filter | يرشح، يترشح، مصفاة، مرشحة، أداة لكبت بعض الموجات الكهربية والصوتية |
| filter aid | عامل مساعد للترشيح |
| filter bed | مهاد الترشيح، مهاد من رمل أو حصى لتصفية الماء |
| filter cake | العجينة الناتجة عن الترشيح؛ عجينة الترشيح |
| filter cloth | قماش ترشيح |
| filter off | يفصل بالترشيح |
| filter out | يحجز؛ يفصل |
| filter paper | ورق ترشيح |
| filter paper | ورق الترشيح |
| filter press | مكبس ترشيح؛ مرشح ضغطي |
| filter sterilised | التعقيم بالترشيح |
| filterate | ناتج الترشيح |
| filteration test | اختبار الغربلة. اختبار يتم القيام به لتحديد ما غذا كان برنامج حاسبي انتهاكيا أم لا |
| filtered sterilization | التعقيم بالترشيح |
| filtering (wadding for -) | الترشيح (مادة حشو للترشيح) |
| filtering machines | ماكينات الترشيح |
| filtering materials [chemical preparations] | مواد ترشيح [مستحضرات كيميائية] |
| filtering materials [mineral substances] | مواد ترشيح [مواد معدنية] |
| filtering materials [paper] | مواد ترشيح [ورق] |
| filtering materials [semi-processed foams or films of plastic] | مواد ترشيح [رغوية أو أغشية رقيقة نصف معالجة من البلاستيك] |
| filtering materials [unprocessed plastics] | مواد ترشيح [بلاستيك غير معالج] |
| filtering materials | مواد الترشيح [مواد نباتية] |

| | |
|---|---|
| [vegetable substances] | |
| filtering materials of textile | مواد ترشيح من القماش |
| filtering media (ceramic materials in particulate form, for use as -) | وسائط الترشيح (مواد خزفية على شكل دقائق؛ للاستخدام كوسائط ترشيح) |
| filtering preparations for the beverages industry | مستحضرات ترشيح للاستخدام في صناعة المشروبات |
| filtering system | نظام تصفية |
| filter-off | فصل بالترشيح |
| filter-off | المادة المنفصلة بالترشيح |
| filters (cigarette -) | مرشحات (مرشحات السجائر) |
| filters (coffee -), electric | مرشحات (مرشحات القهوة) كهربائية |
| filters (paper coffee -) | مرشحات (مرشحات القهوة الورقية) |
| filters [parts of household or industrial installations] | مرشحات [أجزاء من التجهيزات المنزلية أو الصناعية] |
| filters [parts of machines or engines] | مرشحات [أجزاء من الماكينات أو المحركات] |
| filters [photography] | مرشحات |
| filters for air conditioning | مرشحات لتكييف الهواء |
| filters for cleaning cooling air [for engines] | مرشحات لتنظيف هواء التبريد [في المحركات] |
| filters for drinking water | مرشحات مياه الشرب |
| filters for respiratory masks | مرشحات لأقنعة التنفس |
| filters for ultraviolet rays | مرشحات للأشعة فوق البنفسجية |
| filters for ultraviolet rays, for photography | مرشحات للأشعة فوق البنفسجية للاستخدام في التصوير الفوتوغرافي |
| filtrate | ناتج ترشيح |
| filtrate | يرشح |
| filtrate | ناتج الترشيح |
| filtrate | يصفي، يرشح، يترشح |
| filum | خيط، خييط |
| fin (also vertical stabilizer) | زعنفة؛ موازِن رأسي |
| final arbitral award | حكم تحكيم نهائي |
| final catalytic composite | مادة مركبة تحفيزية نهائية |
| finalized | نهائي؛ منتهي |
| financial irregularity | مخالفة مالية |
| financial management system | نظامالإدارةالمالي |
| financibility | القابلية للتمويل |
| financible invention | اختراع قابل للتمويل |
| find applications in | له استخدامات (تطبيقات) في |
| findable prior art | فن سابق يمكن العثور عليه |
| findings | نتائج بحث |
| fine | نقي؛ صافي |
| fine | ناعم |
| fine | الغرامة |
| fine grained clastic rocks | الصخور الرسوبية صغيرة الحبيبات |
| fine manipulator cell | عينة مقارنة دقيقة |
| fines | دقائق (الخام) |
| fines | مواد دقائقية |
| finger guards | واقيات للأصابع |
| finger rest | مسند الإصبع |
| fingernail polishers [electric or non-electric] | وسائل لتلميع الأظافر [كهربائية أو غير كهربائية] |
| finger-stalls [office requisites] | أغطية واقية للأصابع [متطلبات مكتب] |
| fining preparation (must- -) | مستحضرات تنقية (مستحضرات لتنقية خمر الفطير) |
| finings (wine -) | مواد تنقية (مواد لتنقية الخمر) |
| finish | ينهي |
| finished caping | الغطاء النهائي |
| finishing machines | آلات صقل؛ آلات تشطيب؛ آلات إنهاء |
| finishing plate | لوح تشطيب؛ لوح إنهاء |
| finishing preparations for use in the manufacture of steel | مستحضرات صقل للاستخدام في صناعة الصلب |
| finishing unit | وحدة تشطيب؛ وحدة إنهاء |
| finite differences | فروق منتهية |
| fire (clothing for protection against -) | حريق (ملابس للحماية من الحريق) |
| fire alarms | إنذارات للحريق |
| fire bars | مزلاج للحريق |
| fire beaters | وسائل لسحق الحريق |
| fire blankets | بطانيات لإطفاء الحريق |
| fire boats | مراكب لإطفاء الحريق |
| fire box | صندوق احتراق |
| fire burrs | مثقاب |
| fire detector | كاشف حريق |
| fire engines | سيارات الإطفاء |
| fire escapes | سلم حريق |
| fire extinguishing apparatus | جهاز إطفاء الحريق |
| fire extinguishing compositions | تركيبات لإطفاء الحريق |
| fire hose | خراطيم لإطفاء الحريق |
| fire hose nozzles | فوهات خراطيم إطفاء الحريق |
| fire irons | مكاوي بالنار |
| fire power | قوة النيران |
| fire retardant material | مادة مثبطة للحريق |
| fire screens [domestic] | حاجبة النار [منزلية] |
| firearm sights | مصَّوب للسلاح الناري |
| firearms | أسلحة نارية |
| firearms (ammunition for -) | أسلحة نارية (ذخيرة للأسلحة النارية) |
| firearms (cleaning brushes for -) | أسلحة نارية (فرشاة لتنظيف الأسلحة النارية) |
| fireclay | صلصال حراري |
| firecrackers | مفرقعات نارية |
| fire-dogs [andirons] | مساند للحطب المشتعل [مناصب] |
| fireguards | حواجز النار |
| firelighters | مشاعل النار |
| firemen (asbestos screens for -) | رجال الإطفاء (حاجب من الأسبيستوس لرجال الإطفاء) |
| fireplace bellows [hand tools] | منفاخ للمستوقد [أدوات يدوية] |
| fireplaces [domestic] | مستوقد [منزلي] |
| fireproof cement coatings | طلاء من الأسمنت مقاومة للحريق |
| fireproof paints | دهانات مقاومة للحريق |
| fireproofing preparations | مستحضرات مقاومة للحريق |
| fireside additives | مواد الإضافة المعرضة للهب |
| firestones | أحجار مقاومة للحرارة |

| | |
|---|---|
| firewall | جدار النار؛ الجدار الناري |
| firewall | جدار أو نظام حماية |
| firewood | حطب الوقود |
| fireworks | ألعاب نارية |
| firing | إشعال |
| firing lanyards for explosives | حبل فتح النار للمواد المتفجرة |
| firing order | مواعيد الاشتعال |
| firing pin | إبرة ضرب النار |
| firing platforms | منصات إطلاق النار |
| firing squad | فرقة الإعدام |
| firm | يرسخ، مؤسسة، شركة، ثابت، راسخ |
| firmware | برامج ثابتة |
| firmware upgrade | تحديث البرنامج الثابت |
| first fuel line | خط وقود أول |
| first fuel tank | خزان وقود أول |
| first input | مدخل أول |
| first instance court | محكمة ابتدائية |
| first order ; first-order | من المرتبة الأولى |
| first oxidant line | خط مؤكسد أول |
| first time inventor | مخترع لأول مرة |
| first-aid boxes ; first-aid kits | صناديق الإسعافات الأولية |
| first-sale doctrine | مبدأ البيع الأول.حق المشتري لعمل فكري في إعادة تحويل ملكية العمل الفكري دون إذن من صاحبه الأصلي |
| first-sale doctrine | مبدأ البيع الأول. حق المشتري لعمل فكري في إعادة تحويل ملكية العمل الفكري دون إذن من صاحبه الأصلي |
| fish (food products made from -) | سمك (منتجات الطعام المصنوعة من السمك) |
| fish (salted -) | أسماك (أسماك مملحة) |
| fish [not live] | سمك [غير حي] |
| fish fillets | سمك منزوع العظام (طري) |
| fish hooks | خطافات للسمك |
| fish oil, not edible | زيت سمك، غير صالح للأكل |
| fish plates [rails] | لوح وصل تراكبي [السكة الحديدية] |
| fish spawn | بيض السمك |
| fish, live | سمك، حي |
| fish, preserved | أسماك، محفوظة |
| fish, tinned [canned (am.)] | أسماك، معلبة |
| fisher indole synthesis | تفاعل تخليق الإندول وفقا لفيشر |
| fisheye | عدسة عين السمكة |
| fishfinder | مستكشف السمك أو الباحث عن السمك |
| fishfinder | جهاز استكشاف السمك-الباحث عن الأسماك- مستكشف الأسماك |
| fishing (harpoons for -) | صيد السمك (رماح لصيد السمك) |
| fishing bait [live] | طعم لصيد السمك [حي] |
| fishing baskets | سلال لصيد السمك |
| fishing nets | شبكات لصيد السمك |
| fishing tackle | عدة صيد السمك |
| fishing vessels | مراكب صيد الأسماك |
| fishing vests | صديريات لصيد السمك |
| fishmeal | دقيق سمك |
| fission | يشطر، ينشطر، انشطار، انفلاق |
| fission power | انشطار طاقة |

| | |
|---|---|
| fissionable chemical elements | عناصر كيميائية قابلة للانشطار |
| fissionable material for nuclear energy | مواد قابلة للانشطار للطاقة النووية |
| fit to window | ملاءمة الإطار |
| fit with | يزود بـ |
| fitted toilet lid covers [fabric] | أكسية لأغطية المراحيض بنفس الحجم [أقمشة] |
| fittings | وصلات |
| fittings (bath -) | تركيبات (تركيبات للحمام) |
| fittings (compressed air pipe -), not of metal | تركيبات (تركيبات لماسورة الهواء المضغوط) غير مصنوعة من المعدن |
| fittings for engine boilers | تركيبات لغلايات المحرك |
| fittings of iron (harness -) | تركيبات من الحديد (تركيبات من الحديد لأطقم الفرس) |
| fittings of metal for beds | تركيبات من المعدن للأسرة |
| fittings of metal for building | تركيبات من المعدن للمباني |
| fittings of metal for coffins | تركيبات من المعدن للتوابيت |
| fittings of metal for compressed air ducts | تركيبات من المعدن لخراطيم الهواء المضغوط |
| fittings of metal for furniture | تركيبات من المعدن للأثاث |
| fittings of metal for shoes and boots | تركيبات من المعدن للأحذية العادية والأحذية ذات الرقبة |
| fittings of metal for windows | تركيبات من المعدن للنوافذ |
| fittings, not of metal (bed -) | تركيبات غير مصنوعة من المعدن [تركيبات غير مصنوعة من المعدن للسرير] |
| fittings, not of metal (coffin -) | تركيبات غير مصنوعة من المعدن (تركيبات غير مصنوعة من المعدن للتابوت) |
| fittings, not of metal (door -) | تركيبات غير مصنوعة من المعدن (تركيبات غير مصنوعة من المعدن للباب) |
| fittings, not of metal (furniture - ) | تركيبات غير مصنوعة من المعدن (تركيبات غير مصنوعة من المعدن للأثاث) |
| fittings, not of metal (window -) | تركيبات غير مصنوعة من المعدن (تركيبات غير مصنوعة من المعدن للنافذة) |
| fittings, shaped, for furnaces | تركيبات، ذات شكل، للأفران |
| fittings, shaped, for ovens | تركيبات، ذات شكل، للأفران |
| five-segment color wheel | عجلة ألوان مكونة من خمسة أجزاء |
| fixatives [varnishes] | مثبتات [ورنيش] |
| fixatives for watercolors [watercolours] | مثبتات للألوان المائية (ألوان مائية) |
| fixed bed reactor ; fixed-bed reactor | مفاعل ذي طبقة ثابتة |
| fixed fiber optic sensor network | شبكة استشعار ثابتة بألياف ضوئية |
| fixed focal length | البعد البؤري الثابت |
| fixed offset | إزاحة ثابتة |
| fixed soil | تربة ثابتة |

| | |
|---|---|
| fixing baths [photography] | مغطس تثبيت [التصوير الفوتوغرافي] |
| fixing solutions [photography] | محاليل تثبيت [التصوير الفوتوغرافي] |
| flacky or blocky crystal | بلورة قشريّة أو بلورة كتلية |
| flagpoles | صاري للعلم |
| flags [not of paper] | أعلام [غير مصنوعة من الورق] |
| flags [of paper] | أعلام [مصنوعة من الورق] |
| flakes (corn -) | رقاقات [رقاقات من القمح] |
| flakes (maize -) | رقاقات [رقاقات من الذرة] |
| flakes (oat -) | رقاقات [رقاقات من الشوفان] |
| flakes (potato -) | رقاقات [رقاقات من البطاطس] |
| flame | رسالة مشتعلة: رسالة تحريض مثيرة للآخرين |
| flame | يرسل رسالة مشتعلة |
| flame (on) | يشعل حرب البريد |
| flame atomic absorption spectroscopy | قياس الامتصاص الذري الطيفي اللهبي |
| flame deposition | ترسيب باللهب |
| flame hydrolysis | حل مائي باستخدام اللهب |
| flame retardants | مؤخرات الاحتراق |
| flame thrower | قاذفة لهب |
| flamebait | رسالة تحريض |
| flamefest | حرب ضارية |
| flamer | مشعِل حرب البريد |
| flammability | قابلية الإشعال |
| flammable solvents | مذيبات قابلة للاحتراق |
| flange | شفة |
| flange | حافة ناتئة [خاصة إذا وردت كلمة lip في نفس السياق] |
| flanges for railway wheel tires [tyres] | شفاه لإطارات عجل السكة الحديدية [إطارات] |
| flanges of metal [collars] | شفاه من المعدن [حلقات معدنية] |
| flank | الجناح؛ جناح القوات |
| flanking residues | وحدات بنائية مجانحة |
| flanking sequence | متوالية مجانحة: متوالية تعمل على انحراف/تجنيح موقع إلخ على جانب أو جانبين إلخ |
| flannel (sanitary -) | فانلات [صحية] |
| flannel [fabric] | فانلات [أنسجة] |
| flap | قلابة |
| flap | صمام قلاب |
| flapper valve | صمام قلاب |
| flare | اتساع (نحو الخارج) |
| flare stacks for use in the oil industry | مداخن متوهجة للاستخدام في صناعة البترول |
| flares | إضاءات |
| flare-up | غضب مفاجئ |
| flash charge | شحن الفلاش |
| flash chromatography | الفصل بكروماتوجراف الوميض |
| flash chromatography | كروماتوجراف وميضي |
| flash drive | قرص فلاش |
| flash drum | اسطوانة تقطير وميضي |
| flash indicator | مؤشر الفلاش |
| flash memory | ذاكرة وميضية |
| flash mode | وضع الفلاش |
| flash off | يوقف الفلاش |
| flash off | يخفض الضغط فجائيًا [في المفاعلات] |
| flash point | درجة الوميض: الدرجة الحرارية التي تشتعل عندها أبخرة المشتق النفطي |
| flash points (of reactants) | درجات الوميض (الخاصة بالمواد المتفاعلة) |
| flash standby | وضع استعداد الفلاش |
| flash unit | وحدة وميض |
| flash-bulbs [photography] | مصباح ومضي [للتصوير الفوتوغرافي] |
| flashing | تعريضها لضغط على نحو سريع |
| flashing lights [luminous signals] | ضوء ومضي (علامات مضيئة) |
| flashing of metal, for building | حشوات معدنية للمباني |
| flashing, not of metal, for building | حشوات غير مصنوعة من المعدن للمباني |
| flashlight preparations | مستحضرات صور مصباح ومضي |
| flashlights [photography] | جهاز إضاءة وماض |
| flashlights [torches] | مصابيح كهربائية [مصابيح] |
| flasks for travellers (drinking -) | قوارير للمسافرين [قوارير للمسافرين للشرب] |
| flasks of precious metal | قوارير مصنوعة من المعدن النفيس |
| flasks, not of precious metal | قوارير غير مصنوعة من المعدن النفيس |
| flat cables | كبل مسطح |
| flat commission | عمولة ثابتة |
| flat feet (supports for -) | قدم مسطحة [دعامات من أجل القدم المسطحة] |
| flat file ; flat-file | ملف نصي |
| flat irons [non-electric] | مكواة ثياب، [غير كهربائية] |
| flat irons, electric | مكواة ثياب، كهربائية |
| flat management system | نظام إدارة موحد |
| flat plate crush strength | مقاومة كسر المستوى المسطح |
| flat-bedding | التطبق المستو |
| flat-iron stands | حوامل لمكواة الثياب |
| flatulence | انتفاخ البطن الهوائي |
| flaviviridae | عائلة فيروس الصفراء |
| flavor | نكهة |
| flavorant compound | مركب مكسب للنكهة |
| flavorings for beverages [essential oils] | مكسبات النكهة للمشروبات [زيوت طيارة] |
| flavorings, other than essential oils | مكسبات النكهة، غير الزيوت الطيارة |
| flavorings, other than essential oils, for beverages | مكسبات النكهة، غير الزيوت الطيارة، للمشروبات |
| flavorings, other than essential oils, for cakes | مكسبات النكهة، غير الزيوت الطيارة للكعك |
| flavors | مكسبات النكهة |
| flavour | مادة مكسبة للنكهة؛ مادة منكهة؛ مكسب نكهة |
| flavour | نكهة |
| flavour enhancers | محسنات النكهة |
| flavourings for beverages [essential oils] | مواد منكّهة للمشروبات [زيوت طيارة] |

| | |
|---|---|
| flavourings for cakes [essential oils] | مكسبات النكهة للكعك؛ [زيوت طيارة] |
| flavourings, other than essential oils | مكسبات النكهة،غير الزيوت الطيارة |
| flavourings, other than essential oils, for beverages | مكسبات النكهة؛ غير الزيوت الطيارة للمشروبات |
| flavourings, other than essential oils, for cakes | مكسبات النكهة غير الزيوت الطيارة للكعك |
| flax | الكتان |
| flax breaker | كسارة عيدان الكتان |
| flax meal [fodder] | أطعمة من الأعشاب [علف] |
| flax seeds | بذور الكتان |
| flax straw | قش الكتان |
| fleams | مشارط |
| fledspar | الفلسبار |
| fleece wool | صوف الخراف |
| fleshing knives [hand tools] | سكاكين لنزع اللحم عن الجلد [أدوات يدوية] |
| fleshing machines | آلات لنزع اللحم عن الجلد |
| flex-fuel vehicle | مركبة الوقود المرن |
| flexible storage architecture | بنية التخزين المرن |
| flexible tubes, not of metal | أنابيب مرنة؛ غير مصنوعة من المعدن |
| flexual strenght | مقاومة انثناء |
| flexural modulous | معامل الانثناء |
| flexural strength | مقاومة الثني |
| flexuse strength | مقاومة الانحناء |
| flight (1) | طيران |
| flight (2) | رحلة |
| flight deck (1) | مقصورة الملاحين |
| flight deck (2) | ظهر حاملة الطائرات |
| flight engineer | مهندس جوي |
| flight lieutenant | نقيب طيار |
| flint | الفلنت ( الزلط |
| flint glass | زجاج رصاصي |
| flippers for swimming | زعانف للسباحة |
| float | عوم، طوف |
| float glass | زجاج عائم: زجاج شفاف يتميز بمسطحات مستوية ومتوازية بحيث توفر رؤية واضحة غير مشوهة وانعكاساً صافياً |
| float glass | زجاج عائم: زجاج شفاف يتميز بمسطحات مستوية ومتوازية بحيث توفر رؤية واضحة غير مشوهة وانعكاساً صافياً. وينتج الزجاج العائم بعملية تعويم الزجاج عند خروجه من الفرن عبر حمام من المعدن المصهور |
| floating containers of metal | حاويات عائمة مصنوعة من المعدن |
| floating containers, not of metal | حاويات عائمة غير مصنوعة من المعدن |
| floating docks of metal for mooring boats | أحواض عائمة، مصنوعة من المعدن لإرساء المراكب |
| floating docks, not of metal, for mooring boats | أحواض عائمة، غير مصنوعة من المعدن لإرساء المراكب |

| | |
|---|---|
| floating licensing | ترخيص عائم |
| floats for bathing and swimming | عوامات للاستحمام والسباحة |
| floats for fishing | عوامات للصيد |
| flocculants | مادة الفلوكيولانت (تؤدي إلى التجلط) |
| flock (silk -) | خصلات (خصلات من الحرير) |
| flock (wool -) | خصلات [خصلات من الصوف] |
| flock [stuffing] | خصلات [للحشو] |
| flood | يستطرد (في غرف المحادثة) |
| flood | يغمر |
| flood | يحقن؛ يشبع؛ يغمر: مثل يحقن بالبخار steam flood |
| flooding | الغمر |
| floopy disk | قرص مرن |
| floor | أرضية |
| floor boards (parquet -) | ألواح أرضية [باركيه للأرضية] |
| floor coverings | أغطية للأرضية |
| floor manager | مدير الاستوديو |
| floor tiles, not of metal | بلاطات للأرضية غير مصنوعة من المعدن |
| floor tiles, of metal | بلاطات للأرضية من المعدن |
| floor wax | شمع الأرضية |
| floor wax removers [scouring preparations] | مواد لإزالة شمع الأرضية [مستحضرات للجلي] |
| flooring (parquet -) | أرضيات (باركيه للأرضية) |
| floors of metal | أرضيات مصنوعة من المعدن |
| floors, not of metal | أرضيات غير مصنوعة من المعدن |
| floppy disks | أقراص مرنة |
| flora | بكتيريا طبيعية: توجد في الجسم ومفيدة له |
| floss | مشاقة قطن؛ مشاقة الحرير |
| floss for dental purposes | خيط ناعم للأغراض المتعلقة بالأسنان |
| flounces (skirt -) | أهداب (أطراف التنورة) |
| flour for food | دقيق للطعام |
| flour mill machines | آلات طحن الدقيق |
| flour mills | مطاحن الغلال |
| flour mills | طواحين للدقيق |
| flourinated ethylene-propylene copolymers | بوليمرات مشتركة من البروبيلين والإثيلين تحتوي على الفلور |
| flour-milling products | منتجات من الدقيق المطحون |
| flow | تدفق (ج تدفقات) |
| flow balancing means | وسيلة موازنة تدفق |
| flow control | التحكم في التدفق |
| flow control valve | صمام للتحكم في التدفق |
| flow diagram | مخطط سير عمليات؛ مخطط انسيابي |
| flow diverter | حارف تدفق؛ مفرِّع تدفق |
| flow enriched with components | تدفق غني بالمكونات |
| flow impaired well | بئر يعاني من خلل التدفق؛ بئر مختل التدفق؛ الحفر تحت ضغط اقل من ضغط البئر |
| flow of farm processes | تعاقب العمليات الزراعية |
| flow of gas | تدفق غازي |
| flow sheet | كشف بالعمليات المتتابعة |
| flow slugging | التدفق التتابعي |
| flow stream | تيار التدفق |

| | |
|---|---|
| flowback; flow-back; flow back | تدفق عكسي |
| flowchart ; flow chart | مخطط سير عمليات؛ مخطط انسيابي |
| flower arrangements (foam supports for -) [semi-finished products] | مجموعات منسقة من الأزهار (دعامات للمجموعات المنسقة من الأزهار) [منتجات شبه مكتملة] |
| flower bulbs | بصيلات الأزهار |
| flower perfumes (bases for -) | عطور من الأزهار (مواد قاعدية للعطور المأخوذة من الأزهار) |
| flower pots | قدور للأزهار |
| flower preservatives | مواد حافظة للأزهار |
| flowering plants | نباتات مزهرة |
| flower-pot covers of paper | أغطية لقدور الأزهار مصنوعة من الورق |
| flower-pot covers, not of paper | أغطية لقدور الأزهار، غير مصنوعة من الورق |
| flower-pot pedestals | قواعد معدنية لقدور الأزهار |
| flowers (artificial -) | أزهار، (أزهار صناعية) |
| flowers (extracts of -) [perfumes] | أزهار (مستخلصات من الأزهار) [عطور] |
| flowers (wreaths of artificial -) | أزهار (أكاليل من الأزهار الصناعية) |
| flowers (wreaths of natural -) | أزهار (أكاليل من الأزهار الطبيعية) |
| flowers, dried, for decoration | أزهار مجففة، للزينة |
| flowers, natural | أزهار طبيعية |
| flower-stands [furniture] | حوامل للأزهار [أثاث] |
| flow-through | تدفق نافذ |
| fluctuation | تذبذب؛ تقلب |
| flue | مصرف غازات |
| flue gas | غاز المداخن |
| flue gases | غازاتُ الاِحْتِراق |
| flues (chimney -) | مداخن [مداخن المستوقد] |
| flues for engine boilers | مداخن لغلايات المحرك |
| flues for heating boilers | مداخن لغلايات التسخين |
| fluid | مائع |
| fluid | سائل |
| fluid (power steering -) | مائع (زيت مؤازر القيادة) |
| fluid (transmission -) | مائع (مائع لنقل الحركة) |
| fluid bed | ذو الطبقة المتميعة |
| fluid bed catalytic cracking (fcc) | التكسير الحفزي في وجود طبقة متميعة |
| fluid catalytic cracking | التكسير الحفزي لمائع |
| fluid communication ; fluid connection | اتصال عن طريق المائع |
| fluid diversion | تحويل مائع |
| fluid dynamics | ديناميات السوائل |
| fluid expander | ممدد المائع |
| fluid flow regulator | منظم لتدفق سائل |
| fluid front propagation | الانتشار الأمامي للسائل |
| fluid separation assembly | مجمع فصل الموائع |
| fluidicly | عن طريق مائع |
| fluidics | مائعيات |
| fluidize | يسيل |
| fluidized | مسال |
| fluidized bed | طبقة متميعة؛ طبقة مميعة |
| fluidized bed reactor | مفاعل طبقة متميعة |

| | |
|---|---|
| fluidized catalytic cracking | التكسير الحفزي في وجود طبقة متميعة |
| fluidized solid | صلب مسال |
| fluidly | عن طريق المائع |
| fluids (brake -) | مائع (مائع للفرامل "الكابح") |
| fluids (cutting -) | مائع (مائع القطع) |
| fluids for hydraulic circuits | مائع للدوائر الهيدروليكية |
| fluids for use with abrasives (auxiliary -) | مائع للاستخدام مع المواد الحاكة (مائع مساعدة للاستخدام مع المواد الحاكة) |
| fluoren | فلور |
| fluorescence | الفلورة |
| fluorescence flow cytometry | تعداد الخلايا بالتدفق الفلوري |
| fluorescence intensity | شدة الفلورة |
| fluorescent | وميضي؛ وامض؛ مضئ |
| fluorescent | فلوري |
| fluorescent materials | مواد فلورية |
| fluorescent materials | المواد الوامضة |
| fluorescent screens | شاشات فلورية (فلورسنت) |
| fluorescers | ملونات وميضية |
| fluoride glass | زجاج فلوريد |
| fluoriding agent | عامل لإضافة فلوريد |
| fluoriding agent | عامل إضافة فلوريد؛ عامل معالجة بالفلوريد |
| fluorin | فلور |
| fluorinated products | نواتج تحتوي على الفلور |
| fluorine | فلور |
| fluorine doped tin oxide | أكسيد قصدير مشاب بالفلور |
| fluorochromes | ملونات تألقية |
| fluoroorgano boron compound | مركب بورون فلورو عضوي |
| fluorophore-assisted carbohydrate electrophoresis (face) | الإشراد الكهربائي للكربوهيدرات بمساعدة حاملات التألق |
| fluorophores | حاملات التألق |
| fluoropolymer | بوليمر فلورو |
| fluorouracil | فلورويوراسيل |
| fluorspar compounds | مركبات فلوريد الكالسيوم البلوري |
| flush | غسل |
| flush gas | غاز غسيل |
| flush mounted | يتم تركيبها في نفس المستوى |
| flush with = coplanar with | يقع في نفس المستوى |
| flushable | قابل للغسل بالدفق |
| flushing | تنظيم استخدام الذاكرة |
| flushing apparatus | جهاز غسيل بالدفق |
| flushing tanks | خزانات للدفق |
| flutes | فلوت (أداة موسيقية) |
| flutes (bamboo -) | فلوت (فلوت من الخيزران) |
| flux | يذيب، يسيل، يذوب، تدفق، دفق، الصهور، مادة مساعدة على صهر المعادن؛ مساعد صهر؛ دفق؛ |
| flux normalized at | دفق تمت معادلته عند |
| fluxes (brazing -) | مصهور لحام (مصهور للحام بالنحاس الأصفر) |
| fluxes (soldering -) | مصهور لحام (مصهور للحام بالقصدير) |
| fly ash | رماد متطاير |

| | |
|---|---|
| fly ash | الرماد المتطاير |
| fly catchers [traps or whisks] | صائد الذباب [مصيدة أو صاعقة الحشرات] |
| fly catching adhesives | مواد لاصقة لصيد الذباب |
| fly catching paper | ورق لصيد الذباب |
| fly destroying preparations | مستحضرات للقضاء على الذباب |
| fly glue | صمغ للذباب |
| fly swatters | مضارب للذباب |
| flyer | منشور يرفق بالمجلة أو الصحيفة |
| flying discs [toys] | أقراص طائرة [ألعاب] |
| flying robot | روبوت طائر |
| flyiong officer | ملازم أول طيار |
| flywheel energy storage | مخزن طاقة دولاب الموازنة |
| fly-wheels (machine -) | عجل تنظيم السرعة [عجل تنظيم السرعة للآلة] |
| fm | فمتو مولار |
| fmol | فمتو مول |
| fms | متلازمة الألم العضلي الليفي |
| foam | مادة رغوية |
| foam cell | خلية رغوية |
| foam supports for flower arrangements [semi-finished products] | دعامات رغوية لتنسيق الأزهار [منتجات شبه مكتملة] |
| foaming | تكوين رغاوي |
| focal depth | العمق البؤري |
| focus | البؤرة |
| focus groups | فئة نموذجية |
| focus indicator | مؤشر البؤرة |
| focus lock | قفل البؤرة |
| focus pri | أولوية ضبط البؤرة |
| focus ring | حلقة البؤرة |
| focus ring | حلقة الضبط البؤري |
| focused thinking | تفكير مركز |
| focusing frame | إطار ضبط البؤرة |
| focusing mode | وضع ضبط البؤرة |
| focusing point | نقطة البؤرة |
| focusing system | نظم ضبط البؤرة |
| fodder | علف |
| fodder (additives to -) | علف (مواد إضافية للعلف) |
| fodder milk | لبن لتغذية الحيوان |
| fodder presses | آلات ضغط العلف |
| fodder rack | معلف |
| fog signals, explosive | إشارات متفجرة للضباب |
| fog signals, non-explosive | إشارات غير متفجرة للضباب |
| foil | رقيقة (معدنية) |
| foil (aluminium -) | رقاقات (رقاقات من الألومنيوم) |
| foil (metal -) for painters, decorators, printers and artists | رقاقات (رقاقات من المعدن) للرسامين والمزخرفين والطباعين والفنانين |
| foil (silver -) [leaf] | رقاقات (رقاقات من الفضة) [صحائف] |
| foil of regenerated cellulose, other than for packing | رقاقات من السليولوز المعاد تصنيعه غير المستخدمة في التغليف |
| foils for fencing | رقاقات معدنية للسياجات |
| foils of metal for insulating | رقاقات من المعدن للعزل |
| foils of metal for wrapping and packaging | رقاقات من المعدن للتغليف والتعبئة |
| fold | طية |
| fold | يطوي |
| fold breccia | رواهص الطيات |
| fold potency | فاعلية مضاعفة |
| folder | مجلد |
| folder | وسيلة طي (في مجال الطباعة، والصناعة) |
| folders [stationery] | حافظات أوراق [أدوات مكتبية] |
| folders area | منطقة المجلدات |
| folders for papers | حافظات للأوراق |
| folding doors, not of metal | أبواب قابلة للطي، غير معدنية |
| folding of protein, etc. | طي |
| folds zigzag | الثنيات الملتوية |
| foliage | أوراق |
| foliar application | للاستخدام مع أوراق النبات |
| foliate | ورقي الشكل |
| foliolate | مؤلف من ورقيات |
| folk literature | أدب شعبي. يعد الأدب الشعبي من بين المواد المتمخضة عن المعارف التقليدية والتراثية التي تسعى المجتمعات والشعوب التقليدية إلى توفير حماية لها بموجب الحماية المقررة للمنتجات التقليدية والتراثية. |
| follicular dendritic cells | الخلايا التغضنية الجريبية |
| follow from | ينتج من |
| follow up | يرد (على رسالة) |
| follow up | يتابع |
| follow-on innovation | ابتكار لاحق. ابتكار لاحق على ابتكار سابق |
| follow-up | رد |
| follow-up | متابعة |
| follow-up line | سطر الرد |
| follow-up milk | لبن الفطام |
| fondants [confectionery] | فندان [حلويات] |
| food (pet -) | أطعمة (أطعمة للحيوانات الأليفة) |
| food analysis apparatus | جهاز تحليل الطعام |
| food and agriculture organization, fao | منظمة الأغذية والزراعة |
| food colorants | مواد لتلوين الأطعمة |
| food cooling devices | وسائل لتبريد الأطعمة |
| food crops | محاصيل غذائية |
| food dyes | صبغات للأطعمة |
| food for babies | أطعمة للأطفال الرضع |
| food grade | فئة غذائية |
| food industries | الصناعات الغذائية |
| food preparation machines, electromechanical | آلات لتحضير الطعام، كهروميكانيكية |
| food processors [electric] | أجهزة معالجة الأطعمة (كهربائية) |
| food stamps | بطاقات صرف الطعام |
| food sterilization | تعقيم الطعام |
| food technology | تقنية طعام |
| food, drug and cosmetic colors (fd&c) | ملوّنات الأطعمة والعقاقير ومستحضرات التجميل |
| foodprocessor | كبة |
| foods (farinaceous -) | أطعمة (أطعمة نشوية) |
| foods prepared from fish | أطعمة معدة من السمك |

| | |
|---|---|
| foodstuffs (animal -) | مواد غذائية (مواد غذائية للحيوانات) |
| foodstuffs (chemical substances for preserving -) | مواد غذائية (مواد كيميائية لحفظ المواد الغذائية) |
| foodstuffs (decorations of plastic for -) | مواد غذائية (زينة من البلاستيك للمواد الغذائية) |
| foodstuffs (essences for -) [except etheric essences and essential oils] | مواد غذائية (مواد مستخلصة للمواد الغذائية) [ما عدا المواد المستخلصة من الإتير والزيوت الطيارة] |
| foot | قدم |
| foot and mouth virus disease | مرض الحمى القلاعية |
| foot perspiration (remedies for -) | عرق القدمين (علاج لعرق القدمين) |
| foot perspiration (soap for -) | عرق القدمين (صابون لعرق القدمين) |
| foot scrapers | مكشطة للقدم |
| footage | طول الفيلم |
| football (tables for indoor -) | كرة قدم (مناضد لكرة القدم الداخلية) |
| football boots | أحذية ذات رقبة لكرة القدم |
| football boots [shoes] (studs for -) | أحذية ذات رقبة لكرة القدم [أحذية] (نتوءات لأحذية كرة القدم ذات الرقبة) |
| football shoes | أحذية لكرة القدم |
| foothold | موطئ لقدم |
| footing | أساس؛ قاعدة |
| footmuffs, electrically heated | مدفئ (دفايات) للقدمين يعمل بالكهرباء |
| footmuffs, not electrically heated | مدفئ (دفايات) للقدمين لا يعمل بالكهرباء |
| footpad | باطن القدم |
| footprint | آثار |
| footprint | حيز الإشغال |
| foots oil | زيت القاع |
| footstools | مساند للقدمين |
| footwarmers [electric or non-electric] | مدفئ للقدمين [كهربائية أو غير كهربائية] |
| footway | رصيف المشاة |
| footwear | ألبسة قدم |
| footwear (brushes for -) | ألبسة قدم (فرشاه لألبسة القدم) |
| footwear (orthopaedic [orthopedic] -) | ألبسة قدم (ألبسة قدم تقويمية) |
| footwear (tips for -) | ألبسة قدم (زينة لألبسة القدم) |
| footwear uppers | الأجزاء العلوية من ألبسة القدم |
| for a given purpose | لغرض معين |
| for household purposes | للأغراض المنزلية |
| for prolonged administration | للإعطاء الممتد |
| for pulsed administration | للإعطاء النبضي |
| for servicing purposes | لأغراض الصيانة |
| for timed administration | للإعطاء الموقوت |
| forage | علف |
| forage drying apparatus | جهاز تجفيف العلف |
| force | يجبر، قوة |
| force majeur | قوة قاهرة |
| force majeure clause | بند القوة القاهرة. بند تعاقدي يبين كيفية التعامل في حالة حصول حدث من أحداث القوة القاهرة |
| forced draft evaporative towers | أبراج تبخير ذات سحب قسري |
| forced imbibition | تشرب قسري |
| force-field analysis | تحليل القوى الميدانية |
| forceps | ملاقط |
| forcola | الفوركولا: مسند المجداف |
| foreground | المقدمة |
| foreign filing | الإيداع بالخارج. إيداع طلب عن البراءة بأي بلد أجنبي. |
| foreign arbitral award | حكم تحكيم أجنبي |
| foreign patent | براءة أجنبية |
| foreign patent documents | مستندات براءة أجنبية |
| foreign sovereign immunities act | قانون حصانات السيادة الأجنبية |
| foreman | رئيس المحلفين |
| forensic engineering | هندسة طب شرعي |
| forensic medicine | الطب الشرعي |
| forestry (chemicals for -), except fungicides, herbicides, insecticides and parasiticides | الغابات (كيماويات للغابات) ما عدا مبيدات الفطريات ومبيدات الأعشاب ومبيدات الحشرات ومبيدات الطفيليات |
| forge a charge | يلفق تهمة |
| forge bellows | منفاخ الكير |
| forged | مشكَّل بالطرق |
| forges, portable | مصهر معادن، يمكن حمله |
| fork lift | ونش شوكة (كلارك ) |
| fork lift trucks | شاحنات بونش شوكة |
| fork lifts | رافعات شوكية: يتم تزويد عربات الرفع أو المقطورات بها |
| forklift tines | شوكات بمرفاع شوكي |
| forks | شِوَك |
| form | يكوّن |
| form | يشكل، يصوغ، ينشئ، شكل، صيغة، أنموذج |
| form factor ; form-factor | معامل الشكل |
| formal drawings | رسومات رسمية |
| formamide | فورماميد |
| format | يصيغ (صيغة كيميائية) |
| format (disk etc.) | يهيئ (قرصا إلخ) |
| formate | فورمات |
| formation | تكوين |
| formation brine | محلول ملحي من التكوين |
| formation fluid | مائع التكوين |
| formation of a cyclic phosphonate 1,3-propanediol ester | تكوين إستر فوسفونات حلقي لمركب 1، 3 - بروبان دايول |
| formations and units (ground troops) | التشكيلات والوحدات (للقوات البرية) |
| formats | صور؛ هيئات |
| formatted ligand | مركب ترابطي تمت صياغته |
| formatter | محول |
| formic acid | حمض فورميك |
| formic aldehyde | فورميك الديهيد |
| forms | نماذج |
| forms [printed] | نماذج [مطبوعة] |

| | |
|---|---|
| formualte | يصيغ (صيغة كيميائية) |
| formualtion resistent to alcohol extraction of opioid | الاستخلاص الكحولي لشبيه الأفيون |
| formulate | يصيغ |
| formulation | صياغة (مصدر يصيغ) |
| formulation in intact form | صيغة في صورة سليمة |
| formulations | صيغ |
| formwork | قالب الصب |
| fortran | لغة فورتران: لغة برمجة |
| fortune cookie | كعكة الحظ |
| forum | منتدى |
| forum rules of etiquette | آداب المشاركة في المنتديات؛ الآداب المرعية في المنتديات؛ قواعد المشاركة في المنتديات |
| forward ( a message ) | يرحّل؛ يعيد توجيه (رسالة) |
| forward link | وصلة أمامية |
| forward link ; downlink | التردد الصاعد |
| forward link transmission | إرسال على الوصلة الأمامية |
| forward reaction | تفاعل مباشر |
| forward sequence | متوالية أمامية |
| forward slash | الشرطة المائلة للأمام |
| fosamprenavir | فوسامبرينافير |
| fossil | حفري |
| fossil | حفرية |
| fossil fuel | وقود حفري |
| foster care | رعاية أسرية بديلة مؤقتة |
| foul | يوسّخ؛ يلوّث |
| fouling | اتساخ؛ تكوين أوساخ؛ توسيخ |
| fouling of refinery feedstocks | الاتساخ بخامات تغذية التكرير |
| found analysis | التحليل العملي |
| foundation aid | المعونة المالية الأساسية |
| foundation level | المستوى الأساسي |
| foundation spending | الإنفاق الأساسي |
| foundations for beehives | أساسات لخلايا النحل |
| foundry | مصهر |
| foundry ladles [hand tools] | مغارف سبك [أدوات يدوية] |
| foundry machines | آلات سبك |
| foundry molding [moulding] preparations | مستحضرات تشكيل بالسبك |
| foundry molds [moulds] of metal | قوالب المسبك، مصنوعة من المعدن |
| foundry molds [moulds], not of metal | قوالب المسبك، غير مصنوعة من المعدن |
| foundry sand | رمل المسبك |
| fountain pens | أقلام حبر |
| fountains | نافورات |
| fountains (ornamental -) | نافورات (نافورات للزينة) |
| four different clock-like orientations | الاتجاهات الأربع المختلفة المنتظمة |
| four-component ugi reaction | تفاعل UGI من أربع مكونات |
| fourier transform infrared (ftir) spectrum | طيف تحويل فوريه بالأشعة تحت الحمراء (FTIR) |
| fourier transform infra-red spectrometer (ftir) | جهاز طيف فورير تحت الحمراء |
| four-stroke engine | محرك رباعي الأشواط |

| | |
|---|---|
| fourth-rank (order) | الدرجة الرابعة |
| four-way valve | صمام ذو أربع وجهات |
| four-wheeled vehicle | مركبة ذات أربع عجلات |
| fpga | مصفوفة بوابات لها حقول قابلة للبرمجة |
| fqa, frequently asked questions. | الأسئلة المتكررة |
| frac fluid = fracture fluid | مائع تكسير |
| frac water | جزء الماء |
| fraction | جزء |
| fractional | تجزيئي |
| fractional aircraft ownership | ملكية جزئية للطائرات |
| fractional crystallisation | بلورة تجزيئية |
| fractional crystallization. ... | التبلور التجزيئي |
| fractional distillation | تقطير تجزيئي |
| fractionally distilled | تقطير على أجزاء |
| fractionation | تجزئة |
| fractionation | تقطير تجزيئي أو تجزئة |
| fractionator | مجزئ (برج أو عمود تجزئة) |
| fracture | صدع (في الجيولوجيا، الصخور إلخ) |
| fracture gradient | درجة ميل الصدع |
| fracture network | شبكة التصدع |
| fracture porosity | مسامية المكاسر |
| fracture pressure | الضغط الصدعي |
| fracturing | تصدع |
| fragile | سهل للكسر |
| fragment | شظية: لكل شظية نهايتان ends or termini |
| fragment | جزء |
| fragment | شظية، كسرة |
| fragmented patent landscape | تعبير يطلق على حالة تبعثر البراءات التي يفترض أن تكون مرتبطة ببعضها وعدم توحيدها |
| fragmenting ; fragmentation | تكوين شظيات |
| fragmenting ; fragmentation | تجزئة؛ تقسيم (إلى أجزاء) |
| fragments | شظيات: أجزاء؛ قطع |
| frame | إطار |
| frame relay | طبقة الإطار |
| frame ware ; frameware | إطار |
| frames (embroidery -) | إطارات (إطارات مطرزة) |
| frames (handbag -) | إطارات (إطارات للحقائب اليدوية) |
| frames (hat -) [skeletons] | إطارات (إطارات للقبعات) [هياكل] |
| frames (picture -) | إطارات (إطارات للصور ) |
| frames for bicycles, cycles | إطارات للدراجات |
| frames for handsaws | إطارات للمنشار اليدوي |
| frames for photographic transparencies | إطارات للأفلام الشفافة للصور الضوئية |
| frames for umbrellas or parasols | إطارات للشماسي أو المظلات |
| frames of metal for building | إطارات من المعدن للمباني |
| framework | إطار؛ هيكل |
| framework of metal for building | هياكل للمباني من المعدن |

| | |
|---|---|
| framework of metal for ovens | هياكل للأفران من المعدن |
| framework regions (“frs”) | مناطق إطار (“FRs”) |
| framework variable domain sequence | متوالية نطاق متغير لإطار |
| framework, not of metal, for building | هياكل للمباني غير معدنية |
| frameworks | شدات أو سقالات |
| framing | تشكيل هيكلي |
| franchisability | قابلية الشيء لأن يكون محلا لامتياز |
| franchisable | قابل أن يُمنح فرانشايز |
| franchisable business | عمل تجاري يمكن منح امتياز عنه |
| franchisable business model | نموذج تجاري يسمح بمنح ترخيص امتياز |
| franchise | امتياز |
| franchise advice | مشورة بشأن امتياز |
| franchise agreement | اتفاق لمنح امتياز |
| franchise brokerage | وساطة امتياز |
| franchise disclosure agreement | اتفاق إفصاح متصل بمنح امتياز |
| franchise exclusivity | حصرية امتياز |
| franchise feasibility | جدوى امتياز |
| franchise knowhow | دراية الكيفية في مجال الامتياز |
| franchise territory | إقليم الامتياز |
| franchising negotiations | مفاوضات منح الامتياز. مفاوضات تجري بين طرفين بشأن قيام أحدهما منح الآخر امتيازا |
| franchisor-franchizee relationship | علاقة مانح الامتياز بالحاصل على الامتياز |
| franchizability of a business concept | قابلية المفهوم التجاري لأن يكون محلا لامتياز |
| francium | فرنسيوم |
| frangible | سهل الكسر |
| franking (apparatus to check -) | ختم الرسائل (جهاز لفحص ختم الرسائل) |
| franking machines [stamping machines] | آلات لختم الرسائل (آلات لوضع الطوابع) |
| frat house | بيت الإخاء والتآخي |
| fraud | النصب والاحتيال |
| fraud | خداع، احتيال، حيلة، دجال |
| fraudsters | المزورين |
| fraudulence | خداع، احتيال |
| fraudulent | خدعي، داعي، احتيالي |
| fraudulent patent procurement | شراء براءة احتيالي |
| fraught | مفعم، مشبع، مملوء |
| free base | يحول إلى قاعدة حرة |
| free cell | خلية حرة |
| free cysteine amino acid | حمض السيستين الأميني الحر |
| free end | طرف طليق |
| free flowing extended release matrix formulations | صيغ قالب التدفق الحر ذات الإطلاق الممتد |
| free license | ترخيص مجاني |
| free patent documents | مستندات براءة مجانية. وثائق براءة يمكن الاطلاع عليها مجانا. |
| free perl module installations | إعداد مركبات لغة بيرل |
| free quote | عرض اسـعار مجاني ،عرض أسعار غـير ملزم |
| free radical | شق حر |
| free software | برنامج حر |
| free software foundation | مؤسسة البرامج المجانية |
| free space | حيز خالي |
| free surface | سطح حر؛ سطح طليق |
| free water | ماء حر |
| freebased | حر القاعدة |
| free-fall | يهبط تلقائيا |
| free-flowing ; free flowing | حر التدفق |
| freelance web designer | مصمم شبكي مستقل |
| free-net | شبكة مجانية |
| freestyle race | سباق حر |
| freeware | مجاني |
| freeware | برنامج مجاني |
| freewheels for land vehicles | عجلات حرة للمركبات الأرضية |
| freewheels other than for land vehicles | عجلات حرة لغير المركبات الأرضية |
| freeze-drying | تجفيف بالتبريد |
| freezers | حجرات تجميد |
| freezing wages, to increase wages, allowences, bonus, | تجميد الأجور، زيادة الأجور، البدلات (بدل)، العلاوات |
| french curves | مساطر لرسم المنحنى |
| frequency | تردد |
| frequency curve | منحنى التواتر |
| frequency division multiple access (fdma) system | نظام الوصول المتعدد بتقسيم التردد FDMA |
| frequency hopping | قفز التردد (وثب التردد؛ تغير التردد): الإشارات تنتقل بسرعة من تردد إلى آخر |
| frequency meters | أدوات قياس التردد |
| frequency of plugging | تكرار الانسداد (في خط النقل إلخ) |
| frequency response | الاستجابة الترددية |
| frequency selective fading | خفوت انتقائي ترددي |
| frequency subbands | نطاقات تردد فرعية |
| fresh | جديد |
| fresh feed | مادة تغذية جديدة |
| fresh weight (fw) | الوزن الرطب |
| freshet | سيل؛ طوفان؛ فيض؛ مجرى |
| friable | سهل الانسحاق |
| fricative | احتكاكي |
| friction | حك، فرك |
| friction lighters for igniting gas | قداحات بالاحتكاك لإشعال الغاز |
| frictional | احتكاكي |
| frictional loss | فقد احتكاكي |
| friendly company | شركة صديقة |
| friendly environment | بيئه مناسبه لظروف ما |
| friendly invention | اختراع صديق |
| friendly technology | تقنية صديقة |
| friesian | أبقار الفريزيان |
| frieze [cloth] | أنسجة صوفية غليظة [ملابس] |
| friezing machines | آلات لعمل النسيج الصوفي الغليظ |
| frigate | فرقاطة |
| frill | يُكَشْكِش؛ يهدب |

| | |
|---|---|
| frills [lacework] | كشكشة (أعمال مخرمات) |
| frills for clothing | كشكشة للملابس |
| fringe | شيء إضافي أو ثانوي |
| fringe minority | قلة لا تُذكَر |
| fringes | حواف بارزة (شراشيب القماش) |
| fritting the infrastructure | فريتة البنية الأساسية |
| frizzled proteins | بروتينات Frizzled |
| frocks | عباءات |
| from grades k-12 | مرحلة رياض الأطفال وحتى المرحلة الثانوية |
| from optically active starting materials, or by stereoselective synthesis | من مواد بدء نشطة ضوئيا أو بواسطة تخليق انتقائي فراغي |
| from the inlet 82 to the outlet 86 of the conduit 80 | من المدخل 82 إلى المخرج 87 لقناة التوصيل 80 |
| front line states | دول المواجهة |
| frontal and sub-cortical dementias | العته الجبهي وتحت القشرة |
| front-end | أمامي |
| front-end | طرف أمامي |
| frontier | حدّ |
| frontotemporal | جبهي صدعي |
| frostbite salve | مرهم ملطف للضرر الناتج عن الصقيع |
| frosted fruits | فواكه مجمدة |
| frosting chemicals (glass -) | كيماويات للصنفرة (كيماويات لصنفرة للزجاج) |
| frosty | بارد جدا، مكسو بالصعيق |
| froth | زبد |
| frozen fruits | فواكه مثلجة |
| frozen water | ماء مثلج |
| frozen yoghurt [confectionery ices] | لبن زبادي مثلج [حلويات مثلجة] |
| fruit (alcoholic beverages containing -) | فاكهة(مشروبات كحولية تحتوى على فاكهة) |
| fruit (artificial -) | فاكهة (فاكهة صناعية) |
| fruit (hormones for hastening the ripening of -) | فاكهة (هرمونات لتعجيل نضوج الفاكهة) |
| fruit chips | رقاقات من الفاكهة |
| fruit cups | أكواب للفاكهة |
| fruit extracts (non-alcoholic -) | مستخلصات من الفاكهة [غير كحولية] |
| fruit extracts [alcoholic] | مستخلصات من الفاكهة [كحولية] |
| fruit fly | ذبابة الفاكهة |
| fruit jellies | جيلي الفاكهة |
| fruit jellies [confectionery] | جيلى الفاكهة [حلويات] |
| fruit juice beverages (non-alcoholic -) | مشروبات من عصير الفاكهة [غير كحولية] |
| fruit juices | عصائر فاكهة |
| fruit nectars [non-alcoholic] | رحيق الفاكهة [غير كحولي] |
| fruit peel | قشر الفاكهة |
| fruit pickers [hand tools] | وسائل قطف الفاكهة [أدوات يدوية] |
| fruit preserved in alcohol | فاكهة محفوظة في الكحول |
| fruit presses, electric, for household purposes | وسائل كهربائية لضغط الفاكهة، للأغراض المنزلية |
| fruit pulp | لب الفاكهة |
| fruit residue [marc] | بقايا الفاكهة [تفل الفاكهة المعصورة] |
| fruit roasters | جهاز تحميص الفاكهة |
| fruit salads | سلطة الفاكهة |
| fruit, fresh | فاكهة طازجة |
| fruit, preserved | فاكهة محفوظة |
| fruit, stewed | فاكهة مطهوة ببطء (يخنه الفاكهة) |
| fruits (crystallized -) | فاكهة [فاكهة مبلورة] |
| fruits (frosted -) | فاكهة [فاكهة مجمدة] |
| fruits, tinned [canned (am.)] | فاكهة، معلبة |
| frusto conical ; frustoconical ; frusto-conical | مخروطي ناقص |
| frustoconical portion | جزء على هيئة مخروط ناقص |
| frustoconically shaped | على شكل مخروطي ناقص |
| frustum of a cone | مخروط ناقص |
| frying pans | مقلاة |
| fsk | تعديل تبديل التردد |
| ft | أقدام / قدم |
| ft | الزجاج المسقي بالكامل |
| ft./min. (feet/minute) | قدم/دقيقة |
| ft.-lbs ; ft/lbs | قدم لكل رطل |
| ft/min | قدم بالدقيقة |
| ftir spectrometer | جهاز قياس الطيف FTIR |
| ftpmail | بريد بروتوكول نقل الملفات |
| fucosylated antibodies | الأجسام المضادة التي تمت إضافة فيوكوز إليها |
| fuel | وقود |
| fuel api | درجة نقاء الوقود, نقاوة الوقود |
| fuel cell | خلية وقود |
| fuel cell stack | مجموعة خلية وقود |
| fuel cell system | نظام خلية وقود |
| fuel cell system reformer | وحدة إعادة تشكيل |
| fuel cell van | شاحنة بخلية وقود؛ شاحنة ذات خلية وقود |
| fuel cells | خلايا وقودية |
| fuel conversion apparatus for internal combustion engines | جهاز تحويل الوقود لمحركات الاحتراق الداخلي |
| fuel dispensing pumps for service stations | مضخات توزيع الوقود لمحطات الخدمة |
| fuel economisers | مقتصد الوقود |
| fuel economisers for motors and engines | مقتصد الوقود للموتور والمحركات |
| fuel economy | اقتصاد مرتكز على الوقود |
| fuel efficiency | فعالية الوقود |
| fuel feeder | مغذي وقود |
| fuel for atomic piles | وقود للمفاعلات الذرية |
| fuel gas | غاز الوقود |
| fuel injector | حاقن الوقود |
| fuel mixtures (vaporized -) | خليط من الوقود (خليط من الوقود يتحول إلى بخار) |
| fuel oil | زيت وقود |
| fuel oil | زيت وقود؛ نفط وقود |
| fuel pumps (self-regulating -) | مضخات وقود (مضخات وقود ذاتية التنظيم) |
| fuel tank | خزان وقود |
| fuel with an alcoholic base | وقود له قاعدة كحولية |
| fuel-injection technology | تقنية حقن الوقود |

| | |
|---|---|
| fuel-saving preparations | مستحضرات لتوفير الوقود |
| fulfillment | خدمات تعبئة وشحن أو توصيل للمستهلك |
| full cream | دسم كامل |
| full disclosure | إفصاح كامل |
| full duplex | مزدوج |
| full operational audit & ufw study | مراجعة الاجراءات التشغيلية ودراسة المياه غير المحاسب عليها |
| full time inventor | مخترع يستغرق الاختراع كل وقته |
| fullers [hand tools] | محزاز [أدوات يدوية] |
| fuller's earth for use in textile industry | تراب القصار للاستخدام في صناعة الأقمشة |
| fulling preparations | مستحضرات قصر |
| fulling preparations for use in textile industry | مستحضرات قصر للاستخدام في صناعة الأقمشة |
| fulling tools [hand tools] | أدوات للقصر [أدوات يدوية] |
| full-spec | كامل الخصائص أو المواصفات |
| fully charged | مشحون بالكامل |
| fully closed position | وضع الإغلاق التام |
| fully de-glycosylated | غير مرتبط بالجليكوزيل كليا |
| fully glycosylated | مرتبط بالجليكوزيل كليا |
| fully open position | وضع الفتح التام |
| fully qualified domain name, fqdn | اسم مجال كامل |
| fully retracted position | وضع الانكماش التام |
| fully stoichiometric | المتكافئ تماما |
| fully tempered glass (ft) | زجاج مقسي بالكامل: زجاج تصل صلابته إلى خمس أضعاف الزجاج الملدن، وعند حدوث كسر يتناثر إلى شظايا صغيرة على شكل مكعبات. وهو من النوع الذي يستخدم بوجه عام في أعمال التزجيج التي تحتاج إلى متانة عالية وفي زجاج السلامة الذي يستخدم في الأبواب وجدران المراوش. |
| fully-fledged | كامل المواصفات |
| fumed silica | سيليكا مدخنة |
| fumes | أبخرة |
| fumigating pastilles | كرات التبخير |
| fumigating sticks | أعواد التبخير |
| fumigation apparatus | جهاز تطهير بالبخار |
| fumigation preparations | مستحضرات للتطهير بالبخار |
| fumigation preparations [perfumes] | مستحضرات تبخير [عطور] |
| fuming acid | حمض مدخن |
| function | يشتغل، وظيفة |
| function of | دالة لـ |
| function of position; position function | دالة للموضع |
| function of time | دالة زمنية؛ دالة في الزمن |
| function of variables | دالة من متغيرات |
| functionable | قابل للقيام بالوظيفة |
| functionable invention | اختراع قابل لأداء وظيفته |
| functional | ذو أداء وظيفي جيد |
| functional coating | غلاف وظيفي |
| functional loss of pten | الفقد الوظيفي لـ PTEN |

| | |
|---|---|
| functional t cell immune response | الاستجابة المناعية الوظيفية للخلايا التائية |
| functionality | مجموعة وظيفية |
| functionality | وظيفية |
| functionality | وظيفية |
| functionalized | به مجموعة وظيفية؛ تم إدخال مجموعة وظيفية إليه |
| functionally | وظيفيا |
| functionalzation | إدخال مجموعة وظيفية |
| fund | يمول، تمويل، صندوق |
| fundability | القابلية للتمويل |
| fundable | يمكن تمويله |
| fundable invention | اختراع يمكن أن يحظى بتمويل |
| funding | تمويل |
| fundus | قاع، جوف |
| funerary urns | وعاء لحفظ رماد الموتى (خاص بالدفن) |
| fungicides | مبيدات للفطريات |
| fungicides (chemical additives to -) | مبيدات للفطريات (إضافات كيماوية لمبيدات الفطريات) |
| fungiform | فطري الشكل |
| funiculars | سكك حديدية معلقة |
| funnels | مداخن |
| funnels for locomotives | مداخن للناقلات |
| funnels for ships | مداخن للسفن |
| fur | فراء |
| fur stoles | دُثر من الفراء |
| furan | فيوران |
| furanaldehide | فيورانالدهيد |
| furanyl | فيورانيل |
| furbishing preparations | مستحضرات تلميع |
| furnace | فرن؛ محرقة |
| furnace ash boxes | صناديق لرماد الأفران |
| furnace coke | كوك الأفران |
| furnace fire screens | ستارة واقية من نار الأفران |
| furnace fireguards | واقيات من نار الأفران |
| furnace grates | مواقد للأفران |
| furnaces | أفران |
| furnaces (cement for -) | أفران (أسمنت للأفران) |
| furnaces (coolers for -) | أفران (مبردات للأفران) |
| furnaces (cooling vats for -) | أفران (أحواض تبريد للأفران) |
| furnaces (loading apparatus for -) | أفران (جهاز تعبئة للأفران) |
| furnaces (shaped fittings for -) | أفران (تركيبات مشكلة للأفران) |
| furnaces for laboratory experiments | أفران للتجارب المعملية |
| furnish | تجهيزة؛ المجهز؛ مادة التجهيز: خليط المواد المختلفة التى يتم مزجها في معلق الكتلة والتى يتم منها صنع الورق أو الكرتون، والمكونات الأساسية هي المادة الليفية (اللب)، المواد المالئة، مواد التبويش، مواد التقوية ضد البلل، وأي إضافات أخرى، والأصباغ |
| furniture | أثاث |
| furniture (fittings of metal | أثاث (تركيبات من المعدن |

| | |
|---|---|
| for -) | للأثاث) |
| furniture (leather trimmings for -) | أثاث (زينة من الجلد للأثاث) |
| furniture (loose covers for -) | أثاث (أغطية غير مثبتة للأثاث) |
| furniture (office -) | أثاث (أثاث مكتبي) |
| furniture (partitions of wood for -) | أثاث (فواصل من الخشب للأثاث) |
| furniture (school -) | أثاث (أثاث مدرسي) |
| furniture casters of metal | عجل للأثاث مصنوع من المعدن |
| furniture casters, not of metal | عجل للأثاث، غير مصنوع من المعدن |
| furniture coverings of leather | أغطية للأثاث من الجلد |
| furniture coverings of plastic | أغطية للأثاث من البلاستك |
| furniture coverings of textile | أغطية للأثاث من القماش |
| furniture dusters | منافض الغبار للأثاث |
| furniture especially made for laboratories | أثاث مصنوع خصيصاً للمعامل |
| furniture especially made for medical purposes | أثاث مصنوع خصيصاً للأغراض الطبية |
| furniture fittings, not of metal | تركيبات للأثاث غير مصنوعة من المعدن |
| furniture industry | صناعة الأثاث |
| furniture of metal | أثاث من المعدن |
| furniture partitions of wood | فواصل أثاث خشبية |
| furniture shelves | أرفف للأثاث |
| furrings of wood | تبطين للجدران من الخشب |
| furs [clothing] | فراء [ملابس] |
| fur-skins | جلود فراء |
| further aspects | سمات أخري |
| fuse | يلتحم |
| fuse wire | سلك المصهر |
| fused bicyclic thienopyrimidine and furanopyrimidine compounds | مركبات ثيينو بيريميدين وفيورانو بيريميدين ثنائية الحلقة ملتحمة |
| fused engagement | تعشيق مدمج بالانصهار |
| fused salt | ملح مصهور |
| fused silica [semi-worked goods] other than for building | سيليكا منصهرة [منتجات شبه مشغولة] غير المخصصة للبناء |
| fuselage | بدن الطائرة |
| fuses | مصهرات |
| fuses for explosives | صمامات إشعال للمتفجرات |
| fuses for explosives, for use in mines | صمامات إشعال للمتفجرات للاستخدام في المناجم |
| fusion | اندماج |
| fusion bonded epoxy | إبوكسي ملتحم بالاندماج |
| fusion of sth to sth | دمج كذا بكذا |
| fusion power | انصهار طاقة |
| fusion protein | بروتين اندماج |
| fustian | نسيج قطني (فستيان) |
| futuristic inventions | اختراع مستقبلي |
| fuzzy system | نظام عصبي ضبابي |
| fw | الوزن الرطب |

# G

| | |
|---|---|
| gabardines [clothing] | قماش الغبردين [ملابس] |
| gadolinium | جادولينيوم (عنصر فلزي) |
| gag | وسيلة |
| gag codon | رامز وسيلة |
| gag order | حكم بالتعتيم الإعلامي |
| gage = gauge | مقياس |
| gain | يكسب، مكتسب |
| gain amplifier | مضخم كسب |
| gain of function mutation | طفرة كسب وظيفة |
| gait | مشية |
| gaiter straps | سيور للحذاء النصفي (الجيتر) |
| gaiters | حذاء نصفي (جيتر) |
| galena [ore] | كبريتيد الرصاص الطبيعي [خام] |
| galena crystals [detectors] | بلورات كبريتيد الرصاص الطبيعي [وسائل كشف] |
| galenic product | منتج مستخلص من النبات |
| galenical | من أصل نباتي |
| gall bladder carcinoma | الورم السرطاني بالمرارة |
| gallate (basic -) of bismuth | جالات البيسموت (جالات قاعدية) |
| gallbladder | المرارة |
| gallery | رواق |
| gallery | معرض |
| galley racks [printing] | حوامل لألواح حروف الطباعة [طباعة] |
| gallic acid | حمض الجاليك |
| gallic acid for the manufacture of ink | حمض الجاليك لتصنيع الحبر |
| galling | إهتراء؛ تلاصق؛ التحام |
| gallium | جاليوم (عنصر فلزي) |
| gallnuts | مادة العفصة الجوزية (تضخم نباتي في شجر الجوز) |
| gallotannic acid | حمض جالوتانيك |
| galoshes | أحذية فوقية مطاطية |
| gal-screen reporter gene assay system | نظام تجارب الجين المرشد Gal-Screen |
| galvanic | تيار كهربائي بالتفاعل الكيميائي |
| galvanic batteries | بطاريات كالفانية |
| galvanic belts | سيور كالفانية |
| galvanic cell | خلية غلفانية |
| galvanic cells | خلايا كالفانية |
| galvanic therapeutic appliances | أدوات كالفانية علاجية |
| galvanism | كهربائة محدثة بالتفاعل الكيميائي |
| galvanize | يكلفن |
| galvanizing apparatus | جهاز كلفنة (طلاء بالقصدير والزنك) |
| galvanizing baths | مغاطس مكلفنة |
| galvanizing preparations | مستحضرات جلفنة |
| galvanometer | جلفانومتر |

| | |
|---|---|
| galvanometer | المقياس الكلفاني |
| galvanoscope | المقياس الكلفاني |
| gambier | الكاد الأصفر |
| gamboge | صمغ كمبودي |
| gamboge for painting | صمغ كمبودي للرسم |
| game [dead] | لحوم الصيد [ميتة] |
| game bags [hunting accessory] | حقائب للصيد (كماليات الصيد) |
| game calls (hunting -) | وسائل نداء لحيوانات الصيد (وسائل نداء لحيوانات الصيد من أجل الصيد) |
| game cosoles | منصات الألعاب |
| games | ألعاب |
| games (apparatus for -) adapted for use with television receivers only | ألعاب (أجهزة للعب) معدة للاستخدام مع أجهزة الاستقبال التلفزيونية فقط |
| games (automatic -) other than those adapted for use with television receivers only | ألعاب (ألعاب أوتوماتيكية) غير المعدة للاستخدام مع أجهزة الاستقبال التلفزيونية فقط |
| games (balls for -) | ألعاب (كرات للألعاب) |
| games (bats for -) | ألعاب (مضارب كره للألعاب) |
| games (counters [discs] for -) | ألعاب (عدادات [أقراص] للعب) |
| games (marbles for -) | ألعاب (كرات رخامية للعب) |
| games other than those adapted for use with television receivers only (apparatus for electronic -) | ألعاب غير تلك المعدة للاستخدام مع أجهزة الاستقبال التليفزيونية فقط (أجهزة للألعاب الإلكترونية غير المعدة للاستخدام مع أجهزة الاستقبال التليفزيونية فقط) |
| gamma scintigraphy | قياس (عد) الوميض لأشعة جاما |
| ganglia | عقد (جمع عقدة) |
| gangster movies | أفلام العصابات |
| gantries | رافعات |
| gap | فجوة |
| gap | يحدث ثغرة، ينشق، فجوة، انقطاع في تسلسل |
| garbage bags | حقائب جمع القمامة |
| garbage bags [of paper or of plastics] | أكياس للقمامة [من الورق أو من البلاستيك] |
| garbage cans | صفائح معدنية للقمامة |
| garbage disposals | آلات للتخلص من القمامة |
| garden herbs, fresh | أعشاب الحدائق طازجة |
| garden herbs, preserved | أعشاب الحدائق، محفوظة |
| garden tools [hand-operated] | أدوات للحدائق [تدار يدوياً] |
| gardening gloves | قفازات لشغل البساتين |
| gargle | غرغرة |
| garlands (artificial -) | أكاليل زهور [صناعية] |
| garlic presses [kitchen utensils] | وسائل لضغط الثوم [أدوات مطبخ] |
| garment bags for travel | حقائب ثياب للسفر |
| garment covers [storage] | أغطية للثياب [تخزين] |
| garments for protection against fire | ثياب للحماية من النار |
| garnet | عقيق أحمر |
| garniture | حلية |
| garters | أربطة للجوارب |

| | |
|---|---|
| gas | يرش غازا، غاز |
| gas (solidified -) [fuel] | غاز (غاز متصلب) [وقود] |
| gas alarm | إنذار غاز |
| gas analyser | محلل الغاز |
| gas apparatus (regulating and safety accessories for -) | جهاز يعمل بالغاز (كماليات للتنظيم والأمان للأجهزة التي تعمل بالغاز) |
| gas boilers | غلايات تعمل بالغاز |
| gas burners | مواقد تعمل بالغاز |
| gas burners (brackets for -) | مواقد تعمل بالغاز (مساند للمواقد التي تعمل بالغاز) |
| gas cap | غطاء غازي؛ غاز المكمن |
| gas chilling | تبريد الغاز |
| gas chromatograph/mass spectrometer (gc/ms) | جهاز كروماتوجراف الغاز/مقياس الطيف الكتلي |
| gas chromatography ("gc") | كروماتوجراف الغاز ("GC") |
| gas compressibility | قابلية الغاز للضغط |
| gas condensers [other than parts of machines] | مكثفات غازية [غير أجزاء الآلة] |
| gas containers for cigar lighters | حاويات غاز لمشاعل السيجار |
| gas detector | كاشف غاز |
| gas diffusion | انتشار غازي |
| gas expansion | تمدد الغاز |
| gas flow | تدفق غازي |
| gas for lighting | غاز للإنارة |
| gas generators [installations] | مولدات غاز [تجهيزات] |
| gas lamps | مصابيح غازية |
| gas leak detector | كاشف تسرب غاز |
| gas leak preventer valve | صمام مانع لتسرب الغاز |
| gas lighters | مشاعل غازية |
| gas mixture | خليط غازي |
| gas oil | زيت الغاز |
| gas oil catalytic cracker | وحدة تكسير حفزي لزيت الغاز |
| gas oil feedstock | خام تغذية بزيت غاز |
| gas oil, vacuum gas oil, naphtha or cracked stock, | زيت الغاز، زيت غاز تحت ضغط منخفض، النفثا أو الخام المكسّر |
| gas pipes (regulating and safety accessories for -) | مواسير الغاز (كماليات للتنظيم والأمان لمواسير الغاز) |
| gas proof ; gas-proof | مانع للغاز |
| gas propellents for aerosols | مواد دافعة غازية للايروسول |
| gas purifying preparations | مستحضرات لتنقية الغاز |
| gas scrubbing apparatus | جهاز غسل الغاز |
| gas sensor | جهاز إحساس بالغاز |
| gas stream | تيار غازي |
| gas testing instruments | أدوات لاختبار الغاز |
| gas turbine | توربين غازي |
| gas turbine engine | محرك توربين غازي؛ محرك توربيني؛ محرك نفاث |
| gas turbine engine | محرك توربيني، محرك نفاث |
| gas weapons (tear -) | وسائل إطلاق غازات (أسلحة غازية مثيرة للدموع) |
| gas/liquid separtor | جهاز فصل الغاز/السائل |
| gaseous hourly space velocity | السرعة الفراغية للغاز في الساعة |
| gases (blowing machines for the compression, exhaustion and transport of -) | غازات (آلات نفخ لضغط وإفراغ ونقل الغازات) |
| gases (protective -) for welding | غازات (غازات واقية) للحام |
| gases (solidified -) | غازات (غازات متصلبة) |
| gasification | التحويل إلى غاز |
| gasifiers | مواد للتحويل إلى غاز |
| gas-insulated switchgear device | مجموعة مفاتيح توزيع معزولة بالغاز |
| gasket | حشوة - حشو - حَشِيَةٌ (لمنع التسرب) |
| gaskets | أطواق لمنع التسرب |
| gaskets (fibrous -) for ships | حبال تثبيت الشراع المطوي (حبال ليفية لتثبيت الشراع المطوي) للسفن |
| gas-liquid chromatography ("glc") | كروماتوجراف الغاز - السائل ("GLC") |
| gasoline | بنزين؛ جازولين |
| gasoline (detergent additives to -) | جازولين (مواد إضافة مزيلة للأوساخ للجازولين) |
| gasoline base cut | قطفة أساسها البنزين |
| gasoline car model | نموذج سيارة تسير بالجازولين |
| gasoline electric hybrids | المختلطات ذات الطاقة الكهربائية الجازولينية |
| gasoline gauges | مقياس الجازولين |
| gasoline pumps for service stations | مضخات جازولين لمحطات الخدمة |
| gasoline treatment | معالجة الجازولين |
| gasometers | مستودعات لخزن الغاز وقياس كميته |
| gas-tight ; gastight | مانع لتسرب الغاز - غلاف كتيم للغاز |
| gastric | مَعِدي |
| gastric carcinoma | الورم السرطاني المعدي |
| gastrin | جاسترين (هرمون معدي) |
| gastritis | التهاب المعدة |
| gastroenteritis | التهاب المعدة والأمعاء |
| gastrointestinal | للمعدة والأمعاء |
| gastrointestinal tract | القناة الهضمية |
| gastroparesis | شلل معدي |
| gastroscopes | مناظير للمعدة |
| gate | عبّارة |
| gate stops of metal | حواجز وقوف للبوابات من المعدن |
| gate valve | صمام بوابي |
| gates for car parks (coin-operated -) | بوابات لمواقف السيارات (بوابات لمواقف السيارات تعمل بوضع العملات) |
| gates of metal | بوابات مصنوعة من المعدن |
| gates, not of metal | بوابات غير مصنوعة من المعدن |
| gateway | عبّارة |
| gathering device | جهاز تجميع |
| gating | الإمرار |
| gatrans | عوامل الجَترن |
| gauge | قياس، مقياس |
| gaultheria oil | زيت الغلطرية (نوع من النبات الدائم الخضار) |
| gauntlets (fencing -) | قفازات واقية (قفازات واقية للمبارزة بالسيف) |
| gauss | الجاوس: هو وحدة قياس شدة |

| | |
|---|---|
| | المجال المغناطيسي |
| gaussian probability density | كثافة جاوس الاحتمالية |
| gaussian probability distribution | توزيع جاوس الاحتمالي |
| gauze | شاش |
| gauze [cloth] | شاش (قماش) |
| gauze for dressings | شاش للتضميد |
| gavage tube | أنبوب تغذية |
| gb | جيجا بايت |
| gbq | جيجا بكريل |
| gcc | مجلس التعاون الخليجي |
| gccs | نظام العام للقيادة والسيطرة الأمريكي |
| g-csf | G-CSF؛ عاملG-CSF |
| gear boxes for land vehicles | علب تروس للمركبات الأرضية |
| gear boxes other than for land vehicles | علب تروس لغير المركبات الأرضية |
| gearing for land vehicles | مجموعة مسننات للمركبات الأرضية |
| gears for cycles | تروس للدراجات |
| gears for weaving looms | تروس لنول النسيج |
| gears, other than for land vehicles | تروس غير المخصصة للمركبات الأرضية |
| geek | مهووس؛ خبير |
| geek code | لغة المهووسين بالكمبيوتر |
| gel | هلام؛ جل |
| gel documentation unit | وحدة توثيق الجيلات |
| gel electrophoresis | الإشراد الكهربائي لهلام |
| gel permeation chromotagraphy (gpc) measurements | القياسات الكروماتوجرافية لنفاذ الجل (GPC) |
| gelatin(e) | جيلاتين |
| gelatine for food | جيلاتين للطعام |
| gelcap | أقراص مغلفة بالجيلاتين |
| gelling agent | عامل تكوين جل |
| gelling agents | المواد المكونة للهلام |
| gem substitution | استبدال مزدوج على نفس الذرة |
| geminal | متشابه؛ متماثل؛ توأمي |
| gene | جين (جينة) |
| gene | جين |
| gene carrier | حاملة الجين |
| gene expression | التعبير الوراثي؛ التعبير الجيني |
| gene expression profiling | خصائص التعبير الوراثي |
| gene knockout | تعطيل جيني |
| gene map | الخريطة الجينية |
| gene patent | براءة اختراع مورث بشري. هي حصول جين ما من الجينات البشرية على الحق في الحماية المقررة وفقاً لقوانين الملكية الفكرية لكونه يحمل صفات معينة أو كحامل للأمراض وناقل لها من جيل إلى أخر، أو مساهم في الوقاية أو العلاج من بعض الأمراض، إذ يعد اكتشاف صفة من تلك الصفات في جين معين عملاً جديداً وتم اكتشافه بطريقة إبداعية وقابل للتطبيق وتنطبق عليه كافة الشروط المطلوبة قانوناً لمنح البراءة، التي تعد شروطاً صعبة بل شبه مستعصية في مثل تلك الحالات تحديداً، ويعد الحصول على براءة اختراع على جين معين حقاً لمكتشف صفات هذا الجين في منع الآخرين من استخدامه أو استغلاله تجارياً |
| gene patenting | إصدار البراءة فيما يتصل بالجينات |
| gene therapy | العلاج الجيني |
| general (gen) | فريق أول |
| general affairs | شئون عامة |
| general agreement on tariffs and trade (gatt) | الاتفاقية العامة للتعريفات (الجمركية ) والتجارة (جنيف) |
| general amnesty | عفو عام |
| general elections | انتخابات عامة |
| general linearized model (glm) procedure | إجراء النموذج الخطي العام (GLM) |
| general release of film | العرض العام للفيلم؛ عرض الفيلم للجمهور |
| general shuttle vector | ناقل مكوكي عام |
| generalizations of science | عموميات العلم |
| generalized | عام |
| generate | يؤدي إلى |
| generate | يولد؛ ينتج؛ ينشئ |
| generate | يولد |
| generating output | توليد مخرجات |
| generation | توليد، نسل، ذرية |
| generation software | برنامج توليد |
| generative | مولد |
| generator | مولد |
| generators (current -) | مولدات (مولدات للتيار) |
| generators (gas -) [installations] | مولدات (مولدات للغاز) [تجهيزات] |
| generators of electricity | مولدات للكهرباء |
| generic customizable solutions | حلول عامة يمكن تصنيعها وفق الطلب |
| generic drug | دواء عام. دواء انتهت الحماية المنبثقة عن البراءة الصادرة عنه، فانخفضت قيمته وتم التعامل معه على أنها عام |
| generic patent | براءة عامة. |
| genetic | جيني؛ وراثي |
| genetic code | الشفرة الوراثية: معلومات توجد في حمض الـ دي إن إيه الخاص بالخلية تشير إلى تحدد تركيب الخلية. وتُعد العامل الأساسي في الوراثة |
| genetic engineering | الهندسة الوراثية: طرق علمية لتغيير التركيب الجيني للكائن الحي من أجل الحصول على خصائص معينة في تكوينه |
| genetic enhancement | دعم جيني |
| genetic load | الطفرة الوراثية الضارة بالمجتمع |
| genetic map ; genetic mapping | الخريطة الجينية: تمثيل بياني لترتيب الجينات أو المواقع المتحولة على الكروموسوم |
| genetic material patenting | إصدار براءة عن مواد جينية. |
| genetic susceptibility | استعداد وراثي |

| | |
|---|---|
| genetically engineered | معدل وراثيا |
| genetically modified organisms | كائنات معدلون وراثيا. كائنات تم إخضاعها لتعديلات وراثية. وتطالب بعض الجهات العلمية بمنح الجهات القائمة على تطوير تعديلات وراثية لبعض الكائنات بمنحهم براءات عن تلك التطويرات، وبينما أقر تشريعات بعض البلدان ذلك رفضته تشريعات بلدان أخرى |
| geneticin | جينيتيسين |
| geneticist | إخصائي علم الوراثة. |
| genetics | علم الوراثة: فرع من البيولوجيا يعني بالوراثة، وبخاصة آليات نقل الوراثة وتغير الخصائص الموروثة بين الكائنات المتشابهة أو المرتبطة ببعضها البعض. |
| genius | عبقرية، عبقري |
| genome | مجموعة العوامل الوراثية؛ جينوم |
| genome project | مشروع الجينوم |
| genomic | حامل لمجموعة العوامل الوراثية؛ جينومي |
| genotype | نمط وراثي |
| gentamycin | جنتاميسين |
| gentian | جنتيان |
| gentle | معتدل |
| genus | نوع |
| geo-chemistry | كيمياء أرضية |
| geographic coordinates | إحداثيات جغرافية |
| geographic coordinates system | نظام إحداثيات جغرافي: يعطي إحداثيات كل نقطة على سطح الأرض على شكل زاويتي طول وعرض (N,E) وليس على شكل إحداثيات ديكارتية X وY |
| geographical maps | خرائط جغرافية |
| geolocatable multiple services | خدمات متعددة لتحديد الموضع جغرافيا |
| geometric isomers | أيزومرات هندسية |
| geometries | أشكال هندسية |
| geometry | الخواص الهندسية |
| geo-modeller | ووسيلة تخطيط جيولوجية |
| geophone ; geophone-receiver | سماعة أرضية؛ جيوفون؛ جهاز مَسْحُ الأَرْض؛ مكبر صوت أرضي |
| geophysical data | بيانات جيوفيزيائية |
| geoscience | العلوم الجيولوجية؛ علم الأرض أو الخواص الجيولوجية |
| geotextile ; geo-textile ; geo textile | نسيج أرضي (مادة تبطين للجابيونات) |
| geotextiles | أنسجة للأغراض الجيولوجية |
| geothermal electricity production | إنتاج كهرباء أرضية حرارية (جيوثيرمالية) |
| geothermal energy | طاقة حرارية أرضية، طاقة جيوثيرمالية |
| geothermal energy commercialization | جعل الطاقة الأرضحرارية ذات طبيعة تجارية |
| geothermal heat | سخونة ناتجة عن حرارة الأرض، سخونة جيوثيرمالية |
| geothermal heating | تسخين أرضي حراري، تسخين جيوثيرمالي |
| geothermal power | طاقة أرضية حرارية، طاقة جيوثيرمالية |
| geraniol | كحول سائل عطري |
| germ | جنين البذرة |
| germ (seed -) for botanical purposes | بذور (جنين بذور) للاستخدام الزراعي |
| german silver | فضة ألمانية |
| germanium | جرمانيوم |
| germanium / semiconductor glass | جيرمانيوم / زجاج موصل |
| germicidal burners | مواقد لإبادة الجراثيم |
| germicidal lamps for purifying air | مصابيح إبادة لتنقية الهواء |
| germicides | مبيدات للجراثيم |
| germination | إنبات |
| germinoma | وَرَمٌ جرثومي؛ ورم إنتاشي |
| germlin | سلالة جرثومية |
| germlined antibody | جسم مضاد من سلالة جرثومية |
| germplasm | جبلة جرثومية |
| gettering | امتصاص الشوائب |
| gettering | ماص للشوائب |
| getters [chemically active substances] | مواد مستأصلة [مواد فعالة كيميائياً] |
| getting around the software | التعرف على البرامج |
| gf/in | ثقل جم/ البوصة |
| gg | جيجا جرام |
| gherkin | جيركين (خيار صغير) |
| ghsv | السرعة الفراغية للغاز في الساعة |
| gia | وكالة الاستخبارات العامة |
| giardiasis | الإصابة بالجياردیات |
| gib head key | خابور بذقن |
| gif | صيغة تبادل الرسومات |
| gifted actor | ممثل موهوب |
| gigabases | جيجا قاعدة: وحدة لقياس طول الجزيء. انظر kb(kilobase و megabase |
| gigaseal | عزل ذو مقدار كبيرة: ويسمى أيضا عزل ذو مقاومة عالية high resistance seal |
| gildings | طلاء الذهب |
| gimlets [hand tools] | مثقاب [أدوات يدوية] |
| gin | مسكر قوى |
| ginger [spice] | زنجبيل (توابل) |
| ginger ale | جعة الزنجبيل |
| ginger beer | بيرة الزنجبيل |
| ginger jam | مربى من الزنجبيل |
| gingerbread | خبز من الزنجبيل |
| gingivitis | التهاب اللثة |
| gipo | المكتب الحكومي للمشروع في المصنع |
| girders of metal | عوارض مصنوعة من المعدن |
| girders, not of metal | عوارض، غير مصنوعة من المعدن |
| girdles | أحزمة |
| gis | نظام معلومات جغرافي فضائي -نظام معلومات جغرافي |
| give in the key the city | يسلم مفاتيح المدينة |

| | |
|---|---|
| give off | يصدر؛ يبعث |
| give off (to) | يرسل (إلى) |
| give rise to | يؤدي إلى؛ يكون مصدرا لـ |
| given | مُعطى؛ معين |
| glacial | ثلجي |
| glacial acetic acid | حمض خليك ثلجي |
| gland | حلقة حشو |
| glased tile | القيشاني |
| glass (alabaster -) | زجاج (زجاج من الألبستر) |
| glass (building -) | زجاج (زجاج للمباني ) |
| glass (opacifiers for -) | زجاج (مواد غير منفذة للزجاج) |
| glass (opal -) | زجاج (زجاج متلألئ) |
| glass (preparations for preventing the tarnishing of -) | زجاج (ممستحضرات لمنع فقدان بريق الزجاج) |
| glass (silvered -) [mirrors] | زجاج (زجاج مطلي بالفضة) [مرايا] |
| glass (water -) [soluble glass] | الزجاج (الزجاج المائي) [زجاج قابل للذوبان] |
| glass [receptacles] | زجاجات (أوعية) |
| glass beads | خرزات زجاجية |
| glass bowls | سلطانيات من الزجاج |
| glass bulbs [receptacles] | الزجاج المنتفخ (أوعية) |
| glass caps | أغطية علوية من الزجاج |
| glass ceramic | خزف زجاجي |
| glass cloth | نسيج مصنوع من الزجاج |
| glass covered with an electrical conductor | زجاج مغطى بموصل كهربائي |
| glass fibers [fibres] for textile use | ألياف زجاجية [ألياف] للاستخدام في المنسوجات |
| glass flasks [containers] | قوارير من الزجاج [حاويات] |
| glass for vehicle windows [semi-finished product] | زجاج لنوافذ المركبات [منتجات شبه مكتملة] |
| glass granules for road marking | حبيبات زجاجية لوضع علامات على الطرق |
| glass incorporating fine electrical conductors | زجاج يتضمن موصلات كهربائية دقيقة |
| glass jars [carboys] | برطمانات زجاجية (قنينه لحفظ السوائل) (الدامجانة) |
| glass paper | ورق من الزجاج |
| glass stoppers | سدادات من الزجاج |
| glass transition temperature | درجة حرارة التحول الزجاجي |
| glass transition temperature (tg) | درجة التحول الزجاجي: وهي درجة الحرارة التي يتحول عندها العينة من الحالة الصلبة إلى الحالة المطاطية (rubbery state) . |
| glass vials [receptacles] | قارورة زجاجية؛ قنينة زجاجية [أوعية] |
| glass wool for insulation | صوف زجاجي للعزل |
| glass wool other than for insulation | صوف زجاجي غير المستخدم في العزل |
| glass working machines | آلات لشغل الزجاج |
| glass, unworked or semi-worked [except building glass] | زجاج غير مشغول أو شبه مشغول [ماعدا زجاج المباني] |
| glass-based phenolic | راتنج فينولي أساسه الزجاج |
| glass-cloth [towels] | نسيج مصنوع من الزجاج [فوط] |
| glass-frosting chemicals | كيماويات لصنفرة الزجاج |
| glass-infiltrated ceramic coping | غطاء بورسلين مزجج بالزجاج |
| glass-staining chemicals | كيماويات لتلوين الزجاج |
| glassware (graduated -) | أواني زجاجية (أواني زجاجية مدرجة) |
| glassware (painted -) | أواني زجاجية (أواني زجاجية مزخرفة) |
| glassy | شفافة |
| glassy | زجاجية |
| glaucoma | المياه الزرقاء؛ الجلوكوما؛ ارتفاع ضغط العين: مرض ينتج عن خلل في تصريف السائل المائي الذي يُفرَز في العين، فيزيد الضغط على أنسجة العين الداخلية بما فيها العصب البصري، مما ينتج عنه اضطراب في الرؤية وظهور بقع عمياء في المجال البصري |
| glauconite | جلوكونايت |
| glaze (laundry -) | مواد صقل (مواد صقل للاستخدام في المغسلة) |
| glazes [paints, lacquers] | مواد صقل (دهانات وورنيش اللاكية) |
| glaziers' diamonds [parts of hand tools] | ماس الزجاج [أجزاء من الأدوات اليدوية] |
| glaziers' diamonds [parts of machines] | ماس الزجاج [أجزاء من الآلات] |
| glaziers' putty | معاجين للزجاج |
| glazing | التلميع |
| glazing agents | عناصر ملمعة |
| glazing apparatus for photographic prints | جهاز تلميع للاستخدام في الطباعة الفوتوغرافية |
| glazing irons | مكواة تلميع |
| glazings (ceramic -) | مواد ملمعة (مواد ملمعة للخزف) |
| glean | فهم |
| gliacyte | خلية الغراء العصبي |
| glidant | مزلِّب؛ مادة مزلقة؛ محسِّن انزلاق |
| glider (also sailplane) | طائرة شراعية |
| gliding or strike-slip boundary earthquakes | هزَّاتٍ أرضيَّةً عند حواف الانزلاق لألواح الغلاف الصخريِّ |
| glioblastoma | الورم الدبقي الأولي |
| glioblastoma | ورم الخلايا الأولية الدبقية |
| glioma | ورم دبقي |
| global awareness | وعي العالمية. الإلمام بدائرة الانتماء الكبرى العالمية والشخصية الإنسانية العالمية وأسسها وتعدد الثقافات المكونة لها والمخاطر الكبرى التي يتعرض لها العالم بحسبانه وحدة واحدة ذات مصير مشترك كالتلوث والخطر النووي |
| global economy | اقتصاد العالم |
| global information infrastructure | البنية التحتية المعلوماتية العالمية. اسم للإطار التقني الذي يتم إعداده ليربط |

| | |
|---|---|
| | جميع المجالات التقنية على مستوى العالم. |
| global invention | اختراع عالمي |
| global patent database | قاعدة بيانات براءات عالمية |
| global positioning system | نظام تموضع عالمي |
| global positioning system (gps) | نظام تحديد المواقع العالمي |
| global prior art search | بحث متصل بالفن السابق على مستوى العالم |
| global system for mobile communications (gsm) | النظام العالمي للإتصالات عن طريق الهواتف المحمولة: طريقة للإتصال عن طريق الهواتف المحمولة الرقمية تستخدم على نطاق أوروبا وغيرها من الأماكن الأخرى في العالم. يستخدم هذا النظام ثلاث موجات من الترددات هي: MHz 900 - MHz 1800 - Mhz 1900. |
| global system for mobile telecommunication | النظام العالمي للاتصال عن طريق الهواتف المحمولة |
| global warming | ارتفاع الحرارة العالمي؛ الاحتباس العالمي |
| globes (terrestrial -) | كرات (كرات أرضية) |
| globular | كروي |
| glomerulonephritis | التهاب كبيبات الكلى |
| glomerulosclerosis | تصلب الكبيبات |
| glossary | مسرد لشرح الكلمات الصعبة |
| glossettes | أقراص حلوة المذاق |
| glove stretchers | أدوات توسيع القفازات |
| gloves (baseball -) | قفازات (قفازات للعبة البيسبول) |
| gloves (boxing -) | قفازات (قفازات للعبة الملاكمة) |
| gloves (fencing -) | قفازات (قفازات خاصة بالمبارزة) |
| gloves (gardening -) | قفازات (لأعمال البساتين) |
| gloves (golf -) | قفازات (قفازات للعبة الجولف) |
| gloves (insulating -) | قفازات (قفازات عازلة) |
| gloves (polishing -) | قفازات (قفازات للتلميع) |
| gloves [clothing] | قفازات [ملابس] |
| gloves for divers | قفازات للغواصين |
| gloves for games | قفازات للألعاب |
| gloves for massage | قفازات للتدليك |
| gloves for protection against accidents | قفازات للوقاية من الحوادث |
| gloves for protection against x-rays for industrial purposes | قفازات للوقاية من أشعة أكس للأغراض الصناعية |
| glow plugs for diesel engines | شمعات توهج لمحركات الديزل |
| glucinium [beryllium] | جلوسنيوم [بريليوم] (عنصر فلزي) |
| glucocorticoid | قشراني سكري |
| glucocorticoid | قشراني سكري؛ جلوكوكرتيكويد |
| glucose for food | جلوكوز للطعام |
| glucose for medical purposes | جلوكوز للأغراض الطبية |
| glucose tolerance test (gtt) | تحليل منحنى تحمل السكر |
| glucoside | جلوكوسيد |
| glucuronidation | التحويل إلى حمض جلوكويورونيك |
| glue (fly -) | صمغ [صمغ للذباب] |
| glue for stationery or household purposes | صمغ للأغراض المكتبية أو المنزلية |
| glue guns, electric | مسدسات صمغ، كهربائية |
| glue-heating appliances | أدوات لتسخين الصمغ |
| glue-pots | مغراة |
| glutamate | جلوتامات |
| gluten | جلوتين |
| gluten [glue] for stationery or household purposes | غراء (صمغ) للأغراض المكتبية أو المنزلية |
| gluten for food | جلوتين (مادة بروتينية) للطعام |
| glutinous tree-banding preparations | مستحضرات من الجلوتين لترقيع الأشجار |
| glutinous tree-grafting preparations | مستحضرات من الجلوتين لتطعيم الأشجار |
| glycerides | جليسريد |
| glycerine | جليسرين |
| glycerol | جليسيرول |
| glycerol monostearate or glycerol stearate | مونو ستيارات الجليسيرول أو ستيارات الجليسيرول |
| glycerophosphate | جليسروفوسفات |
| glycogen storage diseases | تخزين الجليكوجين |
| glycol | جليكول |
| glycol ether | إيثر جليكول |
| glycolate sodium celulose | جليكولات سليولوز الصوديوم |
| glycoprotein | بروتين سكري |
| glycoside | جلوكوسيد |
| glycosylated | مرتبط بالجليكوزيل |
| glycosylated mammalian biological molecules" | الجزيئات الحيوية الثديية المرتبطة أصليا بالجليكوزيل |
| glycosylation | ارتباط بالجليكوزيل؛ إدخال مجموعة جليكوزيل |
| glycosylation of protein | ارتباط البروتين بالجليكوزيل |
| glycovariants | صور السكر المتغيرة |
| glyoxylic acid | حمض الجليوكسيليك |
| gnu | نظام التشغيل GNU |
| gnu general public license | ترخيص عام. نوع خاص من الترخيص بموجبه يمنح الترخيص لكافة المستعملين |
| gnu/linux | نظام التشغيل GNU/Linux |
| goals | أهداف |
| goblets of precious metal | كؤوس مصنوعة من المعادن النفيسة |
| goblets, not of precious metal | كؤوس غير مصنوعة من المعادن النفيسة |
| goffering irons | مكواة للثني |
| goggles for sports | نظارات واقية للرياضيين |
| gold (dental amalgams of -) | ذهب (زئبق ممزوج بالذهب للأسنان) |
| gold (objects of imitation -) | ذهب (منتجات من الذهب المقلد) |
| gold and silver ware, other than cutlery, forks and spoons | أواني ذهبية وفضية، غير السكاكين والشوك والملاعق |
| gold beaters' skin | جلد للمطارق الذهبية |
| gold embroidery | تطريز ذهبي |
| gold particles | جسيمات ذهب |

| | |
|---|---|
| gold salts | أملاح ذهب |
| gold solder | سبيكة لحام من الذهب |
| gold thread [jewellery, jewelry (am.)] | خيوط ذهبية [مجوهرات] |
| gold, unwrought or beaten | ذهب غير مشكل أو مطروق |
| golden syrup | أشربه ذهبية |
| golf bags, with or without wheels | حقائب لعبة الجولف، مزودة بعجل أو بدونه |
| golf carts | عربات صغيرة للعبة الجولف |
| golf clubs | مضارب للعبة الجولف |
| golf gloves | قفازات للعبة الجولف |
| goloshes | كلوش (حذاء فوقى غير منفذ للماء) |
| gonad msufficiency | قصور الغدة التناسلية |
| gongs | أجراس قرصية الشكل |
| good | سلعة، جيد |
| good mouth feel | شعور مريح للفم |
| goodpasture syndrome | متلازمة جودباستشار |
| goods | سلع |
| goods handling carts | عربات صغيرة لنقل المنتجات |
| goofy invention | اختراع رسوم متحركة |
| gouges [hand tools] | أزاميل مقعرة [أدوات يدوية] |
| goulard water | ماء جولارد |
| gourd | يقطين (قرع) |
| gourds (bottle -) | قرع (زجاجات على شكل قرع) |
| gout | نقرس |
| gouty arthritis | التهاب المفاصل الناتج عن النقرس |
| governance | قيادة |
| governance | حوكمة |
| governing jurisdiction | السلطة القضائية الحاكمة |
| governing law clause | فقرة القانون الساري أو النافذ |
| governing law clause | بند القانون الحاكم. بند تعاقدي يحدد القانون الذي يحكم العقد وتفسير بنوده، وربما الذي يحكم التحكيم وإجراءاته |
| government grant | المعترضون يقولون أنه منحة حكومية وليس حقا أصيلاً |
| government monolopoly | احتكار الحكومة |
| government operation | عملية حكومية |
| government-granted monopoly | احتكار بموجب قرار حكومي |
| government-owned invention | اختراع مملوك للحكومة |
| governor setpoint signal | إشارة نقطة ضبط حاكمة |
| gowns (dressing -) | عباءات (للارتداء) |
| gp/gmet/hr | جم من بوليمر أوليفين لكل جم من الميتالوسين في الساعة |
| gpa | جيجا باسكال |
| gpe/(gas.hr) | جرام من بوليمر إيثلين لكل جم من المادة الحاملة المنشطة لكل ساعة |
| gpo | مكتب الحكومي للمشروع |
| g-protein coupled receptors | والمستقبلات المقترنة ببروتين G |
| gprs | هى خدمة تعني بترقية خدمة بيانات الإتصالات الخاصة بشبكات الهواتف المحمولة لإتاحة إمكانية رفع معدل إرسال البيانات (نظريا) لحده الأقصى البالغ 115 كيلوبايت. |
| gps | النظام العالمي لتحديد المواقع هو نظام راديو (لاسلكي) يعتمد على الأقمار الصناعية في توفير معلومات معينة عن مواقع خدمة الإتصالات ليتسنى للمشتركين في هذا النظام الإستفادة منها حيثما كانوا على نطاق الكرة الأرضية. |
| gpu | معالج الرسوم |
| gr/h | جم/ساعة (وبخاصة لكتلة، وزن لتيار تغذية، محفز إلخ) |
| graben or trough faults | الصدوع الأخدودية |
| grade | يعطي تقديرا |
| grade | فئة |
| graded-bedding | التدرج الحبيبي |
| grader | مصنفة الحبوب/ الجذور |
| gradient | كمية متدرجة |
| gradient function | دالة تدرج |
| gradient indicators | مؤشرات مدرجة للميل |
| grading | التقدير: استخدام التقديرات/الدرجات |
| gradually warmed to | ليدفأ تدريجيا إلى درجة حرارة الغرفة |
| graduate student's patent rights | حقوق البراءة الخاصة بطلاب الجامعة |
| graft | طُعم؛ جزء مزروع |
| graft copolymers | بوليمرات مشتركة مطعمة |
| graft into, grafted into | يطعّم كذا على كذا |
| graft polymer | بوليمر تطعيمي |
| graft versus host disease; graft-versus-host-disease; graft-versus-host disease (gvhd) | الأمراض المتعلقة برفض العائل للجزء المزروع |
| graft versus host disease; graft-versus-host-disease; graft-versus-host disease (gvhd) | مرض متعلق برفض العائل للجزء المزروع |
| graft vs. host reaction | رد فعل الجزء المستقبل للجزء المزروع |
| grafting mastic for trees | صمغ المصطكا لتطعيم الشجر |
| grafting tools [hand tools] | أدوات تطعيم الأشجار [أدوات يدوية] |
| grafting wax for trees | شمع تطعيم للشجر |
| grain (blowing machines or fans for the compression, sucking and carrying of -) | حبوب [آلات نفخ أو مراوح لضغط وشفط وحمل الحبوب] |
| grain fabric | طراز الراسب |
| grain husking machines | آلات تقشير الحبوب |
| grain separators | آلات فصل الحبوب |
| grain shape | شكل الحبيبات |
| grain size and packing | حجم الحبيبات والترتيب ( أو التعبئة ) |
| grain stripper | درّاسة |
| grains [cereals] | حبوب [رقاقات من الحبوب] |
| grains [seeds] | حبوب [بذور] |
| grains for animal consumption | حبوب للاستهلاك الحيواني |
| grains, cereals | الحبوب |
| grammage | الوزن النوعي: الكتلة الفعلية |

| | |
|---|---|
| | للورق أو الكرتون، ويعبر عنها عادة (جرام/متر المربع) |
| gram-negative | سلبي الجرام |
| gram-positive bacteria | بكتيريا موجبة لجرام (جرام هو نوع صبغ) |
| granite | جرانيت |
| granite cobble conglomerates | مدملكات الحصى الجرانيتي |
| grant | يمنح، يوافق، يقبل، منح، وافق على، منحة، موافقة |
| grant clause | بند المنح: المادة التي تنظم منح الترخيص باستخدام البراءة من قبل صاحب البراءة للمرخص إليه، والتي تشمل تحديد نطاق البراءة وما إذا كانت محملة بإتاوة أم لا |
| grant of representation | تفويض بالتصرف |
| grant relief | يحكم أو يقضي بمعالجة قضائية |
| granted monopoly | احتكار ممنوح |
| granted patent | براءة مَمنوحة |
| granted patent application | طلب براءة مقبول |
| grantee | الطرف الممنوح |
| grantee of a trademark right | الطرف الممنوح حق العلامة التجارية |
| grants | موافقات |
| granulate | ناتج التحبيب |
| granulation | تحبيب |
| granulator | جهاز تحبيب |
| granules | حبيبات |
| granulocyte | خلية محببة |
| granulocyte macrophage colony stimulating factor (gm-csf) | عامل تنبيه مستعمرة خلايا ملتهمة كبيرة لخلايا حبيبية |
| granulocyte macrophage colony stimulating factor; granulocyte-macrophage colony stimulating factor (gm-csf) | عامل منبه لمستعمرة خلايا ملتهمة كبيرة لخلية محببة |
| granulomatous | متعلق بورم حبيبي |
| granulomatous | مكون من أورام حبيبية |
| grape must [unfermented] | عصير العنب [غير متخمر] |
| grape tomatoes | طماطم عنقودية |
| grapefruit | جريب فروت |
| grapes, fresh | عنب طازج |
| graph | رسم بياني |
| grapheme transistor | مقحل غرافيمي، ترانزيستور |
| graphic designer | مصمم جرافيكي |
| graphic prints | صور مطبوعة بيانية |
| graphic representations | تصويرات بيانية |
| graphic reproductions | نسخ بيانية |
| graphical summary | ملخص بياني |
| graphite | جرافيت (رصاص أسود) |
| graphite (lubricating -) | جرافيت (جرافيت مزلق) |
| grapnels (automatic -) for marine purposes | مرساة (مرساه أوتوماتيكية) للأغراض البحرية |
| grass (esparto -) | عشب (عشب حلفاء التي يصنع من أليافها السلاسل والأكياس) |
| grass root | على مستوى القاعدة |
| grasses for upholstering | عشب للتنجيد |
| grassroots employee-driven innovation | ابتكار من قبل موظف بسيط |
| grass-roots units ; grass roots units | الوحدات الجديدة |
| graters [household utensils] | مبشرة [أدوات منزلية] |
| grates (furnace -) | مواقد (مواقد للأفران) |
| grating machines for vegetables | آلات لبشر الخضراوات |
| gratings of metal | حاملة وقود من المعدن |
| grave or tomb enclosures, not of metal | محتويات القبر أو المدفن غير مصنوعة من المعدن |
| gravel | حصى |
| gravel pack | حشوة حصى |
| gravel packing | حشوة حصوية |
| gravestone slabs of metal | ألواح لشاهد الضريح مصنوعة من المعدن |
| gravestone slabs, not of metal | ألواح لشاهد الضريح غير مصنوعة من المعدن |
| gravestones | شاهد للضريح |
| gravestones of metal | شاهد الضريح مصنوع من المعدن |
| gravies (meat -) | صلصة مرق (صلصة مرق اللحم) |
| gravimetric method | طريقة القياس الوزني |
| graving tools [hand tools] | أدوات حفر [أدوات يدوية] |
| gravitate | يجتذب |
| gravitation | جذب |
| gravitational | جاذب |
| gravitational energy | طاقة جاذبة |
| gravitational separation | الفصل بفعل الجاذبية |
| gravity | الوزن النوعي، الثقل النوعي [وبخاصة في الموضوعات المتعلقة بلزوجة أنواع النفط المختلفة] |
| gravity | الجاذبية |
| gravity fed | تتم تغذيته بفعل الجاذبية |
| gravity feed hopper gun | مسدس له قادوس للتغذية بفعل الجاذبية |
| gravity feeding | التغذية بفعل الجاذبية |
| gravity override | تجاهل الثقل النوعي |
| gravity separation | فصل بفعل الجاذبية الأرضية |
| gravity separation | الفصل بفعل الجاذبية |
| gray-scale image; gray scale image | صورة رمادية؛ صورة بتدرج الرمادي:هي صورة رقمية ناتجة من قياس شدة الإضاءة intensity فقط وليس الألوان colors، حيث قيمة البكسل تتناسب مع شدة الإضاءة. أخفض قيمة هي اللون الأسود وأكبر قيمة هي الأبيض |
| graywacke | جرايواكي |
| grease | شحم؛ دهن |
| grease (illuminating -) | شحم (شحم للإنارة) |
| grease boxes [parts of machines] | صناديق تشحيم [أجزاء من الآلة] |

| | |
|---|---|
| grease for arms [weapons] | شحم للأسلحة [الأسلحة النارية] |
| grease for belts | شحم السيور |
| grease for boots | شحم للأحذية ذات الرقبة |
| grease for leather | شحم للجلود |
| grease for shoes | شحم للأحذية |
| grease nipples | حلمات التشحيم |
| grease rings [parts of machines] | حلقات التشحيم [أجزاء من الآلات] |
| grease-removing preparations for use in manufacturing processes | مستحضرات لإزالة الشحم للاستخدام في عمليات التصنيع |
| greases (anti-rust -) | شحم (شحم مضاد للصدأ) |
| greases (preparations for the separation of -) | شحوم (مستحضرات لفصل الشحوم) |
| greases for cosmetic purposes | مواد زيتية لأغراض التجميل |
| greases for veterinary purposes | شحوم للأغراض البيطرية |
| green | أخضر، يخضر |
| green beans | فاصوليا خضراء |
| green chemistry | كيمياء خضراء |
| green computing | احتساب أخضر |
| green energy | طاقة خضراء |
| green energy source | مصدر طاقة خضراء |
| green growth | نمو أخضر. نمو صديق للبيئة ومواجه للتلوث |
| green invention | اختراع أخضر. اختراع معزز للبيئة. |
| green it infrastructure | بنية تحتية خضراء لتقنية المعلومات. بنية تحتية لتقنية المعلومات معززة للبيئة |
| green lamp | المصباح الأخضر |
| green patent | براءة خضراء. براءة معززة للبيئة. |
| green peas/ marrow peas (marrowfat) | بسلة خضراء/ بسلة كبيرة |
| green technology | تقنية خضراء |
| green vehicle | مركبة خضراء |
| greener | أكثر خضرة |
| greengage | برقوق أخضر |
| greenhouse | صوبة زجاجية |
| greenhouse frames of metal | إطارات للدفيئة مصنوعة من المعدن |
| greenhouse frames, not of metal | إطارات للدفيئة غير مصنوعة من المعدن |
| greenhouse gas | غاز احتباس حراري |
| greenhouse gases | الغازات الرافعة لدرجة الحرارة؛ غازات الصوبة الزجاجية |
| greenhouse gases | الغازات المسببة للاحتباس الحراري |
| greenhouses | صوبات زراعية |
| greenhouses of metal, transportable | دفيئة مصنوعة من المعدن، قابلة للنقل |
| greenhouses, transportable, not of metal | دفيئة، قابلة للنقل غير مصنوعة من المعدن |
| greening | تخضير |
| green-lipped mussel (e.g., perna canaliculus). | بلح البحر الأحمر (وهو نوع من المحار اسمه العلمي على سبيل المثال (Perna canaliculus). |
| greentech | تقنية خضراء |
| green-tech | تعبير يعني التقنية الخضراء |
| green-tech innovation | ابتكار أخضر تقني. ابتكار يراعي البيئة وتوفير الطاقة |
| greeting cards | بطاقات تهنئة |
| grey mold | العفن الرمادي |
| grey mould ; grey mold | العفن الرمادي |
| grid applications | تطبيقات شبكية |
| grid north | الشمال الإحداثي |
| gridded earth formation | تكوين أرضي شبكي |
| gridded simulation model | نموذج محاكاة شبكي |
| gridder | وسيلة عمل شبكة |
| griddles [cooking appliances] | صواني للخبز [أدوات للطهي] |
| griddles [cooking utensils] | صواني للخبز [أدوات للطهي] |
| gridiron supports | دعامات للشواية |
| grids for batteries | ألواح للبطاريات |
| grill supports | دعامات للمشواة |
| grilles of metal | مشواة مصنوعة من المعدن |
| grills [cooking appliances] | مشواة [أدوات للطهي] |
| grills [cooking utensils] | مشواة [أدوات طهي] |
| grind | الطحن |
| grinders/crushers, electric, for household purposes | مطاحن/ وسائل عصر كهربائية للأغراض المنزلية |
| grinding machines | آلات طحن |
| grinding preparations | مستحضرات للطحن |
| grinding wheels (emery -) | عجلات للطحن ( صنفرة) |
| grindings | مواد مجروشة |
| grindstones [hand tools] | أحجار تجليخ [أدوات يدوية] |
| grindstones [parts of machines] | أحجار التجليخ [أجزاء من الآلات] |
| grip pressure sensor | جهاز إحساس بقبضة الضغط |
| grit | الجريت ( حجر الطاحون ) |
| groats for human food | برغل للطعام البشرى |
| groats for poultry | برغل للطيور الداجنة |
| grog | مادة مقاومة للصهر: مادة متوهجة مقاومة للصهر؛ جروج (أنواع مشروبات روحية) |
| groove | حز؛ شق؛ تجويف |
| grooving | تشقق |
| gross income | إجمالي الدخل |
| gross negligence | إهمال جسيم |
| gross negligence | إهمال جسيم |
| grosso modo | تقريبا |
| ground acceleration | التعجيل الأفقي للهزة |
| ground rice | الأرز المجروش |
| ground robot | روبوتات أرضي |
| ground water | مياه جوفية |
| ground-breaking invention | اختراع مؤثر |
| grounded | متصل بطرف أرضي |
| groundnut | الفول السوداني |
| group bit order | مجموعة من ترتيب الرقم الثاني؛ مجموعة ترتيب الرقم الثاني |
| group captain | عقيد طيار |
| grout | ملاط (رقيق)؛ جص |

| | |
|---|---|
| grow | ينمو |
| growing media | أوساط الإنماء |
| growth | نمو |
| growth factor receptor tyrosine kinases | إنزيمات تيروسين كيناز لمستقبل عامل النمو |
| growth in renewable energy patent applications | نمو في طلبات البراءات المنصبة على الطاقة المتجددة |
| growth innovative activity | النشاطات الابتكارية المتعلقة بالنمو |
| growth of knowledge | نمو المعرفة |
| growth of scientific knowledge | نمو المعرفة العلمية |
| growth regulating preparations (plant -) | مستحضرات تنظيم النمو (مستحضرات لتنظيم نمو النبات) |
| gruel, with a milk base, for food | عصيدة ذات قاعدة من اللبن الحليب للطعام |
| gsm | جم/متر2 |
| gsm 1800 | هى شبكة الهاتف المحمول التي تستخدم الموجة 1800 MHz مثل التي تستخدمها شركتا اورانج وتي موبايل في بريطانيا وغيرهما من الشركات في مختلف أنحاء العالم. |
| gstp | الخطة العامة لاختبار النظم |
| gua | أنشطة تمارسها الحكومة |
| guaiacol for pharmaceutical purposes | نبات عود الأنبياء (جويفم) للأغراض الصيدلانية |
| guanidine | جوانيدين |
| guano | سماد الغوانو الطبيعي |
| guanosine | جوانوسين |
| guanylyl | جوانيليل |
| guar gum | صمغ الغوار |
| guard devices for lighting | وسائل حماية للإنارة |
| guard rails of metal | حواجز حماية مصنوعة من المعدن |
| guards (fire -) | أجزاء واقية (أجزاء واقية من الحريق) |
| guards [parts of machines] | أجزاء واقية [أجزاء من الآلة] |
| guava | جوافة |
| guest-star | ضيف الشرف |
| gui | واجهة تطبيق رسومية للمستخدم |
| guidance technology | تقنية التوجيه السلاح |
| guide agent | عامل توجيه |
| guide plate | لوح دليلي |
| guide tube | أنبوب دلالة |
| guide wheel | عجلة دليلية |
| guided missile | قذيفة موجهة |
| guided-wave system | نظام موجات موجَّه |
| guides | دلائل |
| guides for machines | موجهات للآلات |
| guidewires (medical -) | أسلاك توجيه (أسلاك توجيه طبية) |
| guillain-barre syndrome | متلازمة جيان – باريه: (التهاب الجذور والأعصاب الحاد المجهول السبب) |
| guilty intention | نية إجرامية |
| guinea pig | خنزير غينيا؛ خنزير هندي |
| guineapig | الخنزير الغيني |
| guirrilla warfare | حرب العصابات |
| guitars | جيتار |
| gulf cooperations council, gcc | مجلس التعاون الخليجي |
| gully dish | غطاء المصرف |
| gum | صمغ |
| gum (chewing-) | لبان (لبان للمضغ) |
| gum (tragacanth -) | صمغ (صمغ الكثيراء) |
| gum acacia | صمغ السنط |
| gum arabic | صمغ عربي |
| gum ghatti | صمغ جاتي |
| gum resins | راتنج صمغي |
| gum solvents | مذيبات للصمغ |
| gum tragacanth | صمغ الكثيراء |
| gum tragacanth and gum acacia | وصمغ الكثيرات وصمغ الأكاسيا |
| gum tragacanthh | صمغ الكثيراء |
| gum xanthan | صمغ الزانتان |
| gum-lac | صمغ اللك |
| gummed cloth | نسيج مصمغ |
| gummed tape [stationery] | شرائط مصمغة [أدوات مكتبية] |
| gun barrels | مواسير الأسلحة |
| gun carriages [artillery] | عربات المدفع [سلاح المدفعية] |
| gun cases | الغلاف الخارجي للسلاح |
| gun cotton | قطن البارود |
| gun racks | مشد الأسلحة |
| gunboat | زورق مسلح |
| gunner | فرد المدفعية |
| gunpowder | بارود |
| guns (artillery -) [cannons] | مدافع (مدافع لسلاح المدفعية) |
| guns (glue -), electric | مسدسات كهربائية (مسدسات شمع) |
| guns (hammers for -) | بنادق (طارق للبنادق) |
| guns (harpoon -) [sports articles] | أسلحة (أسلحة لإطلاق الرماح (الحربون)) [أدوات رياضية] |
| guns (harpoon -) [weapons] | أسلحة (أسلحة إطلاق (الحربون)) [أسلحة] |
| guns (noise-suppressors for -) | أسلحة (وسائل كاتمة للصوت خاصة بالأسلحة) |
| guns (paintball -) [sporting apparatus] | أسلحة (أسلحة للكرات الملونة) [أجهزة رياضية] |
| guns (sighting mirrors for -) | أسلحة (مرايا للرؤية خاصة بالأسلحة) |
| guns (spray -) for paint | أسلحة (أسلحة رشاشة) للدهان |
| guns [hand tools] | أسلحة (أدوات يدوية) |
| guns [tools using explosives] | أسلحة [أدوات تستخدم مواد متفجرة] |
| guns [weapons] | أسلحة [أسلحة] |
| guns, hand-operated, for the extrusion of mastics | أسلحة لقذف المواد الصمغية تدار يدوياً |
| gunstocks | مقابض البندقية |
| gunylyl | جوانيلايل |
| gurjun [gurjon, gurjan] (balm of -) for making varnish | جورجون (بلسم من شجر جورجون) لصناعة الورنيش |
| gurjun [gurjon, gurjan] balsam for medical | بلسم جورجون للأغراض الطبية |

| | |
|---|---|
| Purposes | |
| guru | مرشد |
| gust | عصف |
| gut flora | فلورا الأحشاء |
| gut for fishing | أمعاء حيوانات لصيد السمك |
| gut for making sausages | أمعاء حيوانات لعمل المقانق |
| gut for rackets | أوتار لمضارب التنس |
| guttapercha | مادة الجاتابرشا الشبيهة بالمطاط |
| gutter pipes of metal | مواسير البالوعات المصنوعة من المعدن |
| gutter pipes, not of metal | مواسير البالوعات، غير المصنوعة من المعدن |
| gutters of metal | بالوعات مصنوعة من المعدن |
| gutters, not of metal | بالوعات غير مصنوعة من المعدن |
| gut-trophic | تكثر في الأحشاء |
| gymnasium mats | سجاجيد للجمنازيوم |
| gymnastic mats | سجاجيد للجمباز |
| gymnastic shoes | أحذية للجمباز |
| gymnastics (appliances for -) | لعبة الجمباز (أجهزة للعبة الجمنازيوم) |
| gynecological | المتعلقة بطب النساء |
| gynecology | علم أمراض النساء |
| gypsophilia | جصِّية (نبات) |
| gypsum | الجص |

# H

| | |
|---|---|
| haberdashery , except thread | خردوات، ما عدا الخيوط |
| hackers | الهاكرز (لصوص الكمبيوتر) |
| hacking | اختراق؛ لصوصية |
| hacking | تعديل الأجهزة |
| hacking software | برنامج لاقتحام الحواسيب |
| hackles [hand tools] | أمشاط الكتان [أدوات يدوية] |
| hackling of flax | تمشيط ألياف الكتان |
| hacks | تعديلات |
| haematogen | مولد الدم |
| haemocytometer | مقياس الخلايا الدموية |
| haemoglobin | هيموجلوبين |
| haemolytic uremic syndrome | متلازمة انحلال الدم البوليني |
| haemophilus influenzae | بكتيريا الأنفلونزا المولعة بالدم |
| haemorrhagia | نزيف |
| haemorrhoid preparations | مستحضرات للبواسير |
| haemostatic pencils | أقلام قاطعة للنزف |
| hafnium [celtium] | هفنيوم [سلتيوم] (عنصر فلزي) |
| hague agreement for the protection of cultural properties 1899 | اتفاق لاهاي لعام 1899. |
| hague agreement for the protection of cultural properties 1907 | اتفاق لاهاي لعام 1907. |
| hainault scythes | مناجل هينولت |
| hair | شعر |
| hair (bows for the -) | شعر (أقواس للشعر) |
| hair (false -) | شعر [شعر مستعار] |
| hair (plaited -) | شعر (شعر مضفر) |
| hair (tresses of -) | شعر (ضفائر من الشعر) |
| hair band | رباط للشعر |
| hair bands | أربطة للشعر |
| hair clippers for animals [hand instruments] | وسائل لقص شعر الحيوانات [أدوات يدوية] |
| hair clippers for personal use [electric and non-electric] | وسائل قص الشعر للاستخدام الشخصي [كهربائية أو غير كهربائية] |
| hair clipping machines for animals | آلات لقص شعر الحيوانات |
| hair colorants | مواد لتلوين الشعر |
| hair coloring caps | أغطية رأس لتلوين الشعر |
| hair curlers [other than hand implements], non-electric | وسائل تجعيد الشعر (غير الأدوات التي تدار باليد) غير كهربائية |
| hair curling (hand implements for -) non-electric | تجعيد الشعر (أدوات يدوية لتجعيد الشعر) غير كهربائية |
| hair curling papers | ورق لتجعيد الشعر |
| hair curling pins | دبابيس لتجعيد الشعر |
| hair cutting machines for animals | آلات لقص الشعر للحيوانات |
| hair driers [dryers] | آلات لتجفيف الشعر [مجففات] |
| hair dyes | صبغات للشعر |
| hair for brushes | شعر للفرش |
| hair grips [slides] | مشابك للشعر [وسائل منزلقة لشبك الشعر] |
| hair growth preparations (medicinal -) | مستحضرات لنمو الشعر [مستحضرات دوائية لنمو الشعر] |
| hair lotions | غسول (لوسيون) للشعر |
| hair nets | شبكات للشعر |
| hair ornaments | زينة للشعر |
| hair pins | دبابيس للشعر |
| hair prostheses | زرع الشعر |
| hair spray | أسبراي للشعر |
| hair waving preparations | مستحضرات لتمويج الشعر |
| haircloth [sackcloth] | نسيج من وبر الجمل [خيش] |
| hair-curlers, electrically heated | وسائل لتجعيد الشعر، يتم تسخينها كهربائياً |
| hairdressers' chairs | مقاعد للحلاقين |
| hairpin | دبوس شعر - مشبك |
| hair-removing tweezers | ملاقط لإزالة الشعر |
| hairy cotton | قطن وبري |
| half cream cheese | جبن نصف دسم |
| half life | نصف العمر |
| half-boots | أحذية ذات رقبة نصفية |
| half-frame ; half frame | ذو إطار نصفي |
| half-hardy | متوسطة التحمل |
| half-life | فترة نصف عمر؛ عمر نصفي |
| half-maximal response | استجابة نصف قصوى |
| half-mers | الوحدات النصفية |
| half-molcules ; half molcules | الجزيئات النصفية |
| halftone | تدرج اللون: التدرج اللوني من الأسود إلى الأبيض عند طبع الصورة |
| half-track vehicles | مركبات نصف جنزير |
| hall | صالة؛ قاعة |
| hallmark | مميزة |
| hallmark positions | مواضع مميزة |
| hallmark residues | وحدات بنائية مميزة |
| halogenating reagent | مادة تفاعل هلجنة؛ كاشف هلجنة |
| halt | يوقف |
| halvah | نبات الحلفاء |
| ham | لحم خنزير |
| hammer | مطرقة؛ شاكوش |
| hammer | إبرة إطلاق النار |
| hammer mill | كسارة بالمطرقة |
| hammer sharpeners | مسننات للمطارق |
| hammers (pneumatic -) | مطارق (مطارق هوائية) |
| hammers [hand tools] | مطارق [أدوات يدوية] |
| hammers [parts of machines] | مطارق [أجزاء من الآلات] |
| hammers for guns and rifles | مطارق للمسدسات والبنادق |
| hammocks | أرجوحة شبكية |
| hampers [baskets] | سلال كبيرة ذات غطاء [سلال] |
| hamster | حيوان قارض |
| hand cars | عربات خفيفة |
| hand drills [hand tools] | مثقاب يدوي [أدوات يدوية] |

| | |
|---|---|
| hand drying apparatus for washrooms | جهاز تجفيف يدوي لحجرات الغسيل |
| hand labelling appliances | أجهزة يدوية لوضع الإشارات والأرقام |
| hand lever | الرافعة اليدوية |
| hand milking | حلب يدوي |
| hand pumps | مضخات يدوية |
| hand stripping | جني القطن يدويا |
| hand tools, hand-operated | أدوات يدوية تدار يدوياً |
| handbag frames | إطارات للحقائب اليدوية |
| handbags | حقائب يدوية |
| handbells [musical instruments] | أجراس يدوية [أدوات موسيقية] |
| handbooks [manuals] | كتيبات [أدلة] |
| handcuffs | قيود |
| handheld device | جهاز يمسك باليد |
| hand-held tools, other than hand-operated | أدوات تُحمل يدويا، غير التي تدار يدوياً |
| handkerchiefs of paper | مناديل من الورق |
| handkerchiefs of textile | مناديل من القماش |
| handle | مقبض: مقبض أو يد أي أداة يمكن أن تمسكها منه |
| handle | مقبض، يتعامل مع |
| handle bars for bicycles, cycles | مقود الدراجات |
| handles (ferrules of metal for -) | مقابض [حلقات من المعدن للمقابض] |
| handles (suitcase -) | مقابض [مقابض لحقائب السفر] |
| handles (tool -) not of metal | مقابض (مقابض للأدوات) غير مصنوعة من المعدن |
| handles (walking stick -) | مقابض (مقابض لعصى المشي) |
| handles, not of metal | مقابض غير مصنوعة من المعدن |
| (knife -) | [مقابض للسكاكين] |
| handling | تداول |
| handling and work devices | وسائل تداول وتشغيل |
| handling apparatus for loading and unloading | جهاز تعبئة وشحن للتحميل وإفراغ الحمولة |
| handling machines, automatic [manipulators] | آلات تعبئة وشحن أتوماتيكية [يدوية] |
| handling pallets, not of metal | منصات نقالة للتعبئة والشحن غير مصنوعة من المعدن |
| hand-off | خاصية التحويل |
| handouts | النشرات |
| hand-rests for painters | سنادات لليد للرسامين |
| hands (clock -) [clock- and watchmaking] | عقارب الساعة (عقارب لساعات الحائط) (صناعة ساعات اليد وساعات الحائط) |
| hand-to-hand fighting | قتال يدا بيد؛ قتال بالأيدي؛ تشابك بالأيدي |
| handwriting specimens for copying | نماذج الكتابة للنسخ |
| hang | يعلق |
| hang gliders | وسائل منزلقة للتعليق |
| hangar | حظيرة الطائرات |
| hanged | معلق |
| hanger | جهاز تعليق |
| hangers (coat -) | وسائل تعليق (وسائل لتعليق المعاطف) |

| | |
|---|---|
| hangers [parts of machines] | وسائل تعليق [أجزاء من الآلات] |
| hangings (wall -), not of textile | مواد (مواد معلقة على الجدار) غير مصنوعة من القماش |
| hangings for lamps | تعليقات للمصابيح |
| hank, jute bags, jute factory | شلة قطن، أجولة جوت، مصنع جوت |
| haploid | أحادي المجموعة الكروموسومية؛ أحادي الصبغيات |
| haploid | أحادي المجموعة الكروموسومية |
| haplotype | نمط فردي |
| haptic (tactile) | لمسي |
| hapticicity | ملامسة؛ تلامس |
| harassing tactics | أساليب التحرش |
| harbour | يأوي (أفراد التنظيم) |
| hard disc drive | محرك القرص الصلب |
| hard drive | محرك صلب |
| hardening preparations (metal -) | مستحضرات تصليد (مستحضرات تصليد معدنية) |
| hardening substances (limestone -) | مواد تصليد (مواد تصليد من الحجر الجيري) |
| hardware | معدات؛ أجهزة؛ عتاد: أي جزء معدني. فمثلا علبة الكمبيوتر والشاشة تندرج تحت مسمى معدات. |
| hardware of metal [small] | خردوات مصنوعة من المعدن [صغيرة] |
| hardware set | مجموعة معدات |
| hardware solutions | حلول باستخدام الأجهزة |
| hard-wired | سلكي؛ متصل بسلك. عكس لاسلكي wireless |
| hardy | شديدة التحمل |
| harmful invention | اختراع ضار |
| harmonic directional measurements | القياسات الاتجاهية التوافقية |
| harmonicas | هرمونيكا |
| harmoniums | الأرغن |
| harness | طقم أحزمة تثبيت أو أمان؛ حزام تثبيت أو أمان |
| harness | يسخر |
| harness (climbers' -) | عدة تسلق الجبال أو أطقم الفرس لقافز السدود |
| harness (security -) for vehicle seats | عدد (أطقم أمان) لمقاعد المركبات |
| harness belts | أحزمة أمان |
| harness fittings of iron | تركيبات لأطقم الفرس من الحديد |
| harness fittings of precious metal | تركيبات لأطقم الفرس من المعادن النفيسة |
| harness fittings, not of precious metal | تركيبات لأطقم الفرس غير مصنوعة من المعدن النفيس |
| harness for animals | عدة وأطقم للحيوانات |
| harness for sailboards | عدة الألواح الشراعية |
| harness of metal for handling loads | عدد من المعدن لتداول الحمولة |
| harness straps | أربطة لأطقم الفرس |

| | |
|---|---|
| harness traces | حبال أطقم الفرس الخاصة بجر العربة |
| harness, not of metal, for handling loads | عدد، غير مصنوعة من المعدن لتداول الحمولة |
| harnessing | تسخير |
| harnessing energy | تسخير الطاقة |
| harp strings | أوتار القيثارة |
| harpoon guns [sports articles] | أسلحة الحراب (الحربون) [أدوات رياضية] |
| harpoon guns [weapons] | أسلحة الحراب (الحربون) [أسلحة] |
| harpoons | حراب |
| harpoons for fishing | حراب لصيد السمك |
| harps | قيثارات |
| harrows | آلات لتمهيد التربة |
| harvest | حصد |
| harvesting machines | آلات حصاد |
| hash clusters | عروض الجداول المميزة |
| hashimoto thyreoiditisand primary myxedemia | التهاب الدرقية لهاشيموتو |
| hashing functions | وظائف hashing |
| hat boxes of cardboard | صناديق من الورق المقوى للقبعات |
| hat boxes of leather | صناديق من الجلد للقبعات |
| hat frames [skeletons] | إطارات للقبعات [هياكل] |
| hat linings, of textile, in the piece | بطانة للقبعات من القماش بداخل القبعة |
| hat ornaments [not of precious metal] | زينة للقبعة [غير مصنوعة من المعدن النفيس] |
| hat ornaments [of precious metal] | زينة للقبعة [مصنوعة من المعدن النفيس] |
| hat stands | حوامل للقبعات |
| hatchback | هاتشباك |
| hatchets | فؤوس صغيرة |
| hatching | التظليل بخطوط متوازية |
| hats | قبعات |
| hats with bells [musical instruments] | قبعات ذات أجراس [أدوات موسيقية] |
| haulage apparatus [mining] | جهاز جر [تعدين] |
| hauling machines (net -) [fishing] | آلات جر [آلات جر الشبكة] [صيد السمك] |
| have (with) | يعمل مع |
| haversacks | أجربه المؤن |
| hay | تبن |
| hay fever | حمى الخريف؛ حمى الكلأ |
| hazardous invention | اختراع خطير |
| hazardous material | مادة خطرة |
| hazardous waste | نفايات خطرة |
| hazelnuts | بندق |
| h-chain | سلسلة ثقيلة |
| hcl | حمض هيدروكلوريك |
| hct | هيماتوكريت: قياس حجم كرات الدم الحمراء وتظهر كنسبة مئوية لإجمالي حجم الدم. |
| hcv | التهاب الكبد الوبائي C |
| hcv infection | عدوى فيروس HCV |
| hcv ns3 protease inhibitors | مثبطات بروتياز NS3 لـ HCV |
| hd | رمز حرب كيمائية لغاز الخردل |
| hdbk | كتيب |
| hdd | محرك قرص صلب |
| hd-dvd rom drive | مشغلات أقراص HD-DVD |
| hdlc | تحكم عالي المستوى في روابط البيانات |
| hdtvs (high-definition televisions) | التلفزيونات عالية التعريف |
| head cleaning tapes [recording] | أشرطة لتنظيف رأس التسجيل [التسجيل] |
| head x tail | رأس × ذيل |
| headache (articles for -) | صداع (أدوات للصداع) |
| headache pencils | أصابع طبية للصداع |
| headbands [clothing] | أربطة رأس [ملابس] |
| headbox | صندوق رأسي |
| header | مقدمة {كمبيوتر} |
| header | طوب مستعرض |
| header | مجمع علوي؛ أنبوب صاعد {وصف المفاعلات} |
| header tank | خزان علوي |
| headgear for wear | ألبسة رأس للارتداء |
| heading | التزهير |
| headings clause | البند الخاص بالعناوين. بند تعاقدي يبين أن عناوين بنود العقد واردة لمجرد التوضيح |
| headlights for automobiles | مصابيح أمامية للسيارات |
| head-mounted display | شاشة/أداة عرض مثبتة على الرأس |
| headphone jack | مقبس سماعة رأس |
| headphones | سماعات رأس |
| headquarters | المقر الرئيسي |
| head-rests [furniture] | سنادات رأس [أثاث] |
| head-rests for vehicle seats | سنادات رأس لمقاعد المركبات |
| heads up display, or hud technology | تكنولوجيا HUD |
| head-stalls | جزء من اللجام يحيط بالرأس |
| headwall | جدار ظهري |
| health insurance portability and accountability act (hipaa) | قانون التأمين الصحي وإمكانية الحمل والمحاسبة |
| health monitoring | المراقبة السليمة |
| healthy | سليم |
| healthy | صحي؛ متمتع بالصحة |
| healthy | معافى |
| hear regulator | منظم للسمع |
| hear the case | ينظر قضية |
| hearing aids for the deaf | وسائل مساعدة للصُم على السماع |
| hearing protectors | وسائل واقية للسمع |
| hearings | جلسات استماع (بالبرلمان)؛ جلسة استماع |
| heart failure | قصور القلب |
| heart pacemakers | ضابطات لنبضات القلب |
| heart rate variability | تغيرية معدل نبضات القلب |
| hearths | مواقد |
| heat | يسخن، سخونة |
| heat (compositions to prevent the radiation of -) | حرارة (تركيبات لمنع إشعاع الحرارة) |
| heat (non-conducting materials for retaining -) | حرارة (مواد غير موصلة لحجز الحرارة) |
| heat accumulators | مراكم حرارية |

| | |
|---|---|
| heat adhesive patches for repairing textile articles | رقعات لاصقة بالحرارة لإصلاح المواد من القماش |
| heat balance | ميزان الحرارة |
| heat content | المحتوى الحراري |
| heat energy | طاقة سخونة |
| heat energy gathering device | جهاز مجمع للطاقة الساخنة |
| heat exchange fluids | مائع للتبادل الحراري |
| heat exchanger | مبادل الحرارة |
| heat exchangers [not parts of machines] | وسائل تبادل الحرارة [غير أجزاء الآلات] |
| heat exchangers [parts of machines] | وسائل تبادل الحرارة [أجزاء من الآلات] |
| heat inactivated fetal bovine serum (fbs) | مصل جنيني بقري غير منشَّط بالحرارة |
| heat jackets | أغلفة حرارية |
| heat path | مسار الحرارة |
| heat pumps | مضخات الحرارة |
| heat recovery | استخلاص الحرارة |
| heat recovery steam generator unit | وحدة مولد بخار تعمل باستخلاص الحرارة |
| heat regenerators | معيد توليد الحرارة |
| heat regulating apparatus | جهاز تنظيم الحرارة |
| heat seeking detection systems | أجهزة الكشف التي تتعقب الحرارة؛ أنظمة الكشف الباحثة عن الحرارة |
| heat shock protein | بروتين الصدمة الحرارية |
| heat sink | مبدد حرارة |
| heat strengthened glass (hs) | زجاج مقوى بالحرارة: زجاج تصل صلابته إلى ضعف صلابة الزجاج الملدن وعند حدوث كسر فإنه يتناثر على هيئة شظايا أكبر قليلاً من شظايا الزجاج المسقي بالكامل ، وهو من النوع الذي يستخدم بوجه عام في أعمال التزجيج التي تحتاج إلى متانة إضافية |
| heat transfer | انتقال الحرارة |
| heat transfer | تحويل السخونة |
| heat treated flat glass | زجاج مسطح معالج حرارياً: يصنف إلى مجموعتين مختلفتين |
| heater | سخان؛ جهاز تسخين |
| heater | مسخن |
| heaters (immersion -) | سخانات (سخانات غاطسة) |
| heaters for baths | سخانات للحمامات |
| heaters for feeding bottles, non-electric | سخانات لزجاجات الرضاعة، غير كهربائية |
| heaters for heating irons | سخانات لتسخين المكواة |
| heaters for vehicles | سخانات للمركبات |
| heaters, electric, for feeding bottles | سخانات كهربائية لزجاجات الرضاعة |
| heat-exchanged gas ; heat exchanged gas | غاز حدث له تبادل حراري |
| heating apparatus | جهاز تسخين |
| heating apparatus for defrosting windows of vehicles | جهاز تسخين لإزالة الصقيع عن نوافذ المركبات |
| heating apparatus for solid, liquid or gaseous fuels | جهاز تسخين للوقود الصلب أو السائل أو الغازي |
| heating apparatus, electric | جهاز تسخين كهربائي |
| heating boilers | غلايات للتسخين |
| heating cushions [pads], electric, for medical purposes | وسائد تسخين (كمادات) كهربائية للأغراض الطبية |
| heating elements | عناصر تسخين |
| heating filaments, electric | فتائل تسخين كهربائية |
| heating furnace | فرن المعالجة الحرارية |
| heating installations | تجهيزات تسخين |
| heating installations (hot water -) | تجهيزات تسخين(تجهيزات تسخين للماء الساخن) |
| heating installations [water] | تجهيزات تسخين [ماء] |
| heating pad | كِمادة مسخنة |
| heating plates | أطباق تسخين |
| heating value of the residue gas | القيمة الحرارية للغاز المتبقي (أم القدرة الحرارية) |
| heat-insulated containers | حاويات معزولة الحرارة |
| heavy chain constant domain | نطاق ثابت ذو سلسلة خفيفة |
| heavy chain domain ; heavy-chain domain | نطاق ثقيل السلسلة |
| heavy chain variable domain | نطاق متغير ثقيل السلسلة |
| heavy industries | الصناعات الثقيلة |
| heavy machine gun (hmg) | رشاش ثقيل |
| heavy minerals | معادن ثقيلة |
| heavy pitches | المواد القارية الثقيلة |
| heavy shelling | قصف عنيف |
| heavy water | ماء ثقيل |
| hectograph | هكتوجراف (منضحة) |
| hectometre | هكتو متر: 100 متر |
| hedge funds | صناديق التحوط |
| heel-making machines | آلات لعمل كعوب الأحذية |
| heelpieces for boots and shoes | أجزاء كعب الحذاء للأحذية العادية والأحذية ذات الرقبة |
| heelpieces for stockings | أجزاء الكعب للجوارب |
| heels | كعوب |
| hegemony | سيطرة |
| helical spring | نابض لولبي |
| helicobacter pylori | بكتيريا حلزونية |
| helicopter | هليكوبتر؛ طائرة عمودية؛ حوامة |
| helicopter carrier | حاملة هليكوبتر |
| helicopter gunship | هليكوبتر مسلحة |
| heliographic apparatus | أجهزة هليوجراف (تلسكوب لتصوير الشمس) |
| heliogravure | الطباعة الغائرة |
| heliotropine | بلورات هليوتروبين |
| helium | هليوم |
| helix | الحلزون |
| helmet mount | وصلة الخوذة |
| helmets (protective -) | خوذات (خوذات واقية) |
| helmets (protective -) for sports | خوذات (خوذات واقية) للرياضة |
| hemangioma | ورم وعائي دموي |
| hematimeters | هيماتيميتر (عداد كريات الدم) |
| hematogen | مولد الدم |
| hematology parameters | العوامل المتغيرة لأمراض الدم |
| hematoma | ورم دموي |

| | |
|---|---|
| hematopoiesis | تكون وتطور الدم |
| hematopoietic | مساعد على تكون الدم |
| hemectant | مادة ماصة للرطوبة |
| hemi | نصفي |
| hemiester | نصف إستر |
| hemihydrate; hemi-hydrate; hemi hydrate | نصف هيدرات |
| hemi-hydrate; hemi hydrate | نصف هيدرات |
| hemline markers | وسائل لوضع علامات خطوط الحاشية |
| hemming machines | آلات لعمل الحواشي |
| hemochromatosis | مرض التلون الدموي |
| hemodynamic | متعلق بسرعة تيار الدم |
| hemoglobin | هيموجلوبين |
| hemoglobinopathy | انخفاض الهيموجلوبين |
| hemolytic anemia | فقر الدم الانحلالي |
| hemorrhage | نزف |
| hemorrheologic agents | عوامل جريان الدم |
| hemorrhoid preparations | مستحضرات للبواسير |
| hemostatic pencils | أصابع طبية لقطع النزف |
| hemothorax | صدر دموي؛ تجمع دموي في التجويف البلوري |
| hemp | خيوط القنب الهندي |
| hemp bands | أربطة مصنوعة من خيوط القنب |
| hemp cloth | أقمشة مصنوعة من خيوط القنب |
| hemp fabric | أنسجة مصنوعة من خيوط القنب |
| hemp thread and yarn | خيوط وغزول القنب |
| hems (false -) | حواشي الثياب (حواشي منفصلة للثياب) |
| heparin lock = heparinized syringe | إبرة هيبارين لمنع تجلط الدم |
| heparinised | معالج بالهيبارين |
| hepatic first-pass metabolism | أيض العبور الأول الكبدي |
| hepatitis | التهاب الكبد |
| hepatitis c virus replication inhibitors | مثبطات نسخ فيروس التهاب الكبد الوبائي |
| hepatocellular | كبدية خلوية |
| hepatocellular carcinoma | الورم السرطاني المتعلق بالخلايا الكبدية |
| hepatocyte | خلية كبدية |
| heptocyte clearance | تصفية خلية كبديّة |
| herbicide safeners | عوامل مقننة لسمية مبيدات الأعشاب |
| herbicides | مبيدات الأعشاب |
| herbs (medicinal -) | أعشاب (أعشاب دوائية) |
| herbs for smoking | أعشاب للتدخين |
| herbs teas | أعشاب شاي |
| herbs, fresh (garden -) | أعشاب طازجة (أعشاب طازجة من البساتين) |
| hereditary non~polyposis colorectal cancer | السرطان القولوني المستقيمي بغير البوليب الوراثي |
| hereunto annexed | مرفق طيه |
| herg)-encoded potassium channel | قناة مشفرة بجين hERG |
| heritage knowledge | ثقافة تراثية |
| heritage project | المشروع التراثي |
| hermetical | معزول عن الهواء |
| hernia bandages | ضمادات للفتق |
| herniated/ruptured/prolapsed intervertebral disk syndrome | متلازمة القرص بين الفقاري المفتوق/ المتمزق/ الساقط |
| herpes gestationis | هربس الحمل |
| herpetic | حلائي |
| herringbone-style packing | حشو من نوع herringbone |
| herrings | سمك الرنجة |
| heter- ; hetero-, prefix | سابقة لغوية بمعنى: مغاير |
| hetero | غير متجانسة |
| heteroaryl | مجموعة أريل غير المتجانسة |
| heteroatom ring member | ذرة غير متجانسة في الحلقة |
| heterocycle | حلقة غير متجانسة |
| heterocyclic | حلقي غير متجانس |
| heterocyclic alkyl | ألكيل حلقي غير متجانس |
| heterocycloalkyl | سيكلو ألكيل غير متجانس |
| heterocyclyl | مجموعة حلقية غير متجانسة |
| heterocyclyl group | مجموعة حلقية غير متجانسة |
| heterocyclyltin | مجموعة حلقية غير متجانسة محتوية على القصدير |
| heterodimer | دايمر غير متجانس |
| heterodimeric complex | دايمري غير متجانس |
| heteroduplex molecule | جزيء مضاعف غير متجانس |
| heterogeneity | انعدام تجانس |
| heterogeneous | غير متجانس |
| heterologous | متغاير التكوين |
| heterologous genes (transgenes) | جينات متغايرة التكوين؛ جينات محوَّلة |
| heteromultimers | عديدات الوحدات غير المتجانسة |
| heterophasic | غير متجانسة الطور |
| heteropoly | متعدد غير متجانس |
| heteroscedasticity | تغاير تفاوتي |
| heterospecific | غير متجانس النوعية |
| heterozygote | اللاقحة المخالفة |
| het-het fused systems | أنظمة ملتحمة مع هت-هت |
| hexagonal | مسدس الشكل |
| hexahydrocannabinol | هكسا هيدروكانابينول |
| hexamer | هكسامر: وحدة بنائية سداسية |
| hexamethylenetetraamine | هكسا ميثلين تترا أمين |
| hexan | هكسان |
| hexane and ethanol isocratic system | نظام متساوي التأثير مكون من هكسان وإيثانول |
| hexapod robot | روبوت سداسي الأرجل |
| hexose | هكسوز |
| hexoses | وحدات الهكسوز |
| hexyl | هِكسيل |
| hf | تردد عال |
| hfa | هيدرو فلورو ألكان |
| hg | هكتو جرام |
| hhc | مقر القيادة وسرية مقر القيادة |
| h-hour | ساعة بدء القتال (ساعة-س) |
| hi sp | سرعة عالية |
| hidden curriculum | المنهج الخفي |
| hiding pigments | خضابات الإخفاء |
| hierarchical structure | هيكل هرمي |
| high chairs for babies | مقاعد عالية للأطفال الرضع |
| high colour | لون واضح |
| high definition | عالي التعريف |
| high hydrocarbons | هيدروكربونات عالية الكربون |

| | |
|---|---|
| high impact velocities | سرعات تصادم عالية |
| high molecular weight basic substance | المادة القاعدية مرتفعة الوزن الجزيئي |
| high networth individuals | أصحاب الأصول المالية الكبيرة |
| high pass filter; high-pass filter | مرشح تمرير الترددات العالية |
| high pressure processing | معالجة الضغط العالي |
| high pressure pumps | مضخات عالية الضغط |
| high pressure washers | آلات للغسل بالضغط العالي |
| high resistance seal | عزل ذو مقاومة عالية |
| high resolution sector field icp-ms | جهاز ICP-MS ذو مجال قطاعي عالي الدقة |
| high shear mixer | خلاط عالي القص |
| high shear mixture | خليط عالي القص |
| high stringency | ظروف عالية الصرامة |
| high tensile (strength) layer | طبقة عالية المقاومة للشد |
| high tension batteries | بطاريات عالية الجهد |
| high vac | على فراغ عالي |
| high value patent drawings | رسومات براءة ذات قيمة عالية |
| high venules | أوردة صغيرة مرتفعة |
| high yield seeds | بذور وفيرة الغلة |
| high-end computers | أجهزة الكمبيوتر المتقدمة |
| higher carbon compounds: | مركبات عالية الكربون |
| higher hydrocarbons | الهيدروكربونات الأعلى |
| high-frequency apparatus | جهاز عالي التردد |
| highgraded model | نموذج محسَّن النوعية أو الفئة |
| highgrading (a model) | تحسين نوعية أو فئة (أحد النماذج) |
| highly attenuative | عالية التخفيف |
| highly classified invention | اختراع سري للغاية |
| highly-opaque; highly opaque | عالية الإعتام |
| high-order | عالي الرتبة |
| high-performance liquid chromatography ("hplc") | كروماتوجراف السائل عالي الأداء ("HPLC") |
| high-shear | عالي مقاومة القص |
| high-stakes assessment | تقييم عالي المخاطرة |
| high-tech | تكنولوجي حديث |
| high-tech | تعبير يعني التقنية عالية المستوى |
| high-temprature | عند درجة حرارة عالية؛ عالي درجة الحرارة |
| high-throughput ; high throughput | معالجة البيانات (الضخمة) بمعدل سريع |
| high-transmission glass; high-transmittance glass | زجاج عالي النفاذية/الإنفاذية |
| hijacked (zombie) computers | أجهزة الكمبيوتر المختَرَقة [والتي يُطلَق عليها (زومبي)] |
| himez | نطاق اشتباك بالصواريخ على ارتفاع عال |
| hind leg | ساق خلفية |
| hinge | منطقة مفصلية، مفصلة |
| hinge area | منطقة المفصلة |
| hinge member | جزء مفصلي |
| hinge region | منطقة المفصل؛ المنطقة المفصلية |
| hinge region of iggl antibody. | منطقة المفصلة لجسم مضاد IgGI |
| hinges of metal | مفصلات مصنوعة من المعدن |
| hinges, not of metal | مفصلات، غير مصنوعة من المعدن |
| hippocampus | قرن آمون |
| hips for roofing | أسنمة لعمل الأسقف |
| hire clause | البند الخاص بالاستئجار |
| hired inventor | مخترع أجير لدى الغير |
| histamine type 1 receptor | مستقبل هيستامين من النوع 1 |
| histamine type 2 receptor | مستقبل هيستامين من النوع 2 |
| histamine type 3 receptor | مستقبل هيستامين من النوع 3 |
| histamine type 4 receptor | مستقبل هيستامين من النوع 4 |
| histo, hisito | نسيجي |
| histochemistry | كيمياء الأنسجة |
| histogram | المدرج التكراري |
| histogram | المخططات التكرارية: مخططات تبين التوزيع التكراري لمتغير ما |
| histogram | مخطط تكراري: مخطط يبين التوزيع التكراري لمتغير ما |
| histological sections | قطاعات من الأنسجة |
| histology | علم الأنسجة |
| histomorphometric markers | مرقمات التحديد التاريخي الشكلي |
| historical inventor | مخترع تاريخي |
| hit-and-run | الكر والفر |
| hitching jaw | فك تشبيكي |
| hi-technology patent | براءة في مجال التقنية العالية |
| hm | توجيه آلي نحو الهدف |
| hmmwv | مركبة مدولبة متعددة الأغراض عالية الحركية |
| hoac | حمض أسيتيك |
| hoax | الهوكس-خدعة-رسائل الخداع |
| hockey sticks | عصى لعبة الهوكي |
| hodgkin lymphoma | الورم الليمفاوي لهودكين |
| hoes [hand tools] | معازق [أدوات يدوية] |
| hoist | رفع |
| hoists | آلات رافعة |
| hold | يحجز؛ يثبت |
| hold someone in contempt | يتهمه بإعاقة العدالة |
| hold-downs | مثبتات |
| holder | حامل، صاحب شيء |
| holders (passport -) | حوامل (حوامل لجوازات السفر) |
| holders for checkbooks [cheque books] | حوامل لدفاتر الشيكات (دفاتر الشيكات) |
| holders for electric coils | حوامل للملفات الكهربائية |
| holders for flowers and plants [flower arranging] | حوامل للأزهار والنباتات [تنسيق الأزهار] |
| holders for stamps [seals] | حوامل للأختام [أختام] |
| holding company | شركة قابضة |
| holding devices for machine tools | وسائل حاملة للأدوات الخاصة بالآلات |
| holding patterns | أنماط؛ صور حيازة الأرض |
| holding structure = mounting structure (to hold sth in a certain location) | بنية تثبيت |
| holdup | نسبة احتجاز |
| holdup amount; hold-up amount | الكمية المحتجزة |

| | |
|---|---|
| holing axes | فؤوس مجوفة |
| holistic security | أمن كلي |
| hollow | تجويف |
| hollow body | جسم فارغ |
| hollow cylinder | اسطوانة مجوفة |
| hollowing bits [parts of hand tools] | مثقاب التجويف [أجزاء من الأدوات اليدوية] |
| holmium | هلميوم |
| hologram | صورة مجسمة؛ رسم ثلاثي الأبعاد |
| home automation system | نظام جعل المنزل أوتوماتيكيا |
| home country | دولة الموطن |
| home equity account | حساب ائتماني بضمان المنزل |
| home front | جبهة داخلية |
| home page | الصفحة الرئيسية: أول صفحة لموقعك تظهر دائما لك |
| home robot | روبوت بيت |
| homegrown engineering | هندسة محلية |
| home-host information sharing | التشارك في المعلومات مع (فرع) البلد المضيف |
| homeostasis | اتزان داخلي |
| homeowners association | اتحاد الملاك |
| homestead owners | ملاك الأراضي |
| homicide | جرائم القتل |
| homochiral | أحادي المتشاكل |
| homogenate | مادة متجانسة |
| homogenisation; homogenization | تجانس |
| homogeniser | مُجانس؛ عامل تجانس |
| homogenous ; homogeneous | متماثل؛ متجانس |
| homograft | رقعة متجانسة؛ رقعة متماثلة: رقعة لعضو أو نسيج من متبرع إلى مستقبل بحيث يكونا من نفس النوع، كرقعة من شخص إلى آخر مماثل |
| homologous | فرد متماثل؛ نظير |
| homologue | نظير؛ فرد متماثل |
| homologue ; homolog | نطاق أو منطقة تجانس |
| homology domain | بشكل تحليلي متجانس |
| homolytically | تجانسية الصفات |
| homozygosity | لاقحة متجانسة |
| homozygote | عسل |
| honey | قرص العسل |
| honeycomb | رتبة شرفية |
| honorary rank | غطاء؛ قلنسوة |
| hood | جزء علوي |
| hooding | أغطية في شكل كوخ (غطاء للشفط في شكل كوخ) للمطابخ |
| hoods (extractor -) for kitchens | أغطية واقية للرأس والوجه [ملابس] |
| hoods [clothing] | أغطية علوية [أجزاء من الآلة] |
| hoods [parts of machines] | أغطية في شكل كوخ لعربات الأطفال |
| hoods for baby carriages | أغطية لمحركات المركبات |
| hoods for vehicle engines | أسقف للمركبات |
| hoods for vehicles | يعقف، عقاف، خطاف |
| hook | شرائط تثبيت من نوع الدعامة والمشبك |
| hook and pile fastening tapes | قابل للعقف |
| hookable | |
| hooked | معقوف |
| hook-engageable | قابل للربط عن طريق المعقف |
| hooking section | مقطع خطافي |
| hookload | حمل وزن مواسير الحفر |
| hooks (boat -) | خطافات (خطافات للمراكب) |
| hooks (curtain -) | مشابك خطافية (مشابك خطافية للستائر) |
| hooks (embroidering crochet -) | إبر معقوفة (إبر معقوفة لحبك الخيوط) |
| hooks (fish -) | خطافات (خطافات للسمك) |
| hooks (rug -) | إبر معقوفة (إبر معقوفة لصناعة السجاد) |
| hooks (shoe -) | مشابك خطافية للأحذية |
| hooks [haberdashery] | مشابك خطافية [خردوات] |
| hooks [metal hardware] | مشابك خطافية [خردوات معدنية] |
| hooks for corsets | خطاف للمشد النسائي (الكورسيه) |
| hooks for slate [metal hardware] | خطاف للألواح الإردوازية (خردوات معدنية) |
| hooks of metal for clothes rails | مشابك خطافية مصنوعة من المعدن لمشاجب الملابس |
| hooks, not of metal, for clothes rails | مشابك خطافية، غير مصنوعة من المعدن لمشاجب الملابس |
| hoop cutters [hand tools] | قاطعات حلقية [أدوات يدوية] |
| hoop iron | أطواق حديدية |
| hoop steel | أطواق فولاذية |
| hoops of metal (barrel -) | أطواق مصنوعة من المعدن (أطواق مصنوعة من المعدن للبراميل) |
| hoops, not of metal (barrel -) | أطواق، غير مصنوعة من المعدن (أطواق غير مصنوعة من المعدن للبراميل) |
| hoops, not of metal (cask -) | أطواق غير مصنوعة من المعدن، (أطواق غير مصنوعة من المعدن للأوعية) |
| hooves (animal -) | حوافر (حوافر الحيوانات) |
| hooves (cement for animal -) | حوافر (ملاط لحوافر الحيوانات) |
| hop cones | أقماع من أزهار الجُنجُل |
| hopper | قادوس |
| hoppers [mechanical discharging] | قواديس [للتفريغ الميكانيكي] |
| hoppers [non-mechanical] of metal | قواديس [غير ميكانيكية] مصنوعة من المعدن |
| hops | أزهار الجُنجُل |
| hops (extracts of -) | أزهار الجُنجُل (مستخلصات من أزهار الجُنجُل) |
| hops (extracts of -) for making beer | أزهار الجُنجُل (مستخلصات من أزهار الجُنجُل) لصناعة البيرة |
| horizons | خطوط أفق |
| horizontal | أفقي |
| horizontal | المحور الأفقي |
| horizontal axis | المحور الأفقي |
| horizontal score | علامة / خط أفقي |
| hormone replacement therapy | العلاج البديل بالهرمونات؛ العلاج بالهرمونات البديلة |
| hormones for hastening the ripening of fruit | هرمونات لتعجيل نضوج الفاكهة |

| | |
|---|---|
| horn, unworked or semi-worked | قرون، مشكلة أو شبه مشكلة |
| horns (animal -) | قرون (قرون الحيوانات) |
| horns (drinking -) | قرون (قرون للشرب) |
| horns (powder -) | أقماع للبارود |
| horns [musical instruments] | أبواق [أدوات موسيقية] |
| horns for loudspeakers | أبواق (لمكبرات الصوت) |
| horns for vehicles | أبواق للمركبات |
| horro film | أفلام الرعب |
| horse blankets | بطاطين للفرس |
| horse brushes | فرش للفرس |
| horse collars | أطواق للفرس |
| horse radish peroxidase | انزيم البيروكسيداز المستخلص من نبات الفجل الحار |
| horsehair | شعر ذيل الفرس |
| horsehair for bows [for musical instruments] | شعر ذيل الفرس لقوس الكمان [للأدوات الموسيقية] |
| horsehair gloves for massage | قفازات من شعر الفرس للتدليك |
| horseradish | فجل حار |
| horseradish peroxidase-conjugated streptavidin | ستربتافيدين مقترن ببيروكسيداز الفجل الحار |
| horseshoe games | ألعاب الحدوة |
| horseshoe nails | أظافر نعل الفرس |
| horseshoes of metal | حدوة فرس مصنوعة من المعدن |
| horst | الصدوع المكونة للظهور الصدعية (الهورست |
| horticultural frames, not of metal | إطارات الأعمال البستانية غير مصنوعة من المعدن |
| horticulture | زراعة البساتين |
| horticulture chemicals, except fungicides, herbicides, insecticides and parasiticides | كيماويات للأعمال البستانية، ما عدا مبيدات الفطريات، ومبيدات الأعشاب الضارة ومبيدات الحشرات ومبيدات الطفيليات |
| hose | خرطوم |
| hose (fire -) | خراطيم (خراطيم للحريق) |
| hose (watering -) | خراطيم (خراطيم مياه) |
| hose carts | عربات ذات خراطيم |
| hose connection | وصلة خرطومية |
| hoses (reels, not of metal, non-mechanical, for flexible -) | خراطيم (بكرات لف، غير مصنوعة من المعدن، غير ميكانيكية، للخراطيم المرنة) |
| hoses (winding spools, not of metal, non-mechanical, for flexible -) | خراطيم (مكبات لف، غير مصنوعة من المعدن، غير ميكانيكية، للخراطيم المرنة) |
| hoses of textile material | خراطيم مصنوعة من القماش |
| hosiery | جوارب |
| hosiery (bags for washing -) | جوارب (حقائب لغسل الجوارب) |
| hosiery looms | نول للجوارب |
| hospital beds | أسرة للمستشفيات |
| hospitalize | يدخل إلى المستشفى |
| host | عائل؛ مضيف |
| hostile software | برنامج عدائي |
| hostilities | اشتبكات |
| hot | تدريب تشغيلي |
| hot air apparatus | جهاز الهواء الساخن |
| hot air bath fittings | تركيبات الهواء الساخن للحمامات |
| hot air ovens | أفران الهواء الساخن |
| hot air therapeutic apparatus | جهاز علاجي بالهواء الساخن |
| hot air vibrators | هزازات بالهواء الساخن |
| hot exhaust gas | غاز العادم الساخن |
| hot filling | التعبئة على الساخن، التعبئة في الحالة الساخنة |
| hot flushes | حالات الفوران الحراري الجلدي |
| hot metal composing ; lynotyping | طباعة اللينونيت |
| hot plates | لوحات تسخين |
| hot pots [not electrically heated] | قدور ساخنة [لا يتم تسخينها كهربائياً] |
| hot spot | بقعة ساخنة |
| hot swapping | التبديل الحي |
| hot water bottles | زجاجات ماء ساخن |
| hot-dip | غمر ساخن |
| hotlink protection scripts | برامج حماية الوصلات الساخنة: برامج لحماية الوصلات الهامة من السرقة من خارج الموقع |
| hotplate; hot-plate; hot plate | سطح ساخن |
| hot-press paper | ورقة ضغط ساخن |
| hot-rolling ; hot rolling | الجلفنة على الساخن؛ الدرفلة على الساخن |
| hourly space velocity | سرعة فراغية مقدرة بالساعات |
| hours on stream | ساعات التشغيل |
| house | يأوي |
| house | يبيّت |
| house keeping genes | الجينات الشغالة؛ جينات "التدبير المنزلي": جينات يتم التعبير عنها في كل خلايا الجسم وتسهم في إنتاج مواد ضرورية لصيانة الخلايا والاستقلاب. لكن بعضها الآخر ينتسخ في أماكن أو مراحل معينة فقط. |
| house member | عضو مجلس النواب |
| house numbers (luminous -) | أرقام المنازل [أرقام مضيئة للمنازل] |
| house numbers of metal, non-luminous | أرقام المنازل، مصنوعة من المعدن وغير مضيئة |
| house numbers, not of metal, non-luminous | أرقام للمنازل، غير معدنية، وغير مضيئة |
| house of commons (lower house) | مجلس العموم (البريطاني) |
| house of lords (upper house) | مجلس اللوردات (البريطاني) |
| house of representatives | مجلس النواب |
| house painters' rollers | بكرات لعمال الدهان بالمنازل |
| household containers of precious metal | حاويات منزلية مصنوعة من المعدن النفيس |
| household linen | بياضات من الكتان للمنزل |
| household pets (nesting boxes for -) | حيوانات أليفة منزلية (صناديق لإيواء الحيوانات الأليفة المنزلية) |
| household utensils of precious metal | أدوات منزلية مصنوعة من المعدن النفيس |
| housepower | قدرة ميكانيكية |

| | |
|---|---|
| housing | مبْيَت |
| housing | مبيت |
| housings [parts of machines] | أماكن تسكين (مبيت) [أجزاء من الآلة] |
| hover | يحوم |
| hovercraft | حوامة |
| howitzers | هاوتزرات |
| hp | قدرة حصان |
| hpi | ساعة بعد العدوى؛ ساعة بعد الإصابة بالعدوى |
| hplc | كروماتوجراف السائل مرتفع الأداء |
| hps | مواصفة منتجات المعدات |
| hrs | ساعات |
| hs | الزجاج المقوى بالحرارة |
| hscsd | بيانات الدوائر عالية السرعة: تطوير هام في مجال شبكات الهواتف المحمولة والذي يتيح زيادة سرعة البيانات من 9.6 كيلوبايت إلى 57.6 كيلوبايت وذلك بتوحيد الحيز الزمني. |
| htrf (homogeneous time-resolved fluorescence) receptor-ligand binding assay | اختبار ارتباط المجموعة الترابطية بالمستقبل HTRF (التألق الفلوري المتجانس للتحلل عبر الزمن) |
| http | بروتوكول تحويل النص التشعبي |
| h-type or re ion-exchanged zeolite | زيوليت التبادل الأيوني من النوع H أو من النوع RE |
| hub | محور،مفرع؛ لوحة توصيل؛ لوحة وصل، |
| hub caps | أغطية لمحاور العجلات |
| hubs for vehicle wheels | محاور لعجلات المركبات |
| hull, husk | القشرة |
| hulling machine | ماكينة تقشير |
| hulls (ships' -) | هياكل (هياكل سفن) |
| human | بشري |
| human anti-gcgr antibody | جسم مضاد بشري لـ GCGR |
| human capital | رأس المال البشري. مزيج الخصائص والمهارات والكفاءات المهنية والشخصية التي يكتسبها شخص فتجعل له مكانا في سوق العمل. |
| human c-met variants | صور متغيرة لـ c-Met بشري |
| human consensus framework | إطار توافقي بشري |
| human consensus framework sequence | متوالية إطار توافقي بشري |
| human decision making | صناعة القرار البشرية |
| human ether-a-go-go-related gene (herg) | الجين المسؤل عن تشفير قنوات البوتاسيوم المؤدي لاعادة الاستقطاب القلبي |
| human framework sequence | متوالية إطار بشري |
| human genetic evidence | دليل وراثي مأخوذ من البشر |
| human genome project | مشروع الجينوم البشري. هو من أهم التطورات الدولية للجينات البشرية، وقد بدأ هذا المشروع عام 1990م، وكان من أهم أهدافه اكتشاف جميع المورثات البشرية Genes Human وتحديد التتابع الكامل لأزواج القواعد النيتروجينية |
| human germline gene segment sequences | متواليات جزء جيني من سلالة جرثومية بشرية |
| human il-17a binding igg assays | اختبارات ربط IL-17A بشري بـ IgG |
| human interfaces | أسطح بينية بشرية |
| human kvl .5 potassium channel | قناة بوتاسيوم لـ Kv1.5 بشري |
| human nogo 5+6 gst | NOGO 5+6 GST بشري |
| human security | الأمن البشري. يعد شعار الأمن البشري من شعارات منظمة الأمم المتحدة |
| human tumor nude mouse xenograft models | نماذج فئران مجردة الشعر تم تركيب رقع خارجية لها من ورم بشري |
| human whole blood | دم كامل بشري |
| humanisation ; humanization | التوافق مع البشر؛ جعله متوافقا مع البشر |
| humanized ; humanised | متوافق مع البشر |
| humanized antibody | جسم مضاد متوافق مع البشر |
| humanized milk | لبن مشابه للبن الأم |
| human-level machine intelligence | ذكاء آلي على نفس مستوى البشر |
| humanoid robot | روبوت |
| human-tissues-related invention | اختراع متعلق بالأنسجة البشرية |
| humectant | مرطب |
| humidors | مرطبات (لصندوق السجائر) |
| humint | الاستخبارات البشرية |
| hummus [chickpea paste] | حمص (معجون الحمص) |
| humoral response | الاستجابة الخلطية: الإستجابة المناعية التي تقوم بها الأجسام المضادة Antibodies المفرزة من قبل الخلايا البلازمية plasmocytes المنحدرة من الخلايا البـائية B-cells |
| humus | مادة الدُبال |
| humus top dressing | سماد عضوي من مادة الدُبال |
| hunting firearms | أسلحة نارية للصيد |
| hunting game calls | وسائل نداء لصيد الطيور والحيوانات |
| hunting knives | سكاكين الصيد |
| huntington's chorea | رقص هنتجتنون |
| huqin [chinese violins] | الهيوكين [الكمان الصيني] |
| husked barley | شعير مقشر |
| husked oats | شوفان مقشر |
| husker | مقشرة |
| husking machines (corn and grain -) | آلات تقشير (آلات تقشير للذرة والحبوب) |
| huts | أكواخ |
| hvac | تدفئة وتهوية وتكييف هواء |
| hw | معدات؛ أجهزة |
| hybrid automatic retransmission (h-arq) scheme | نظام إعادة إرسال آلي هجين H-ARQ |
| hybrid electric vehicle | مركبة خليطية كهربائية |
| hybrid integrated circuits | دوائر متكاملة هجينية |

| | |
|---|---|
| hybrid vehicles | سيارات هجينة |
| hybridize | يهجن |
| hybridize (to) | يحدث له تهجين (في) أو يهجن (في) |
| hybridoma | ورم هجين |
| hybrids | المختلطات |
| hydrants | صنابير رئيسية |
| hydrastine | هيدراستين |
| hydrastinine | هيدراستينين |
| hydrate | هيدرات |
| hydrated chloral | هيدرات الكلورال |
| hydrated forms | الصور المميَّهة |
| hydration | تميه؛ إضافة ماء؛ اتحاد بالماء |
| hydraulic | هيدروليكي |
| hydraulic circuits (fluids for -) | دوائر هيدروليكية (مائع للدوائر الهيدروليكية) |
| hydraulic circuits (liquids for -) | دوائر هيدروليكية (سوائل للدوائر الهيدروليكية) |
| hydraulic circuits for vehicles | دوائر هيدروليكية للمركبات |
| hydraulic door openers and closers [parts of machines] | وسائل فتح ووسائل إغلاق هيدروليكية للأبواب |
| hydraulic energy | طاقة هيرو ليكية |
| hydraulic engines and motors | محركات وموتورات هيدروليكية |
| hydraulic fracturing | التصدع الهيدروليكي |
| hydraulic jack stand | رافعة هيدروليكية ثابتة |
| hydraulic nipple | وصلة هيدروليكية |
| hydraulic pressure | ضغط هيدروليكي |
| hydraulic turbines | تربين مائي |
| hydrazine | هيدرازين |
| hydrazine monohydrate | أحادي هيدرات هيدرازين |
| hydrazinolysis | تحليل بالهيدرازين |
| hydroboration | إدخال البورون والهيدروجين |
| hydrobromide | هيدروبروميد |
| hydrocarbon | هيدروكربونات (مركب كربوني) |
| hydrocarbon composition | التركيبة الهيدروكربونية |
| hydrocarbon economy | اقتصاد معتمد على الهيدروكربون |
| hydrocarbon feed | تيار التغذية الهيدروكربوني (وأيضا تيار التغذية بالهيدروكربون) |
| hydrocarbon feedstock | خام تغذية هيدروكربوني؛ خام تغذية بالهيدروكربون |
| hydrocarbon liquid | سائل هيدروكربوني |
| hydrocarbon oil | زيت هيدروكربوني |
| hydrocarbon solvents | مذيبات هيدروكربون |
| hydrochlorate | هيدروكلورات |
| hydrochloric acid | حمض هيدروكلوريك |
| hydroconversion | التحويل الهيدروجيني |
| hydrocracker | وحدة تكسير بالهيدروجين |
| hydrocracking | تكسير بالهيدروجين |
| hydrocyclone | فرازة مخروطية مائية |
| hydrodearomatization | نزع الشكل العطري بالهيدروجين |
| hydrodemetallation | نزع المعدن بالهيدروجين |
| hydrodesulfuration hds and hydrodenitrogenation hdn respectively | نزع الكبريت بالهيدروجين HDS ونزع النيتروجين بالهيدروجين HDN، بالترتيب |
| hydrodesulfurization | نزع الكبريت بالهيدروجين |
| hydrodynamic size of ligands | الحجم الهيدروديناميكي للمركبات الترابطية |
| hydroelectric energy | طاقة هيدروكهربية |
| hydro-electricity | كهرومائية |
| hydrofining | تحسين هيدروجيني |
| hydrofluoric acid | حمض هيدروفلوريك |
| hydroformylation | إدخال مجموعة هيدروفورميل؛ إدخال مجموعة الفورميل المتحد بالهيدروجين |
| hydrogen | هيدروجين |
| hydrogen bond | رابطة هيدروجينية |
| hydrogen bonding | ترابط هيدروجيني |
| hydrogen economy | اقتصاد معتمد على الهيدروجين |
| hydrogen embrittlement | تقصُّف أو تهشيش بالهيدروجين (تهشيش بكذا) |
| hydrogen fuel cells | خلايا وقود هيدروجيني |
| hydrogen peroxide | فوق أكسيد الهيدروجين |
| hydrogen response | الاستجابة للهيدروجين (في صناعة المحفزات) |
| hydrogenate | يهدرج. يمزج هيدروجين. |
| hydrogenation | هدرجة |
| hydrogencracking | تكسير بالهيدروجين |
| hydrogenolysis | تحلل بالهيدروجين؛ التحلل الهيدروجيني |
| hydrogenolysis | التحلل الهيدروجيني |
| hydrogen-rich fuel cell combustion gas | غاز احتراق خلية الوقود الغني بالهيدروجين |
| hydroisomerate | ناتج أزمرة بالهيدروجين |
| hydroisomeration | الأزمرة بالهيدروجين |
| hydrolysation | حل مائي ؛ انحلال مائي |
| hydrolysis | تحليل مائي أو تحلل مائي |
| hydrolyzation | حل مائي ؛ انحلال مائي |
| hydrolyze ; hydrolyse | يحل مائيا |
| hydromel [mead] | شراب من ماء وعسل [الميد شراب مخمر] |
| hydrometers | هيدرومتر (مقياس الثقل النوعي للسوائل) |
| hydromorphone hci & naloxone hc1 | هيدرومورفون HCl ونالوكسون HC1 |
| hydrophile | إلف للماء |
| hydrophilic | آلف للماء؛ قابل للذوبان في الماء |
| hydrophobic | غير آلف للماء؛ غير قابل للذوبان في الماء |
| hydrophobic frit | فريت غير آلف للماء |
| hydrophobicity | عدم الألفة للماء؛ عدم القابلية للذوبان في الماء |
| hydrophone | سماعة مائية |
| hydroplanes | طائرات مائية |
| hydroprocessing | معالجة بالهيدروجين |
| hydrostatic beds | أسِرَّة هيدروستاتية |
| hydrotalcite | تالكيت مائي |
| hydrothermal | حراري مائي |
| hydrotreatment | المعالجة بالهيدروجين |
| hydroxy functional polyacrylate | أكريلات بها مجموعة هيدروكسي وظيفية |
| hydroxy thiol ester composition | تركيبة إستر هيدروكسي ثيول |
| hydroxypropylcellulose | سيليولوز هيدروكسي بروبيل |

| | |
|---|---|
| hygienic bandages | أربطة صحية |
| hygienic basins | أحواض صحية |
| hygienic paper | ورق صحي |
| hygrometers | جهاز قياس الرطوبة النسبية في الجو |
| hygroscopic | استرطابي؛ ماصة للرطوبة |
| hygroscopicity | الاسترطاب: امتصاص الرطوبة |
| hymophilia | الاستعداد النزفي |
| hyper compressor | ضاغط من النوع الفائق |
| hyperactive bladder | المثانة مفرطة النشاط |
| hyperalgesia | فرط التألم |
| hyperandrogenic chronic anovulation | انقطاع الإباضة المزمنة المتميزة بفرط إفراز الأندروجين |
| hyperandrogenism | فرط إفراز الأندروجين |
| hyperapolipoproteinemia | زيادة نسبة البروتين الخالي من الدهن في الدم |
| hyperbaric | مفرط الضغط أو الوزن |
| hyperbetalipoproteinemia | فَرْطُ بروتيناتِ الدَّمِ الشَّحْمِيَّةِ البيتائِيَّة |
| hyperbolic paraboloid | قطع مكافئ زائدي |
| hypercalcaemia | فرط كالسيوم الدم |
| hypercholesteraemia | فرط كوليستيرول الدم |
| hyperglycaemia | الزيادة المفرطة للسكر في الدم |
| hyperglycemia | فرط سكر الدم |
| hyperhidrosis | فرط العرق |
| hyperinsulemia | فرط الإنسولين في الدم |
| hyperinsulinemia | فرط الإنسولين في الدم |
| hyperkinetic | مفرط الحركة |
| hyperleptinemia | زيادة اللبتين في الدم |
| hyperlipidaemia | ارتفاع نسبة الدهون في الدم |
| hyperlipidemia | فرط دهون الدم |
| hyperlipoproteinaemia | فرط البروتينات الشحمية في الدم |
| hyperoxic | مفرط الأكسجين |
| hyperparathyroidism | فرط نشاط الغدد جار الدرقية |
| hyperplasia | فرط التنسج |
| hyperproliferative | فرط التكاثر |
| hyperproliferative diseases | الأمراض مفرطة التكاثر |
| hyperreactive airways | المسالك الهوائية مفرطة التفاعلية |
| hypertension | ارتفاع ضغط الدم |
| hypertension | ارتفاع الضغط |
| hyperthermic | مفرط أو مرتفع الحرارة |
| hyperthymic | مفرط التوتة |
| hyperthyreosis | فرط الدرقية |
| hypertonic | مفرط التناضح |
| hypertriglyceridemia | فرط ثلاثي الجليسريد في الدم |
| hypertriglyceridemia-hypertrigliceridemia | فرط تكوُّن الجلسريدات الثلاثية في الدم |
| hypertrophic | متضخم |
| hypertrophy | تضخم |
| hyperuricemia | فرط حمض يوريك الدم |
| hypervariable | مفرط التغير |
| hypervariable positions | مواضع مفرطة التغير |
| hypoalphalipoproteinemia | نقص البروتين الشحمي من النوع ألفا بالدم |
| hypochloride (potassium -) | هيبو كلوريد (هيبوكلوريد البوتاسيوم) |
| hypochlorite of soda | هيبوكلوريت من الصودا |
| hypochlorous acid | حمض هيبوكلوروز |
| hypocotyl | سويق الجنين |
| hypodermic | تحت الجلد |
| hypodermic needle | إبرة حقن |
| hypodermic syringes | محقنة تحت الجلد |
| hypogammaglobulinemia | انخفاض جاماجلوبين الدم |
| hypogastric belts | أحزمة للمنطقة البطنية الوسطى أسفل السرة |
| hypoglycaemia | انخفاض حاد في مستوى السكر في الدم |
| hypokinetic | ضعيف النشاط |
| hypopharynx carcinoma | الورم السرطاني بالبلعوم السفلي |
| hypophosphorylated | منخفض المعالجة بالفوسفور |
| hyposulphites | هيبو سلفيت |
| hypotension | انخفاض ضغط الدم |
| hypothalamus | غدة تحت المهاد بالمخ |
| hypothermic | فاتر الحرارة |
| hypotonic | ناقص التوتر |
| hypoventilation (respiratory depression) | نقص التهوية |
| hypoxanthine | هيبوزانتين |
| hypoxic-ischemic encephalopathy | اعتلال دماغي ناتج عن نقص الأكسجين مصحوب بقصور الدم الموضعي |
| hysterectomized women | النساء مستأصلَة الرحم |

# I

| | |
|---|---|
| icao | الهيئة الدولية للطيران المدني التابعة للأمم المتحدة |
| ice (dry -) [carbon dioxide] | ثلج (ثلج جاف) [ثاني أكسيد الكربون] |
| ice bags | أكياس ثلج (للأغراض الطبية) |
| ice bath | حمام ثلج |
| ice boxes | ثلاجات |
| ice buckets | دلاء للثلج |
| ice chests | أوعية محكمة للثلج |
| ice cold | بارد |
| ice cream | بوظة (أيس كريم) |
| ice cream (binding agents for -) | بوظة (عوامل رابطة للبوظة) |
| ice cube molds [moulds] | قوالب لمكعبات الثلج |
| ice for refreshment | ثلج منعش |
| ice machines and apparatus | آلات وأجهزة لصناعة الثلج |
| ice moulds of metal | قوالب ثلج من المعدن |
| ice nails [climbing irons] | مسامير للثلج [حدائد تسلق] |
| ice pails | سطل ثلجي |
| ice picks | حفار الثلج |
| ice skates | لوحات تزلج على الجليد |
| ice water | ماء مثلج |
| ice, natural or artificial | ثلج طبيعي أو اصطناعي |
| ice-cold ; ice cold | بارد |
| ice-cooled condition | ظروف تبريد بالثلج |
| iced tea | شاي مثلج |
| ices (binding agents for edible -) | مثلجات (عوامل رابطة للمثلجات الصالحة للأكل) |
| ices (edible -) | مثلجات (مثلجات صالحة للأكل) |
| ices (powder for edible -) | مثلجات (مسحوق للمثلجات الصالحة للأكل) |
| icosahedron | مجسم له عشرين وجه |
| icp-aes | القياس الطيفي للانبعاث الذري - البلازما المقترن حيثياً |
| ict | تكنولوجيا الاتصالات والمعلومات |
| ict awareness | وعي تقنية الاتصالات والمعلومات |
| ict incident report | تقرير الأحداث المتصلة بتقنية المعلومات والاتصالات |
| ict's industry trends | توجهات صناعة تقنية المعلومات والاتصالات |
| ict-driven society | مجتمع تسوقه تقنية المعلومات الحاسبية |
| icv | داخل بطين المخ |
| icv | قيمة فحص متكاملة |
| id | قطر داخلي |
| id | في الجلد |
| id. | نفسه |
| idea | فكرة |
| idea commercialization | جعل الفكرة ذات طبيعة تجارية |

| | |
|---|---|
| idea documentation | توثيق فكرة |
| idea expression | التعبير عن الفكرة |
| idea materialization | تحقق الفكرة |
| idea promoters | مروجو الأفكار |
| idea testability | قابلية الفكرة للاختبار |
| idea theft | سرقة فكرة |
| idea's inventability | قابلية الفكرة للاختراع |
| idea's feasibility | جدوى فكرة |
| ideas-driven growth | نمو تسوقه الأفكار |
| ideas-driven society | مجتمع تسوقه الأفكار |
| identifiability | قابلية الشيء للتعريف |
| identifiable | قابل للتعريف |
| identification | تعريف |
| identification | تعريف |
| identification bracelets of metal, for hospitals | أساور تعيين هوية مصنوعة من المعدن للمستشفيات |
| identification bracelets, not of metal, for hospitals | أساور لتعيين الهوية، غير مصنوعة من المعدن، للمستشفيات |
| identification device | جهاز تعريف |
| identification scheme | مخطط التعريف |
| identification sheaths for electric wires | أغلفة تحديد للأسلاك الكهربائية |
| identification systems | نظام تعرف |
| identification threads for electric wires | خيوط تحديد للأسلاك الكهربائية |
| identify | يحدد |
| identity | هوية |
| identity cards, magnetic | بطاقات هوية، مغناطيسية |
| identity plates of metal | لوحات هوية، مصنوعة من المعدن |
| identity plates, not of metal | لوحات هوية غير مصنوعة من المعدن |
| identity theft penalty enhancement act | قانون تفعيل عقوبة سرقة الهوية |
| ideological differences | خلافات عقائدية |
| idf(s) | إطار (إطارات) لتوزيع الوسيطة |
| idiopathic | ذاتي المنشأ؛ مجهول السبب؛ غامض. |
| idiopathic epilepsy | صرع ذاتي المنشأ؛ صرع مجهول السبب: صرع لم ينشأ عن اضطراب عقلي ويبدأ أثناء الطفولة أو المراهقة |
| idiopathic pulmonary fibrosis | التليف الرئوي ذاتي المنشأ |
| idiopathic purpura | فرفرية ذاتية المنشأ |
| idiopathic thrombocytopenic purpura | الفرفرية ذاتية المنشأ بانحلال الصفيحات |
| idiopathy | مرض ذاتي المنشأ؛ مرض مجهول السبب: مرض ينشأ عفويا أو من سبب مجهول |
| idiotype | نمط ذاتي |
| idiotypic | متعلق بالنمط الذاتي |
| idl | رابطة بيانات دولية |
| idle speed | سرعة الدوران؛ سرعة التباطؤ |
| iec | لجنة كهروتقنية داخلية |
| ieee | معهد مهندسي الكهرباء والإلكترونيات |
| ies | جمعية هندسة الإضاءة |
| iex | تبادل أيوني |
| ifpp | تعليمات لتحضير العرض |

| | |
|---|---|
| igeneous rock | صخور نارية |
| igg antibody | جسم مضاد IgG |
| igg2 bulk antibody | جسم مضاد سائب IgG2 |
| igne beads | مسبحيات IGNE |
| igniting apparatus, electric, for igniting at a distance | جهاز إشعال كهربائي للإشعال عن بعد |
| igniting devices for internal combustion engines | وسائل إشعال لمحركات الاحتراق الداخلي |
| igniting magnetos | مغنيط الإشعال |
| igniting magnetos for engines | مغنيط إشعال للمحركات |
| ignition (electric apparatus for remote -) | إشعال (جهاز كهربائي للإشعال عن بعد) |
| ihc | كيمياء الأنسجة والمناعة |
| il-17r fc fusion protein | بروتينات اندماج IL-17R Fc |
| il-18 receptor antigen binding protein | بروتين ربط مولد ضد بمستقبل IL-18 |
| ileitis | التهاب لفائفي |
| ileocolitis | التهاب لفائفي قولوني |
| iliac | حرقفي |
| il-ir igg2 antibody | جسم مضاد IgG2 لـ IL-IR |
| illegitimate patent | براءة غير شرعية. براءة قائمة على أسس غير سليمة. ومن أبرز الأسس غير السليمة التي تتأسس عليها البراءات الادعاء بعدم وجود اختراعات سابقة، وهي التي تعرف بالفن السابق |
| illicit gains | مكاسب غير مشروعة |
| illuminatable | قابل للإضاءة |
| illuminate | يضيء |
| illuminating grease | شحم إنارة |
| illuminating wax | شمع إنارة |
| illumination | إضاءة |
| illuminator | مضيء |
| illustrate | يوضح |
| illustration | توضيح |
| illustrations | توضيحات، رسوم توضيحية |
| illustrative | الرسوم التوضيحية الخاصة بالبراءة |
| illustrator | مختص بالرسوم التوضيحية |
| ils | إسناد لوجستي متكامل |
| ilsp | خطة الإسناد اللوجستي المتكامل |
| im | إدارة المعلومات |
| im | في العضل |
| im | رسالة فورية |
| image | صورة |
| image advertising | ترويج المفهوم؛ الترويج الرمزي؛ الترويج الانطباعي |
| image converter | محولٌ للصورة |
| image counter (current image) | عداد الصور (الصورة الحالية) |
| image intensification technology | تقنية تكثيف الصورة |
| image intensifier | مكثف صورة |
| image quality | جودة الصورة |
| image quality/size/record mode indicato | مؤشر جودة الصورة/الحجم/وضع التسجيل |
| image recognition | التعرف إلى الصورة |
| image resizer | مُعيد ضبط حجم الصورة |
| image resolution | صفاء الصورة |
| image rotator | مُدورٌ للصورة |
| image sensing surface | سطح مستشعر للصورة |
| image sensor | جهاز إحساس بالصورة |
| image size | حجم الصورة |
| image size indicator | مؤشر حجم الصورة |
| image transmission | نقل صورة |
| imageable document | مستند ممكنٌ تصويره |
| imagery | صورة، فن صنع التمثيل أو الأصنام الأيقونات |
| imaging | تصوير |
| imaging technology | تقنية تصوير |
| imidazo | إميدازو |
| imidazole | إميدازول |
| imine | إيمين |
| imines and oximes | مركبات الإيمين والأوكسيم |
| imino acid | حمض إميني |
| imitation gold (objects of -) | ذهب مقلد (مواد مصنوعة من الذهب المقلد) |
| imitation leather | جلد مقلد |
| immaterial expression | تعبير غير مادي |
| immersed | منقوع |
| immersion heater | مسخِن غاطس |
| immersion heaters | سخانات غاطسة |
| immiscible | غير قابل للامتزاج |
| immobile time | زمن عدم التحرك |
| immortalize | تتم المحافظة عليه حياً |
| immortalizing the cells | الاحتفاظ بالخلايا حية |
| immune | منيع |
| immune milk | لبن محصن ضد الأمراض |
| immune response domain (ird) | نطاق استجابة مناعية |
| immune-mediated disease | مرض مناعي (مثل مرض مناعة ذاتية) |
| immunity | مناعة |
| immunization | تحصين |
| immunize | يحصّن (مناعياً) |
| immunize | يحصن ، يوفر المناعة |
| immunized | معطى المناعة |
| immunizer | محصن، معطي المناعة |
| immunoadhesin | عامل الالتصاق المناعي؛ لاصق مناعي |
| immunoadhesive | لاصق مناعي |
| immunoadjuvant therapy | العلاج بالمساعد المناعي |
| immunoassay | مقايسة مناعية |
| immunoconjugates | مقترنات مناعية |
| immunogen | مولد المناعة |
| immunogenicity | توليد مناعة |
| immunoglobulin | جلوبيولينات مناعية |
| immunoglobulin gene | جين الغلوبلينات المناعية |
| immunoglobulin single variable domain | نطاق متغير مفرد لجلوبيولين مناعي |
| immunoglobuline vl or vh domains | نطاقات خفيفة أو ثقيلة السلسلة لجلوبيولين مناعي |
| immunoglobulins | الجلوبيولينات المناعية |
| immunologic | مناعي |
| immunological | متعلق بالتحصين |
| immunologist | عالم مناعة |

| | |
|---|---|
| immunology | علم المناعة |
| immunomer | مونومر مناعي |
| immunopotentiation | تأثير (مفعول) مناعي |
| immunoprecipitation | ترسيب مناعي |
| immunosuppressive | كابت المناعة |
| impact driving cap | غطاء تحريك صدمي |
| impact mill | مطحنة صدمية |
| impact pile driver | مشغل دق ركائز صدمي |
| impact strength | مقاومة الصدمات |
| impair | يعوق |
| impaired | مَعُوق |
| impaired glucose tolerance | التحمل الضعيف للجلوكوز |
| impaired glucose tolerance | اختلال تحمل الجلوكوز |
| impairer | عائق |
| impairment | إعاقة |
| impart sth | يكشف عن كذا |
| impart sth to sth (impart sth sth) | إضفاء أو منح خاصية كذا لكذا |
| impedance | مُعَاوَقَةٌ |
| impedance convertor | محول معاوقة |
| impede | يعوق |
| impeder | عائق |
| impediment | عائق |
| impeding | إعاقة |
| impeding innovation | إعاقة الابتكار |
| impinging beam | حزمة واردة |
| implant | غريسة |
| implant | غريسة: نسيج أو جهاز مزروع (طعم)، يزرع |
| implantable device | جهاز قابل للزرع |
| implantable medical device | جهاز طبي قابل للزرع |
| implantation | زرع |
| implanted | مزروع |
| implanter | زارع |
| implants | زراعات |
| implants (surgical -) [living tissues] | أنسجة حية مزروعة (أنسجة حية مزروعة جراحياً) [أنسجة حيه] |
| implement | أداة؛ وسيلة |
| implement | ينفذ |
| implementability | قابلية الشئ للتنفيذ |
| implementable invention | اختراع قابل للتطبيق |
| implementations | تطبيقات؛ استخدامات |
| implementer | منفذ |
| impregnate | يشرّب (المصدر تشريب) |
| impregnated dressings | ضمادات نقع |
| impregnating chemicals (leather) | كيماويات تشرب (كيماويات تشرب للجلد) |
| impregnating chemicals (textile) | كيماويات تشرب (كيماويات تشرب للقماش) |
| impregnation | تشريب |
| impressed | مسلّط |
| impression | طبعة؛ طبع (أسنان) |
| imprinters (credit card -), non-electric | آلات طباعة (آلات طباعة الفواتير لبطاقات الائتمان) (غير كهربائية) |
| improve | يحسن |
| improvement | تحسين |
| improvement feasibility | جدوى التحسين |
| improvement invention | اختراعات تتعلق بالتطوير |
| improving permucosal absorption" | (تركيبة تُعطى عن طريق المخاط وطريقة لتحسين الامتصاص عن طريق المخاط) |
| impulse physics | فيزياء الدفع |
| in % of control | في صورة % للعينة العيارية |
| in % of day 0 | في صورة % من اليوم صفر |
| in a 5 % co2 atmosphere | في جو به تركيز يبلغ 5% من CO2 |
| in a closed position | في وضع الإغلاق |
| in a flush manner | في نفس المستوى |
| in a follow-up study | في دراسة تكميلية |
| in a freeze-dried (lyophilized) condition | في حالة تجفيف بالتجميد (تجفيد) |
| in a given direction | في اتجاه معلوم |
| in a liquefied medium | في وسط مسال |
| in a liquid medium | في وسط سائل |
| in a loaded position | في وضع التحميل |
| in a melt | في صورة صهير |
| in a proportion of | بنسبة قدرها |
| in a single pass | في ممر مفرد |
| in a vacuum | في وسط مفرغ = تحت التفريغ |
| in a vacuum oven | في فرن وسط مفرغ |
| in an ice-salt bath | في حمام ملح مثلّج |
| in an open manner | بطريقة مفتوحة |
| in approximate weight percent | في صورة نسبة مئوية تقريبية بالوزن |
| in bold | مكتوب بخط خليظ |
| in bulk | كبير الحجم |
| in bursts | على دفعات |
| in conjuction with | جنبا إلى جنب مع |
| in effect | في حيز/نطاق التنفيذ |
| in face-to-face relation to ; in face-to-face relationship with | مقابل |
| in fluid communication with ; in fluid contact with | على اتصال عن طريق مائع مع |
| in his capacity | بصفته |
| in ice bath | في حمام ثلج |
| in impurity amounts | في صورة كميات توجد كشوائب |
| in italics | مكتوب بخط مائل |
| in its entirety | بالكامل؛ في مجمله |
| in kit form | في شكل طقم؛ في شكل مجموعة |
| in microgravity | تحت تأثير الجاذبية الدقيقة |
| in need thereof | في حاجة إليه |
| in one portion | دفعةً واحدةً |
| in one stroke | دفعة واحدة |
| in par with | تتماشى مع |
| in parrallel | على التوازي |
| in particular | بشكل محدد |
| in portions | على أجزاء |
| in prism | باستخدام المنشور |
| in re | المشار إليه (برقم مرجعي) |
| in rem | عيني |
| in series | |

| | |
|---|---|
| in situ | في الموقع |
| in the clear | بدون تشفير |
| in the order of | في حدود |
| in the range of | في حدود |
| in unit dosage form | في صور وحدة جرعة |
| in unit gravity | تحت تأثير وحدة الجاذبية |
| in use | أثناء الاستخدام |
| in vacuo | في وسط مفرغ = تحت التفريغ |
| in vitro | في المختبر |
| in vitro, in situ, and in vivo diagnosis | التشخيص في المختبر، وفي الموضع، وفي جسم الكائن الحي |
| in vivo | في جسم الكائن الحي |
| in. | بوصة |
| in/hr | بوصة في الساعة |
| in/out knob | زر دخول/خروج |
| inaccessible knowledge | معرفة لا يمكن الوصول إليها |
| inactivation | إبطال فعالية |
| inactive patent | براءة غير مفعلة |
| inactive patent portfolio | محفظة براءات غير مفعلة |
| inadequate security awareness | وعي أمني غير كاف |
| inapplicable invention | اختراع غير قابل للتطبيق |
| inbred, in-bred | مهجن داخليا |
| incandescent burners | مواقد متوهجة |
| incense | بخور |
| incense (insect repellent -) | بخور (بخور طارد للحشرات) |
| inch | بوصة |
| incidence | سقوط (الأشعة إلخ) |
| incident angle | زاوية سقوط |
| incident beam | موحد ألوان |
| incident beam of penetrating radiation | حزمة ساقطة من أشعة نافذة |
| incident light | ضوء ساقط |
| incident x-ray beam | حزمة الأشعة السينية الساقطة |
| incinerator | فرن إحراق |
| incinerators | أفران إحراق القمامة |
| incipient failure | تعطُّل أولي |
| incipient wetness techniques | أساليب الترطيب الابتدائية |
| incite | يحرض |
| inclination | الميل |
| inclination switch | مفتاح ميل |
| inclined ways for boats | مساند إنزال مائلة للمراكب |
| inclined well | بئر مائلة |
| inclinometers | مقياس الميل |
| include | يشتمل على |
| include but are not limited to | يتضمن على سبيل المثال لا الحصر |
| inclusion | تضمين |
| inclusion and exclusion criteria | معايير الاختيار والإقصاء |
| inclusion bodies | أجسام اشتمال |
| inclusion criteria | معايير الاختيار |
| inclusions | شوائب دخيلة |
| incoming mixture | الخليط الداخل |
| incomplete capacity | أهلية غير كاملة |
| incomplete disclosure | إفصاح غير كامل |
| incomplete invention | اختراع جزئي |

| | |
|---|---|
| incontinence sheets | أغطية للسرير لسلس البول |
| incontinents (napkins for -) | مرضى سلسل البول (مناشف لمرضى سلسل البول) |
| incontinents (pants, absorbent, for -) | مرضى سلس البول (سراويل تحتية ماصة لمرضى سلس البول) |
| incoporeal right | حق معنوي |
| incore | في الذاكرة الرئيسية |
| incorporate | يضمّن؛ يدمج |
| incorporation | إدراج / مدرج |
| increased propensity | الميل المتزايد |
| incremental | تزايدي؛ اضطرادي |
| incremental improvement | تحسين طفيف |
| incremental invention | اختراع إضافي |
| incremental patent | براءة إضافية، براءة مؤسسة على ابتكار طفيف |
| incremental value model | نموذج القيمة الإضافية. طريقة لاحتساب القيمة المالية للممتلكات الفكرية |
| incubate (with) | يحتضن (باستخدام) |
| incubation medium | وسط حضانة |
| incubator | جهاز حضانة؛ حاضن؛ حاضنة؛ حضّان: يستخدم لحفظ وتحضين العينات عند درجات حرارة مختلفة |
| incubator for babies | جهاز حضانة للأطفال |
| incubator for bacteria culture | جهاز حضانة لمزارع البكتريا |
| incubator with varying temperatures | جهاز حضانة عند درجات حرارة مختلفة |
| incubators for eggs | حضانات للبيض |
| incurable patent invalidity | بطلان براءة غير قابل للإزالة |
| indan | إندان |
| indazol | إندازول |
| indecency | خدش الحياء |
| indemnification and hold harmless clause | بند عدم تحميل المسئولية: بند تعاقدي يبين تحمل طرف المسئولية بالنيابة عن الطرف الآخر في حالة نشوء مطالبات قانونية أو ما إذا ذلك من قبل الغير في مواجهته نتيجة إخلال الطرف الأول وفق شروط معينة |
| indene resin | راتنج الإندين |
| indentation | تسنين؛ تثلم |
| indentation test | اختبار التحزز؛ اختبار التثلم |
| indenting | تعاقد على السندات |
| independent arbitration | تحكيم مستقل |
| independent claim | ادعاء مستقل |
| Independent contractors clause | البند الخاص باستقلال المتعاقدين. بند تعاقدي يبين أن كلا من المتعاقدين مستقل عن الآخر وأن الاتفاق لا يعني نشوء علاقة وظيفية أو علاقة شركة محاصة بين الطرفين. |
| independent innovation | ابتكار مستقل |
| independent inventing | القيام بعملية الاختراع على نحو مستقل. |
| independent invention | اختراع مستقل |
| independent inventor | مخترع مستقل |
| independent patent searcher | باحث براءات مستقل |
| independent patent strategist | إستراتيجي براءات مستقل |

| | |
|---|---|
| independent variable | متغير مستقل |
| independently developed idea | فكرة مطورة على نحو مستقل |
| indeterminacy of culture | لاحتمية الثقافة |
| index | أس |
| index | يفهرس، فهرست، مؤشر |
| index area | منطقة الفهرس |
| index cabinets [furniture] | خزائن مفهرسة [أثاث] |
| index cards [stationery] | بطاقات مفهرسة [أدوات مكتبية] |
| index display | عرض فهرسي |
| index of refraction | معامل الانكســار؛ دليل الانكسار |
| indexes | فهارس |
| indian inks | حبر هندي |
| indicate (by) | يشير إليه (بـ) |
| indicating device | وسيلة بيان |
| indicating mechanism | آلية البيان |
| indication | دلالة |
| indication mechanism | آلية البيان |
| indications | أعراض |
| indicative of | تدل على |
| indicator | مؤشر (دال) |
| indicators (quantity -) | مؤشرات [مؤشرات للكمية] |
| indicators (speed -) | مؤشرات [مؤشرات للسرعة] |
| indicators (water level -) | مؤشرات [مؤشرات لمنسوب الماء] |
| indicators [electricity] | مؤشرات [كهرباء] |
| indict officially | يتهم رسميا |
| indigenous | محلي؛ من أهل البلد |
| indigenous idea | فكرة من بنات أفكار أهل البلد. فكرة من الأفكار التي أنتجتها عقول أهل البلد |
| indigenous invention | اختراع محلي |
| indigenous people's invention | اختراع خاص بشعب محلي |
| indigenous peoples' knowledge | معرفة خاصة بشعوب محلية |
| indigo [colorant] | صبغة النيلة الزرقاء [مواد ملونة] |
| indinavir | إندينافير |
| indirect licensing | ترخيص غير مباشر |
| indirect patent infringement | انتهاك براءة غير مباشر |
| indium | انديوم (عنصر فلزي) |
| individual fiber layer as a function of total panel volume | طبقة ليفية فردية كدالة في الحجم الكلي للوح |
| individual ministries | وزارات فردية |
| individual well flowlines | خطوط تدفق بئر فردي |
| individual well prediction models | نماذج تنبؤ للآبار الفردية |
| individually or in any combination | بمفرده أو في توليفة |
| indole moiety | جزء إندول |
| indole nitrogen | ذرة نيتروجين للإندول |
| indolyl-sulfanyl arylamines | مركبات إندونيل-سالفانيل أريل أمين |
| indoor aquaria | أحواض تربية الكائنات المائية بالمنزل |
| indoor football (tables for -) | كرة قدم منزلية (مناضد لكرة القدم المنزلية) |
| indoor terrariums [plant cultivation] | مربى يابس للاستخدام في الداخل [الزراعة النباتات] |
| indoor terrariums [vivariums] | مربى يابس للاستخدام في الداخل [مربى للحيوانات] |
| indoor window blinds [shades] [furniture] | ستائر للنوافذ للاستخدام في الداخل [ستائر النوافذ] [أثاث] |
| indpendently | على حدة |
| indpendently selected | التي يتم اختيارها على حدة |
| induce | يحث؛ يستحث |
| induce | يستحث؛ يُحدِث: تحث أو تؤدي إلى حدوث كذا |
| induce | يحفز، يغري |
| induce (with) | يحرض بـ أو يعالج بـ |
| induced magnetic field | المجال المغناطيسي المستحث |
| inducement | تحفيز |
| inducers | عوامل حثّ |
| inducible | قابل للحث |
| inductance | دائرة محاثة |
| inductive heating | تسخين حثّي |
| inductor | عضو حث |
| inductors [electricity] | ملفات حاثة [كهرباء] |
| indurated | متصلب |
| industrial | صناعي |
| industrial accidents analysis | تحليل الحوادث الصناعية |
| industrial applicability | القابلية للتطبيق الصناعي |
| industrial applicability test | اختبار القابلية للتصنيع. اختبار يتم إجراءه لقياس مدى استحقاق الاختراع أن يصدر عنه براءة وذلك من خلال تقييم إمكانيات تصنيع الاختراع ووضعه موضع التطبيق الصناعي |
| industrial applicability test | اختبار القابلية للتصنيع. اختبار يتم إجراءه لقياس مدى استحقاق الاختراع أن يصدر عنه براءة وذلك من خلال تقييم إمكانيات تصنيع الاختراع ووضعه موضع التطبيق الصناعي |
| industrial arbitration | التحكيم الصناعي |
| industrial architecture | الهندسة الصناعية؛ العمارة الصناعية |
| industrial chemicals | كيماويات صناعية |
| industrial chemistry, councils, associations, chambers | الكيمياء، المجالس، الاتحادات، الغرف الصناعية |
| industrial city | مدينة صناعية |
| industrial civilization | الحضارة الصناعية |
| industrial complex | مجمع صناعي |
| industrial cooperation | تعاون صناعي |
| industrial coordination | تنْسِيق أو تَنْظِيم صناعي |
| industrial design | نموذج صناعي |
| industrial development bank | بنك التنمية الصناعية |
| industrial diversificaiton | التنوع الصناعي |
| industrial fair | معرض المنتجات الصناعية |
| industrial grease | شحم صناعي |
| industrial growth | نمو صناعي |
| industrial information | الإعلام الصناعي |
| industrial medicine | طب الصناعات |
| industrial methylated spirit | كحول ميثيلي مستخدم في |

| | |
|---|---|
| | الصناعة (سبرتو أحمر) |
| industrial oil | زيت صناعي |
| industrial policies | سياسات صناعية |
| industrial production; industrial output | الإنتاج الصناعي |
| industrial programming, psychology, research | البرمجة؛ علم النفس؛ البحوث الصناعية |
| industrial robot | روبوت صناعي |
| industrial safety, industrial insurance | الأمن الصناعي؛ التأمين الصناعية |
| industrial sector's structure | هيكل القطاع الصناعي |
| industrial sustainability | الاستدامة الصناعية |
| industrial technology | تكنولوجيا الصناعة |
| industrial technology | تقنية صناعية |
| industrial wax | شمع صناعي |
| industrialisation | التصنيع |
| industrialised countries | الدول الصناعية |
| industrialist | رجل صناعة |
| industrializability | قابلية الشيء للتصنيع |
| industrialization | تصنيع |
| industrialization of a patent | تصنيع براءة |
| industrialize | يصنع |
| industrialized | مصنع، صناعي |
| industrially | صناعيا؛ في المجال الصناعي |
| industrially inapplicable invention | اختراع غير قابل للتطبيق الصناعي |
| industries | صناعات |
| industry | صناعة |
| industry vertical | المجال الرأسي للصناعة (المجال النوعي أو التخصصي للصناعة) |
| industry-shaking invention | تعبير يطلق على الاختراع ذو التأثير الشديد |
| industry-shaking patent | براءة تهز الصناعة |
| industry-specific patent legislation | تشريع براءات خاص بصناعة معينة |
| inequality | عدم التكافؤ، التباين، تفاوت |
| inequitable | قائم على عدم المساواة، غير منصف، غير إنصافي |
| inert | خامل |
| inert solvent | مذيب خامل |
| inertised | مخمد |
| infancy, doli incapax | دون السن؛ سن المسائلة القانونية |
| infant walkers | مشايات للأطفال |
| infantry (ground force) | المشاة (قوات البر؛ قوات برية) |
| infantry battlion | كتيبة مشاة |
| infantryman | فرد المشاة |
| infarct | احتشاء |
| infarction | احتشاء |
| infected | مصاب بالاحتشاء |
| infectious arthritis | التهاب المفاصل المعدي |
| inferometric refractometer | قياس الانكسار للتداخل الضوئي |
| infertile soil | تربة مجدبة |
| infiltration | اِرْتِشاح ؛ تَرَشُّح ؛ تَرْشِيح |
| infirngability | القابلية للانتهاك |
| inflammable gas | غاز قابل للاشتعال |
| inflammatory | التهابي |
| inflammatory bowel disease | داء الأمعاء الالتهابي |
| inflammatory bowel diseases | أمراض الأمعاء الالتهابية |
| inflammatory conditions associated with ligamentous sprain | حالات التهابية مرتبطة بالالتواء الرباطي |
| inflammatory disorders of the gastrointestinal tract | الاضطرابات الالتهابية بالمسار المعدي المعوي |
| inflammatory infiltrates | ارتشاحات التهابية |
| inflammatory mediators | عوامل وسيطة التهابية؛ عوامل وسيطة للالتهاب |
| inflatable publicity objects | مواد إعلان قابلة للنفخ |
| inflate | ينفخ |
| inflation | تضخم (مالي) |
| inflation-indexed individual tax returns | ضرائب الدخل الشخصي المرتبطة بنسبة التضخم |
| inflection point | نقطة انقلاب |
| inflow | دفق داخل؛ تدفق داخل؛ فيض داخل |
| influent | تيار متدفق (داخل). قارن effluent |
| influential patent | براءة مؤثرة. براءة ذات تأثير في وضع شركة |
| influenza induced pneumonia | الالتهاب الرئوي الناتج من الأنفلونزا |
| influx | تدفق |
| info | معلومات |
| informal drawings | رسومات غير رسمية |
| informal sketches | رسوم تخطيطية غير رسمية. الرسوم التي يرفقها بعض طالبي البراءات ضمن أوراق الطلب التي أحيانا يكون باعث إرفاقها عدم الانتهاء نهائيا من إعداد الرسوم الرسمية |
| information | معلومات |
| information alert | المعلومات التنبيهيه |
| information economies | اقتصاديات المعلومات |
| information exchange | تبادل المعلومات |
| information filtering system | نظام تصفية المعلومات |
| information infrastructure | بنية تحتية معلوماتية |
| information leakage prevention system | نظام منع تسرب (تسريب) المعلومات |
| information machine | آلة معلومات |
| information revolution | ثورة معلومات |
| information security | أمن المعلومات |
| information sharing agreement | اتفاق بشأن مشاركة معلومات. اتفاق يتوخى طرفاه تنظيم مشاركتهما معلومات معينة وذلك تجنباً لانتهاك حقوق النشر وحقوق الملكية الفكرية |
| information society | مجتمع معلومات |
| information storage system | نظام تخزين معلومات |
| information storing system | نظام تخزين معلومات |
| information system | نظام معلومات |
| information technology driven innovation | ابتكار تقوده التقنية. جهد ابتكاري يسير على هدى من وضع التقنية وتطورها |
| information technology operation | عملية تقنية معلومات |
| informational empowerment | تمكين معلوماتي |
| informational security | الأمن المعلوماتي |

| | |
|---|---|
| information-oriented society | مجتمع ذو وجهة معلوماتية |
| informed contractors clause | البند الخاص بإحاطة المتعاقدين. بند تعاقدي يبين أن كلا من المتعاقدين قد استوفق وحصل على المعلومات اللازمة لجعله على دراية بالاتفاق ومستلزماته |
| infotainment | برنامج تثقيفي ترفيهي؛ برنامج معلوماتي ترفيهي |
| infrared | تحت الحمراء (أشعة تحت الحمراء) |
| infrared filter | مصف للأشعة تحت الحمراء |
| infrared heat-seeking missiles | صواريخ متتبعة للحرارة بالأشعة دون الحمراء |
| infrared light emitter | باعث أشعة تحت حمراء |
| infrared spectroscopy ("ir") | قياس طيف الأشعة تحت الحمراء ("IR") |
| infrastructure | البنية الأساسية |
| infrastructure | بنية |
| infringable | يمكن انتهاكه |
| infringable technology | تقنية قابلة للانتهاك |
| infringe | ينتهك، يمس |
| infringed | منتهك |
| infringed drug | دواء منتهك |
| infringed patent | براءة منتهكة |
| infringement | انتهاك، مساس |
| infringement ownership rights | انتهاك حقوق الملكية |
| infringement test | اختبار للتحقق من حصول انتهاك |
| infringements | انتهاكات |
| infringer | منتهك |
| infringibility | القابلية للانتهاك |
| infringible | قابل للانتهاك |
| infringible drug | دواء عرضة للانتهاك |
| infringible patent | براءة قابلة للانتهاك |
| infringing drug | دواء انتهاكي |
| infuse | يدخل سائل في الوريد؛ يسرب سائل إلى الوريد |
| infusible | قابلة للتسريب |
| infusion | تسريب |
| infusion medium | وسط تشريب (نقع) |
| infusion pump | مضخة التسريب |
| ingenious | حاذق، بارع، مبدع |
| ingenious improvement | تحسين حاذق. تحسين ماهر لبراءة غير بديهي. |
| ingenuity | براعة |
| ingestion | ابتلاع |
| ingot | صبة: قالب أو كتلة معدة للتشكيل |
| ingots of common metal | قوالب للتشكيل من المعدن العادي (غير النفيس) |
| ingots of precious metals | قوالب للتشكيل من المعدن النفيس |
| ingress | دخول |
| inguinal hernia | الفتق الأربي |
| inhalability | قابلية الشيء للاستنشاق |
| inhalable | قابل للاستنشاق |
| inhalant | نشوق |
| inhalant | مادة للاستنشاق |
| inhale | يستنشق |
| inhaled | مستَنشَق |
| inhaler | بخّاخ؛ جهاز استنشاق: لدفع الدواء إلى الرئة كرذاذ يمكن استنشاقه. |
| inhaler | مستنشق |
| inhaling | القيام بالاستنشاق |
| inherent availability | إتاحة ذاتية |
| inheritance | الوراثة |
| inhibit | يثبط؛ يمنع؛ يعوق |
| inhibition | تثبيط؛ منع؛ إعاقة |
| inhibition of cdk4/cdk6 | تثبيط إنزيمي CDK4/CDK6 |
| inhibitor of matrix metalloproteases (mmps) | مثبط لإنزيمات ماتريكس ميتالوبروتياز MMPs |
| initial average temperature | متوسط درجة حرارة أول |
| initial invention | اختراع مبدئي |
| initial invention review | مراجعة مبدئية للاختراع |
| initial purification and molecular cloning | التنقية المبدئية والاستنساخ الجزيئي |
| initiatory pleading | صحيفة دعوى |
| injectable | قابل للحقن |
| injectable | عقار أو مادة قابلة للحقن |
| injectable | قابل للحقن |
| injectable filler | حشوة قابلة للحقن |
| injectate | ناتج الحقن |
| injection molding | القولبة بالحقن |
| injection timing | مواعيد حقن الوقود |
| injective function | دالة متباينة: المتغيرات المتباينة (المختلفة) لها مقابلات مختلفة حسب هذه الدالة |
| injector | حاقن |
| injector | حاقن |
| injector head | رأس حقن |
| injectors for engines | وسائل حقن للمحركات |
| ink | حبر |
| ink (printing -) | حبر (حبر الطباعة) |
| ink [toners] for photocopiers | حبر [تنر] للطابعات الضوئية |
| ink ejector | مخرج الحبر |
| ink for leather | حبر للجلود |
| ink for skin-dressing | حبر لتغطية الجلد |
| ink matrix | شبكة حبر؛ مصفوفة حبر |
| ink reservoir | خزان الحبر، احتياطي الحبر |
| ink sticks | أعواد حبر |
| ink stones [ink reservoirs] | أحجار حبر [خزانات حبر] |
| inking apparatus for printing machines | جهاز تحبير لآلات الطباعة |
| inking pads | ختامات لتحبير الأختام |
| inking ribbons | شرائط تحبير |
| inking ribbons for computer printers | شرائط تحبير لطابعات الكمبيوتر |
| inking sheets for document reproducing machines | لوحات تحبير لآلات نسخ المستندات |
| inking sheets for duplicators | لوحات تحبير لآلات النسخ |
| inking sytsem lacquers | ورنيشات نظام التحبير |
| inkstands | حوامل حبر |
| inkwells | محابر |
| inlet channel | قناة دخول |
| inlet end | طرف دخول |
| inlet opening | فتحة للإدخال |
| inlet velocity | سرعة الدخول |
| in-licensing business model | نموذج تجاري يعتمد على |

| | |
|---|---|
| | الحصول على التراخيص من الغير |
| in-line; in line | متوازي؛ متحاذي |
| in-line blending | مزج متوازي |
| in-line roller skates | لوحات تزلج ذات عجلات على محور واحد |
| in-line static mixer | خلاط ستاتيكي متوازي |
| inner dosage component | مكون جرعة داخلي |
| inner soles | النعال الداخلية |
| inner tubes (adhesive rubber patches for repairing -) | إطارات داخلية (رقعات لاصقة من الكاوتشوك لترميم الإطارات الداخلية) |
| inner tubes (repair outfits for -) | إطارات داخلية(معدات تصليح الإطارات الداخلية) |
| inner tubes for bicycles, cycles | إطارات داخلية للدراجات والدراجات الثلاثية |
| inner tubes for pneumatic tires [tyres] | إطارات داخلية للإطارات الخارجية الهوائية |
| inner tubes of tires [tyres] (compositions for repairing -) | إطارات داخلية للإطارات الخارجية (تركيبات لترميم الإطارات الداخلية للإطارات الخارجية) |
| innermost | الأعمق: الأدنى للداخل |
| innocent infringement | انتهاك برئ |
| innocent patent infringement | انتهاك براءة برئ |
| innovate | يبتكر |
| innovation | ابتكار |
| innovation commercializability assessment | تقييم قابلية الابتكار لأن يصبح ذا طبيعة تجارية |
| innovation credibility | مصداقية ابتكارية |
| innovation drivers | العوامل التي تقود حركة الابتكار، محفزات الابتكار |
| innovation enabler | مُمَكن للابتكار |
| innovation process | عملية الابتكار |
| innovation studies literature | أدبيات الدراسات المتصلة بالابتكار. المواد المكتوبة المعرفة بالاختراع. |
| innovational activity | نشاط ابتكاري |
| innovation-based entrepreneurship | مضاربة مرتكزة على الابتكار |
| innovation-centered economy | اقتصاد مرتكز حول الابتكار |
| innovation-driven competitiveness | تنافسية يقودها الابتكار |
| innovation-driven growth | نمو يسوقه الابتكار |
| innovation-oriented mind | ذهن ذو وجهة ابتكارية |
| innovation-oriented worker | عامل صاحب توجهات ابتكارية |
| innovations | ابتكارات |
| innovative activity | نشاطات ابتكارية |
| innovative country | بلد ذو نزعة ابتكار خلاقة. بلد تنتشر فيه الأعمال الإبداعية الابتكارية الخلاقة |
| innovative goods | سلع ابتكارية |
| innovative green solutions | حلول |
| innovative robot | روبوت ابتكاري |
| innovator | مبتكر |
| innovators | مبتكرون |
| inoculate | يلقّح؛ يطعم |
| inoculation | تلقيح؛ تطعيم |
| inoculum | مادة تلقيح؛ مادة تطعيم |
| inorganic | غير عضوية |
| inorganic acid salts | أملاح الأحماض غير العضوية |
| inorganic chemistry | كيمياء غير عضوية |
| inorganic fertilizers | أسمدة غير عضوية |
| inorganic limestone | الحجر الجيري الغير عضوي |
| inorganic material | مادة غير عضوية |
| inorganic or organic acid addition salts | أملاح الإضافة للأحماض العضوية وغير العضوية |
| inosine | إينوزين |
| in-process samples | العيّنات الحاليّة: تلك التي يتم العمل عليها تمييزا لها عن المادة الخام وكذلك المنتجات النهائية |
| input | مدخل؛ إدخال |
| input | يدخل بيانات |
| input | يدخل، مُدخل |
| input device | جهاز مدخلات |
| input end | طرف إدخال |
| input mixture | خليط الإدخال |
| input or output device | جهاز إدخال أو إخراج |
| input voltage | جهد الدخل |
| inputs | مدخلات |
| inputs | مدخلات |
| ins | بوصة |
| insane | مجنون؛ مختل القوى العقلية |
| insanity | جُنُون: خلل عقلي |
| insect repellent incense | بخور طارد للحشرات |
| insect repellents | مواد طاردة للحشرات |
| insect screens | شبكات منخلية للحشرات |
| insect traps | مصيدة للحشرات |
| insecticide | مبيد حشري |
| insecticide atomizers [hand tools] | مرذاذ مبيد للحشرات [أدوات يدوية] |
| insecticide sprayers [hand tools] | بخاخ (أسبراي) لإبادة للحشرات [أدوات يدوية] |
| insecticides (chemical additives to -) | مبيدات حشرات (مواد إضافة كيميائية لمبيدات الحشرات) |
| insect-like robot | روبوت مشابه للحشرة |
| insects (electric devices for attracting and killing -) | حشرات (وسائل كهربائية لجذب الحشرات وقتلها) |
| insemination (semen for artificial -) | تخصيب (منى للتخصيب الصناعي) |
| insert | وليجة؛ غريسة |
| insert | ملحق يرفق بالصحيفة |
| insert | ملحق: جهاز أو جزء ملحق |
| insert | يدخل |
| insert choke | صمام اختناق مُقحَم |
| insertion | إدخال؛ إدراج |
| insomnia | أرق |
| inspection warrant | أمر بالتفتيش |
| inspiring environment | بيئة ملهمة |
| installable system | نظام قابل للتركيب |
| installation | تركيب؛ وحدة |
| installation security | أمن المنشآت |

| | |
|---|---|
| installed capacity | سعة مركّبة |
| installer | ملف تثبيت (برنامج) |
| installers | عمال التركيب |
| instant blood mediated inflammatory reaction | التفاعل الالتهابي الفوري الذي يحدث عبر الدم |
| instant messageing (im) | الرسائل الفورية |
| instant messaging technology | تقنية إرسال الرسائل الفورية |
| instant milk powder | لبن مجفف سريع الذوبان |
| instant security feature | ميزة التأمين الفوري |
| instantiation | تمثيل؛ تجسيد |
| instep | مشط القدم |
| institute | معهد |
| institute | يؤسس، معهد |
| institute of inventors | معهد المخترعين |
| institution | مؤسسة تعليمية |
| institution | مؤسسة |
| institution | مؤسسة، إقامة، تأسيس |
| institutional arbitration | تحكيم مؤسسي |
| institutional constriants | ضوابط مؤسساتية |
| instruction | تعليم |
| instruction | تعليمات |
| instructional | تعليمي |
| instructor | مدرس |
| instrument | أداة |
| instrument | أداة |
| instrument cases for use by surgeons and doctors | علب أدوات لاستخدام الجراحين والأطباء) |
| instrument of censorship | أداة رقابة. يدعي مناهضو الملكية الفكرية أن حق النشر هو صورة من صور الرقابة. وهم يصنفونه بحسبانه حق راقبة خاصة |
| instrumentality | استخدام الأجهزة |
| instruments (musical -) | أدوات (أدوات موسيقية) |
| insufficience | عدم كفاية، نقص |
| insufficient disclosure | إفصاح غير كاف |
| insufflation | نفخ |
| insufflators | أدوات للنفخ |
| insulating buildings against moisture (substances for -) | عزل المباني ضد الرطوبة (مواد لعزل المباني ضد الرطوبة) |
| insulating case | صندوق عازل |
| insulating fabrics | أنسجة عازلة |
| insulating felt | لباد عازل |
| insulating flasks | أوعية عازلة |
| insulating glass | زجاج عازل للحرارة: ويتكون من طبقتين أو أكثر من الزجاج معزولة بإحكام على كامل المحيط الخارجي ويعبأ الفراغ بينهما عامة بهواء جاف، ويمكن استخدام غازات أخرى لتعبئة الفراغ لتحسين خاصية العزل الحراري |
| insulating glass [building] | زجاج عازل [مباني] |
| insulating gloves | قفازات عازلة |
| insulating materials | مواد عازلة |
| insulating oils | زيوت عازلة |
| insulating paints | دهانات عازلة |

| | |
|---|---|
| insulating paper | ورق عازل |
| insulating plaster | لاصقات عازلة |
| insulating tape and band | شرائط وأربطة عازلة |
| insulating varnish | ورنيش (دهان) عازل |
| insulation (metal foil for -) | عزل [رقاقات معدنية للعزل) |
| insulation holder | حامل عازل |
| insulators | مواد عازلة |
| insulators for electric mains | عوازل الكهرباء الرئيسية |
| insulin independent type ii diabetes | مرض السكر من النوع 2 غير المعتمد على الإنسولين |
| insulin resistance | مقاومة الإنسولين |
| insulin sensitivity | حساسية للإنسولين: حساسية أنسجة الجسم، عضو إلخ للإنسولين |
| insulinotropic | المُفرز للإنسولين |
| insulinotropic hormone | الهرمون المفرز للإنسولين |
| insulitis | التهاب الجزر البنكرياسية |
| insurable | قابل للتأمين عليه |
| insurance | تأمين، وسيلة تأمين |
| insure | يؤمن |
| insured | مؤمن عليه، شخص مؤمن عليه |
| insurer | المؤمِّن: سواء شخص أو شركة |
| insurer | مؤمن |
| int.memory | الذاكرة الداخلية |
| intact antibody | الجسم المضاد السليم |
| intaglio printing | الطباعة الغائرة |
| intake | مدخل؛ سحب |
| intake | مدخل: منفذ |
| intake | دخول |
| intake air temperature sensor | جهاز استشعار درجة حرارة الهواء الداخل |
| intangible assets | أصول غير ملموسة. من أمثلتها البراءات |
| intangible value | قيمة غير ملموسة |
| intangibleness | اللامادية، اللاملموسية |
| intangibles | أمور غير ملموسة |
| integer | عدد صحيح |
| integral (to) | متكامل (مع) |
| integratability | قابلية الشيء للتكامل |
| integratable | قابل للتكامل |
| integratable component | مكون قابل للتكامل |
| integrate | يتكامل ، يكامل |
| integrated asset modeling process | العملية المتكاملة لعمل نماذج للموجودات |
| integrated circuit | دائرة متكاملة |
| integrated circuit cards [smart cards] | بطاقات ذات دوائر متكاملة [بطاقات ذكية] |
| integrated circuits | دوائر متكاملة |
| integrated circuits | دوائر متكاملة |
| integrated patent portfolio | محفظة براءات متكاملة |
| integrated production: | الإنتاج المتكامل، وذلك في منشأة يكون فيها إنتاج الورق أو الكرتون مرتبط مباشرة بإنتاج اللب |
| integrated solutions | حلول متكاملة |
| integrating and reconciling all aforementioned | تكامل كل نطاقات المحاكاة سالفة الذكر والتوفيق بينها. |

| | |
|---|---|
| simulation domains | |
| integration charge | رسم إدماج |
| integrin | إنتجرين |
| integrity management | إدارة السلامة |
| intel or intell | استخبارات |
| intellectual activity | نشاط ذهني |
| intellectual capital | رأس المال الفكري |
| intellectual capital management | إدارة رأس المال الفكري |
| intellectual creations | ابتكارات خلاقة ذهنية |
| intellectual creativity | إبداع فكري |
| intellectual credibility | مصداقية فكرية |
| intellectual gap | فجوة فكرية |
| intellectual monopoly | احتكار فكري |
| intellectual piracy | قرصنة فكرية |
| intellectual property | ملكية فكرية |
| intellectual property assignment agreement | اتفاق بشأن التنازل عن ممتلك فكري |
| intellectual property attorney | وكيل ملكية فكرية |
| intellectual property clause | بند الملكية الفكرية. البند الوارد في مختلف العقود التي تنظم التزامات الطرفين وواجباتهما فيما يتصل بالحقوق المتصلة بالملكية الفكرية |
| intellectual property detective | مخبر مختص بحقوق الملكية الفكرية |
| intellectual property due diligence | مراجعة واجبة بشأن الملكية الفكرية. تقييم وضع الممتلكات الفكرية ذات الصلة بالنشاط التجاري بما في ذلك العلامات التجارية والبراءات للوقوف على عناصر القوة والضعف والهشاشة، ويتم القيام بالمراجعة الواجبة في مناسبات مختلفة أبرزها عند اتخاذ قرار تجاري مهم بالنسبة للشركة مثل دمجها أو الاستحواذ عليها |
| intellectual property empowerment | تمكين متصل بالملكية الفكرية |
| intellectual property ethics | أخلاقيات الملكية الفكرية |
| intellectual property infringement | انتهاك ملكية فكرية |
| intellectual property infringement investigation | تحريات منصبة على انتهاك ملكية فكرية |
| intellectual property institution | مؤسسة ملكية فكرية. مؤسسة لها دور في مجال الملكية الفكرية أو في وضع سياسات وقوانين الملكية الفكرية موضع التنفيذ |
| intellectual property intensive industry | صناعة يعد حضور الملكية الفكرية فيها كبيرا |
| intellectual property investigator | تحر مختص بالملكية الفكرية |
| intellectual property law firm | مؤسسة قانونية للبراءات |
| intellectual property laws | قوانين ملكية فكرية |
| intellectual property lawyer | محامي ملكية فكرية |
| intellectual property literacy | الإلمام بالملكية الفكرية |
| intellectual property lobby | تجمع للاستمالة العامة خاص بالملكية الفكرية. تجمع قائم على افتراض وجود مصلحة مشتركة لأعضائه في استصدار التشريعات والقرارات التي تخدم ذلك التجمع ومن يمثله فيما يتصل بالملكية الفكرية. |
| intellectual property lobbyist | مختص بالاستمالة المتوخية في حقل الملكية الفكرية. مختص بالاستمالة التي تتوخى إصدار التشريعات والقرارت التي تصب في مصلحة تجمع الاستمالة ومن يمثله في حقل الملكية الفكرية |
| intellectual property market | سوق الملكية الفكرية |
| intellectual property officer | المسئول عن الملكية الفكرية |
| intellectual property portfolio audit | تدقيق محفظة ملكية فكرية |
| intellectual property portfolio management | إدارة محفظة ملكية فكرية |
| intellectual property right culture | ثقافة ملكية فكرية. انتشار احترام نظام الملكية الفكرية |
| intellectual property rights | حقوق ملكية فكرية |
| intellectual property security agreement | اتفاق لتقديم أملاك فكرية كضمان. اتفاق ينظم قيام طرف بتقديم حقوق ملكية فكرية تخصه كضمان لسداد مبلغ للغير |
| intellectual property system | نظام الملكية الفكرية |
| intellectual property transfer agreement | اتفاق بشأن تحويل ملكية ممتلك فكري |
| intellectual work | عمل فكري |
| intelligence system | نظام استخبارات |
| intelligent building system | نظام مبنى آلي |
| intelligent document | مستند ذكي |
| intelligent software assistant | مساعد برنامج ذكي |
| intended for = designed for | مصممة لـ |
| intense cutaneous flushing | احمرار جلدي كثيف |
| intensification | تكثيف |
| intensification technology | تقنية تكثيف |
| intensifier | مكثف |
| intensify | يكثف |
| intensity regulators for mechanical pianos | منظمات شدة الصوت لآلات البيانو الميكانيكية |
| intensive expansion | التوسع الزراعي الرأسي |
| intentional exposure to radiation | تعرض عمدي للأشعة |
| inter alia | ضمن أشياء أخرى |
| inter se | فيما بينهم |
| interaction pressure | ضغط تفاعل |
| interactions | تداخلات |
| interactive eyeglasses | نظارات تفاعلية |
| interactively | تباديا |
| intercalator | عامل إقحام |
| intercalators | روابط بينية |
| intercell interference | تداخل بين الخلايا |
| intercept | محصورة (رياضيات) |
| intercept (a message) | يلتقط رسالة: يعترض رسالة (قبل وصولها للطرف الآخر) |

| | |
|---|---|
| interceptor | طائرة اعتراضية |
| interchain | داخل السلسلة |
| intercommunication apparatus | جهاز اتصال بيني |
| interconnected coil springs | نوابض ذات ملفات متصلة فيما بينها |
| interconnected networks | شبكات اتصال متصلة فيما بينها (شبكات متصلة داخليا) |
| interconnection body | جهاز ربط |
| interconverting any variable groups /interconversions | تحويل داخلي لأي مجموعات متغيرة |
| intercropping | زراعة المقحمات |
| intercrystaline porosity | مسامية بين البلورات |
| interdigitate (with) | يتداخل بينيا (مع) |
| interdigitating dendritic cells | الخلايا الشجرية المتشابكة بينياً |
| interface | وصلة بينية؛ سطح بيني |
| interface | واجهة |
| interface | يصل بينيا |
| interface | السطح البيني، الواجهة البينية |
| interfaces | أسطح بينية، واجهات بينية |
| interfacial (surface) tension | توتر سطحي بيني |
| interfacial energy | طاقة بيسطحية أو واقعة بين سطحين |
| interfere | يتدخل |
| interference | يتعارض، يتصادم، يتدخل، يتداخل |
| inter-governmental maritime consultative organization, imaco, | المنظمة الاستشارية الحكومية الدولية للملاحة البحرية (لندن) |
| intergranular porosity | المسامية الأولية بين الحبيبات |
| interim arbitral award | حكم تحكيم وقتي |
| inter-interlace interleaving | توليف بين التشابكات |
| interlace interleaving: | عمليات توليف التشابك |
| interleave | يدرج |
| interleaves | تداخلات |
| interleaving | التوليف: إعادة ترتيب تيار الرموز في متوالية، وبذلك يحدث توزيع عشوائي للأخطاء المحتملة الناتجة عن انخفاض كفاءة القناة |
| interlock | تشابك |
| intermediary industries | الصناعات الوسيطة |
| intermediate ester | إستر المركب الوسيط |
| intermediate insulating channel | قناة وسطى عازلة |
| intermediate material | مادة وسيطة |
| intermediate release formulation | صيغة ذات إطلاق متوسط |
| intermediate section | مقطع متوسط |
| intermediates | المركبات الوسيطة |
| intermeshing | معشقة (مثل مسامير ملولبة معشقة؛ إلخ) |
| intermetallic | سبيكي |
| intermolecular ; intramolecular | بين الجزيئات |
| internal combustion engines (anti-knock substances for -) | محركات احتراق داخلي [مواد مضادة للخبط لمحركات الاحتراق الداخلي) |
| internal glazing | الألواح الزجاجية الداخلية |
| internal memory | ذاكرة داخلية |
| internal volume of the header | الحيز الداخلي للمجمع العلوي |
| internal workfare | معونة اجتماعية بشرط العمل |
| internalization | تأثير داخلي |
| internalization | امتصاص |
| internalize | يمتص (يدمج) |
| international aid organizations | منظمات المعونة الدولية |
| international arbitration tribunal | محكمة تحكيم دولية |
| international atomic energy agency, iaea | الوكالة الدولية للطاقة الذرية (فيينا) |
| international civil aviation organization, icao | منظمة الطيران المدني الدولية (مونتريال) |
| international commercial arbitration | تحكيم تجاري دولي |
| international communications union, itu | الاتحاد الدولي للمواصلات السلكية واللاسلكية |
| international development association (ida) | مؤسسة التنمية الدولية (واشنطن) |
| international finance corporation (ifc) | المؤسسة المالية الدولية |
| international fund for agriculture development | الصندوق الدولي للتنمية الزراعية |
| international labour office | مكتب العمل الدولي |
| international labour organization | منظمة العمل الدولية (جنيف) |
| international preliminary examination report | تقرير الفحص الدولي التمهيدي |
| international relief coordinator, irc | منسق الأمم المتحدة لإغاثة منكوبي الكوارث |
| international search report | تقرير البحث الدولي |
| international, regional orgs | منظمات وكتل إقليمية ودولية |
| internationalization | جعل الشيء ذا طبيعة دولية |
| internationalization of inventive activity | جعل النشاط الفكري ذا طبيعة دولية |
| internationalization of patent activity | جعل نشاط البراءات ذا طبيعة دولية |
| internationalization of patent law | جعل قانون البراءات ذا طبيعة دولية |
| internationally-banned weapons | أسلحة محرمة دوليا |
| internet awareness | وعي الشبكة. الإلمام بالشبكة ومخاطرها ومغرياتها وإمكانيات التعرض للأذى المادي والمعنوي من الغير من خلالها |
| internet engineering task force | فريق مهام هندسة الإنترنت |
| internet industry | صناعة الشبكة |
| internet infrastructure | البنية التحتية للشبكة البينية |
| internet patent | براءة شبكية، براءة شبكة المعلومات |
| internet service provider | مزود خدمة الإنترنت |
| internet tbd | TDBالخاص بالإنترنت |
| internet telephony | الإرسال الهاتفي على الإنترنت؛ التهاتف عبر الإنترنت |
| internet ticketing solutions | حلول إصدار تذاكر عبر الشبكة البينية |

| | |
|---|---|
| internode | مسافة بين عقدتين |
| interoperability | قابلية التشغيل البيني |
| interoperability | قابلية عنصر أن يكون موضع تشغيل ضمن منظومة عناصر متكاملة |
| interoperable | قابل للتشغيل البيني |
| interpersonal | شخصي اجتماعي |
| interplate earthquakes | هزّاتٍ أرضيَّةٍ بين ألواح الغلاف الصخري |
| interpolation | استكمال؛ استيفاء |
| interpolymerized units | وحدات مبلمرة بينياً |
| interposed transformer | محول بيني |
| interposition | إقحام؛ توسّط؛ تموضع بيني؛ تخلل |
| interpret | يفسر |
| interpretation | تفسير |
| inter-recative | تفاعلية فيما بينها |
| interrogate | يستجوب |
| interrupt | يعترض |
| interruption unit | وحدة قطع؛ وحدة مقاطعة |
| interruptions | فواصل |
| interspecies | من فصائل انتقالية |
| interspecific | نوعي (تهجين نوعي مثلا) |
| interstitial | بيني أو مقحَم |
| interstitial | بيني أو خلالي |
| interstitial cell-stimulating hormone | الهرمون المنبه للخلايا البينية؛ الهرمون المنبه للخلايا الخلالية |
| interstitial cystitis | التهاب المثانة الخلالي |
| interval | مسافة فاصلة |
| interval | فترة زمنية فاصلة |
| intervening atoms | ذرات مشتركة (بين مجموعتين) |
| intervening prior art | فن سابق متداخل |
| inter-well regions | مناطق ما بين الآبار |
| inter-zonal | داخل نطاق |
| intestinal flora | الفلورا المعوية: بكتيرية معوية |
| intestine | أمعاء |
| intestine carcinoma | الورم السرطاني بالأمعاء |
| intima | بطانة |
| intra- interlace interleaving | توليف في التشابكات |
| intra-arterialtd | في الشريان |
| intraarticular | في المفصل |
| intrabasinal | داخل حوضيه |
| intrabodies | أجسام مضادة داخلية |
| intrabursal | داخل الجراب |
| intracellular | بين الخلايا؛ بين خلوي |
| intracerebral | داخل المخ |
| intracerebroventricular (icv) | في بطين المخ |
| intracisternal | في الحوض |
| intracranial | داخل الجمجمة |
| intradermal | في الأدمة |
| intraformational breccia | رواهص داخل حوضية |
| intraformational conglomerates | مدملكات داخل حوضية |
| intramuscular | داخل العضل |
| intranasal | داخل الأنف |
| intranet | إنترانت؛ شبكة داخلية |
| intraosseous | في العظم |
| intrapersonal | شخصي ذاتي |
| intrasternal | في القص |
| intrathecal | داخل الغمد |
| intrathecal administration | عن طريق الحقن داخل الغمد |
| intravenous | بالحقن في الوريد؛ بالتسريب إلى الوريد |
| intraventricular | في البطين |
| intrep | تقرير استخبارات |
| intreq | طلب استخبارات |
| intrinsic | أصلي؛ داخلي المنشأ |
| intrinsic asthma | ربو داخلي المنشأ |
| intrinsic properties | خواص أصيلة |
| intrinsically safe electrical components | مكونات كهربائية آمنة ذاتيا |
| introduce into | يُدخل إلى |
| introduce into | يدخل في |
| introgressed dna | الحمض النووي DNA الذي تم إدخال جينات مستزرعه منه |
| introgression | إدخال جينات مستزرعة |
| introgression line (il) | سلالة إدخال جينات مستزرعة |
| intrusion detection | اكتشاف مقتحم. رصد من يقوم باقتحام حواسيب الغير |
| intrusion detection software | برنامج لاكتشاف المقتحمين. تعبير يطلق على عملية رصد من يقوم بافتحاسم حواسيب الغير |
| intrusion detection system | نظام كشف تدخل |
| invade | يقتحم |
| invalid patent claim | ادعاء غير سليم خاص ببراءة |
| invalid prior art | فن سابق غير سليم |
| invalid status | حالة غير صالحة |
| invalidate | يبطل |
| invalidated patent claim | ادعاء خاص ببراءة تم إثبات عدم براءته |
| invalidation | إبطال |
| invalidity | بطلان، عدم صلاح |
| invalids' hoists | رافعات للعجزة |
| invariant | ثابت؛ لامتغير |
| invasion | غزو؛ هجوم المرض |
| invasion (of tissues) | غزو (الأنسجة ) |
| invasive | اقتحامي |
| invasive technology | تقنية اقتحامية |
| invasiveness of tumour cells | تغلغل الخلايا الورمية (في النسيج إلخ) |
| inventability | قابلية الشئ للاختراع |
| inventable | قابل للاختراع |
| invented | تم اختراعه، مُخترع |
| inventing | اختراع |
| invention | اختراع |
| invention | اختراع |
| invention advice | مشورة بشأن اختراع |
| invention agreement | اتفاق اختراع |
| invention assignment | التنازل عن اختراع |
| invention assignment agreement | اتفاق بشأن التنازل عن اختراع. من أبرز تطبيقاته الاتفاق الذي يبرمه رب العمل مع الموظف عند تعيينه بشأن تنازل الموظف عن الاختراعات التي قد يخترعها خلال عمله لصالح رب العمل |

| | |
|---|---|
| invention commercialization | جعل الاختراع ذا طبيعة تجارية |
| invention commercialization assessment | تقييم مسألة جعل الاختراع ذا طبيعة تجارية |
| invention conception | مفهوم للاختراع |
| invention criteria | معايير الاختراع |
| invention design | تصميم اختراع |
| invention documentation | توثيق اختراع |
| invention drivers | العوامل التي تقود حركة الاختراع، محفزات الاختراع |
| invention embodiment | تجسد الاختراع |
| invention ethics | أخلاقيات الاختراع |
| invention failure | تعطل الاختراع، إخفاق الاختراع |
| invention fundability | قابلية الاختراع لأن يحظى بتمويل |
| invention funding | تمويل للاختراع |
| invention funding advice | مشورة بشأن إيجاد تمويل لغرض الاختراع |
| invention industrial applicability | قابلية الاختراع للتطبيق الصناعي |
| invention literature | أدبيات الاختراع. المواد المكتوبة المعرفة بالاختراع. |
| invention marketer | مسوق اختراعات |
| invention marketing | تسويق الاختراع |
| invention marketing company | شركة تسويق اختراعات |
| invention nurturing | رعاية الاختراع |
| invention obviousness | وضوح الاختراع. كون الاختراع شديد البساطة مما يجعلها مفتقرا لمتطلب الاختراعية ومن ثم غير جدير بأن تصدر عنه براءة |
| invention of questionable patentability | اختراع إمكانية صدور براءة عنه موضع تساؤل |
| invention of unquestionable patentability | اختراع إمكانية صدور براءة عنه ليست موضع تساؤل |
| invention promoter | مروج اختراعات |
| invention promotion | ترويج اختراعات |
| invention promotion company | شركة ترويج اختراعات |
| invention prototype | النموذج الأولي للاختراع |
| invention review | مراجعة الاختراع |
| invention review checklist | قائمة المهام اللازمة لمراجعة الاختراع |
| invention review process | عملية مراجعة الاختراع |
| invention scope | نطاق الاختراع |
| invention secrets | أسرار الاختراع |
| invention success | نجاح الاختراع |
| invention theft | سرقة اختراع |
| invention usability | قابلية الاختراع للاستعمال |
| invention viability | جدوى الاختراع |
| invention viability assessment | تقييم جدوى الاختراع |
| invention/ patent exclusive licence agreement | اتفاق بشأن ترخيص براءة اختراع حصريا |
| invention's applicability | قابلية الاختراع للتطبيق |
| invention's commercializability | قابلية الاختراع أن يكون ذا طبيعة تجارية |
| invention's complexity | تعقيد الاختراع |

| | |
|---|---|
| invention's conceivability | قابلية الاختراع للتخيل |
| invention's designability | قابلية الاختراع للتصميم |
| invention's envisionability | قابلية الاختراع للتخيل |
| invention's functionability | قابلية الاختراع للقيام بالوظيفة المطلوبة |
| invention's implementability | قابلية الاختراع للتنفيذ |
| invention's industrializability | قابلية الاختراع للتصنيع |
| invention's manufacturability | قابلية الاختراع للتصنيع |
| invention's market value | قيمة الاختراع السوقية |
| invention's marketability | قابلية الاختراع للتسويق |
| invention's monetizability | قابلية الاختراع أن يتحول إلى نقد |
| invention's operability | قابلية الاختراع للتشغيل |
| invention's operationability | قابلية الاختراع للتشغيل |
| invention's patentability | إمكانية صدور براءة عن اختراع، قابلية الاختراع أن تصدر عنه براءة |
| invention's profitability | قابلية الاختراع لتحقيق ربح |
| invention's salability | قابلية الاختراع للبيع |
| invention's sustainability | قابلية الاختراع للاستدامة |
| invention's workability | قابلية الاختراع للتشغيل |
| invention-focused education | تعليم مهتم بالاختراع |
| invention-focused website | موقع شبكي مهتم بالاختراعات |
| invention-friendly environment | بيئة مواتية للاختراع |
| inventions | اختراعات |
| invention's feasibility | جدوى الاختراع |
| inventions capacity | أهلية الاختراعات. هي مدى أهمية العمل الابتكاري الاستكشافي الجديد وملاءمته وأحقيته في أن يحصل على البراءة، أو يتم تسجيله. هذا، ولقد حدثت اختلافات واسعة النطاق بين الدول الكبرى بشأن أهلية المواد البيولوجية وبرامج الحاسوب في الحصول على البراءة. |
| invention's commercial feasibility | جدوى الاختراع التجارية |
| inventions commercial potentialities | إمكانيات الاختراع تجارية |
| invention's financibility | قابلية الاختراع أن يحصل على تمويل |
| invention's manufacturing feasibility | جدوى تصنيع اختراع |
| invention's monetizability | قابلية الاختراع لأن يصبح ذا قيمة نقدية |
| invention's non-reducibility | عدم قابلية الاختراع لأن يتم وضعه موضع التنفيذ |
| inventive activity | نشاط اختراعي |
| inventive concept | مفهوم اختراعي |
| inventive cycle | دائرة اختراعية |
| inventive expertise | خبرة اختراعية |
| inventive mind | ذهن ذو نزعة اختراعية |
| inventive person | شخص ذو نزعة اختراعية |
| inventive requirement | متطلب الاختراعية |
| inventive skills | مهارات اختراعية |
| inventive spirit | روح اختراعية |
| inventive step | خطوة ابتكاريه |
| inventive step test | اختبار الخطوة الابتكارية. اختبار يتم |

| | |
|---|---|
| | إجراءه لقياس مدى استحقاق الاختراع أن يصدر عنه براءة وذلك من خلال تقييم مدى انطواء الاختراع على خطوة ابتكارية إبداعية |
| inventive thinking | تفكير ذو توجه اختراعي |
| inventive worker | عامل مبتكر |
| inventiveless person | شخص عديم الاختراعية |
| inventiveness requirement | مُتطلب الاختراعية. وجوب أن ينطوي العمل الفكري المطلوب منحه براءة على اختراع معين |
| inventor | مخترع |
| inventor collaboration | تعاون فيما بين مخترعين |
| inventor collaboration networks | شبكة تعاون المخترعين |
| inventor collaboration over distance | تعاون فيما بين مخترعين تباعد بينهم مسافة |
| inventor fraud | الاحتيال المتصل بالمخترع |
| inventor network | شبكة مخترعين |
| inventor profile | تعريف موجز بالمخترع |
| inventor profile services | خدمات توفير التعريفات الموجزة للمخترعين |
| inventor's agent | وكيل مخترع |
| inventor's biography | سيرة المخترع |
| inventor's engageability | قابلية المخترع للارتباط بجهة |
| inventor's preferred embodiments | التجسيدات المفضلة في نظر المخترع. التجسيدات المفضلة للاختراع من وجهة نظر المخترع |
| inventor's self evaluation | تقييم المخترع لاختراعه بنفسه |
| inventor-friendly company | شركة صديقة للمخترع |
| inventor's credibility | مصدقية المخترع |
| inventorship | الاختراعية. نسبة الاختراع لجهة. |
| inventorship dispute resolution services | خدمات حل النزاعات المتصلة بالاختراعات |
| inverse fast fourier transform unit | وحدة تحويل فورير السريعة المعكوسة |
| inversion | عكس؛ قلب |
| inversion | انقلاب |
| inverted microscope | المجهر ثلاثي العدسات العينية: يستخدم في فحص الخلايا الحية في الأنسجة المزروعة معمليا |
| inverters [electricity] | مقوم عكسي [كهرباء] |
| investigation | فحص، بحث، دراسة |
| investigation | تحريات |
| investigation device | جهاز فحص |
| investigational new drug | دواء جديد تحت التجربة؛ دواء تجريبي جديد. |
| investigator | باحث |
| investigator | تحر، مفتش |
| investment environment | بيئه استثماريه |
| invisible light | ضوء غير مرئي |
| in-vivo | داخل جسم الكائن الحي. |
| in-vivo anti-inflammatory wheal and flare model | نموذج الطفح والاحمرار الجلدي المضاد للالتهاب في جسم الكائن الحي |
| invoicing machines | ماكينات/أجهزة إعداد فواتير |
| in-wheel motor | تقنية المحرك في كل عجلة |
| iodated compound | مركب يودات |
| iodic acid | الحامض اليودي |
| iodide | يوديد |
| iodine | يود |
| iodised albumen | زلال معالج باليود |
| iodised salts | أملاح معالجة باليود |
| iodo | يودو |
| iodoform | يودوفورم |
| iodophor | حامل لليود |
| ion exchange | تبادل أيوني |
| ion exchange chromatogeaphy | الفصل الكروماتوجرافي للتبادل الأيوني |
| ion exchange membrane | غشاء تبادل أيوني |
| ion exchangers [chemical preparations] | وسائل للتبادل الأيوني [مستحضرات كيميائية] |
| ion sequestration | تنحية الأيونات |
| ion-exchanged water | ماء حدث به تبادل أيوني |
| ion-exchanged zeolite | زيوليت التبادل الأيوني |
| ionisation apparatus for the treatment of air | جهاز تأين لمعالجة الهواء |
| ionizing ionic compound | مركب أيوني مؤين |
| ionizing radiation | إشعاع مؤين |
| ion-leaching treatment | المعالجة بالنض الأيوني |
| ionomer | وحدة أيونية |
| ionomers | أيونومرات |
| ionone [perfumery] | سائل يونون [عطور] |
| iontophoresis | الإشراد الأيوني؛ الرحلان الأيوني |
| ion-trap ; ion trap | احتجاز الأيونات |
| ip | بروتوكول الانترنت |
| ip | داخل الغشاء البريتوني |
| ip assessor | مقيم براءات |
| ip driven company | شركة تسوقها الملكية الفكرية، شركة يسوقها بروتوكول الانترنت |
| ip engine highlight | IP Engine Highlight |
| ipa | كحول أيزو بروبيل |
| ipdl | مكتبة الويبو الرقمية للملكية الفكرية |
| ipea | إدارة الفحص التمهيدي الدول. |
| iper | تقرير الفحص التمهيدي الدولي |
| ipoa - international peace operations association | رابطة عمليات السلام الدولية |
| ipod | جهاز الموسيقي المحمول الخاص بشركة آبل |
| ipsilateral | على نفس الجانب |
| ipx | تبادل رزم بيانات دولية |
| ir | الأشعة تحت الحمراء |
| iraqi fund for external development | الصندوق العراقي للتنمية الخارجية |
| iridium | إيريديوم (عنصر فلزي) |
| iridocyclitis | التهاب القزحية والجسم الهدبي |
| irish moss | طحالب أيرلندية |
| iron (chrome -) | حديد [حديد كرومي] |
| iron (molybdenum -) | حديد [حديد الموليبدنيوم] |
| iron (silicon -) | حديد [سيليكون الحديد] |

| | |
|---|---|
| iron and steel industry | صناعة الحديد والصلب |
| iron bands (stretchers for -) [tension links] | أربطة حديدية (حلقات توسيع للأربطة الحديدية) [توصيلات الشد] |
| iron core | قلب حديدي |
| iron ores | خام الحديد |
| iron salts | أملاح الحديد |
| iron slabs | لوحات حديدية |
| iron spiked sample | بها نسبة عالية من الحديد |
| iron strip | شرائح حديدية |
| iron thiocyanate chelation | عامل خلابي عبارة عن حديد ثيو سيانات؛ حديد ثيو سيانات كعامل خلابي |
| iron wire | أسلاك حديدية |
| iron, unwrought or semi-wrought | حديد مطروق أو شبه مطروق |
| ironing board covers [shaped] | أغطية للوح الكي [ذات شكل] |
| ironing boards | ألواح الكي |
| ironing machines | آلات كي |
| ironmongery | الحدائد والأدوات المعدنية |
| irons (beak -) [bick-irons] | حديد [طرف السندان المُحدد] |
| irons (flat -), electric | مكواة [مكواة مسطحة] كهربائية |
| irons [non-electric hand tools] | مكواة [أدوات يدوية غير كهربائية] |
| ironstone formations | المتكونـــات الرســوبية الحــديدية |
| ironwork for doors | مشغولات حديدية للأبواب |
| ironwork for windows | مشغولات حديدية للنوافذ |
| irradiation | تعريض للإشعاع |
| irregular slugs of crude oil, etc. | تدفقات هائلة غير منتظمة |
| irrelevant prior art | فن سابق غير ذي صلة |
| irrevocable license | ترخيص غير قابل للرجوع فيه |
| irrigation and draining | الري والصرف |
| irrigation canal | قناة ري |
| irritable bowel syndrome and gastritis | متلازمة تهيج الأمعاء والتهاب المعدة |
| irs | مصلحة الضرائب الفدرالية |
| is | سرية المعلومات |
| isa search report | تقرير إدارة البحث الدولي |
| ischaemic = ischemic | متعلق بقلة الدم الموضعية |
| ischemic and hemorrhagic stroke | السكتة النزفية أو الناتجة عن قصور الدم الموضعي |
| ischemic apoplcxia- apoplexy | النزف المخي النسيجي المصحوب بقصور الدم الموضعي |
| ischemic cerebral embolism | الانصمام (الانسداد؛ التجلط) المخي المصحوب بقصور الدم الموضعي |
| ischemic cerebral thrombosis | التجلط المخي المصحوب بقصور الدم موضعي |
| ischemic heart condition | حالة قصور الدم الموضعي إلى القلب |
| isdn | الشبكة الرقمية للخدمات المتكاملة |
| isentropic | متساوي القصور الحراري |
| isentropic dense fluid expanders (hydraulic turbines) | ممدات مائع كثيف متساوي الإنتروبيا (توربينات هيدروليكية). |
| isinglass | غراء السمك |
| islamic development bank | البنك الإسلامي للتنمية |
| island position | موقع عائم |
| islet | جزيرة؛ كتلة نسيجية منعزلة |
| iso | الأيزو: المنظمة الدولية للتوحيد القياسي |
| iso- | متماثل |
| iso-butyl | أيزو-بيوتيل |
| isocratic | متساوي التأثير؛ متساوي النسب |
| isodewaxed | منزوعة الشمع بطريقة متماثلة |
| isoelectric point (iep) | نقطة التعادل الكهربائي، نقطة تساوي الكهربائية، نقطة متساوية الكهربائية |
| isoform | صورة متماثلة |
| isoforms | مكونات متشاكلة |
| isogenic | إسوي النمط الجيني |
| isolatability | قابلية الشيء للعزل |
| isolatable | قابل للعزل |
| isolate | يعزل |
| isolate | يعزل |
| isolated from | معزول من (تم أخذه من كذا ) |
| isolates | نواتج عزل |
| isolation | عزل |
| isomerate | ناتج الأزمرة |
| isomeric | أيزومري: في صورة أيزومرات |
| isomerism | أزمرة |
| isomers | الأيزومرات |
| isometric drawing | رسم منظوري؛ مجسم منظوري |
| isoparaffin | أيزو بارافين |
| iso-paraffins | الأيزو-بارافينات |
| iso-propyl | أيزو-بروبيل |
| isopropyl acetate | أسيتات أيزو بروبيل |
| isostatic | متوازن التضاغط |
| isostatics | خُطوطُ التضاغط المتوازن |
| isostere | مماثل فراغي |
| isotactic | متماثلة الترتيب؛ نمطي؛ منتظم التكرار |
| isotherm | منحنى التماثل الحراري |
| isothermal | في درجة حرارة ثابتة |
| isothermal | ثابت الحرارة. على سبيل المثال isothermal system أي نظام ثابت الحرارة؛ وفيه يحفظ النظام في درجة حرارة ثابتة ويعزل فيها النظام عن الوسط المحيط مما لا يسمح بتبادل الحرارة ويسمى هذا النظام Adiabatic . فمثلا زجاجة ديور Dewar flask وهي عبارة عن ترموس يمكن اعتبا |
| isothermic bags | حقائب للحفاظ على درجات الحرارة ثابتة |
| isotonic | متساوي التوتر |
| isotonic beverages | مشروبات متساوية التوتر |
| isotonic phosphate buffer | محلول فوسفات منظم متساوي التوتر |
| isotonic with | متساوية التوتر مع |
| isotope | نظير مشع |
| isotopically-labeled | مركب معلَّم (أو مرقَّم) بالنظائر |

| | |
|---|---|
| Compound | |
| isotropic | موحد الخواص |
| isotype | نوع شبيه |
| isourea | يوريا مناظرة |
| isoxazol | أيزوكسازول |
| isozymes | إنزيمات مماثلة |
| isp | مزود خدمات إنترنت؛ شركة مزودة بخدمات الإنترنت |
| issuability | القابلية للصدور |
| issuable patent | براءة قابلة للصدور |
| issued patent | براءة صادرة |
| ist | تعليمات لتقديم العطاء |
| it | تقنية المعلومات |
| it for small bussiness | تكنولوجيا المعلومات للأعمال الصغيرة |
| it greener solutions | حلول تقنية اتصالات ومعلومات أشد خضرة |
| it infrastructure | البنية التحتية التقنية |
| it optimization | رفع كفاءة تقنية المعلومات إلى المستويات القصوى |

# J

| | |
|---|---|
| jacket | غلاف |
| jacketed 3-neck round bottom flask | دورق ذي غلاف مستدير القاع بثلاث فوهات |
| jackfruit | جاك فروت |
| jamming | تشويش |
| jaywalking | عبور الشارع بشكل منافٍ لقانون المرور |
| jcd | وثيقة ضبط المهمة |
| jd | دكتوراه في القانون |
| jejunum | المعي الصائم |
| jet engine | محرك نفاث |
| jet fuel | وقود الطائرات النفاثة |
| jet mill | طاحنة نفثية |
| jet nozzle | فوهة تدفق |
| jet-lag ; jeg lag | إعياء الطيران: عدم انتظام النوم أو الإنهاك الشديد نتيجة السفر لمسافات طويلة وتفاوت التوقيت بين مكان المغادرة والوصول |
| jetting shoe | غلاف دفق |
| jg | جول/جم |
| jingle | أغنية دعائية؛ دعاية غنائية |
| jinning industry, yarn | محالج القطن؛ الغزل (خيوط) |
| joining pin | دبوس وصل؛ مشبك |
| joint inventorship | اختراعية مشتركة |
| joint portions | أجزاء مفصلية |
| joint school district | مقاطعة المدارس المشتركة |
| joint tenancy | حيازة مشتركة |
| jointly and severally | مجتمعين وفرادى |
| jointly-owned invention | اختراع مملوك ملكية مشتركة |
| joule thomson | ظاهرة جول وطمسون |
| journal | مرتكز؛ مقعدة (عمود) |
| joystick | عصا ألعاب: عصا توجيه |
| jpeg compression | الضغط بتنسيق JPEG |
| judder | اهتزازات سريعة |
| judge advocate | نائب أحكام |
| judgement | حكم |
| judicial commission | لجنة قضائية |
| judicial duty list | لائحة الواجبات القضائية |
| judicial opinion | رأي قضائي. رأي قانوني يكتبه القاضي شرحا لحكم قضائي صادر عنه. |
| jugular vein | الوريد الوِداجيّ |
| juice concentrate | كناتج تركيز عصير |
| juicer-mixer | عَصَّارَة ; مِعْصَرَة |
| junction portion | الجزء التوصيلي |
| juncture material | مادة وصل؛ وصلة |
| juristic acts | أعمال قانونية (شرعية ) |
| juristic rights | حق اعتباري |
| jus cogens | قواعد الزامية- مبادئ سامية |
| jute | الجوت: ألياف تستخدم في صنع الخيش |
| jute plant (long-bodded jute), jute plant (round-bodded jute) | نبات الجوت الأحمر؛ نبات الجوت الأبيض |
| jute waste | نفايات الجوت |

# K

| | |
|---|---|
| keep under surveilance | يضع تحت المراقبة |
| kelly | عمود مضلّع |
| keratin | قرنين |
| keratinocyte | خلية تقرنية |
| keratitis | التهاب القرنية |
| keratoconjunctivitis | التهاب القرنية والملتحمة |
| keratoleukoma | سحابة القرنية |
| keratolytics | مقشرات الطبقة القرنية للجلد |
| kernel | النواة؛ الحبة |
| kettle | غلاية |
| key | مفتاح |
| key logger | مسجل لضربات المفاتيح |
| keyboard overlay | تراكب لوحة المفاتيح |
| keynote | محور الفيلم |
| keypad | لوحة مفاتيح صغيرة: القسم الأيمن من اللوحة (يحتوي على الأرقام وأزرار الأوامر) |
| keystroke monitoring software | برنامج لمراقبة ضربات لوحة المفاتيح |
| keyway | مجرى الخابور |
| keyword | كلمة أساسية؛ كلمة مرشدة |
| kg | كجم |
| kgf | ثقل كجم |
| kgmol/h | كجم مول/ساعة |
| khaos turbo charger | شاحن الهواء التوربيني كاوس |
| khz | كيلو هرتز |
| kick-off point (kop) | نقطة البداية؛ نقطة ضربة البداية |
| kid invention | اختراع لطفل |
| kid tracking | تعقب الأطفال |
| kidney dialysis; haemodialysis | غسيل الكُلى (دَيْلزة الكُلى) أو غسيل الدم |
| kidney parenchym carcinoma | الورم السرطاني بالخلايا المتنية بالكلى |
| kieselgel | كيسيلجل |
| kieselguhr | كيسيلجور |
| kiln | تنور |
| kilogramme | كيلو جرام |
| kilometre | كيلو متر |
| kinamatic viseosity | اللزوجة الكينماتيكية |
| kinase | إنزيم كيناز |
| kinematic ; kinetic | حركي |
| kinematic viscosity | لزوجة حركية |
| kinematically | بشكل حركي |
| kinematics ; kinetics | علم الحركة: يعنى بالخواص الحركية للأجسام |
| kinetic energy | طاقة الحركة |
| kinetic energy | طاقة تنشيط حركي |
| kit with an item for adminstration | طقم يضم وسيلة للإعطاء |

| | |
|---|---|
| kits | أطقم (علاجية) |
| kj | كيلو جول |
| km | كيلومتر |
| kmol | كيلو مول |
| kmph or km/h | كيلومتر كل ساعة |
| kn | كيلو نيوتن |
| k-na tartrate | طرطرات K-Na |
| knapsacks | حقائب ظهر (من الجلد أو الخيش) |
| kneading apparatus | جهاز عجن |
| knee bandages | أربطة خاصة بالركبة |
| knife | سكين؛ سكينة |
| knight commander | من رتبة قائد فرسان |
| knightsbridge safe deposit centre | مركز صناديق أمانات نايتسبريدج |
| knitting needle | إبرة حياكة |
| knock out | فصل بفعل الجاذبية الأرضية |
| knock resistance | مقاومة الخبط؛ مقاومة الدق |
| knockdown ; | تنزيل الجين |
| knockin ; knock-in ; knock in | تشغيل الجين |
| knockout ; knock out ; knock-out | تعطيل مثل تعطيل جيني gene knockout |
| knot | عقدة = ميل بحري |
| knowhow | دراية الكيفية |
| knowhow transfer | دراية الكيفية |
| know-hows | درايات الكيفية |
| knowledge | معرفة، علم |
| knowledge age | العصر المعرفي |
| knowledge assets | أصول معرفية. |
| knowledge capital | رأس المال المعرفي |
| knowledge economy | اقتصاد المعرفة |
| knowledge exchange | تبادل المعرفة |
| knowledge gap | الفجوة المعرفية |
| knowledge intensive economy | اقتصاد ذو حضور كبير للمعرفة فيه |
| knowledge management | إدارة المعرفة |
| knowledge management system | نظام إدارة المعرفة |
| knowledge transfer | تحويل المعرفة |
| knowledge worker | عامل في مجال معرفة |
| knowledge workers | العاملون في قطاع/قسم المعلومات؛ |
| knowledgeable | ملم، واسع الاطلاع |
| knowledge-intensive company | شركة يُعد حضور العلم والمعرفة فيها كبيرا |
| knowledge-intensive environment | بيئة ذات حضور كثيف للمعرفة |
| knowledge-intensive industry | صناعة يعد حضور المعرفة فيها كبير |
| known | معلوم، معروف |
| known prior art | فن سابق معلوم |
| knsm | كيلو نيوتن ثانية م |
| knurled head | رأس مخرش أو مفرز |
| kp - kiloponds | كيلو بوند |
| kpa | كيلو باسكال |
| kpa-gauge | كيلو باسكال بالمقياس |
| kph | كم/س |
| kpsi | ألف رطل لكل بوصة مربعة |

| | |
|---|---|
| kraft pulp | لب كرافت: اللب المستخلص كيميائيا باستخدام كبريتات الصوديوم كمادة طبخ أساسية |
| krebs | محلول كريبس |
| ksi | كيلو رطل/بوصة |
| kte | جهاز هاتف بأزرار |
| ku | وحدات كربس |
| kuwait fund for arab economic development | الصندوق الكويتي لتنمية الاقتصاد العربي |
| kv | كيلو فولت |
| kv1.3 overexpressing hek 293 cells ; hek 293 cells overexpressing kv1.3 | الخلايا HEK 293 التي تعبر وراثيا بإفراط عن قناة Kv1.3 |
| kva | كيلوفولت أمبير |
| kvcm-1 | كيلو فولت سم |
| kw | كيلووات |
| kw/kgc.hour-1 | كيلو واط/ كيلو جرام من الكربون في الساعة -1 |
| kwh | كيلو واط . ساعة |

# L

| | |
|---|---|
| lab | مختبر |
| lab scale fixed bed reactor | مفاعل ذي طبقة ثابتة من الفئة المعملية |
| label | علامة؛ يعلّم (بعلامة)؛ يرقّم؛ يضع بطاقة بيان المحتوى |
| label claim | المُعلَن عنه (في بطاقة استخدام المنتج) |
| labelled | مُعلَّم؛ مُرقم |
| labellers [machines] | آلات لصق بطاقات العناوين [آلات] |
| labels [cloth] | بطاقات العناوين [أقمشة] |
| labels of floppy disks | بطاقات عنونة على الأقراص المرنة |
| labels, not of textile | بطاقات عناوين غير مصنوعة من القماش |
| labial carcinoma | كارسينوما شفوية: الورم السرطاني الشفوي |
| labile | متحول: متغير؛ غير مستقر؛ متأثر ب؛ غير ثابت |
| lability of prodrugs | الطبيعة غير المستقلة للعقاقير الأولية |
| labor intensive solutions | حلول ذات حضور كثيف للعمالة |
| laboratories | مختبرات |
| laboratory | مختبر |
| laboratory burners | مواقد للمختبرات |
| laboratory lamps | مصابيح للمختبرات |
| laboratory scale fixed bed reactor | مفاعل ذي طبقة ثابتة من الفئة المعملية |
| laboratory stage | مرحلة المعمل |
| laboratory trays | أحواض مسطحة للمختبرات |
| labour, skilled labour, semi-skilled labour | الأيدي العاملة، العمال المهرة، العمال نصف المهرة |
| lab-scale ; laboratory-scale | من الفئة المعملية |
| lace boots | أحذية ذات رقبة بالرباط |
| lace for edgings | رباط للحواف |
| lace making machines | آلات لعمل الرباط |
| lace trimming | زركشة للرباط |
| lace trimmings | إكسسوارات للرباط |
| laceration | تهتك |
| laces (leather -) | أربطة [أربطة جلد] |
| laces (shoe -) | أربطة (أربطة للأحذية) |
| laces (woollen -) | شرائط زينه (شرائط زينه صوفية) |
| lack | يفتقر، الافتقار |
| lack of an invention disclosure | الافتقار إلى الإفصاح عن الاختراع |
| lack of inventiveness | الافتقار إلى الاختراعية |
| lack of novelty | الافتقار إلى الجدة |
| lack of unity of invention | الافتقار إلى وحدة الاختراع |
| lacquer (dental -) | ورنيش اللك (ورنيش اللك للأسنان) |
| lacquer-removing preparations | مستحضرات لإزالة ورنيش اللك |

| | |
|---|---|
| lacquers | ورنيش اللك (لاكيه) |
| lacquers (thinners for -) | ورنيش اللك (مخففات لطلاء اللك) |
| lactalbumin | الزلال اللبني |
| lactation period | فترة الإدرار |
| lacteal flour [for babies] | دقيق لبنى [للأطفال] |
| lactic acid | حامض اللاكتيك |
| lactobacillus | لاكتوباسيليس |
| lactodensimeter | مقياس كثافة اللبن |
| lactometer | مقياس اللبن |
| lactoprotein | بروتين اللبن |
| lactose | لاكتوز (سُكّرُ اللّبَن) |
| lacuna | ثغرة، فجوة |
| ladder tapes for venetian blinds | شرائط سلّمية للستائر العمودية |
| ladders (rope -) | سلالم (سلالم من الحبال) |
| ladders of metal | سلالم من المعدن |
| ladders of wood or plastics | سلالم من الخشب أو البلاستيك |
| laden solvent ; loaden solvent | مذيب محمّل |
| ladle carriages | عربات ذات مغرفة |
| ladle cars | سيارات ذات مغرفة |
| ladles [hand tools] | مغارف [أدوات يدوية] |
| lag | فاصل زمني (في تقنية الكاميرات) |
| lag phase | الطور (نمو الخلايا) التمهيدي: مستهل النمو (زيادة بسيطة في العدد؛ تأقلم) |
| lagoon | الهَوْر: بحيرة ساحلية |
| lah | هيدريد ألومنيوم ليثيوم |
| laid texture | نسيج مرقد |
| laid-open | التي تم الكشف عن محتواها الفني |
| lambda | سلسلة لامدا |
| laminar flow | تدفق صفحي |
| laminate | لدينة رقائقية |
| laminated (glass) | رقاقي (زجاج رقاقي) |
| laminated glass | زجاج رقائقي: يتكون من طبقتين أو أكثر من الزجاج بالتبادل مع طبقات بينية من مواد مقوية. وتعمل الطبقات البينية على مقاومة الاختراق وامتصاص الصدم المفاجئ للزجاج كما تعمل على تماسك الزجاج في مكانه وتمنع تناثر الشظايا بشكل واسع |
| laminated structure | بنية صفائحية |
| lamination strength | مقاومة ترقيق |
| laminators (document -) for office use | وسائل تغليف شفاف (وسائل تغليف شفاف للمستندات) لاستخدام المكتب |
| lamp black [pigment] | سخام المصابيح [صبغة] |
| lamp casings | أغلفة للمصابيح |
| lamp chimneys | زجاجة القنديل |
| lamp glasses | زجاجة المصباح |
| lamp globes | كرات للمصابيح |
| lamp hanging supports | دعامات لتعليق المصابيح |
| lamp mantles | رتينة للمصباح |
| lamp reflectors | عواكس للمصابيح |
| lamp shades | كمة المصباح (وسيلة لتغطية المصباح لتقليل توهجه) |

| | |
|---|---|
| lamp wicks | فتائل المصباح |
| lamp-glass brushes | فُرش لزجاج المصباح |
| lamps | مصابيح |
| lamps (burners for -) | مصابيح (مواقد للمصابيح) |
| lamps (darkroom -) [photography] | مصابيح (مصابيح للحجرات المظلمة) [للتصوير الفوتوغرافي] |
| lamps (electric -) | مصابيح (مصابيح كهربائية) |
| lamps (globes for -) | مصابيح (كرات للمصابيح) |
| lamps for directional signals of automobiles | مصابيح للعلامات التوجيهية للسيارات |
| lampshade holders | حوامل مظلة المصباح |
| lan | شبكة اتصالات محلية |
| lan jack | مقبس شبكة محلية |
| lance corporal (lc) | وكيل عريف |
| lancets | مشارط مستدقة الطرف |
| land degradation | تدهور التربة؛ تدهور الأرض |
| land development | تنمية الأراضي |
| land reclamation | استصلاح الأراضي |
| land slides | انزلاقات أرضية |
| landfill | ردم أرضي |
| landing | حط |
| landing gear (also undercarriage) | عُدة الحط |
| landing nets for anglers | شبكات إنزال للصيادين |
| landing nipple | وصلة هبوط بين أنبوبين |
| landing profile | وصلة جانبية أرضية |
| landing zone | منطقة للهبوط (الطائرة) |
| landmarks | علامات بارزة |
| landplaster | ملاط أرضي |
| landscape | تنسيق المواقع: مثل تنسيق منطقة بالأشجار؛ تنسيق حديقة |
| landscape | يسوي، يعبد، يهيئ، مشهد، منظر عمومي |
| landscapes | مناظر طبيعية |
| landscaping | تسوية |
| lane | محاكاة شبكة الاتصالات المحلية |
| lanes 1-5 | مسارات 1- 5 |
| language-specific | المتحدثون بلغات محلية مختلفة |
| lanolin | لانولين (دهن الصوف) |
| lanterns | فوانيس |
| lanterns (optical -) | مصابيح (مصابيح بصرية) |
| lanterns for lighting | فوانيس للإنارة |
| lanthanide chelates | مركبات اللانثانيد الخلابية |
| lanthanide cryptates | مركبات كريبتات اللانثانيد |
| lanthanides | لنثانيد |
| lanthanum | لنثانوم |
| lanthanum aluminosilicate crystal powder | سيليكات ألومنيوم الانثانوم |
| lap belt | حزام الفخذ |
| lap shoulder belt | حزام الفخذ والكتف |
| laptop computers | حاسبات آلية محمولة |
| lard for food | دهن الخنزير للطعام |
| large scale procedure | إجراء على نطاق واسع |
| large scale projected reconstruction | مخطط إعادة بناء على نطاق واسع |
| large-scale fighting | قتال على نطاق واسع |
| large-scale map | خريطة ذات مقياس رسم كبير |
| larvae exterminating preparations | مستحضرات لإبادة اليرقات |
| laryngeal | الحنجرة |
| larynx carcinoma | الورم السرطاني بالحنجرة |
| laser diffraction granulometer | مقياس التحبب باستخدام حيود الليزر |
| laser doppler velocimeter | مقياس سرعة تدفق شعاع الليزر |
| laser energy | طاقة ليزر |
| laser physics | فيزياء الليزر |
| laser sensors | أجهزة إحساس بالليزر |
| lasers for medical purposes | أجهزة ليزر للأغراض الطبية |
| lasinavir | لاسينافير |
| lasts (darning -) | قوالب أحذية (قوالب أحذية الإسكافي) |
| lasts [shoemakers' hand tools] | قوالب أحذية [أدوات يدوية لصانعي الأحذية] |
| lasts for shoes [parts of machines] | قوالب أحذية [أجزاء من الآلات] |
| latch bars of metal | قضبان المزلاج مصنوعة من المعدن |
| latches of metal | مزلاج مصنوع من المعدن |
| latches, not of metal | مزلاج غير مصنوع من المعدن |
| late diagenetic dolomitization | الدلمتة المتأخرة |
| latent heat of vaporization | الحرارة الكامنة للتبخر |
| latent period | فترة كمون |
| lateral apartment | شقق متلاصقة |
| lateral fault | الصدع الجانبي |
| laterally | عرضيا |
| latex | مادة لثية: عصارة الشجر |
| latex [rubber] | اللثى [كاوتشوك] (عصارة الشجر) |
| latex paint | دهان لثي |
| lathes [machine tools] | مخرطة [أدوات الآلة] |
| laths of metal | شرائح؛ مصنوعة من المعدن |
| laths, not of metal | شرائح؛ غير مصنوعة من المعدن |
| latissimus dorsi | عضلة ظهرية عريضة |
| latte | قهوة باللبن |
| lattice | شبكية |
| latticework of metal | شبك مصنوع من المعدن |
| latticework, not of metal | شبك غير مصنوع من المعدن |
| launchers | قاذفات؛ قاذفة (صواريخ) |
| launches | زوارق بخارية |
| laundry bleach | مواد تبييض للغسيل |
| laundry blueing | زهرة الغسيل |
| laundry dryers, electric | مجففات للمغسلة؛ كهربائية |
| laundry glaze | مواد تلميع للغسيل |
| laundry preparations | مستحضرات للغسيل |
| laundry room boilers | غلايات لحجرات الغسيل |
| laundry soaking preparations | مستحضرات نقع للغسيل |
| laundry starch | نشا للغسيل |
| laundry wax | شمع للغسيل |
| lauryl methacrylate | ميث أكريلات لوريل |
| lav | عربة مدرعة خفيفة |
| lava rocks for use in barbecue grills | صخور اللافا للاستخدام في المشواة |

| | |
|---|---|
| lavender oil | زيت لافندر |
| lavender water | ماء لافندر |
| law | قانون |
| law and notary office | مكتب التوثيق والتقاضي |
| law clause | البند الخاص بالقانون |
| law enforcement | إنفاذ القانون |
| law firm | مؤسسة قانونية |
| law of tort | قانون الضرر |
| lawn clippers [hand instruments] | أدوات جز العشب [أدوات يدوية] |
| lawnmowers [machines] | آلات جز العشب [آلات] |
| laws | قوانين |
| lawsuit | دعوى (قانون) |
| lawsuit | دعوى قانونية |
| lawyer | قانوني، محام |
| laxatives | مواد ملينة للأمعاء |
| layered security | الحماية ذات الطبقات |
| layering | تكوين الطبقات |
| layettes [clothing] | كسوة الطفل المولود [ملابس] |
| layouts | مخططات |
| lazy susans | صواني دوارة |
| lb | رطل |
| lb/hr | رطل/الساعة |
| lbmol | رطل مول |
| lbs | رطل |
| lc purity | نقاء عن طريق كروموتوجراف سائل |
| lcarte menu | قائمة الطعام |
| lcat | لتر من المحفز |
| lcc | قائد العناصر البرية |
| lcd | شاشة العرض البلورية LCD |
| lcd brightness | سطوع شاشة LCD |
| lcd color | لون شاشة LCD |
| lcd screen | شاشة LCD |
| l-chain | سلسلة خفيفة |
| lcms | التنظير الطيفي لكتلة الكروماتوجراف السائل |
| lcms | القياس الطيفي لكتلة الكروماتوجراف السائل |
| ld/lc | خط الانطلاق/خط التماس |
| ldm | نموذج بيانات منطقي |
| leach | استخلاص |
| leached glass | زجاج منضوض |
| leaching | النض |
| lead | رصاص؛ سلك موصل؛ سلك توصيل؛ وصلة تسجيل: نظام خاص للتوصيلات الكهربية لتسجيل الجهد الكهربي لعضو حي |
| lead (orange -) | رصاص (رصاص برتقالي) |
| lead (red -) | رصاص (رصاص أحمر) |
| lead (white -) | رصاص (رصاص أبيض) |
| lead acetate | أسيتات الرصاص |
| lead arsenate | زرنيخات الرصاص |
| lead molecules | جزيئات LEAD: جزيئات بروتينات طافرة قيادية |
| lead oxide | أكسيد الرصاص |
| lead seals | موانع تسرب مصنوعة من الرصاص |
| lead shot for hunting | طلقات رصاص للصيد |
| lead water | ماء رصاص |

| | |
|---|---|
| lead, unwrought or semi-wrought | رصاص غير مطروق أو شبه مطروق |
| leaded zinc oxide | أكسيد زنك معالج بالرصاص |
| leader peptide (or leader) | ببتيد قيادي |
| leader sequence | متوالية قيادية |
| lead-in area of the disc | منطقة دخول القرص |
| leading and trailing ends | الأطراف الأمامية والخلفية |
| leading edge | الحافة الأمامية؛ الطرف الأمامي |
| leading lady | بطلة الفيلم |
| leading patent portfolio | محفظة براءات صاحبة صدارة في المجال |
| leading the digital | رائدة التكنولوجيا الرقمية |
| leading the witness | استدراج الشاهد |
| lead-out area of the disc | منطقة خروج القرص |
| leads | بروتينات طافرة قيادية |
| leads (leather -) | موجهات (موجه للأطفال أو للحيوانات من الجلد) |
| leaf | مصراع، صفيحة رقيقة، ورق |
| leaf blade | نصل الورقة |
| leaf curl | تجعد الأوراق |
| leaf node | عقدة خارجية |
| leaf patterned | مطرزة بأوراق شجر؛ مشجّرة |
| leaf spring | نابض ورقي |
| leafminer | نقاب الورق |
| league | فرسخ |
| leak | يتسرب، تسرب، يرشح |
| leak detector | كاشف تسريب |
| leakage | ارتشاح، تسرب، شيء مرتشح |
| leakage current | تيار التسرب |
| leakage flux | فيض تسرب |
| leaks | تسربات |
| leaks (chemical compositions for repairing -) | فتحات تسرب (تركيبات كيميائية لترميم فتحات التسرب) |
| leaky | راشح، سَرِب. تنفذ السوائل منه أو إليه |
| lean | يميل، يتكئ، ميل |
| lean solvent | مذيب ضعيف |
| lean tissues | الأنسجة اللحمية أو الهبرية (أي قليلةِ الدهن أو الخاليةِ منهُ |
| learning | تعلُّم |
| learning machine | آلة متعلمة |
| learning technology | تقنية تعلم |
| learning transfer | تحويل التعلم (من موقف إلى آخر) |
| lease | يؤجر، عقار مؤجر، عقد إيجار |
| leashes (leather -) | مقود الحيوانات (مقود الحيوانات من الجلود) |
| least mean squares method | طريقة متوسط المربعات الصغرى |
| least squares method | طريقة المربعات الصغرى |
| least squares method | طريقة اقل مربعات؛ المربعات الأقل |
| least squares regression | تراجع أقل المربعات |
| leather (appliances for measuring the thickness of -) | جلود [أجهزة لقياس كثافة الجلود] |
| leather (clothing of -) | جلود (ملابس من الجلود) |
| leather (clothing of imitations of -) | جلود (ملابس من الجلود المقلدة) |
| leather (creams for -) | جلود (كريمات للجلود) |

| | |
|---|---|
| leather (currying preparations for -) | جلود (مستحضرات تنظيف الجلود وتجهيزها) |
| leather (grease for -) | جلود (شحوم للجلود) |
| leather (imitation -) | جلود [جلود مقلدة] |
| leather (ink for -) | جلود (حبر للجلود) |
| leather (mastic for -) | جلود (مصطكا للجلود) |
| leather (mordants for -) | جلود (مواد مثبتة للون للجلود) |
| leather (polishing -) | جلود (جلود للتلميع) |
| leather (preservatives for -) [oils and greases] | جلود (مواد حافظة للجلود) [زيوت وشحوم] |
| leather (stains for -) | جلود (صبغات للجلود) |
| leather bleaching preparations | مستحضرات تبييض للجلود |
| leather glues | صمغ للجلود |
| leather industry | صناعة الجلود |
| leather leads | موجه للحيوانات من الجلود |
| leather leashes | مقود للحيوانات من الجلود |
| leather paring machines | آلات لتشذيب الجلود |
| leather preservatives [polishes] | مواد حافظة للجلود [مواد تلميع] |
| leather shoulder belts | أحزمة جلدية للكتف |
| leather straps | شرائط من الجلد |
| leather strops | شرائط من الجلد لجعل الموسى أكثر حدة (مسنات) |
| leather thongs | سيور جلدية |
| leather thread | خيوط جلدية |
| leather twist | جدائل من الجلود |
| leather, unworked or semi-worked | جلود غير مشغولة أو شبه مشغولة |
| leatherboard | ألواح من الجلد المقوى |
| leather-dressing chemicals | كيماويات لدباغة الجلود |
| leather-impregnating chemicals | كيماويات تشريب للجلود |
| leather-renovating chemicals | كيماويات لإصلاح الجلد |
| leathers (stirrup -) | جلود (معلاق الركاب) |
| leather-waterproofing chemicals | كيماويات للجلود مقاومة للماء |
| leather-working machines | آلات لشغل الجلود |
| leaven | خميرة |
| leaving group | مجموعة تاركة |
| leber's hereditary optic atrophy | ضمور ليبر البصري الوراثي |
| lec | عملاء محاكاة شبكة الاتصالات المحلية |
| lecithin [raw material] | ليستين [مادة خام] |
| lecs | خادم تهيئة محاكاة شبكة الاتصالات المحلية |
| lecterns | منصات القراءة (منضدة خاصة بالتلاوة في الكنائس) |
| lecture bottle | اسطوانة غاز مضغوط |
| led (light emitting diodes) | الديود الباعث للضوء: بث الضوء المقوّى الذي يستخدم في شاشات التلفزيون والكمبيوتر والمعروف باسم الصمامات الثنائية.. باختصار الـ LED عبارة عن لمبة ضوء الكترونية اي لا تحتوي على فتيلة ولا تسخن كما في المصابيح الكهربية. فهي تصدر الضوء من خلال حركةالالكترونات |
| led system | نظام LED |
| ledgers [books] | دفتر الأستاذ (محاسبية) [دفاتر] |
| leeches | العلق (ديدان ماصة للدم) |
| leeks | كُراث |
| left ventricular remodeling | إعادة تشكيل البطيني الأيسر |
| legacy | هالة |
| legal counsel | مستشار قانوني، محام |
| legal dispute | نزاع قانوني |
| legal entitlement | استحقاق قانوني. حق المرء في الحصول على مزية أو فائدة يقرر القانون أنه يستحقها |
| legal excuse | عذر قانوني |
| legal infrastructure | البنية التحتية القانونية |
| legal opinion | رأي قانوني |
| legal self-defence | دفاع شرعي عن النفس |
| legel precedence | سابقة قانونية؛ سبق قانوني |
| legend | القائمة التفسيرية للشكل |
| leggings | كسوة للساق |
| legion of merit | وسام الاستحقاق الأمريكي |
| legislate | يشرع |
| legislation | تشريع |
| leishmaniasis | داء الليشمانيات |
| lemon (essential oils of -) | ليمون (زيوت عطرية من الليمون) |
| lemonades | عصير ليمون |
| lengthening pieces, not of metal, for chimneys | قطع تطويل، غير مصنوعة من المعدن للمداخن |
| lens | العدسة |
| lens | عدسة، عدسة العين، يصور للسينما |
| lens filter | مرشح العدسة |
| lens hoods | أغطية للعدسات |
| lenses (optical -) | عدسات (عدسات بصرية) |
| lenses (preparations for preventing the tarnishing of -) | عدسات (مستحضرات لمنع فقدان العدسات لبريقها) |
| lenses [intraocular prostheses] for surgical implantation | عدسات [بدائل صناعية بداخل المقلة] للاستزراع الجراحي |
| lenses for astrophotography | عدسات للتصوير الفوتوغرافي للفلك |
| lentile, beans, soya beans, peanuts | العدس، الفول، فول الصويا، الفول السوداني |
| lentils, fresh | عدس طازج |
| lentils, preserved | عدس محفوظ |
| leprosy | جذام |
| les | خادم محاكاة شبكة الاتصالات المحلية |
| lesion | آفة |
| let down ; letdown | يخفّض |
| let through a flow | يسمح بمرور تدفق |
| letdown | المادة المتروكة |
| letdown in pressure = reduced in pressure | ضغط منخفض |
| letter boxes of masonry | صناديق بريد مبنية بالطوب |
| letter boxes of metal | صناديق بريد مصنوعة من المعدن |
| letter boxes, not of metal or masonry | صناديق بريد غير مصنوعة من المعدن أو مواد البناء |
| letter scales | موازين للخطابات |
| letter trays | حاويات مسطحة القاع للبريد |

| | |
|---|---|
| letters [type] | حروف [مطبعية] |
| letters and numerals [of common metal], except type | حروف وأرقام [من المعدن العادي (غير النفيس)]، ما عدا الحروف والأرقام المطبعية |
| letters for marking linen | حروف لوضع علامات الكتان |
| letters patent | براءة إختراع |
| lettuce | خس |
| leucin zippers | زمامات اللوسين المنزلقة: ببتيدات ربط |
| leucine residue | وحدة ليوسين بنائية |
| leukocyte | كرية بيضاء |
| leukopenia | قلة كرات الدم البيضاء |
| leukophoresis | رحلان كرات بيضاء طبيعي لمتبرع بشري |
| leukotrienes | مركبات الليوكوترايين |
| leutinizing hormone- releasing hormone (lhrh) | هرمون إطلاق الهرمون اللوتيني أو الملوتن |
| level | مستوى؛ ميزان (البنّاء): لمعرفة إن كان سطح ما مستوي أم لا |
| level adjustment | ضبط المستوى |
| level controlling valves in tanks | صمامات للتحكم في المنسوب في الخزانات |
| level marker | محدد المستوى |
| levelling instruments | أدوات تسوية |
| levelling staffs [surveying instruments] | قامة التسوية [أدوات قياس] |
| levels [instruments for determining the horizontal] | موازين ضبط الاستواء [أدوات لتحديد الأفق] |
| levers | رافعات |
| leviratic marriage | الزواج من أرملة الأخ |
| lewis acid | حمض لويس |
| lf(s) | قوة (قوات) برية |
| lfc | خرائط الطيران المنخفض |
| lfoc | مركز عمليات القوات البرية |
| lfpt | فريق تخطيط القوات البرية |
| lhsv | السرعة الفراغية للسائل في الساعة |
| liber | لحاء |
| liberal party | حزب الأحرار |
| liberating the optically active amine compound | إطلاق مركب الأمين النشط ضوئيا |
| library | مجموعة متواليات: خليط من عديدات الببتيد غير المتجانسة أو الأحماض النووية |
| library shelves | أرفف للمكتبات |
| libre knowledge | معرفة حرة. شعار مفاده وجوب جعل المعرفة حرة من أي قيود بما في ذلك قيود الملكية الفكرية يطالب مناهضو الملكية الفكرية وأنصار تحرير العلم والمعرفة به |
| licensability | قابلية الشئ للترخيص |
| licensable | قابل للترخيص |
| licensable patent | براءة قابلة للترخيص |
| licensable patent portfolio | محفظة براءات يمكن ترخيصها |
| license | ترخيص |
| license agreement | اتفاق بشأن ترخيص |
| license exclusivity | حصرية ترخيص |
| license plate | لوحة ترخيص |
| license seeker | الراغب في الترخيص |
| license territory | إقليم الترخيص |
| license to distribute | ترخيص للتوزيع |
| license to have manufactured | ترخيص للتصنيع لدى الغير |
| license to have manufactured | ترخيص للتصنيع لدى الغير |
| license to manufacture | ترخيص للتصنيع |
| license to publicly display | ترخيص للعرض العام |
| license to publicly perform | ترخيص للأداء العام |
| license to reproduce | ترخيص لإعادة الإنتاج |
| license to transmit | ترخيص للنقل |
| license to use | ترخيص يمكن وضعه موضع التنفيذ |
| license valuation | تقييم ترخيص |
| license value | قيمة ترخيص |
| licensed | مرخص، مرخص له |
| licensed drug | دواء مرخص |
| licensed know-how | دراية كيفية مرخصة |
| licensed software | برنامج مرخص |
| licensees | المرخص لهم |
| licenses | تراخيص، رخص |
| licenses manager | مدير تراخيص |
| licensing | ترخيص، إصدار ترخيص أو رخصة |
| licensing agreement | اتفاق ترخيص |
| licensing behavior | السلوك الترخيصي |
| licensing funding | تمويل للترخيص |
| licensing funding advice | مشورة بشأن إيجاد تمويل لغرض الترخيص |
| licensing industry | صناعة التراخيص |
| licensing know-how | دراية الكيفية في مجال التراخيص |
| licensing manager | مدير ترخيص |
| licensing negotiations | مفاوضات الترخيص. مفاوضات تجري بين طرفين بشأن قيام أحدهما منح الآخر ترخيصا |
| licensing society | جمعية ترخيص |
| licensor-licensee relationship | علاقة مانح الترخيص بالحاصل على الترخيص |
| lichen planus | الحزاز المسطح |
| lid switch | مفتاح إضاءة الشاشة |
| lie detection technology | تقنية كشف الكذب |
| lie detector | جهاز الكشف عن الكذب |
| lien waivers | تنازل عن الحجز |
| lieutenant | ملازم أول بحري |
| lieutenant (lt.) ; first lieutenant | ملازم أول؛ ملازم أول |
| lieutenant colonel (lt. col) | مقدم |
| lieutenant commander | نقيب بحري |
| lieutenant general | فريق |
| lieutenant general (lt. gen.) | فريق |
| life | حياة |
| life belts | أحزمة نجاة |
| life buoys | طافيات إنقاذ |
| life imprisonment / life sentence | السجن المؤبد |
| life jackets | سترات نجاة |
| life nets | شبكات الإنقاذ |
| life saving apparatus and | أجهزة ومعدات الإنقاذ |

Equipment
life sciences-driven company شركة تقودها العلوم الحياتية
life-saving rafts أطواق النجاة
lift مِصْعَدٌ؛ رفع
lift belts سيور المصعد
lift gas غاز رفع (يستخدم لرفع الزيت في بئر من خلال حقن غاز من أسفل فيها)
lift gas injection system of the wells نظام حقن بغاز رفع للآبار
lift operating apparatus جهاز تشغيل المصعد
lifting apparatus جهاز رفع
lifting cars [lift cars] سيارات رافعة
lifting device جهاز إزالة
lifting jacks, hand-operated رافعة للسيارة تدار يدوياً
lifts (ski -) مصاعد (مصاعد التزلج)
lifts (tailboard -) [parts of land vehicles] رافعة (رافعة الباب الخلفي) [أجزاء من المركبات الأرضية]
lifts [other than ski-lifts] مصاعد [غير مصاعد التزلج]
ligand مركب ترابطي؛ جزيء ربط؛ جزيء ترابطي
ligand formats صيغ المركب الترابطي
ligate يُلحق
ligating إلحاق
ligature وعاء دموي
light يضيء، ضوء
light amplification تضخيم الضوء
light amplifier مضخم الضوء
light bulbs لمبات للإضاءة
light bulbs for directional signals for vehicles لمبات للإضاءة؛ للإشارات التوجيهية للمركبات
light bulbs, electric لمبات للإضاءة؛ كهربائية
light chain domain ; light-chain domain نطاق خفيف السلسلة
light chain variable domain sequence متوالية نطاق متغير خفيف السلسلة
light conducting filaments [optical fibers [fibres]] شعيرات موصلة للضوء [ألياف بصرية]
light creme قشدي فاتح
light diffusers أجهزة نشر الضوء
light dimmers [regulators] [electric] خافت الأنوار [منظمات] [كهربائية]
light duty تشغيل خفيف
light effects مؤثرات ضوئية
light emitter باعث ضوء
light end gases غازات ذيلية خفيفة
light energy طاقة الضوء
light environment بيئة ضوء
light hydrocarbonaceous feed gas stream تيار تغذية بغازات هيدروكربونية خفيفة
light industries الصناعات الخفيفة
light machine gun (lmg) رشاش خفيف
light reflecting material مادة عاكسة للضوء
light scatterer مفرق الضوء
light scattering بعثرة الضوء
light tanks دبابات خفيفة
light truck عربة نقل خفيف
light vehicle مركبة خفيفة
light-chain promiscuity اقتران خفيف السلسلة
light-emitting electronic pointers مؤشرات إلكترونية لانبعاث الضوء
lighters مشاعل
lighters (gas -) مشاعل (ولاعات بالغاز)
lighters for smokers مشاعل المدخنين
light-heat absorbing efficiency فعالية امتصاص الضوء والسخونة
light-heat absorbing material مادة تمتص الضوء والحرارة
light-heat gathering device جهاز تجميع الضوء والسخونة
light-heavy interchain bond residues 127-133 وحدات بنائية شريط داخل السلسلة الخفيفة والثقيلة 127-133
lighting إنارة
lighting (batteries for -) إنارة (بطاريات للإنارة)
lighting (gas for -) إنارة (غاز للإنارة)
lighting (paper spills for -) إنارة (لفافات ورقية للإنارة)
lighting (wood spills for -) إنارة (لفافات خشبية للإنارة)
lighting apparatus and installations أجهزة وتركيبات إنارة
lighting apparatus for vehicles جهاز إنارة للمركبات
lighting ballast جهاز موازنة التيار لوسائل الإنارة
lighting conditions ظروف الإضاءة
lighting control solutions حلول للتحكم في الإضاءة
lighting fixtures تركيبات الإضاءة
lighting fuel وقود إنارة
lighting installations for air vehicles تركيبات إنارة للمركبات الجوية
lighting slabs لوحات للإنارة
lightning arresters واقيات صواعق
lightning conductors [rods] موصلات للإنارة [قضبان]
light-reflectable material مادة عاكسة للضوء
lights (diving -) أضواء (أضواء للغطس)
lights for automobiles أضواء للسيارات
lights for vehicles أضواء للمركبات
lights, electric, for christmas trees أضواء كهربائية، لشجر الكريسماس
lignin اللجنين: هذه هى المادة اللاصقة للألياف الطبيعية وهى عبارة عن بوليمر عضوي معقد وله تركيب غير منتظم
lignite الفحم البني أو الليجنيت
ligroin ليجروين (نفط)
likeliehood function دالة الاحتمال
limbs (artificial -) أطراف (أطراف اصطناعية)
lime جير
lime (nitrogenous -) [manure] جير (جير نيتروجيني) [سماد]
lime (preparations of -) for pharmaceutical purposes جير (مستحضرات من الجير) للأغراض الصيدلانية
lime acetate اسيتات الجير
lime carbonate كربونات الجير

| | |
|---|---|
| lime chloride | كلوريد الجير |
| lime for animal forage | جير لعلف الحيوانات |
| lime softener | مزيل الجير من الماء |
| lime wash | طلاء جيري مائي |
| limestone | حجر جيري |
| limestone hardening substances | مواد تصليد الحجر الجيري |
| limited contractual liability clause | البند الخاص بحدود المسئولية التعاقدية. بند تعاقدي يبين حدود المسئولية التعاقدية التي يتوجب تحملها في حالة الإخلال. |
| limited liability clause | بند تحديد المسئولية. بند يقرر حدود التعويضات التي يجوز لطرف الحصول عليها من طرف آخر في حالة حصول خلل من جانبه مثل الخلل الناتج عن وجود عطل في البرنامج الحاسبي المبيع. |
| limited license | ترخيص محدود |
| limited monolopoly | احتكار محدود. يقوم نظام الملكية التقليدي على فكرة أحقية تمتع صاحب الحق الفكري باحتكار محدود للعائد المالي المنبثق عن العمل الفكري مقابل نشر العمل الفكري واستفادة الناس منه على أن يدخل العمل الفكري النطاق العام بعد فترة معينة |
| limited patentability | إمكانية محدودة لإصدار براءة |
| limited proteolysis | التحلل البروتيني المحدود؛ تحلل البروتين المحدود |
| limiters [electricity] | محددات [كهرباء] |
| limiting mechanism | آلية تأطير للحماية |
| limiting the invention | تقييد الاختراع؛ تحديد مجاله |
| limonite | ليمونيت |
| limp mode | وضع بطئ |
| limp tail | ذيل مترهل |
| linage | سلالة |
| line | خط |
| linear actuators | المشغلات الخطية |
| linear alignment | محاذاة خطية |
| linear elastic fracture mechanics | الخواص الميكانيكية لصدع خطي مرن |
| linear higher carbon c6 and above paraffins | البارافينات الخطية التي بها عدد ذرات مرتفع من الكربون C6 وأعلى |
| linear interpolation | اِسْتِكْمَالٌ خَطِّيٌّ |
| linear spatial configuration | تصميم فراغي خطي |
| linear sweep voltammogram | مقياس فرق الجهد بالمسح الخطي |
| linear up/log down trapezoidal rule | قاعدة شبه المنحرف خطي إلى أعلى / لوغاريتم إلى أسفل |
| linear velocity | سرعة خطية اتجاهية |
| lined with | مبطنًا بـ |
| linen (bed -) | ملاءات (شراشف) (ملاءات للأسّرة) |
| linen (body -) [garments] | ملابس كتانية (ملابس كتانية للجسم) [ملابس] |
| linen (diapered -) | كتان (كتان مشجر أو مضلع) |
| linen (household -) | بياضات (بياضات للمنزل) |
| linen (letters for marking -) | كتان (حروف لتعليم الكتان) |
| linen (numerals for marking -) | كتان (أرقام لتعليم الكتان) |
| linen (raw -) [flax] | كتان (كتان خام) [ألياف الكتان] |
| linen (sachets for perfuming -) | بياضات (أكياس معطرة لتعطير البياضات] |
| linen cloth | قماش الكتان |
| linen fibers | ألياف الكتان |
| linen thread and yarn | خيوط وغزل من الكتان |
| linen, drapery | أقمشة ومنشوجات كتانية، كتان |
| liner | بطانة |
| lines for fishing | شص لصيد السمك |
| lingerie fabric | قماش للملابس التحتية النسائية |
| linguistic invention | اختراع لغوي |
| lingula | لُسَين [ج:لُسَينات] |
| liniments | مراهم |
| lining | بطانة |
| lining (brake -) for vehicles | بطانة (للمكبح) للمركبات |
| lining (clutch -) | بطانة القابض (الدبرياج) |
| lining (hat -), of textile, in the piece | بطانة (للقبعات) من القماش، مثبتة في المنتج |
| lining (ready-made -) [parts of clothing] | بطانة (جاهزة) [أجزاء من الملابس] |
| lining [textile] | بطانة [أقمشة] |
| lining fabric for shoes | قماش تبطين للأحذية |
| lining materials (brake -), partly processed | مواد تبطين (مواد تبطين للمكبح) معالجة جزئياً |
| lining of metal [building] | بطانة مصنوعة من المعدن [مباني] |
| lining, not of metal, for building | بطانة غير مصنوعة من المعدن للمباني |
| link (to) | يربط أو يرتبط (بـ) |
| linkage ; linkages | ارتباط؛ ارتباطات |
| linkage group | مجموعة ربط |
| linkage map | خريطة ارتباطات |
| linkages of metal (cable -) [non-electric] | توصيله من المعدن (توصيله للكبل من المعدن) [غير كهربائية] |
| linker | رابط: مادة ربط |
| links (cuff -) | حلقات (حلقات لطرف كم القميص) |
| link-tooth saw | منشار جنزير |
| linoleum | لينوليوم (مشمع فرش الأرضيات) |
| linseed | بذور الكتان |
| linseed meal | مجروش بذور الكتان |
| lint content | نسبة التيلة |
| lint for medical purposes | ضمادة كتانية معقمة للاستخدام في الأغراض الطبية |
| lintel | عتبة علوية |
| lintels of metal | نوافذ علوية مستعرضة من المعدن |
| lintels, not of metal | نوافذ علوية مستعرضة ليست من المعدن |
| linter | نسالة القطن |
| linters of cotton | زغب القطن |
| lipid binding domains | مناطق ارتباط الجسم الشحمي |
| lipid kinases | إنزيمات كيناز الشحمية |
| lipid substrate | ركيزة شحمية |

lipidic peroxidation تكون البيروكسيد الدهني
lipids دهون
lipofection العدوى الدهنية: نقل العدوى بواسطة جسيم دهني أو شحمي
lipogenic مولد الدهون
lipophile إلف للدهون
lipophilic مستشحم
lipoprotein بروتين دهني
lipoprotein associated coagulation inh مثبطات التجلط المتعلقة بالبروتين الدهني
liposarcoma سركوما شحمية
liposome جسم دهني
lipsticks أحمر الشفاه
liquefaction إسالة؛ تمييع أو سيولة؛ تميع
liquefied مسال
liquefied natural gas غاز طبيعي مسال
liqueur sets أطقم أواني المشروبات الكحولية
liqueurs المشروبات الكحولية
liqueurs (colorants for -) المشروبات الكحولية (مواد ملونة للمشروبات الكحولية)
liqueurs (preparations for making -) المشروبات الكحولية (مستحضرات لتصنيع المشروبات الكحولية)
liquid chloride absorbing material مادة سائلة ماصلة للكلوريد
liquid chromatogeaphy الفصل الكروماتوجرافي للسائل
liquid diluent مادة مخففة سائلة
liquid effluent التيار المتدفق السائل
liquid fuel (containers, not of metal, for -) وقود سائل (أوعية الوقود السائل ليست من المعدن)
liquid handler وسيلة تداول السائل
liquid matrix طبقة سائلة
liquid metal ladles مغارف للمعدن السائل
liquid natural gas (lng) غاز طبيعي مسال
liquid nitrogen economy اقتصاد مرتكز على النيتروجين السائل
liquid paraffin بارافين سائل
liquid pressure sensor جهاز إحساس بضغط السوائل
liquid rubber مطاط سائل
liquid seal مانع تسرب السائل
liquid stream تيار سائل
liquids for removing sulphates from batteries سوائل لإزالة الكبريتات من البطاريات
liquifies petroleum gas غاز البترول المسال
liquifying chemicals مواد إسالة كيميائية (مواد كيميائية
(starch- -) [ungluing agents] لإسالة النشا) [عوامل إزالة الغراء]
liquor مادة سائلة - أو مائية
liquorice [confectionery] عرق سوس [حلويات]
l-isomer أيزومر يساري الدوران
listening device جهاز سمع
literacy الإلمام بحق المؤلف
literary أدبي
literature مراجع
literature أدب، أدبيات
literature procedures للإجراءات الموجودة بالمراجع
litharge الليثارج [أول أكسيد الرصاص]

lithia [lithium oxide] الليثيا [أول أكسيد الليثيوم]
lithia water ماء الليثيا
lithiation إضافة ليثيوم
lithic wacke الواكي الصخري
lithification التصخر
lithium الليثيوم
lithium economy اقتصاد مرتكز على الليثيوم
lithium ion battery بطارية الليثيوم أيون
lithium ion battery pack مجموعة بطاريات الليثيوم أيون
lithium metal polymer battery بطارية ليثيوم بوليمر
lithium perchlorate بيركلورات الليثيوم
lithographic stones أحجار الطباعة
lithographic works of art الأعمال الفنية بالطباعة
lithographs طبعات حجرية
lithologic units الوحدات الصخرية
lithostatic pressure الضغط الليثوستاتيكي
litigable قابل للتقاضي، يمكن أن تقام من أجله دعوى
litigant متقاض
litigate يقاضي، ينازع قضائيا
litigation تقاض
litigator مختص بالنزاعات القضائية
litigious كثير إقامة الدعاوى، كثير الخصام
litmus paper ورق عباد الشمس
litre لتر
litter (products for animal -) فرش الدواب (منتجات لفرش الدواب)
litter boxes [trays] for pets صناديق سُرر من القش [صواني] للحيوانات المنزلية
litter peat تبن الدواب
live animals الحيوانات الحية
live telecast إذاعة على الهواء مباشرة
livedo تزرق
liver لحم الكبد
liver fibrosis تليف الكبد
liver pâté فطائر الكبد
liveries البزات [زي مميز للخدم]
livestock fattening preparations مستحضرات تسمين الماشية
livestock marking tools أدوات وضع علامات على الماشية
lixiviation تصفية
lltr توجيه عبور على ارتفاع منخفض
lng غاز طبيعي مسال
lng plant وحدة غاز طبيعي مسال
lo sp سرعة منخفضة
load bearing body جسم محمل الحمل
load bearing capacity سعة تحميل الحمل
load bearing sheath غمد سعة حمل
load cell خلية حِمل
load center مركز التحميل
load handling (braces of metal for-) تعبئة وشحن الحمولة (مقابض من المعدن لتعبئة وشحن الحمولة)
load handling (harness of تعبئة وشحن الحمولة (عُدد

| | |
|---|---|
| metal for -) | معدنية لتعبئة وشحن الحمولة) |
| load handling (straps of metal for -) | تعبئة وشحن الحمولة (أطواق معدنية لتعبئة وشحن الحمولة) |
| loaden solvent | مذيب تم تحميله؛ تعبئته |
| loading apparatus for furnaces | جهاز تحميل للأفران |
| loading capacity | سعة تحميل |
| loading gauge rods, not of metal, for railway waggons [wagons] | قضبان أجهزة تحديد قياس التحميل، ليست من المعدن لعربات نقل البضائع في السكة الحديدية |
| loading gauge rods, of metal, for railway waggons | قضبان أجهزة تحديد قياس التحميل من المعدن لعربات نقل البضائع في السكة الحديدية |
| loading header | مجمع تحميل |
| loading of the catalyst | شحنة المفاعل |
| loading pallets, not of metal | منصات نقالة للتحميل ليست من المعدن |
| loading pallets, of metal | منصات نقالة للتحميل من المعدن |
| loading ramps | منصات تحميل منحدرة |
| loading/unloading the cassette | إدخال/إخراج الشريط |
| loads (belts, not of metal, for handling -) | الحمولة (سيور ليست من المعدن لتعبئة وشحن الحمولة) |
| loads (slings of metal for handling-) | الحمولة (حبال الرفع من المعدن لتعبئة وشحن الحمولة) |
| loads (slings, not of metal, for handling -) | الحمولة (حبال الرفع ليست من المعدن لتعبئة وشحن الحمولة) |
| loads (straps, not of metal, for handling -) | الحمولة (أحزمة ليست من المعدن لتعبئة وشحن الحمولة) |
| loam | طفال رملي |
| loam-based compost | سماد طفلي |
| lobby | تجمع، تجمع استمالة |
| lobbying | استمالة |
| lobbyist | محترف الاستمالة |
| lobsters (spiny -) [live] | سرطان (جراد) البحر (الشوكي) [حي] |
| lobsters (spiny -) [not live] | سرطان (جراد) البحر (الشوكي) [غير حي] |
| lobsters [live] | سرطان (جراد) البحر [حي] |
| lobsters [not live] | سرطان (جراد) البحر [غير حي] |
| loc | خط الاتصالات |
| local | موضعي |
| local anesthetic | مخدر موضعي |
| local dance and theater groups | فرق المسرح والرقص المحلية |
| local index | فهرس محلي |
| local layer | طبقة موضعية |
| local pressure | ضغط موضعي |
| local value | قيمة موضعية |
| locality | محلية |
| locally | موضعيا |
| locatability | إمكانية تعيين موقع الشيء |
| locate | يحدد موقع؛ يحدد موضع |
| locate | يعين موقع |
| locate (in) | يوجد في |
| location | موقع |
| location | تعيين موقع |
| location of qtls | موضع مواقع QTLs |
| locator | معين الموقع |
| locator device | جهاز تعيين موضع |
| loci | مواقع |
| lock bolts | مزاليج القفل |
| lock hoppers | قواديس الإغلاق |
| lock indicator | مؤشر القفل |
| lock washer | حلقة تثبيت |
| lockers | خزانات قابلة للغلق |
| locking = closing | إغلاق |
| locking = fixing | تثبيت |
| locking device | وسيلة إقفال |
| locking key | مفتاح إقفال |
| locking pin | مسمار تثبيت |
| locking screw | لولب تثبيت |
| locking unit | وحدة إقفال |
| locks [other than electric] of metal | أقفال [بخلاف الأقفال الكهربائية] من المعدن |
| locks [other than electric], not of metal | أقفال [بخلاف الأقفال الكهربائية] ليست من المعدن |
| locks of metal for bags | أقفال من المعدن للحقائب |
| locks of metal for vehicles | أقفال من المعدن للاستخدام في المركبات |
| locks, electric | أقفال كهربائية |
| locks, not of metal, for vehicles | أقفال ليست من المعدن للاستخدام في المركبات |
| loco parentis | في مكان او مقام الوالد او الوالدة |
| locomotion | تحرك، تنقل، سفر |
| locomotives | المركبات |
| locust bean gum | صمغ الخروب |
| locust beans | بذور الخروب |
| log | لوغاريتم؛ سجل |
| log in | يسجل دخول |
| log phase | طور (نمو الخلايا) اللوغاريتمي: النمو السريع (تضاعف العدد بمعدل ثابت) |
| log plate count | قيمة لوغاريتم العد في أطباق |
| log scale | تدريج لوغاريتمي |
| logging | تسجيل أداء؛ تسجيل قياسات: تسجيل بيانات البئر |
| logging while drilling (lwd) | تسجيل الأداء أثناء الحفر |
| logging while drilling tool | أداة تسجيل الأداء أثناء الحفر |
| logical connections | توصيلات منطقية |
| logical row id | معرف الصف المنطقي |
| logistics | شئون الإعاشة؛ اللوجستيا؛ الإمدادات التموينية |
| log-linear scale ; log linear scale | مقياس لوغاريتمي خطي |
| logoff | تسجيل الخروج |
| logon | تسجيل الدخول |
| logon/logoff | تسجيل الدخول / تسجيل الخروج |
| log-rank | لوغاريتم الرتب؛ لوغاريتم الفئات |
| logs [measuring instruments] | معدات قياس [معدات قياس سرعة السفينة] |
| long form | دعاية تلفزيونية طويلة |

| | |
|---|---|
| long standing rule | قاعدة راسخة |
| long staple cotton, medium staple cotton, and short staple cotton | قطن طول التيلة، متوسط التيلة، وقصير التيلة |
| longitudinal or torsional | طولي أو ملتوي |
| longitudinal study | دراسة طولية |
| longitudinal waves | الموجات القصية المستعرضة |
| long-range artillery | مدفعية طويلة المدى |
| long-term lease right | الحِكْر |
| look-ahead logging system ; look ahead logging system ; lookahead loggiing system | نظام تسجيل قياسات قبلي (أو موجه نحو المقدمة أو موجه نحو الأمام): جهاز لقياس المناطق أو السمات الجيولوجية قبل (أداة) حفرة البئر) |
| look-around loggying system ; look around loggying system ; lookaround loggying system | نظام تسجيل قياسات محيطي (أو موجه نحو المحيط) [القياس المناطق أو السمات الجيولوجية المحيطة بـ (أداة) حفرة البئر) |
| loom | النول |
| loom shafts | سيقان النول |
| looms | الأنوال |
| looms [machines] | الأنوال [ماكينات] |
| loop | حلقة |
| loop element | عنصر حلقي |
| loop reactor | مفاعل حلقي |
| looping | تثبيت المدرس مع الطلاب |
| loose end of a coil | طرف سائب لملف |
| loose-leaf binders | روابط الإضبارة للأوراق السائبة |
| loosely | بحرية؛ على نحو حر؛ على نحو سائب؛ بطرف حر |
| loosely closed | غير محكم الإغلاق |
| loq | حد التقدير الكمي |
| lorries | شاحنات |
| los | خط البصر |
| loss | خسارة، خسران |
| loss circulation | الدوران المفقود |
| loss indicators (electric -) | مؤشرات الفقد (مؤشرات الفقد الكهربائي) |
| loss leader | المجتذبة بخسارة |
| loss of function mutation | طفرة فقدان وظيفة |
| loss of patent rights | خسران الحقوق في البراءة |
| loss of potential royalty | خسارة إتاوة محتملة |
| loss of priority | فقدان الأولوية. فقدان طلب البراءة للأولوية. |
| loss of rights | خسران الحقوق |
| loss of royalty | خسارة الإتاوة |
| losses | حدوث فقد؛ فقد؛ فقود |
| lossless | بدون فقد |
| loss-on-ignition (loi) | الفقد بالاحتراق؛ الفقد عند الاحتراق؛ الفقد بالإحماء؛ الفقد بالإشعال |
| lost circulation | الدوران المفقود |
| lot | تشغيلة |
| lot number | رقم تسلسلي |
| lotion | غسول |
| with cosmetic -) | ورقية مشبعة بغسولات التجميل) |
| lotions (tissues impregnated | غسولات (لوسيون) (مناديل |

| | |
|---|---|
| with pharmaceutical -) | ورقية مشبعة بلوسيون صيدلاني) |
| loudspeakers | مكبرات الصوت |
| low ambient light environment | بيئة محاطة بضوء خافت |
| low battery | بطارية ضعيفة |
| low boiler | مكون ذي درجة غليان أقل low- boiling component |
| low carbon olefins | أوليفينات منخفضة الكربون |
| low compression | ضغط منخفض |
| low energy vehicle | مركبة ذات طاقة منخفضة |
| low fat milk | لبن قليل الدهون |
| low light | الضوء الخافت |
| low molecular ethylene (co)polymer | بوليمر إيثيلين (مشترك) منخفض الوزن الجزيئي |
| low molecular ethylene copolymer | بوليمر إيثيلين مشترك منخفض الوزن الجزيئي |
| low molecular weight thrombin inhibitors | مثبطات ثرومبين منخفضة الوزن الجزيئي |
| low of superposition | قانون تعاقب الطبقات |
| low risk solutions | حلول ذات كلفة فعالة ومخاطرة ضئيلة |
| low stringency | ظروف منخفضة الصرامة |
| low temperature coated particles | جسيمات مغلفة عند درجة حرارة منخفضة |
| low volume assay plate | طبق اختبار لحجم قليل |
| low/big-budget films | أفلام ذات ميزانية منخفضة؛ كبيرة |
| low-e glass | زجاج الانبعاث المنخفض :(Low Emissivity) زجاج يتسم بطبقة شفافة على الزجاج تسمح بمرور موجات الطاقة الشمسية القصيرة من خلالها ولكنها تعكس الموجات الطويلة عن جهة الغرفة أو تعكس الطاقة الحرارية الخارجية |
| lower | صغرى |
| lower alkylaminoalkylcarboxy- | ألكيل أمينو ألكيل كربوكسي- صغرى |
| lower animals | حيوانات لا فقارية |
| lower basal bv8 expression = lower basal level of bv8 expression | مستوى قاعدي أقل من التعبير الوراثي عن Bv8 |
| lower boiling hydrocarbon products | منتجات الهيدروكربونات ذات درجة الغليان الأقل |
| lower boiling hydrocarbons | الهيدروكربونات ذات درجة الغليان الأقل |
| lower flammability limit | أدني مدي للاشتعال |
| lower rank | يخفض الرتبة أو الدرجة |
| low-flying aircraft | طائرات على ارتفاع منخفض |
| low-grade tumor | ورم منخفض الدرجة |
| low-mass main sequence star | نجم تسلسل رئيسي ذو كتلة منخفضة |
| low-temperature gas mixture separation | فصل خليط غازي عند درجة حرارة منخفضة |
| low-temperature gas separation | فصل الغاز عند درجة حرارة منخفضة |
| low-yield solutions | حلول ذات مردود منخفض |

| | |
|---|---|
| lozenge | قرص استحلاب |
| lozenges | حلوى على شكل المعين الهندسي |
| lp mode | وضع LP (التشغيل الطويل) |
| lsd | وحدة عرض شاشة كبيرة |
| lter ego | نفس أو شخصية أخرى |
| lube oil | زيت تزليق |
| lubricant | مزلق؛ مادة مزلقة |
| lubricating agents | عوامل تزليق |
| lubricating graphite | جرافيت التزليق |
| lubricating grease | شحم تزليق |
| lubricating oil | زيت تزليق |
| lubricating pumps | مضخات تزليق |
| lubrication | تزليق |
| lubricators [parts of machines] | مزلقات [أجزاء من ماكينات] |
| lubroring | حلقة تزليق |
| luddites | محطموا الآلات |
| luetic neuropathy | الاعتلال العصبي الزهري |
| luggage carriers for vehicles | حوامل الأمتعة في المركبات |
| luggage nets for vehicles | شباك الأمتعة في المركبات |
| luggage trucks | عربات شحن الأمتعة |
| lumber | ألواح الخشب المنشور |
| lumen | تجويف |
| lumen | لومن (وحدة قياس تدفق الضوء) |
| lumen of their hd catheter | تجويف أنبوبة قسطرة HD |
| luminescent materials | مواد مضيئة |
| luminous house numbers | أرقام المنازل المضيئة |
| luminous paper | الورق المضيء |
| luminous paving | الأرصفة المضيئة |
| luminous tubes for lighting | أنابيب الإنارة المضيئة |
| lunch boxes | علب الغذاء |
| luni | واجهة شبكة مستخدم محاكاة شبكة الاتصالات المحلية |
| lupulin for pharmaceutical purposes | شعيرات نبات اللوبولين للاستخدام في الأغراض الصيدلانية |
| lupus erthematosus | ذئبة حُمامية |
| lupus erythematodes disseeminatus | الذئبة الإحمرارية التي تعم الجسم كله |
| lupus nephritis | التهاب كلوي ذأبي |
| lures for hunting or fishing | طُعم للاستخدام في الصيد أو صيد الأسماك |
| lute | طين خاص لإحكام غلق وصلات الأنابيب |
| luteinizing hormons | الهرمون اللوتيني |
| lutetium [cassiopium] | اللوتشيوم [كاسيبيوم] |
| luxury brand industry | صناعة العلامات الفاخرة |
| luxury goods industry | صناعة السلع الفاخرة |
| Lv | البطيني الأيسر |
| lwvont cotton plant | نبات القطن الشجري الأسيوي |
| lye washtubs | أحواض الغسيل بالمحاليل القلوية القوية |
| lyme disease | داء لايم |
| lymph | ليمفي |
| lymph node | عقد لمفية |
| lymph node enlargement | تضخم العقد الليمفاوية |
| lymphatic system | جهاز لمفي |
| lymphatics | أوعية لمفية |
| lymphocytes | خلايا لمفية |
| lymphoid interstitial | التهاب الرئوي الخلالي |
| pneumonitis | الليمفواني |
| lymphomas | الأورام الليمفاوية |
| lymphoneogenesis | تكون العقد الليمفاوية |
| lymphoprep | مستحضر ليمفي |
| lyophilize / lyophilise | يجفف بالتجميد |
| lyophilized cake | عجينة مجففة بالتجميد |
| lypholizer (freeze dryer) | جهاز التجفيف بالتجميد: يستخدم لعمل تجفيف وتركيز العينات الموجودة في صورة سائلة مثل البروتينات والأحماض النووية بطريقة بالضغط بالشفط. |
| lyres | القيثارة |
| lysate | ناتج انحلال (الخلايا) |
| lyse | يحلل أو يخضع للتحليل |
| lysis | تحلل |
| lyslate | ناتج ذوبان الخلايا |
| lysosome | جسم حال |

# M

| | |
|---|---|
| mabs | أجسام مضادة أحادية النسيلة mAbs |
| mac | التحكم في الوصول للوسائط |
| macadam | حصى الرصف |
| macaroni | المكرونة |
| macaroons [pastry] | المكرون [حلوى من بياض البيض والسكر واللوز] |
| mach number | رقم ماخ |
| machetes | مناجل |
| machine | آلة، ماكينة |
| machine belt fasteners of metal | سحابات سيور الماكينات من المعدن |
| machine belts (reinforcing materials of metal for -) | سيور الماكينات (مواد دعم من المعدن في سيور الماكينات) |
| machine fly-wheels | عجلات تنظيم السرعة في الماكينات |
| machine gun | رشاش؛ مدفع رشاش |
| machine intelligence | الذكاء الآلي |
| machine learning technology | تقنية تعلم الآلة |
| machine milking | حلب آلي |
| machine tools | عُدد الماكينات |
| machine wheels | عجلات الماكينات |
| machine wheelwork | مجموعة عجلات الماكينات |
| machineability | القابلية للتشغيل الآلي |
| machineable | قابل للتشغيل الآلي |
| machinelike | آلة نظم افتراضية |
| machinery | الآلات |
| machines | آلات |
| machines for the textile industry | ماكينات للاستخدام في صناعة المنسوجات |
| machining (apparatus for -) | التشغيل الآلي (جهاز للتشغيل الآلي) |
| machinist | العامل الذي يتعامل مع الآلة، ميكانيكي |
| machinization | الميكنة |
| machinized | مزود بالآلات |
| machinze | يزود بالآلات |
| macro lenses | عدسات مجهرية |
| macrophage | خلية ملتهمة كبيرة |
| macrophage mannose receptor (mmr) | مستقبل مانوز خلية ملتهمة كبيرة |
| macropinocytosis | الإرتشاف الخلوي الدقيق. انظر pinocytosis |
| macropores | المسام الكبيرة (المسام المرئية) |
| macroporous; macr-oporous | ذو مسام كبيرة |
| macroscopic | عِياني |
| macular | بقعي |
| macular degeneration | التنكس أو الضمور (الانحلال) البقعي |
| magazine | خازنة البندقية |
| magazine racks | حوامل المجلات |

| | |
|---|---|
| magazines [periodicals] | المجلات [دوريات] |
| magic lanterns | الفوانيس السحرية |
| magnefite | الماجنفيت: عملية استخلاص اللب بطريقة كبريتيت الماغنسيوم القاعدية |
| magnesia | المغنيسيا؛ أكسيد المغنسيوم |
| magnesia cement | ملاط المغنيسيا |
| magnesite | مغنيسيت |
| magnesium | المغنيسيوم |
| magnesium carbonate | كربونات المغنيسيوم |
| magnesium chloride | كلوريد المغنيسيوم |
| magnesium filaments for lighting | فتائل المغنيسيوم للإنارة |
| magnesium overbase | مغنسيوم عالي القاعدة |
| magnesium overbased composition | تركيبة مغنسيوم عالي القاعدة |
| magnesium stearate | ستيارات المغنسيوم |
| magnesium turnings | رقاقات مغنسيوم |
| magnet holding members = magnet holders | أعضاء تثبيت مغناطيس |
| magnet mounting portion | جزء تثبيت مغناطيس |
| magnetic | مغنطيسي |
| magnetic beads | الخرزات الممغنطة |
| magnetic data media | وسائط البيانات المغناطيسية |
| magnetic encoders | أجهزة تشفير مغناطيسية |
| magnetic energy | طاقة مغناطيسية |
| magnetic fluid | مائع مغناطيسي |
| magnetic north | قطب شمالي |
| magnetic proximity switch | مفتاح تقارب مغناطيسي |
| magnetic ranging | تحديد مدى المجال المغناطيسي |
| magnetic resonance imaging | التصوير بالرنين المغناطيسي |
| magnetic resonance imaging | التصوير بواسطة الرنين المغناطيسي |
| magnetic susceptibility balance (msb) | جهاز قياس المغنطيسية |
| magnetic tape units [for computers] | وحدات الشريط المغناطيسي [في الحاسبات الآلية] |
| magnetic tapes | شرائط مغناطيسية |
| magnetic wires | أسلاك مغناطيسية |
| magnetics | مغنطيس |
| magnetometer | مقياس المغناطيسية: هو جهاز يستخدم لقياس شدة الحقل المغناطيسي أو اتجاه الحقل المغناطيسي القريب من الجهاز |
| magnetometers | المقاييس المغناطيسية |
| magnetostrictive | تخصُّر مغناطيسي (متعلق بالتخصر المغناطيسي) |
| magnetostrictive sensors (mss) | أجهزة استشعار التغير المغناطيسي |
| magnets | مغناطيسات |
| magnets (decorative -) | مغناطيسات (مغناطيسات زخرفية) |
| magnifying glasses [optics] | عدسات مكبرة [بصريات] |
| magnitude | المقدار: الكمية القياسية يمكن تحديدها |
| mah-jong | المهيونج [لعبة صينية الأصل] |
| mail bags | حقائب البريد |

mailing list manager مدير قوائم البريد
main role = title role دور رئيسي
mainframe computer كمبيوتر عملاق
mains plug قابس التيار الرئيسي
mainstream technology تقنية الاتجاه السائد
maintain يبقي على
maintainability القابلية للإبقاء
maintenance dose جُرْعَةُ المُداوَمَة: جرعة أقل من الجرعة المبدئية
maintenance drug دَواءُ المُداوَمَة
maintenance therapy علاج المُداوَمَة
maintenance therapy العلاج الدائم؛ العلاج المستدام؛ العلاج المستمر: الذي يُعطى بعد الجرعات الأولى أو بعد الشفاء (لمنع تكرار المرض) ويستمر عليه المريض بعد ذلك.
maize الذرة
maize [milled] الذرة [مطحونة]
maize [roasted] الذرة [محمصة]
maize cake for cattle كُسب الذرة للماشية
maize flakes رقاقات الذرة
maize flour دقيق الذرة
maize meal مجروش الذرة
maize oil زيت الذرة
maize starch نشا الذرة
majolica الميوليق [ضرب من الخزف الإيطالي مزخرف ومطلي بالمينا]
major & minor كبير وصغير
major (maj) رائد
major : minor isomer ratio نسبة الأيزومر الكبير:الصغير
major end items بنود أساسية رئيسية
major general (maj. gen.) لواء
major peaks القمم العظمى
make inroads يحقق تقدما
make-up المكياج
make-up تعويض
make-up (appliances for removing -) [non-electric] المكياج (أدوات إزالة المكياج) [غير كهربائية]
make-up (chem) تركيب كيميائي
make-up (napkins for removing -) [cloth] المكياج (مناديل إزالة المكياج) [قماش]
make-up powder مساحيق المكياج
make-up preparations مستحضرات المكياج
make-up removing appliances, electric أجهزة كهربائية لإزالة المكياج
make-up removing preparations مستحضرات إزالة المكياج
make-up water ماء معوِّض
making صناعة، جعل، عمل
malaria الملاريا
male screw قلاووظ ذكر
maleate ماليات-أملاح حمض الماليك
malice القصد الجنائي
malice in fact توافر القصد الجنائي
malice in law عدم توافر السند الجنائي
malignancies أورام خبيثة
malignant خبيث
mallets [hand instruments] المطارق [معدات يدوية]
malls تشتيت أشعة الليزر بزوايا متعددة
malpractice تقصير مهني
malpractice suit دعوى بشأن تقصير مهني
malt ملت
malt albumen زلال الشعير
malt beer بيرة الشعير
malt biscuits بسكويت الشعير
malt caramel [food colorant] كرميل الشعير [مادة ملونة للطعام]
malt colorants مواد تلوين الشعير
malt extract for food مستخلص الشعير للاستخدام في الطعام
malt for brewing and distilling الشعير للاستخدام في التخمير والتقطير
malt for human consumption الشعير للاستهلاك البشري
malt roaster جهاز تحميص الشعير
malt wort منقوع الشعير
malted milk beverages مشروبات اللبن بالشعير المنبت
maltose الملتوز [سكر الملت أو الشعير]
malware برامج حاقدة
malware detection اكتشاف حزم البرمجيات الضارة التي ترسل لمستخدم الشبكة البينية
manage يدير
manageable ممكنةٌ إدارتُه
managed مدار
management إدارة
management software برنامج للإدارة
management solutions حلول إدارية
management system نظام إدارة
manager مدير
managing director مدير مباشر
mandated lead arranger البنك المسئول عن القرض
mandatory arbitration تحكيم إلزامي
mandolins المندولين
mandrel شياق
maneuver مناورة
maneuver يناور
manganate منجنات [ملح الحامض]
manganese المنجنيز
manganese (ic and ous) منجنيك ومنجنوز
manganese dioxide ثاني أكسيد المنجنيز
mangers for animals معالِف الدواب: أوعية تأكل منها العلف
mangers for livestock معالِف الماشية: أوعية تأكل منها العلف
mangles المكاوي الأسطوانية
mangrove bark لحاء شجر المنجروف الاستوائي
manhole covers of metal أغطية فتحة الصيانة من المعدن
manhole covers, not of metal أغطية فتحة الصيانة ليست من المعدن
manhunt مطاردة
manicure sets معدات تقليم وطلاء الأظافر

| | |
|---|---|
| manicure sets, electric | معدات كهربائية لتقليم وطلاء الأظافر |
| manifold | مشعب: وصلة بفتحات ربط جانبية أو أنبوب متعدد التشعبات الجانبية |
| manifold (exhaust -) for engines | مشعب (مشعب العادم) في المحركات |
| manifolds [stationery] | حافظات [قرطاسية] |
| manifolds of metal for pipelines | مشعبات من المعدن في خطوط الأنابيب |
| maniples | الذراعة [جزء من ثياب القداس يوضع على الذراع اليسرى] |
| manipulation | معالجة |
| manipulative robot | روبوت قادر على التحكم في الأشياء |
| mannequins | المانيكان [تمثال لعرض الملابس] |
| mannequins (resuscitation -) [teaching apparatus] | مانيكان (مانيكان لتمثيل عملية الإفاقة) [أجهزة تعليمية] |
| mannose glycosylated ; mannose-glycosylated | مرتبط بالجليكوزيل من نوع المانوز |
| mannose glycosylation | ارتباط بالجليكوزيل من نوع المانوز |
| mannosylation | الارتباط بالمانوز |
| manometer | مقياس الضغط |
| manometers | أدوات قياس ضغط الغازات والأبخرة |
| manoses | وحدات المانوز |
| manpower | القوى العاملة |
| manslaughter | قتل الخطأ |
| mantillas | أوشحة قصيرة رقيقة |
| mantle | قشرية |
| mantlepieces | أرفف المستوقد |
| manual | يدوي |
| manual eject button | زرار إخراج يدوي |
| manual operation | تشغيل يدوي |
| manually operated scheduling system | نظام جدولة يشغل يدويا |
| manuals [handbooks] | كتيبات |
| manufacturability | قابلية الشيء للتصنيع |
| manufacturable | قابل للتصنيع |
| manufacturer | مصنع |
| manufacturing | تصنيع |
| manufacturing driven inventing | القيام بعملية الاختراع على هدى من متطلبات التصنيع |
| manufacturing greening | تخضير التصنيع. جعل التصنيع معززا للبيئة. |
| manufacturing lacunae | ثغرة تصنيعية |
| manure | سباخ؛ سماد |
| manure for agriculture | الأسمدة الزراعية |
| map | خريطة؛ يرسم خريطة؛ يحدد موضع: مثل تحديد مواضع الجينات على أجسام الكروموسومات |
| map (to) | يعيّن (إلى) |
| mapi | واجهة برامج تطبيق الرسالة |
| maple | نبات القيقب |
| mapping | مخطط؛ تعيين (كذا إلى كذا)؛ تحديد موضع أو موضعة؛ إنشاء خريطة أو مخطط (لخزان أو تكوين إلخ)؛ رسم خرائط أو تحديد معالم |
| mapping a reservoir | إنشاء خريطة أو مخطط لخزان؛ تخطيط الخزان |
| maps (geographical -) | خرائط (خرائط جغرافية) |
| marabouts [cloth] | المربوت [نوع من قماش الحرير] |
| marble | رخام |
| marbles for games | كرات رخامية أو زجاجية للاستخدام في الألعاب |
| marc | كُسب الفاكهة المعصورة |
| margarine | المارجرين [سمن صناعي نباتي] |
| marine compasses | البوصلة الملاحية |
| marine current power | طاقة التيار المائي |
| marine depth finder | جهاز تعيين العمق البحري |
| marine engineering | هندسة بحرية |
| marine locator device | جهاز تعيين موقع بحري |
| marine transgression | الاعتداء البحري |
| marionettes | الدُمى المتحركة |
| maritime invention | اختراع بحري |
| marker | واسم (الجمع: واسمات) |
| market | يسوق، سوق |
| market driven innovation | ابتكار يقوده السوق. جهد ابتكاري يسير على هدى من وضع السوق والمنافسين والحصص السوقية ذات الصلة |
| market driven innovation | ابتكار تسوقه قاطرة السوق. جهد ابتكاري يسير على هدى من وضع السوق والمنافسين والحصص السوقية ذات الصلة |
| market economy | اقتصاد السوق |
| market information system | نظام معلومات السوق |
| market intelligence systems | نظام استخبارات السوق. نظم حاسوبية تستخدم في الحصول على معلومات دقيقة في السوق |
| market needs | احتياجات السوق |
| market value model | نموذج القيمة السوقية. طريقة لاحتساب القيمة المالية للممتلكات الفكرية |
| marketability | قابلية الشيء للتسويق |
| marketable | قابل للتسويق |
| marketable idea | فكرة قابلة للتسويق |
| marketable invention | اختراع يمكن تسويقه |
| market-driven inventing | القيام بعملية الاختراع على هدى من متطلبات السوق |
| marketing company | شركة تسويق |
| marketing literature | أدبيات التسويق. المواد المكتوبة المستخدمة في التسويق. |
| marking buoys | وسائل طافية للاستدلال |
| marking chalk | طباشير التعليم |
| marking gauges [joinery] | وسائل قياس للتحديد [نجارة] |
| marking ink for animals | حبر لوضع علامات على الحيوانات (الوسم) |
| marking linen (numerals or letters for - ) | بياضات تعليم (أرقام أو حروف بياضات التعليم) |
| marl (calcareous -) | طين (طين جيري) |

| | |
|---|---|
| marline spikes | مخرزات لفصل الحبال أثناء جدلها |
| marmalade | المرملاد [مربى أو هلام مشتمل على قطع من الفاكهة وقشورها] |
| marmoset | القشة (قرد أمريكي صغير) |
| marrow | الكوسا |
| marrow (animal -) for food | نخاع العظم (نخاع عظم الحيوانات) للاستخدام في الطعام |
| marten-proof plastic tubing | أنبوب بلاستيك ضد القوارض |
| martyrdom operation = kamikaze operation | عملية فدائية؛ عملية استشهادية |
| marzipan | المرزبانية [حلوى من مسحوق اللوز والسكر وزلال البيض] |
| mascara | الماسكرا |
| mash for fattening livestock | الهريس لتسمين الماشية |
| mash-up | مواقع دمج الخدمات |
| masks (beauty -) | أقنعة (أقنعة التجميل) |
| masks (divers' -) | أقنعة (أقنعة الغطاسين) |
| masks (fencing -) | أقنعة (أقنعة المبارزة) |
| masks (protective -) | أقنعة (أقنعة للحماية ) |
| masks (theatrical -) | أقنعة (أقنعة مسرحية) |
| masks (toy -) | أقنعة (أقنعة اللعب) |
| masks for use by medical personnel | أقنعة لاستخدام العاملين في المجال الطبي |
| masonry | بناء |
| masonry (oil for the preservation of -) | المباني (زيت لحفظ المباني) |
| masonry preservatives, except paints and oils | مواد حافظة للمباني بخلاف الدهانات والزيوت |
| masons' hammers | مطارق البناءين |
| masquerade costumes | ملابس الحفلات التنكرية |
| mass apci | مقياس كتلي للتأين الكيميائي تحت الضغط الجوي العادي |
| mass average particle diameter | متوسط قطر الجسيم بالكتلة |
| mass balance | التوازن الكتلي |
| mass cell | خلية بدينة |
| mass concrete | خرسانة كتلية |
| mass flow | تدفق كتلي |
| mass innovation | ابتكار جماهيري |
| mass motorization | نشر المتحركات ناشرا عاما |
| mass number | عدد كتلي |
| mass production | الإنتاج بالجملة |
| mass resolution of | درجة وضوح الكتلية |
| mass space velocity | سرعة فراغية كتلية |
| mass spectra | أطياف الكتلة |
| mass spectrometrry (lc-ms) | مقياس طيف الكتلة |
| mass spectrometry | قياس الطيف الكتلي |
| mass storage device | جهاز تخزين كبير السعة |
| mass transfer | انتقال الكتلة |
| mass transfer | تحويل الكتلة |
| massage (gloves for -) | التدليك (قفازات التدليك) |
| massage apparatus | جهاز التدليك |
| massage tables | مناضد التدليك |
| massing | تكوين حبيبات |
| massive or poor turnout | إقبال هائل أو ضعيف على الانتخابات |
| mass-storage industry | صناعة التخزين الجماعي |
| master clocks | الساعات الرئيسية |
| master robot | روبوت رئيسي |
| mastic (grafting -) for trees | صمغ المصطكا (راتنج المصطكا للتطعيم) للأشجار |
| mastic [natural resin] | صمغ المصطكا [راتنج طبيعي] |
| mastic for leather | صمغ المصطكا للجلود |
| mastic for tires [tyres] | صمغ المصطكا للإطارات |
| mastics (dental -) | صمغ المصطكا (صمغ المصطكا للاستخدام في طب الأسنان) |
| mastics (guns, hand-operated, for the extrusion of -) | صمغ المصطكا (مسدسات تُشغل باليد لبثق صمغ المصطكا) |
| mastitis | التهاب الثدي |
| mastocytosis | الارتيكاريا الملونة |
| masts | أعمدة |
| masts [poles], not of metal | صواري [أعمدة] ليست من المعدن |
| masts for sailboards | صواري ألواح التزحلق على الأمواج |
| masts for wireless aerials | صواري الهوائيات اللاسلكية |
| masts of metal | صواري من المعدن |
| match boxes | علب الثقاب |
| match holders | حوامل الثقاب |
| matches | أعواد الثقاب |
| mate sth with sth | لاقتران كذا بكذا |
| material | مادة |
| material (textile -) | مادة (مادة المنسوجات) |
| material balance | المتبقي من المواد |
| material expression | تعبير مادي |
| material prior art | فن سابق جوهري |
| material testing instruments and machines | معدات وماكينات لاختبار المواد |
| materializability | القابلية للتنفيذ |
| materializability of inventive concept | قابلة تنفيذ المفهوم الاختراعي |
| materializable | قابل للتحقيق |
| materializable idea | فكرة قابلة للتحقق |
| materializable invention | اختراع قابل للتحقيق |
| materialization | تحقيق |
| materialization of invention | تحقيق الاختراع |
| materializeble inventive concept | مفهوم اختراعي قابل للتطبيق |
| material-related invention | اختراع متعلق بالمواد |
| materials of metal for funicular railway permanent ways | مواد من المعدن لطرق السكة الحديدية الدائمة المعلقة |
| maternity belts | حمالات الولادة |
| mathematical correlation | ارتباط رياضي |
| mathematical instruments | أدوات الحساب |
| mathematical physics | فيزياء حسابية |
| mating electrical plug | قابس مزاوجة كهربائي |
| matrices (boxes for -) [printing] | مصفوفات نقطية (علب المصفوفات النقطية) [طباعة] |
| matrices for use in printing | مصفوفات نقطية للاستخدام في الطباعة |

| | |
|---|---|
| matrix | مصفوفة؛ نسيج شبكي؛ كتلة؛ بناء شبكي؛ قالب؛ مادة مكونة للقالب |
| mats | الحصر |
| mats (place -) [not of paper] | حصر (حصر المنازل) [ليست من الورق] |
| mats for beer glasses | قطع قماش مخرمة توضع تحت أكواب البيرة |
| mats of woven rope for ski slopes | حصر من الحبال المنسوجة تستخدم في منحدرات التزحلق |
| mats, removable, for sinks | حصر قابلة للإزالة للبالوعات |
| matter | يهم، مادة، أمر، شأن |
| matters | مواد، موضوعات، مسائل، قضايا |
| mattocks | المعاول |
| mattress (straw -) | مراتب (مراتب من القش) |
| mattress covers | أغطية المراتب |
| mattresses | مراتب |
| mattresses (childbirth -) | مراتب (مراتب الولادة) |
| mattresses (spring -) | مراتب ( مراتب ذات زنبرك) |
| mau | وحدة |
| max or max | حد أقصى |
| maxabs | أقصى امتصاص |
| maximal oxygen uptake | أقصى امتصاص للأكسجين |
| maximising battery life | إطالة عمر البطارية |
| maximum preparedness | درجة الاستعداد القصوى |
| maximum security | إجراءات أمنية قصوى/ مشددة |
| maximum tensile stress | إجهاد الشد الأقصى |
| mayonnaise | مايونيز |
| mazut | مازوت |
| mb | ميجابايت |
| mb/s | ميجابت في الثانية |
| mbar | ملي بار |
| mbar(a) | ملي بار (مطلق) |
| mbarg | ملي بار بالمقياس |
| mbs | الحد الأقصى لحجم الرشقة النيرانية |
| mc | مركز الإدارة؛ جزء من تجهيزات إسناد النظام |
| mcdt | الحد الأقصى لوقت التوقف التصحيحي |
| mcg | ميكرو جرام |
| mcg&l | إعداد الخرائط والرسوم والمسح التطبيقي والصور |
| mci | ملي كوري |
| mci | الخلل الإدراكي البسيط |
| mcl | ميكرو لتر |
| m-commerce | التجارة المتنقلة؛ التجارة المحمولة |
| mcpba | حمض ميتا - كلورو بيروكسي بنزويك |
| mcr | الحد الأدنى لمعدل خلية التنسيق |
| mcu | وحدة مؤتمرات متعددة النقاط |
| mcwg | مجموعة عمل الاتصالات |
| md | ملي دارسي (مقياس permeability) |
| mdf | إطار التوزيع الرئيسي |
| mdgs e-enabler | مُمكن إلكتروني لأهداف التنمية الخاصة بالألفية |
| mdi | جهاز استنشاق بجرعة مقننة |
| me | ميثيل |
| mead [hydromel] | الميد [الماسل] [مشروبات مخمرة] |
| meal | جريش |
| meal | وجبة (طعام) |
| meal for animals | جريش للحيوانات |
| mean ± sd | متوسط ± الانحراف المعياري |
| mean fluorescence intensity | متوسط شدة الفلورة |
| mean free path | متوسط المسار الحر |
| mean number of cells/40x field | العدد المتوسط للخلايا/مجال بقوة تكبير 40 مرة |
| mean square error | متوسط مربع الخطا |
| mean-square deviation; mean square deviation | متوسط مربع الانحراف |
| measles | حصبة |
| measure | مقاس أو حجم؛ يقيس، قياس |
| measured variables | المتغيرات المقاسة |
| measurement | قياس |
| measuring apparatus | جهاز قياس |
| measuring devices, electric | وسائل قياس كهربائية |
| measuring glassware | أواني زجاجية للقياس |
| measuring inhalation devices | وسيلة استنشاق محددة الجرعة |
| measuring instrument | جهاز قياس |
| measuring spoons | ملاعق قياس |
| meat | اللحم |
| meat (chemical preparations for smoking -) | اللحم (مستحضرات كيميائية لتدخين اللحم) |
| meat chests, not of metal | صناديق اللحم ليست من المعدن |
| meat choppers [hand tools] | مفارم اللحم [عُدد يدوية] |
| meat choppers [machines] | مفارم اللحم [آلات] |
| meat extracts | مستخلصات اللحم |
| meat gravies | صلصة مرق اللحم |
| meat jellies | هلام اللحم |
| meat mincers [machines] | مفارم اللحم [آلات] |
| meat pies | فطائر اللحم |
| meat safes of metal | خزائن اللحم من المعدن |
| meat tenderizers | أدوات تطرية اللحم |
| meat, preserved | لحم محفوظ |
| meat, tinned [canned (am.)] | اللحم المعلب |
| meats (salted -) | اللحوم (اللحوم المملحة) |
| mechanical (mechanical load, flux, link, etc.) | ميكانيكي (حمل ميكانيكي، تدفق ميكانيكي، وصلة ميكانيكية، إلخ) |
| mechanical bicker of cotton | ماكينة جني القطن |
| mechanical energy | طاقة ميكانيكية |
| mechanical force | قوة ميكانيكية |
| mechanical latching system | نظام تثبيت آلي |
| mechanical pulp | استخلاص اللب ميكانيكيا: عملية صناعة لب الورق بطريقة ميكانيكية تماما من مواد خام متنوعة، مثل طحن الخشب، أو إمرار نشارة الخشب أو قطع الخشب الصغيرة خلال مصفاة |
| mechanical resistence | مقاومة آلية |
| mechanical signs | إشارات ميكانيكية |
| mechanical strength | متانة ميكانيكية |
| mechanical stress | الإجهاد الميكانيكي |
| mechanical weathering | التجوية الميكانيكية |
| mechanically | بطريقة ميكانيكية؛ ميكانيكيا |
| mechanically formed | صخور رسوبية ميكانيكية النشأة |

| | |
|---|---|
| sediments | |
| mechanichal photography | التصوير الميكانيكي |
| mechanism | آلية |
| mechanisms | آليات |
| mechanized livestock feeders | آلات تغذية الماشية مجهزة بمعدات ميكانيكية |
| mechanoreceptor | مستقبل آلي |
| medal | ميدالية |
| medallions [jewellery, jewelry (am.)] | الرصائع [ميداليات كبيرة] [مجوهرات] |
| medevac | إخلاء طبي |
| media for bacteriological cultures | مستنبتات أوساط مزارع بكتريولوجية |
| media for bacteriological cultures | أوساط المزارع البكتيرية |
| media gateway control function | وظيفة التحكم في بوابة وسائط |
| median pore diameter | متوسط قطر مسام |
| mediastinal | منصفي |
| mediate | يساهم |
| mediated ; -mediated | بواسطة؛ عبر؛ الذي يساهم فيه كذا (الذي يشارك في إحداثه والتسبب فيه) |
| mediation | وساطة |
| mediation clause | بند الوساطة. بند ينظم عملية الفصل في النزاع بين المتعاقدين من خلال الوساطة. ويعد من البنود النمطية العامة التي تتضمنها عقود الملكية الفكرية |
| mediator | وسيط |
| medical apparatus and instruments | أجهزة ومعدات طبية |
| medical device | جهاز طبي |
| medical guidewires | أسلاك توجيه طبية |
| medical monitoring device | جهاز مراقبة طبية |
| medical negligence | إهمال طبي |
| medical officer (mo) | ضابط طبيب |
| medical traditional knowledge | معرفة طبية تقليدية |
| medicare | برنامج الرعاية الطبية ميدي كير |
| medicated soap | صابون العلاج الطبي |
| medicinal alcohol | كحول طبي |
| medicinal chemistry | كيمياء طبية |
| medicinal drinks | مشروبات طبية |
| medicinal hair growth preparations | مستحضرات طبية لنمو الشعر |
| medicinal herbs | أعشاب طبية |
| medicinal infusions | تشريبات طبية |
| medicinal oils | زيوت طبية |
| medicinal roots | جذور طبية |
| medicinal tea | الشاي الطبي |
| medicine (spoons for administering -) | الدواء (ملاعق لتناول الدواء) |
| medicine cabinets | خزائن طبية |
| medicine cases [portable] [filled] | صناديق العقاقير [محمولة] [مملوءة] |
| medicines | أدوية |
| medico-legal officer | طبيب شرعي |
| medium (pl. media) | وسط |
| medium (pl. media) | وسيطة |
| medium absorption setting | وضع الامتصاص المتوسط |
| medium grained clastic rocks | الصخور الفتاتية متوسطة الحبيبات |
| medium industries | الصناعات المتوسطة |
| medium machine gun (mmg) | رشاش متوسط |
| medium pressure liquid chromatography | فصل كروموتوجرافي لسائل عند ضغط متوسط |
| medium stringency | ظروف متوسطة الصرامة |
| mediumi-sized industries | صناعات متوسطة الحجم |
| mediums (bacteriological culture -) | مستنبتات (مستنبتات مزارع بكتريولوجية) |
| medregrep | تقرير التنظيم الطبي |
| medstat | تقرير الموقف الطبي |
| medullary thyroidea carcinoma | الورم السرطاني النخاعي الدرقي |
| medulloblastoma | ورم الأرومة النخاعية |
| meerschaum | المرشوم |
| meeting point channel | قناة نقطة التقاء |
| megabase | ميجا قاعدة: وحدة لقياس طول الجزيء. انظر kilobase و gigabase |
| megabases | ميجا قاعدة: وحدة لقياس طول الجزيء. |
| megakaryocytes | الخلايا كبيرة النواة |
| megaphones | الأبواق (مضخمات الصوت) |
| megapixel ccd | عدسة تصوير ذات درجة وضوح بالميجا بيكسل |
| meiotic crossing-over | العبور الوراثي الفتيلي |
| melanogenesis | توليد الميلانين |
| melanoma | ورم ميلانيني |
| melanoma | الورم النخاعي؛ ورم ميلانيني |
| melanophore cell | خلية ناقلة للميلانين |
| melatoninergic system | جهاز ميلاتوني الفعل |
| melissa water | ماء المليساء |
| melt blending | خلط بالانصهار؛ مزج بالانصهار |
| melt flow ratio (mfr) | نسبة تدفق المصهور |
| melt fracture | تصدع أو تشدخ المصهور |
| melt index | معامل الانصهار |
| melt mixing | خلط بالانصهار |
| melt point depressing agent | عامل مقلل لنقطة الانصهار؛ عامل مخفض لنقطة الانصهار |
| melt viscosity | لزوجة انصهار |
| melting point | نقطة الانصهار |
| melting point temperature ™ | درجة حرارة الانصهار: وهي درجة الحرارة التي تتحول عندها العينة من الحالة الصلبة إلى السائلة. |
| melting pot | بواتق صهر المعدن |
| melt-phase | في الطور المنصهر |
| member | عضو |
| member atom | ذرة (في الحلقة) |
| membrane bound type 1 protein | بروتين مرتبط بالغشاء من النوع الأول |
| membrane preps | مستحضرات غشاء |
| membrane-proliferative glomerulonephritis type ii | التهاب كبيبات الكلى المتكاثر بالغشاء من النوع II |

| | |
|---|---|
| memorandum of incorporation | مذكرة تأسيس |
| memorandum of understanding | مذكرة تفاهم |
| memorial plaques, not of metal | أنصبة تذكارية ليست من المعدن |
| memorial plaques, of metal | أنصبة تذكارية من المعدن |
| memorial plates of metal | ألواح تذكارية من المعدن |
| memory card adapter | مهايئ بطاقة الذاكرة |
| memory card recovery software | برنامج لاستعادة بطاقة الذاكرة |
| memory chip | شريحة للذاكرة |
| memory gauge | مقياس الذاكرة |
| memory slot cover | غطاء شق ذاكرة |
| memory space | مساحة الذاكرة |
| memory t cell | خلية الذاكرة التائية |
| memory techniques | أساليب تذكر |
| memory type indicator | مؤشر نوع الذاكرة |
| menagerie animals | حيوانات للعرض (مثل في السيرك أو حدائق الحيوانات) |
| meningioma | الورم السحائي |
| meningitidis | الالتهابات السحائية |
| meningococcal | المكوري السحائي |
| meningoencephalitis | التهاب السحايا والدماغ |
| menopause | سن اليأس؛ سن انقطاع الدورة الشهرية؛ سن انقطاع الطمث: فترة فيما بين 45 و55 من العمر عندما يتوقف الطمث لدى المرأة ولا تستطيع الإنجاب. تُسمَّى أيضا change of lifeو climacteric |
| menstruation bandages | ضمادات الحيض |
| menstruation knickers | لباس نسوى للحيض |
| menstruation pads | فوط الحيض |
| menstruation tampons | سدادات قطنية لدم الحيض |
| mental activity | نشاط ذهني، نشاط عقلي |
| mentha | مينثا |
| menthen | مينثين |
| menthol | المنتول |
| mentoring | النصح - الإشراف |
| menu card holders | حوامل بطاقات قوائم الطعام |
| meoh | ميثانول |
| mepa | وكالة الأرصاد الجوية والحماية البيئية |
| meq | ملي مكافئ |
| mercaptan | مركبات المركابتان |
| mercaptanized epoxidized ester composition | تركيبة إستر معالجة بالمركبتان والإيبوكسي |
| mercaptanized unsaturated ester composition | تركيبة إستر غير مشبعة معالجة بالمركابتان |
| mercerised cotton | قطن له لمعان الحرير الطبيعي |
| merchandisability | القابلية للترويج كسلعة والقابلية للمتاجرة |
| merchandisable | قابل أن يكون منتجا |
| mercurial ointments | مراهم زئبقية |
| mercuric oxide | أكسيد الزئبق |
| mercury | الزئبق |
| mercury salts | أملاح الزئبق |
| merger | شهادة اندماج |

| | |
|---|---|
| mergers | شؤون الاندماج |
| merits | وقائع (قانون)؛ الحقوق القانونية أو وقائع الدعوى |
| mesenteric | مساريقي |
| mesenteric lymph nodes | عقد لمفية ميساريقية |
| mesh | تعشيقة؛ تعشق؛ شبكة؛ بنية شبكية؛ يتعشق أو يعشق |
| mesh seives | مناخل شبكية؛ غرابيل شبكية |
| meshing | معشّق |
| mesocorticolimbic system | الجهاز الحرقفي القشري |
| mesohydrogentartrate | ميزو هيدروجين طرطرات |
| mesophilic | أليف للحرارة المتوسطة |
| mesopores | المسام المتوسطة |
| meso-porous; mesoporous | ذو مسام متوسطة |
| meso-tartaric acid | حمض الميزو طرطريك |
| meso-tartrate | الميزو طرطرات |
| mesothelioma | مرض الطلائية الوسطى |
| messaging technology | تقنية إرسال رسائل |
| mess-tins | قدور الطعام |
| mesylate | يضيف مجموعة مسيل إليه؛ تتم مسيلته |
| met | علم الأرصاد الجوية |
| meta(ortho or para) substituted aromatic compounds | مركبات عطرية بها استبدال في الموضع ميتا |
| metabolic acidosis | نقص قلوية الدم الأيضية |
| metabolic profile | شكل التمثيل الغذائي |
| metabolically labile | متحول تأيضيا |
| metabolisms | نواتج تأيض |
| metabolite | ناتج التمثيل الغذائي |
| metabolites | نواتج التمثيل الغذائي؛ النواتج الأيضية |
| metabotropic | منشط للإنزيمات |
| meta-chloroperbenzoic acid | حمض ميتا-كلورو بير بنزويك |
| metachromatic dye | متغيرة التلون |
| metadata | بيانات تعريفية |
| metal | معدن؛ فلز |
| metal alloys (wires of -) [fuse wire] | خلائط معدنية (أسلاك من خلائط معدنية) [سلك الصهيرة] |
| metal annealing preparations | مستحضرات تقوية (تصلب) المعادن |
| metal band stretchers [hand tools] | أدوات توسيع طوق المعادن [عُدد يدوية] |
| metal base | قاعدة فلزية |
| metal detector | جهاز الكشف عن المعادن |
| metal drawing machines | ماكينات سحب المعادن |
| metal dusting | تعفير معدني |
| metal dusting corrosion | التآكل المسبب للتعفير المعدني |
| metal earths | الأتربة المعدنية |
| metal enzyme | إنزيم معدني |
| metal foil for painters, decorators, printers and artists | رقاقات معدنية لاستخدام عمال الدهان وفنيين الديكور وعمال الطباعة والفنانين |
| metal hardening preparations | مستحضرات تقسية المعادن |
| metal inert gas (mig) | غاز معدني خامل |
| metal ion catalysts | محفزات أيون فلزي |
| metal or metal oxide layer | طبقة الفلز أو أكسيد الفلز |
| metal residue | المتبقي من الفلز |
| metal salts | الأملاح المعدنية؛ أملاح الفلزات |
| metal straightening machine | آلة جعل المعادن مستقيمة |

| | |
|---|---|
| metal structure | هيكل معدني |
| metal support ; metallic support | دعامة معدنية |
| metal tempering preparations | مستحضرات معالجة المعادن |
| metalated species | أنواع مضاف إليها مجموعة معدنية |
| metalating agents | عوامل إضافة مجموعة معدنية |
| metallated | معالجة بمعدن |
| metallocene | ميتالوسين |
| metalloids | أشباه الفلزات |
| metallurgy | سبائك فلزية |
| metals (alkaline -) | فلزات (فلزات قلوية) |
| metals (alkaline-earth -) | فلزات (فلزات التربة القلوية) |
| metals in powder form for painters, decorators, printers and artists | معادن على شكل مسحوق لاستخدام عمال الدهان وفنيين الديكور وعمال الطباعة والفنانين |
| metalworking machines | ماكينات صنع الأدوات المعدنية |
| metastase | نقيلة |
| metastases | الأورام الثانوية. انظر metastasis |
| metastasis | الانتشار السرطاني الثانوي؛ الانتقال السرطاني بالانتشار: إنتشار مرض خبيث من موضعه الأصلي إلى موضع أو مواضع أخرى بالجسم، وعادة ما يتم ذلك بواسطة الأوعية الدموية أو الجهاز الليمفاوي؛ نمو سرطاني ثانوي؛ تورم سرطاني ثانوي |
| metastatic | ثانوي: وصف لورم أو سرطان. انظر metastasis |
| metathesis | تبادل مزدوج: نوع من التفاعلات الكيميائية مزدوجة التبادل |
| metathesis reaction | تفاعل مزدوج التبادل؛ تفاعل إبدال؛ تفاعل متبادل؛ تفاعل التبادل المزدوج |
| meteoric rocks | صخور نيزكية |
| meteorological balloons | مناطيد الأرصاد الجوية |
| meteorological instruments | معدات الرصد الجوى |
| meter | متر؛ عداد (مياه، غاز، كهرباء) |
| metering | قياس بالمتر |
| metering compressors | ضواغط ذات عدد قياس |
| metering valve | صمام معايرة |
| meters | عداد القياس |
| metformin | ميتفورمين (دواء خافض لسكر الدم) |
| methanation | إدخال مجموعة الميثان |
| methane | ميثان |
| methane sulfonic acid | حمض الميثان سلفونيك |
| methanesulfonic anhydride | أنهيدريد ميثان سلفونيك |
| methanol fuel | وقود ميثانول |
| methanolic ammonia | أمونيا كحولية |
| methanone | ميثانون |
| methionin residue | وحدة مثيونين بنائية |
| method | طريقة |
| method of payment clause | البند الخاص بطريقة السداد. بند تعاقدي يبين كيفية سداد سعر العقد |
| methyl | ميثيل |
| methyl benzene | بنزين الميثيل |
| methyl benzol | بنزول الميثيل |
| methyl ether | إتير الميثيل |
| methylated spirit | كحول الميثيل |
| methylmagnesium bromide | بروميد ميثيل مغنسيوم |
| methylmercaptobenzaldehyde | ميثيل مركابتو بنزالديهيد |
| methyl-paraben | ميثيل-باربن |
| methylpropanamide | ميثيل بروبان أميد |
| methylsulfonylbenzamine | ميثيل سلفونيل بنزين أمين |
| metre | متر؛ عداد (مياه، غاز، كهرباء) |
| metric | متري |
| metronomes | بندول إيقاع |
| mezzanine floor | الطابق النصفي |
| mf | ملي فاراد |
| mf resin | راتنج MF: راتنج فورمالدهيد الميلانين |
| mfi | متوسط شدة الفلورة |
| mfon | شبكة ألياف ضوئية |
| mg | ملي جرام (مجم) |
| mg/dl | مجم/ديسي لتر |
| mg/kg body weight | مجم/كجم من وزن الجسم |
| mge | صيغة داخلية في الرسم البياني |
| mgmt | إدارة |
| mgso4 | كبريتات مغنسيوم |
| mhe | معدات مناولة المواد |
| mhz | ميجا هرتز |
| mi | معامل انصهار |
| mica | الميكا |
| mica spangles | ترتر الميكا للملابس |
| mica, raw or partly processed | ميكا، خام أو معالجة جزئياً |
| mice (preparations for destroying -) | الفئران (مستحضرات للقضاء على الفئران) |
| micellar | مذيلي؛ أرومي |
| micelle | مذيلة (وحدة حيوية افتراضية) |
| micritic texture | النسيج الغروي |
| microaerophilic | محب للهواء القليل |
| microangipathy | اعتلال الشعيرات الدموية |
| microbial stability | مقاومة للميكروبات |
| micro-billing | نظام تحرير الفواتير الإلكتروني |
| micro-carbon residue mcr | المتبقي من الكربون الدقيق |
| microcarrier beads | خرز حامل دقيق (الذي تتعلق بسطحه الخلايا في المفاعل الحيوي) |
| microcentrifuge filter | مرشح طرد مركزي دقيق |
| micro-chip | شريحة مصغرة |
| microcirculatory | في الدورة الدموية الدقيقة |
| microcline | الميكروكلين |
| micro-credit | القروض التجارية الصغيرة |
| microcrystalline | دقيق البللورات |
| microcrystalline cellulose | سيليولوز دقيق البلورات |
| microdistillation column | عمود التقطير الدقيق |
| microencapsulated delivery systems | نظم توصيل ذات التغليف الدقيق |
| micro-enterprise | المشروعات الصغيرة |
| microfabricated array | صفوفة دقيقة الصنع |
| microflora | المجموعة النباتية الدقيقة |
| microfractionator | عمود التجزئة الدقيق |
| micro-gravity robot | روبوت ذو جاذبية جزئي. روبوت يستطيع أن يشتغل في أحوال تتسم بعدم توافر جاذبية كاملة |

| | |
|---|---|
| microinjection | حقن بالممص الدقيق |
| microinjection | حقن دقيق |
| micromechanical properties | خواص ميكانيكية دقيقة |
| micrometer gauge | جهاز تحديد قياس ميكرومترية |
| micrometer screws for optical instruments | مسامير لولبية ميكرومترية في المعدات البصرية |
| micrometers | ميكرومترات |
| micron | ميكرون: لقياس القطر |
| micronisation | تحويل إلى مسحوق؛ التقليل إلى حجم الميكرون |
| micronization of the product | طحن المنتج إلى جسيمات ميكرونية |
| micronized | مصغر بحجم الميكرون |
| micron-sized | بحجم الميكرون |
| micron-sized particles | جسيمات بحجم الميكرون |
| microorganism | كائن دقيق، كائن مهجري |
| microorganisms (cultures of -) for medical and veterinary use | أحياء مجهرية (مزارع الأحياء المجهرية) للاستخدام في الأغراض الطبية أو البيطرية |
| microorganisms (cultures of -) other than for medical and veterinary use | أحياء مجهرية (مزارع الأحياء المجهرية) بخلاف المستخدمة في الأغراض الطبية والبيطرية |
| microorganisms (nutritive substances for -) | الأحياء المجهرية (مواد غذائية للأحياء المجهرية) |
| microorganisms (preparations of-) for medical and veterinary use | الأحياء المجهرية (مستحضرات الأحياء المجهرية) للاستخدام في الأغراض الطبية والبيطرية |
| microorganisms (preparations of-) other than for medical and veterinary use | الأحياء المجهرية (مستحضرات الأحياء المجهرية) بخلاف المستخدمة في الأغراض الطبية والبيطرية |
| micropayment | الدفع الإلكتروني |
| microphone attenuator | مخفض صوت الميكروفون |
| microphone jack | مقبس ميكروفون |
| microphones | مكبرات الصوت [ميكروفون] |
| micro-plate ; microplate | طبق دقيق |
| micropores | المسام المكروية أو الدقيقة |
| microporous | دقيقة المسام |
| microprocessor | معالج دقيق؛ معالج صغير: جهاز صغير لمعالجة البيانات |
| microprojectile-mediated transformation | التحويل الوراثي الذي تساهم فيه مقذوفات دقيقة |
| microscope slides (containers for -) | شرائح المجهر (حاويات شرائح المجهر) |
| microscopes | المجاهر |
| microscopy | قياس مجهري؛ قياس ميكروسكوبي؛ فحص مجهري |
| microsoft ethics and copmpliance | الأخلاقيات والالتزام لدى شركة ميكروسوفت |
| microsome | جسم دقيق |
| microsphere | جسم كروي دقيق |
| microsporidiosis | الإصابة الناتجة عن أبواغ دقيقة |
| microstable | مضادة للميكروبات |
| microstructure | بنية صغرية |
| microswitch | مفتاح دقيق |
| microtome | جهاز التقطيع إلى شرائح رقيقة |
| microvascular | الأوعية الدقيقة |
| microvascular and macrovascular complications | المضاعفات التي تحدث بالأوعية الدقيقة والأوعية الكبيرة |
| microwave | ميكرويف |
| microwave cooking (bags for -) | طهي بالميكروويف (أكياس للطهي بالميكروويف) |
| microwave energy | طاقة موجة كهرطاسية |
| microwave heating | تسخين بالميكرويف |
| microwave oven | فرن ميكرويف |
| microwave water cut meter | جهاز قياس قطفة ماء يعمل بالموجات الدقيقة |
| microwaves energy | طاقة الميكروويف |
| microwire supports | مواد حاملة سلكية دقيقة (في مجال الكيمياء والمعالجات الحفزية) |
| middle distillates ; middle distillate products | نواتج التقطير المتوسطة |
| midpoint plane | مستوى نقطة المنتصف |
| mid-roll rewind | ترجيع الفيلم من المنتصف |
| migraine | صداع نصفي |
| migrant farmer | المزارع المتنقل |
| milage recorder for vehicles | جهاز تسجيل المسافات في المركبات |
| mild cognitive impairment | ضعف الإدراك الطفيف |
| mild steel | فولاذ مطاوع؛ صلب طري |
| mildew | عفن فطري |
| mildew (chemical preparations to prevent -) | عفن فطرى (مستحضرات كيميائية لمنع العفن الفطري) |
| mildew (chemical preparations to treat -) | عفن فطرى (مستحضرات كيميائية لمعالجة العفن الفطري) |
| mile | ميل |
| milestones | علامات الميل (علامات الكيلو مترات) |
| miliary | دخني |
| milieu | بيئة أو وسط |
| militarisation | عسكرة |
| military engineer | مهندس عسكري |
| military expinditure | الإنفاق العسكري |
| military government | حكومة عسكرية |
| military governor | الحاكم العسكري |
| military governor ; military commander | الحاكم العسكري |
| military installations | المنشآت العسكرية |
| military inteligence | المخابرات الحربية |
| military law | قانون الأحكام العسكرية |
| military observer group for india and pakistan | فريق مراقبي الأمم المتحدة العسكريين في الهند وباكستان |
| military posts | وظائف عسكرية |
| military robot | روبوت عسكري |
| military vehicles for transport | مركبات عسكرية للنقل |
| milk | اللبن الحليب |
| milk (albuminous -) | اللبن حليب (حليب زلالي) |
| milk (cleansing -) | اللبن (لبن التنظيف) للاستخدام في أغراض التجميل |
| milk (peanut -) [soft drink] | لبن (لبن الفول السوداني) [مشروبات لا كحولية] |
| milk and dairy | الألبان ومنتجاتها |
| milk beverages [milk predominating] | مشروبات اللبن الحليب [يغلب عليها الحليب] |

| | |
|---|---|
| milk conservation | حفظ اللبن |
| milk cooling installations | تجهيزات تبريد اللبن الحليب |
| milk drying | تجفيف اللبن |
| milk ferments | خميرة اللبن الحليب |
| milk of almonds [beverage] | لبن اللوز [مشروب] |
| milk of lime | لبن الكالسيوم |
| milk products | منتجات اللبن الحليب |
| milk sugar [lactose] | سكر اللبن الحليب [لاكتوز] |
| milking grease | شحم الحلب |
| milking machines | ماكينات حلب |
| milking machines (teat cups [suction cups] for -) | ماكينات حلب (أكواب حلمية [أكواب امتصاص] في ماكينات الحلب) |
| millboards (asbestos -) | ورق مقوى (ورق مقوى من الأسبستوس) |
| millidarcy | ملي دارسي (وحدة قياس نفاذية ( permeability |
| millimetre | مليمتر |
| milling | تشكيل بالتفريز؛ فرازة؛ سحق؛ ضرب الأرز |
| milling cutters [hand tools] | قواطع تشكيل [عُدد يدوية] |
| milling machines | ماكينات طحن |
| millipore filter paper | ورق مرشح ميليبور |
| milliwatt = mw | مللى وات |
| mills [machines] | مطاحن؛ أدوات طحن [ماكينات] |
| millstones | أحجار الرحى |
| mimeograph apparatus and machines | أجهزة وماكينات النسخ |
| mimetic | محاكي |
| min | دقيقة |
| min | الحد الأدنى |
| mincing knives [hand tools] | سكاكين الفرم [عُدد يدوية] |
| mind | يمانع، ذهن |
| mind-inspiring environment | بيئة ملهمة للذهن |
| mine | يستخرج (النفط إلخ) |
| mine | يستخرج المعادن، تعبير يطلق على عملية إجراء البحوث |
| mine borers | آلات ثقب المناجم |
| mine cart wheels | عجلات عربات المناجم |
| mine detector | مجس ألغام |
| mine gallary | سرداب منجم (مجال تعدين ومناجم) |
| mine laying | بث ألغام |
| mine robot | روبوت ألغام. روبوت لنزع الألغام |
| mine sweeping | كسح ألغام |
| mineral acids | أحماض معدنية |
| mineral components | عناصر معدنية |
| mineral composition | التركيب المعدني |
| mineral food-supplements | إضافات معدنية للغذاء |
| mineral fuel | وقود معدني |
| mineral grain | حبيبة معدنية |
| mineral oils | زيوت معدنية |
| mineral oxide fines | دقائق خام أكسيد معدني |
| mineral spirits | سوائل كحولية معدنية |
| mineral water (preparations for making -) | مياه معدنية (مستحضرات لصنع المياه المعدنية) |
| mineral water [beverages] | مياه معدنية [مشروبات] |

| | |
|---|---|
| mineral water making machines | ماكينات صنع المياه المعدنية |
| mineral water salts | أملاح المياه المعدنية |
| mineral wool [insulator] | صوف معدني [عازل] |
| miners' lamps | مصابيح عمال المناجم |
| mines [explosives] | ألغام [متفجرات] |
| mineworking machines | ماكينات أشغال الحفر في المناجم |
| mini robot | روبوت متناهي الصغر |
| mini video light (assist lamp) | مصباح الفيديو الصغير (مصباح المساعدة) |
| miniature circuit breaker | قاطع دارة صغير المدى |
| miniaturization technology | تقنية التصغير |
| miniaturize | يصغر |
| miniaturized electronic circuit | دائرة إلكترونية مصغرة |
| minibodies | أجسام دقيقة |
| mini-bus | ميني باص |
| minilocus | موضع صغير |
| minimal | أقل (قدر) من كذا |
| minimal clearance between the rotor and stator | أدنى خلوص بين العضو الدوار والعضو الساكن |
| minimum essential medium (mem) | أدنى وسط أساسي |
| minimum voxel correlation (mvc) criteria | أدنى ارتباط للفوكسلات (MVC) |
| minimum work loss | أدنى فقدان للتشغيل |
| mining | التعدين |
| mining | استخراج المعادن |
| mining for patent documents | إجراء بحوث وتحليلات في مستندات البراءات |
| mini-sd storage card | وبطاقة تخزين ساوث داكوتا |
| minister of education | وزير التعليم |
| ministry of education | وزارة التعليم |
| ministry of justice, experts' office | مكتب الخبراء بوزارة العدل |
| ministry of supply and internal trade | وزارة التموين والتجارة الداخلية |
| minium | ألومنيوم [أكسيد الرصاص الأحمر] |
| minor | قاصر |
| minor patent | براءة فرعية |
| minor technology | تقنية فرعية |
| mint essence [essential oil] | رائحة النعناع [زيت عطري] |
| mint for confectionery | نعناع للاستخدام في الحلويات |
| mint for perfumery | نعناع للاستخدام في العطور |
| mirror sites | مواقع بديلة |
| mirror tiles | آجر المرايا |
| mirroring disk drives | محركات أقراص معكوسة |
| mirrors (rearview -) | مرايا (مرايا الرؤية الخلفية) |
| mirrors (sighting -) for guns and rifles | مرايا (مرايا التسديد) في المسدسات والبنادق |
| mirrors [looking glasses] | مرايا |
| mirrors [optics] | مرايا [بصريات] |
| mirrors for dentists | مرايا لاستخدام أطباء الأسنان |
| mirrors for inspecting work | مرايا لأعمال التفتيش |
| mirrors for surgeons | مرايا الجراحين |
| mis | متر في الثانية |
| miscast | طاقم غير مناسب للفيلم |

| | |
|---|---|
| miscibility | قابلية الامتزاج |
| misdemeanour | جنحة |
| misfile | يخطئ في وضع الملف في مكانه السليم |
| misfiling | الخطأ في وضع الملف في مكان السليم |
| misfolding of protein, etc. | طي على نحو سيء |
| missile boat | زورق صواريخ |
| missiles (ballistic -) | صواريخ (صواريخ باليستية) |
| misuse | يسيء الاستعمال، استعمال مسيء |
| miters [hats] | تيجان الأسقف [قبعات] |
| mitigating circumstance | ظرف مخفف |
| mitigation | تقليص، تخفيف |
| mitigation sales | مبيعات التخفيف |
| mitogenesis | تولد أو تكون الانقسام الفتيلي |
| mitosis | انقسام خيطي |
| mitre [miter (am.)] boxes [hand tools] | صناديق أدوات ضبط الزوايا [عُدد يدوية] |
| mittens | قفازات لليد والرسغ تكسو الأصابع الأربع معاً وتكسو الإبهام منفرداً |
| mitts (washing -) | قفازات (قفازات الغسيل) |
| mix and match | الخلط والتوفيق |
| mixed connective tissue | داء النسيج الضام المختلط |
| mixed dyslipidemia | اختلال دهون الدم المختلط |
| mixer | خلاط |
| mixer taps for water pipes | صنابير الخلط للاستخدام في أنابيب الماء |
| mixers [machines] | خلاطات [ماكينات] |
| mixers, manual [cocktail shakers] | خلاطات يدوية [أدوات لمزج الكوكتيل] |
| mixing | خلط (كذا بكذا) |
| mixing machines | ماكينات المزج |
| mixing machines, non-electric, for household purposes | ماكينات المزج غير كهربائية للاستخدام في الأغراض المنزلية |
| mixing partners | شركاء الخلط |
| mixing spoons [kitchen utensils] | ملاعق المزج [أدوات المطبخ] |
| mixing zone | منطقة خلط |
| mixture | خليط |
| mixture bed demineralization unit | وحدة نزع المعادن ذات طبقة مختلطة |
| mixtures | خلائط |
| mkn45 cell lysates | نواتج انحلال خلايا MKN45 |
| mkn45- conditioned medium | الوسط المهيأ بـ MKN45 |
| ml | حاسب محمول متنقل |
| ml | ملي لتر |
| mlb/hr | مل رطل في الساعة |
| mm | ملي متر |
| mm | مم |
| mm hg | مم زئبق؛ مم زئبقي |
| mm of hg | مم من الزئبق |
| mm2 | مم2 |
| mmax-ct | الحد الأقصى لوقت الصيانة التصحيحية |
| mmf | ألياف متعددة الأوضاع |
| mmol | ملي مول |
| mn | ميجا نيوتن |
| mn | دقيقة |
| mn/m | ملي نيوتن/م |
| mobile account | حساب محمول |
| mobile advertising patent | براءة متصلة بالإعلان عبر الجوال |
| mobile and/or stationary wireless communication devices | وسائل الاتصال اللاسلكية المتنقلة و/أو الثابتة |
| mobile chat | المحادثة الهاتفية |
| mobile internent | إنترنت الهاتف (المحمول)؛ إنترنت المحمول |
| mobile malware | فيروسات الأجهزة المحمولة؛ البرامج الحاقدة التي تهاجم الأجهزة المحمولة |
| mobile nodes (mns) | النقاط المتنقلة |
| mobile phase | طور متحرك |
| mobile phone | الهاتف المحمول |
| mobile robot | روبوت متحرك |
| mobile service | خدمة محمول (خدمة الهواتف المحمولة) |
| mobile social networking technology | تقنية تأسيس الشبكمات الاجتماعية الجوالة |
| mobile technology | التكنولوجيا المتنقلة |
| mobile technology | تقنية جوال |
| mobile terminal | وحدة طرفية متنقلة |
| mobile top-up card | كارت شحن موبايل؛ بطاقة شحن المحمول |
| mobile wireless communication devices | وسائل الاتصال اللاسلكية المتنقلة |
| mobile workforce software | برنامج حاسبي خاص بقوة عمل متحركة |
| mobile x-ray backscatter imaging system | نظام تصوير متنقل بالتشتت العكسي يستخدم أشعة سينية |
| mobiles [decoration] | أثاث متحرك [للزينة] |
| mobilise | يعبئ |
| mobility | التنقل |
| mobilize hydrocarbon | يميّع (يحول إلى مائع) الهيدروكربون |
| mobilized fluid | مائع متميع: إلى موائع في تكوين يحتوي على هيدروكربون قادرة على التدفق نتيجة لمعالجة حرارية للتكوين |
| mock cells | خلايا غير معالجة أو كاذبة |
| mode | صيغة، شكل، حالة |
| mode dial | قرص تحديد الوضع |
| mode indicator | مؤشر الوضع |
| mode of administration | نظام الإعطاء |
| mode of operation | حالة التشغيل |
| model | موديل؛ ينمذج، نموذج |
| model vehicles (scale -) | نماذج مركبات (مركبات مشكلة وفقاً لنموذج له نفس الأبعاد الحقيقية) |
| modeling ; modelling | عمل نموذج؛ نمذجة: إنشاء نموذج لخزان، تكوين، إلخ |
| modeling tool | أداة عمل نموذج |
| modelling clay | طين التشكيل |
| modelling materials | مواد التشكيل |
| modelling paste | معجون التشكيل |
| modelling wax | شمع التشكيل |
| models (architects' -) | نماذج (نماذج المهندسين |

| | |
|---|---|
| | (المعماريين) |
| modem | جهاز المودم: يُستخدم لتحقيق الاتصال فيما بين أجهزة الكمبيوتر |
| modem jack | مقبس مودم |
| moderating materials for nuclear reactors | مواد تهدئة المفاعلات النووية |
| modifications | تحويرات |
| modified mercalli mm scale | مقياس مارسيلي المطور |
| modularity | قابلية التعديل |
| modulate | يعدِّل |
| modulates | تضمينات |
| modulation | تضمين .. |
| modulation diversity | تنوع التضمين |
| modulation of pi3 kinase function | تعديل وظيفة إنزيم PI3 كيناز |
| modulation symbols | رموز تضمين |
| modulator | معدل؛ مضمِّن: جهاز تعديل/تضمين |
| modulator | ينتقل من نغمة إلى أخرى |
| modulators | ينتقلوا من نغمة إلى أخرى |
| module | وحدة نمطية |
| module | وحدة قياس |
| modules | وحدات (أو وحدات نمطية) |
| modulus | معامل |
| modulus of elasticity | معاير المرونة |
| modulus of rupture | معامل التمزق |
| moi | تعدد العدوى |
| moiety | جزء؛ شطر. انظر radical |
| moisteners [office requisites] | مواد ترطيب [لوازم مكتبية] |
| moisteners for gummed surfaces [office requisites] | مواد ترطيب الأسطح الصمغية [لوازم مكتبية] |
| moistening [wetting] preparations for use in bleaching | مستحضرات ترطيب للاستخدام في التبييض |
| moistening [wetting] preparations for use in dyeing | مستحضرات ترطيب للاستخدام في الصباغة |
| moistening [wetting] preparations for use in the textile industry | مستحضرات ترطيب للاستخدام في صناعة المنسوجات |
| moistening oil | زيت ترطيب |
| moisture (substances for insulating buildings against -) | الرطوبة (مواد عزل الرطوبة عن المباني) |
| moisture cured | معالجة بالرطوبة |
| moisture migration | انتقال الرطوبة |
| mol | مول |
| mol/l | مول / لتر |
| molar concentration (substance concentration) | التَّركيزُ المولِيّ ( تَرْكيزُ المادَّة): التركيز الجزيئي |
| molar ratio | النسبة المولارية: نسبة جزيئية |
| molar volume | الحجم الجزيئي؛ الحجم المولي |
| molasses for food | دبس السكر للاستخدام في الطعام |
| mold | قالب |
| mold releasability | عملية التحرر من القالب |
| moldable wood | خشب قابل للتشكيل |
| moldic porosity | مسامية القالب |
| molding irons | مكاوي التشكيل |
| molding machines | ماكينات التشكيل |
| molding preparations | مستحضرات التشكيل |
| (foundry -) | (مستحضرات تشكيل المسبوكات) |
| molding wax for dentists | شمع التشكيل لاستخدام أطباء الأسنان |
| moldings for picture frames | زينة لأطر الصور |
| moldings of metal for cornices | حُلى من المعدن للأفاريز |
| moldings, not of metal, for building | قوالب ليست من المعدن للبناء |
| moldings, not of metal, for cornices | زينة ليست من المعدن لتزين أسقف المباني |
| mold-release preparations | مستحضرات إزالة العفن |
| molds (ebonite -) | قوالب (قوالب الإبونيت) |
| molds (ice cube -) | قوالب (قوالب مكعبات الثلج) |
| molds [kitchen utensils] | قوالب [أدوات المطبخ] |
| molds [parts of machines] | قوالب [أجزاء من ماكينات] |
| mole | مول |
| mole fraction | النسبة الجزيئية |
| mole percent ; mol % | %بالمول |
| mole ratio | النسبة بالمول: نسبة جزيئية |
| molecular devices plate reader | قارئ أطباق جزيئي |
| molecular mass | كتلة جزيئية |
| molecular nano technology | تقنية نانوية جزيئية |
| molecular oxygen/steam-containing atmosphere | جو يحتوي على الأكسجين الجزيئي/البخار |
| molecular oxygen-containing gas | غاز يحتوي على الأكسجين الجزيئي |
| molecular sieves | مناخل جزيئية |
| molecular weight control agent | عوامل تحكم في الوزن الجزيئي |
| molecular weight-increasing | تزيد الوزن الجزيئي |
| molecules assembled in a close-packed left-handed helix | الجزيئات المجمعة في حلزون أيسر مجمع معا |
| moleskin [fabric] | فرو الخلد [قماش] |
| moleskin [imitation of leather] | فرو الخلد [تقليد الجلود] |
| molten | منصهر |
| molten cryolite | كريوليت منصهر |
| molten sulfur | كبريت منصهر |
| molybdenum | موليبدنيوم |
| molybdenum trioxide | ثالث أكسيد الموليبدنوم |
| moment | عزم |
| moment of inertia | عَزْمُ الْقُصُورِ الذَّاتِيِّ |
| monedentate | أحادية الترابط |
| monetary | نقدي |
| monetary base | قاعدة نقدية |
| monetary default | إخلال مالي |
| monethanolamine | مونو إيثانول أمين |
| monetizable | قابل لأن يتحول إلى نقد |
| monetization | جعل الشيء ذا عائد نقدي |
| monetize | جعل الشيء ذا عائد نقد |
| money belts [clothing] | أحزمة النقود [ملابس] |
| money boxes of metal | علب النقود من المعدن |
| money clips of common metal | مشابك النقود من المعادن غير النفيسة |

| | |
|---|---|
| money counting and sorting machines | ماكينات عد وتصنيف النقود |
| money scoops | أدوات تفريغ النقود |
| monitizability | قابلية الشيء أن يتحول إلى نقد |
| monitizability | قابلية الشيء للتحول لكي يصبح ذا عائد نقدي |
| monitizable idea | فكرة قابلة أن تتحول إلى مال |
| monitizable innovation | ابتكار قابل لأن يصبح ذا قيمة مالية |
| monitizable invention | اختراع يمكن أن يصبح ذا قيمة نقدية |
| monitor | الشاشة |
| monitor | يراقب، مرقاب، شاشة |
| monitorability | قابلية الشيء للمراقبة |
| monitorable | يمكن مراقبته |
| monitoring | مراقبة |
| monitoring | مراقبة |
| monitoring apparatus, electric | جهاز المراقبة الكهربائي |
| monitoring device | جهاز مراقبة |
| monitoring of device failure | مراقبة تعطل الجهاز |
| monitoring of system performance | مراقبة أداء النظام |
| monitoring technology | تقنية مراقبة |
| monitors [computer hardware] | شاشات عرض [المكونات المادية في الحاسبات الآلية] |
| monitors [computer programs] | شاشات عرض [برامج الحاسب] |
| mono acylated derivative | مشتق مضاف إليه مجموعة أسيل أحادية |
| mono- and dicarboxylic unsaturated acids | أحماض كربوكسيلية أحادية وثنائية غير مشبعة |
| mono-alchol selectivities | انتقائيات الكحول الأحادية |
| monoamine neurotransmitters serotonin and/or noradrenaline in the brain | مستوى السيروتونين و/أو النورأدرينالين للمرسلات العصبية أحادية الأمين في المخ |
| monoamine oxidase inhibitors | مثبطات إنزيم أكسيداز أحادي الأمين |
| mono-and di-alkyl amino groups | مجموعات أمينو أحادية وثنائية الألكيل |
| monobasic | أحادية القاعدية |
| monobodies | أجسام مضادة أحادية التكافؤ |
| monocation | كاتيون أحادي |
| monocline | ثنية وحيدة الجانب |
| monoclinic | أحادي الميل |
| monoclonal | أحادي الاستنساخ؛ أحادي/وحيد النسيلة |
| monoclonal antibody " mab" | جسم مضاد أحادي النسيلة "mAb": جسم مضاد تم إنتاجه من نسيلة أو مجموعة متجانسة جينيا من الخلايا الهجين الملتحمة، بمعنى خلية ورم هجين. يتم استنساخ الخلايا الهدين لتحديد نسائل الخلايا التي تنتج جسم مضاد أحادي النسيلة محدد متجانس كيميائيا ومناعيا. |
| monocyte | خلية أو كرية بيضاء وحيدة النواة |
| mono-ethylenically unsaturated monomers | مونمرات غير مشبعة إيثيلينياً في موضع واحد |
| monogram tabs for marking linen | عراوي المونوجرام لتعليم القماش |
| monohull | بدنة واحدة |
| monohydrate | أحادي هيدرات؛ هيدرات أحادية |
| monohydric alchols | كحوليات أحادية الهيدروكسيل |
| monoline | شركة متخصصة؛ شركة مالية ذات سلعة وحيدة؛ مؤسسة مالية ذات خدمة واحدة |
| monoline insurance agency | شركة تأمين أحادية الخط؛ شركة تأمين ذات خط واحد |
| monolithic | متواحد؛ أحادي |
| monolithic integrated circuit | دائرة إلكترونية أحادية |
| monomer | مونومر |
| monomeric | مونومري |
| mono-methyl-branched paraffins | مركبات بارافين متفرعة أحادية الميثيل |
| mono-methyl-heptanes | مركبات هبتان أحادية الميثيل |
| monominerallic | وحيدة المعدن |
| mono-pegylated | مضاف إليه أحادي بولي إيثيلين جليكول |
| monophonic ring tone | نغمات غير إيقاعية |
| monopolist | محتكر |
| monopoly | احتكار |
| monopoly on information | احتكار معلومات |
| monopoly on use of gene | احتكار استعمال جين. |
| mono-protected piperazine | ببرازين محمي بمجموعة حامية أحادية |
| monoradical | أحادي الشق |
| monoradical or a diradical | أحادية أو ثنائية الشق |
| monospecific | أحادي النوعية |
| monostearate | مونو ستيارات |
| mono-substituted alkyl | ألكيل بها أستبدال أحادي |
| monotherapy | علاج أحادي الدواء؛ معالجة أحادية الدواء |
| monovalent | أحادي التكافؤ |
| montage | مونتاج |
| montmorillonite | منتموريلونايت |
| monuments of metal | معالم تذكارية من المعدن |
| monuments, not of metal | معالم تذكارية ليست من المعادن |
| mooring boats (floating docks of metal, for -) | قوارب الإرساء (الأرصفة العائمة من المعدن في قوارب الإرساء) |
| mooring boats (floating docks, not of metal, for -) | قوارب الإرساء (الأرصفة العائمة ليست من المعدن في قوارب الإرساء) |
| mooring bollards of metal | مرابط حبال الإرساء من المعدن |
| mooring bollards, not of metal | مرابط حبال الإرساء ليست من المعدن |
| mooring buoys of metal | عوامات إرشاد في المرسى من المعدن |
| mooring buoys, not of metal | عوامات إرشاد في المرسى ليست من المعدن |
| moped | دراجة بمحرك صغير |
| mopping-up operations | عمليات تطهير المواقع من العدو |
| mops | مسّاحات |
| moral machine | آلة أخلاقية |
| moral robot | روبوت أخلاقي |
| morality | أخلاقية، درس أخلاقي، مبادئ أخلاقية |
| morbidity | مرض |
| mordant | مثبت ألوان |
| mordants | مواد ترسيخ الصبغ |

| | |
|---|---|
| mordants for leather | مواد تثبيت صبغ الجلود |
| mordants for metals | مواد ترسيخ لون المعادن |
| mordenite | موردينايت |
| more economical | أكثر توفيرا من الناحية الاقتصادية |
| more stringent erasure detection criterion | معيار أكثر صرامة للكشف عن المحو |
| morphogenetic | مخلق |
| morpholino | مورفولينو |
| morpholinothieno | مورفولينو ثيينو |
| morpholinyl | مورفولينيل |
| morphology | بنية شكلية |
| mortar | هاون |
| mortar (troughs of metal for mixing-) | ملاط (أحواض من المعدن لخلط الملاط) |
| mortar (troughs, not of metal, for mixing -) | ملاط (أحواض ليست من المعدن لخلط الملاط) |
| mortar for building | ملاط للمباني |
| mortars | هاونات |
| mortars [firearms] | مدافع الهاون [أسلحة نارية] |
| mortars for pounding | هاون السحق |
| mortise axes | بُلَط النقر |
| mortise chisels | أزاميل النقر |
| mortising machines | ماكينات النقر |
| mosaic | متراكب؛ فسيفساء |
| mosaics for building | فسيفساء البناء |
| mosaics of glass, not for building | فسيفساء من الزجاج بخلاف المستخدمة في البناء |
| mosm | ملي أسمول |
| mosquito nets | الناموسيات |
| moss (irish -) | طحلب (طحلب أيرلندي) |
| most developed countries | البلدان الأكثر نموا |
| most related prior art | فن سابق ذو علاقة أكثر من غيره |
| most relevant prior art | فن سابق ذو صلة أكثر من غيره |
| mother liquor | المحلول الأم |
| mother-of-pearl [unworked or semi-worked] | اللؤلؤ [مشغول أو نصف مشغول] |
| mothproofing paper | ورق مقاوم للعته |
| mothproofing preparations | مستحضرات مقاومة للعته |
| motif | الموتيف؛ تصميم ذو شكل محدد |
| motif on the cover | رسم على الغلاف |
| motifs | تتابعات تنظيمية |
| motile | متحرك |
| motility | حركية |
| motion picture | فيلم سينمائي |
| motive power | قدرة محركة |
| motor | محرك؛ موتور |
| motor buses | حافلة |
| motor cars | السيارات |
| motor coaches | حافلة ميكانيكية |
| motor fire engines | سيارات ميكانيكية لإطفاء الحريق |
| motor fuel | وقود محركات |
| motor fuel (chemical additives to -) | وقود محركات (مواد إضافة كيميائية لوقود المحركات) |
| motor homes | المنازل المتنقلة على عربات |
| motor oil | زيت محركات |
| motor prosthetic implants | زراعات محرك ترقيعية |
| motor vehicle | مركبة تعمل بمحرك |
| motorcycles | دراجات بخارية |
| motorcycles (kick starters for -) | دراجات بخارية (وسائل بداية تشغيل الدراجات البخارية) |
| motorists' clothing | ملابس سائقي السيارات |
| motorization | تحريك |
| motorized | يزود بمتحرك |
| motorized cultivators | آلات زراعية حاصدة بمحرك كهربائي |
| motorized mobility | التنقل بمحركات |
| motorized weapons | أسلحة متحركة بمحرك ذاتي |
| motors for boats | موتورات القوارب |
| motors for cycles | موتورات الدراجات |
| motors for land vehicles | موتورات المركبات الأرضية |
| motors, electric, for land vehicles | موتورات كهربائية للاستخدام في المركبات الأرضية |
| motors, electric, other than for land vehicles | موتورات كهربائية لغير الاستخدام في المركبات الأرضية |
| motors, other than for land vehicles | موتورات بخلاف الاستخدام في المركبات الأرضية |
| mottling | تبقع |
| mould | قالب |
| mouldable wood | خشب قابل للتشكيل |
| moulded | مقولبة (مشكلة في قوالب) |
| moulded polycarbonate plastic | لدائن من البولي كربونات المشكلة |
| moulding irons | مكاوي التشكيل |
| moulding machines | ماكينات التشكيل |
| moulding preparations (foundry -) | مستحضرات التشكيل (مستحضرات تشكيل المسبوكات) |
| moulding wax for dentists | شمع التشكيل لاستخدام أطباء الأسنان |
| mouldings (moulding) | قوالب (قولبة) |
| mouldings for picture frames | حُلى أطر الصور |
| mouldings of metal for cornices | حُليات من المعدن لتجميل الأسقف |
| mouldings, not of metal, for building | قوالب للبناء ليست من المعدن |
| mouldings, not of metal, for cornices | حليات ليست من المعدن لتجميل الأسقف |
| moulds (ebonite -) | قوالب (قوالب الأبونيت) |
| moulds (ice cube -) | قوالب (قوالب مكعبات الثلج) |
| moulds [kitchen utensils] | قوالب [أدوات المطبخ] |
| moulds [parts of machines] | قوالب [أجزاء من ماكينات] |
| mount | تركيب؛ يركب، يثبت؛ حَامِل؛ قاعدة تركيب |
| mountain warfare | الحرب الجبلية |
| mountaineering sticks | عصىّ تسلق الجبال |
| mounted on jeep | محمول على عربة جيب |
| mounted to | مثبت على؛ مركب على |
| mounting bracket | كتيفة تثبيت |
| mounting photographs (apparatus for -) | تركيب الصور الفوتوغرافية (جهاز تركيب الصور الفوتوغرافية) |
| mouse | فأر |
| mouse [data processing equipment] | الفأرة [أداة معالجة البيانات] |
| mouse pads | وسائد الفأرة |
| mouse traps | شراك الفئران |
| moustache wax | شمع الشارب |

| | |
|---|---|
| moustaches (false -) | شوارب (شوارب صناعية) |
| moutain tops | قمم الجبال |
| mouth washes | غسول الفم |
| mouthpieces for cigarette holders | قطع الفم لمباسم السجائر |
| mouthpieces for musical instruments | قطع النفخ في الآلات الموسيقية |
| mouthpieces of yellow amber for cigar and cigarette holders | قطع الفم من الكهرمان الأصفر لمباسم السيجار والسجائر |
| mouthwash | غسول الفم ؛ غرغرة |
| movable shutter | مغلاق متحرك |
| move | يحرك، حركة |
| move down | ينتقل لأسفل |
| move in translation | تتحرك انتقاليًا |
| move left | ينتقل لليسار |
| move right | ينتقل لليمين |
| move upwards | ينتقل لأعلى |
| movement | حركة، حركة جماعية، تحرك |
| movement impairment | إعاقة حركة |
| movements for clocks and watches | الأجزاء المتحركة في ساعات الحائط وساعات اليد |
| moveout | الفرق في زمن وصول الموجات |
| movie files | ملفات الأفلام |
| movie industry | صناعة السينما |
| movie recording time | مدة تسجيل الفيلم |
| moving | متحرك |
| moving average filter | مرشح المتوسط (الحسابي) المتحرك |
| moving bed reactor | مفاعل طبقة متحركة |
| moving pavement [sidewalks] | الأرصفة المتحركة [أرصفة جانبية] |
| moving staircases [escalators] | سلالم متحركة [مصاعد] |
| mowing and reaping machines | ماكينات جز العشب وحصاده |
| mowing machines (knives for -) | ماكينات جز العشب (سكاكين ماكينات جز العشب) |
| mp | نقطة الانصهار |
| mpa | ميلي بواز (مع لزوجة) |
| mpa | ميجا باسكال |
| mpa s | ميجا باسكال في الثانية |
| mpa.s | ملي باسكال في الثانية |
| mpa.s ; mpa s ; mpa-s | ملي باسكال/ثانية |
| mpag | ميجا باسكال وفقًا للمقياس |
| mpas | ملي باسكال/ثانية |
| mph | ميل في الساعة |
| mpk | ملي جرام لكل كيلو جرام |
| mpsi | ميجا رطل على البوصة المربعة |
| mpsoc) | شريحة تحتوي على النظام ومتعددة المعالجات |
| mre | وجبات جاهزة للأكل |
| mrr | الطرق الأقل مخاطرة |
| ms | ملي ثانية |
| ms | شركة ميكروسوفت |
| ms | الطيف الكتلي |
| ms/cm | ميكرو سيمنز لكل سنتيمتر |
| mscf | مليون قدم مربعة معيارية |
| mscf/d | مليون قدم مكعب عياري من الغاز في اليوم |
| mscl | كلوريد ميثان سلفونيل |
| msec | ملي - ثانية |
| msf | ألف قدم مربع |
| msisdn | الشبكة الرقمية للخدمات المتكاملة للمحطات المتنقلة |
| mtbcf | متوسط الزمن بين عطلين حرجين متتاليين |
| mtbcma | متوسط الزمن بين إجراءي صيانة تصحيحية متتالين |
| mtbe | إيثر ميثيل ثلاثي بيوتيل |
| mtbf | متوسط الزمن بين عطلين متتالين |
| mte | عنصر العلاج الطبي |
| mtn banking | سندات متوسطة الأجل؛ سندات خزينية متوسطة الاجل |
| mtp | منفذ تحويل رسالة |
| mtp | جزء تحويل رسالة |
| mu | ميكرو متر |
| mu | وحدة ملي |
| mucilage | مذاب الصمغ في الماء |
| mucoadhesives | مواد تلتصق بالغشاء المخاطي |
| mucoid | شبه مخاطي |
| mucosal | عن طريق الأغشية المخاطية |
| mucosal addressin cell adhesion molecule | جزيء الالتصاق بخلايا الأدريسين في الأغشية المخاطية |
| mucositis | التهاب الغشاء المخاطي |
| mud | وحل |
| mud (medicinal -) | طين (طين علاجي) |
| mud catchers and collectors [machines] | ملاقط وماكينات تجميع الطين [ماكينات] |
| mud drum | اسطوانة تجمع؛ تجميع طين |
| mud fluid | سائل طين الحفر |
| mud for baths | طين المغاطس |
| mud pit | حفرة الوحل |
| mudguards | أجزاء واقية من الوحل |
| muds (drilling -) | طين (طين الحفر) |
| muesli | حبوب الإفطار سويسرية الأصل |
| mufflers for motors and engines | كاتم للصوت في الموتورات والمحركات |
| muffs (pipe -), not of metal | جلبات أسطوانية طرفية (جلبات أسطوانية طرفية للأنابيب) ليست من المعدن |
| muffs [clothing] | الموفة [غطاء أنبوبي طويل مكسو بالفراء .. الخ لتدفئة اليدين] [ملابس] |
| mug | كوب خزفي كبير |
| mugs, not of precious metal | أكواب أسطوانية الشكل ليست من المعادن النفيسة |
| mulch | غطاء عضوي واق |
| mulch (straw -) | دُبال (دُبال القش) |
| mules | الأشخاص الزائفين |
| muller-fischer syndrome | متلازمة مولر - فيشر |
| mulling | سحن؛ سحق؛ دق |
| multi component cure systems | أنظمة معالجة متعددة المكونات |
| multi particulates | جسيمات دقائقية متعددة |
| multi selection indicator | مؤشر التحديد المتعدد |
| multi selector | مفتاح التحديد متعدد الاتجاهات |
| multi-antigen plasmid | بلازميدة متعددة مولدات الضد |
| multi-av cable | كبل AV متعدد |

| | |
|---|---|
| multi-bit symbols | رموز متعددة الأرقام الثنائية |
| multi-brand company | شركة تمتلك علامات عديدة |
| multi-carrier modulation techniques | تقنيات تضمين متعددة الحوامل |
| multicomponent particulate system (i.e., a formation that includes two or more types of particles). | نظام دقائقي متعددة المكونات (على سبيل المثال، صيغة تشتمل على نوعين أو أكثر من الجسيمات) |
| multifunction invention | اختراع ذو وظائف متعددة |
| multi-institutional arbitration | تحكيم يتم من خلال عدد من المؤسسات |
| multilabel | متعدد الترقيم؛ متعدد العلامات: تم تمييزه بعدة علامات tags |
| multi-layer diffractive optical elements | العناصر البصرية الحيودية متعددة الطبقات |
| multi-legged robot | روبوت ذو أرجل عديدة |
| multi-loop reactor | مفاعل متعدد الحلقات |
| multimeric | متعدد الوحدات |
| multimerization | التحويل إلى متعدد وحدات: جعله متعدد وحدات |
| multimerization | التحويل إلى متعدد وحدات؛ جعله متعدد الوحدات |
| multi-national patent portfolio | محفظة براءات متعددة الجنسيات |
| multiparticulate | متعدد الدقائق |
| multi-party arbitration | تحكيم في نزاع متعدد الأطراف |
| multi-party arbitration clause | البند الخاص بكون التحكيم متعدد الأطراف. بند تعاقدي ينظم سير التحكيم عند وجود أكثر من طرفين |
| multi-party patent infringement dispute | نزاع متعدد الأطراف بشأن انتهاك براءات |
| multi-patent dispute | نزاع بشأن عدة براءات |
| multi-peptide synthesizer | وسيلة التخليق متعددة الببتيد |
| multi-phase flow simulations | عمليات محاكاة تدفق متعدد الأطوار |
| multiphase flowmeters | مقاييس التدفق متعددة الأطوار |
| multiple arbitrators | محكمون متعددون |
| multiple function control buttons | أزرار تحكم وظائف متعددة |
| multiple intelligence theory | نظرية الذكاء المتعدد |
| multiple myeloma | ورم نخاعي متعدد |
| multiple patent infringements | انتهاكات متعددة لبراءة |
| multiple sclerosis | تصلب متعدد |
| multiple use invention | اختراع ذو استخدامات عديدة |
| multiple-branched paraffins | البارافينات متعددة التفرعات |
| multiple-in multiple-out (mimo) | الإدخال والإخراج المتعدد |
| multiplet | متعدد |
| multiplexer | مجمع إشارات |
| multiplexing | ارسال تعاقبي متعدد أو إرسال تعددي أو إرسال متعدد |
| multiplexing technology | تقنية الإرسال المتعدد |
| multiplicity of | مجموعة من |
| multi-purpose combat robot | روبوت معارك ذو غايات متعددة |
| multi-purpose invention | اختراع ذو غايات عديدة |
| multispecific | متعدد النوعية |
| multi-tone ring tone | نغمة رنين متعددة النغمات |
| multi-touch screen technology | تقنية لمس الشاشة المتعدد |
| multi-track schedule | نظام الجدول المتغير |
| multi-tubular | متعدد الأنابيب |
| multitude of | مجموعة من |
| multivalent | متعدد التكافؤ |
| multivalent antibody | جسم مضاد متعدد التكافؤ |
| multi-winding antenna | هوائي متعدد اللفات |
| mumps | نكاف |
| mumra | وزارة البلديات والشؤون المدنية والقروية |
| mundane invention | اختراع عادي |
| municipal | بلدية |
| municipal elections | انتخابات بلدية |
| munitions | العتاد الحربي |
| mur | متوسط الزمن اللازم للإصلاح |
| muramyl | ميراميل |
| murder-mystery drama | أفلام الجريمة الغامضة |
| murine antigen binding region | منطقة ربط مولد ضد فأري |
| muscle degeneration | تنكس العضلات؛ ضمور العضلات |
| muscle rigidity | تيبس عضلي؛ تصلب عضلي؛ صمل عضلي |
| muscle smooth | عضلة ملساء |
| muscle spasm | تشنج عضلي |
| muscular dystrophies syndrome | متلازمة اختلال تغذية العضلات |
| musculature | جهاز عضلي |
| musculoskeletal | عضلي هيكلي |
| mushroom spawn for propagation | غزل الفطر (عيش الغراب) للاستخدام في التكاثر |
| mushrooms, fresh | الفطر (عيش الغراب) الطازج |
| mushrooms, preserved | الفطر، محفوظ (عيش الغراب) |
| music cases | الحقائب الموسيقية |
| music industry | صناعة الموسيقى |
| music patent | براءة موسيقية |
| music rolls [piano] | قوائم النوتة الموسيقية [بيانو] |
| music stands | حوامل النوتة الموسيقية |
| music synthesizers | المؤلفات الموسيقية بالطرق الصناعية |
| musical automata (coin-operated-) [juke boxes] | آلات موسيقية أتوماتيكية الحركة (آلات موسيقية أتوماتيكية الحركة تدار بالعملة) [الجوك بوكس] |
| musical boxes | الصناديق الموسيقية |
| musical comedy | الكوميديا الموسيقية |
| musical greeting cards | بطاقات التهنئة الموسيقية |
| musical instruments | آلات موسيقية |
| musical octave | الثماني الموسيقي |
| musk [perfumery] | المسك [عطور] |
| mussels [live] | بلح البحر [حي] |
| mussels [not live] | بلح البحر [غير حي] |
| must | الخمر الفطير [عصير العنب .. الخ قبل التخمر وأثناءه] |
| mustache wax | شمع الشارب |
| mustard | الخردل |
| mustard meal | مجروش الخردل |
| mustard oil | زيت الخردل |

| | |
|---|---|
| mustard plasters | لاصقات الخردل |
| mustard poultices | كمادات الخردل |
| must-fining preparations | مستحضرات التنقية من العفن |
| mutagenesis | إحداث الطفرة |
| mutant | ناتج طفرة؛ طافر |
| mutant ; mutants | ناتج الطفرة |
| mutate | يحدث به طفرة |
| mutated tumor-suppressor gene | الجين المطفَّر الكابت للورم |
| mutation | طفرة |
| mute | يكتم الصوت |
| mutein | بروتين محول منه |
| muteins | نواتج طفرات بروتينية |
| mutes for musical instruments | أدوات تخفيف صوت الآلات الموسيقية |
| mutual fund | صندوق استثمار مشترك |
| mutually assured patent destruction | تدمير براءاتي تبادلي مؤكد. قيام كل من شركتين متنافستين برفع شكاوى ضد البراءات التي للشركة الأخرى حق فيها مما يؤدي إلى توقف فعالية البراءات وتعطلها |
| muzzle | فوهة ماسورة البندقية |
| muzzles | كمامات لفم الحيوان |
| mv | ملي فولت |
| mva | ميجا فولت أمبير |
| mval | ميكرو مكافئ |
| mw | وزن جزيئي |
| mw | موجة دقيقة: موجة ميكرووية |
| mw; mw | ميجا واط |
| mx record changes | إمكانية تغيير عنوان خادم البريد إلى أي خدمة أخرى |
| myalgia | ألم العضلات |
| myasthenia gravis | وهن عضلي وخيم |
| myasthenic lambert-eaton syndrome | متلازمة وهن العضل للامبرت- إيتون |
| mycobacteria | بكتيريا فطرية |
| mycolytic | حال للميوسين |
| mydoom | مايدووم: دودة فيروسية خطيرة |
| myelitis | التهاب النخاع الشوكي |
| myelodysplasia | سوء النمو النخاعي |
| myeloid | شبه نخاعي |
| myeloma | ورم نخاعي |
| myelopathy | اعتلال النخاع |
| myoblast | أرومة عضلية |
| myocardial | متعلق بعضلة القلب |
| myocardial infarction | احتشاء عضلة القلب: تجلط عضلة القلب |
| myocardial ischemic injury | فقر المد الدموي لعضلة القلب؛ فقر الدم الموضعي لعضلة القلب |
| myocarditis | التهاب عضلة القلب |
| myoclonus | تقلص ارتجافي عضلي |
| myocyte | خلية عضلية |
| myofascial pain | الألم المتعلق باللفافة العضلية؛ الألم العضلي الصفاقي |
| myogenic | مولد للنسيج العضلي |
| myonecrosis | موت عظمي |
| myoplasty | تقويم عضلي |
| myositis | التهاب العضل |
| myostatin specific human lgg2 | أجسام مضادة بشرية من النوع LgG2 للمايوستاتين |
| myrobalan bark for pharmaceutical purposes | لحاء شجر الأهليلج للاستخدام في الأغراض الصيدلانية |

# N

| | |
|---|---|
| nail | مسمار (عادي) (مثل مسامير تثبيت الصور، إلخ) |
| nail | يسمر، مسمار |
| nail fold | طية ظفرية |
| nail joints | وصلات مسمارية |
| nail plates | صفيحات وصل مسمارية |
| nail polish | طلاء الأظافر |
| nail pull resistence | مقاومة شد المسمار |
| nailhead | رأس مسمار |
| naïve cell ; naive cell | خلية غير متمايز؛ غير مميز (جديدة) |
| naked antibody | جسم مضاد مجرّد |
| naked antibody | جسم مضاد مجرد: جسم مضاد غير مقترن بعامل علاجي |
| naked mouse | فأر منزوع الشعر |
| n-alkylated derivative | مشتق تم إدخال مجموعة الألكيل به عند ذرة النيتروجين (N) |
| n-alkylated pyrrolidone | بيروليدون يحتوي على مجموعة N- ألكيل |
| naming error | خطأ في التسمية |
| nanboddy | جسم بحجم النانو |
| nano | نانو، جزء من بليون، تعبير يطلق على الشيء متناهي الصغر |
| nano scale | يقاس حجمها بالنانو متر |
| nano technology | تقنية نانوية جزيئئة |
| nano tubes | أنابيب نانوية |
| nanobod (capitalized) or the nanobody | الجسم النانوي |
| nanobodies | أجسام بحجم النانو؛ أجسام متناهية الدقة |
| nanobody | جسم بحجم النانو |
| nanobody (not capitalized) | جسم نانوي |
| nanocomposite | مركبة بحجم نانو |
| nanoemulsions | مستحلبات ذات حجم نانو متري |
| nanofilteration | ترشيح بمرشح تقاس حجم مسامه بالنانو |
| nanometric module | وحدة نانو مترية عيارية |
| nanoparticles | جسيمات بحجم النانو |
| nanopiezo electronics | إلكترونيات نانوبيزية |
| nano-scale needles | إبر مقاسة بوحدات النانو |
| nano-sized | بحجم النانو |
| nanotube storage | مخزن أنبوبي دقيق |
| nano-turf-artificial turf technology | تكنولوجيا نانو-سطح-سطح صناعي |
| nanowires | أسلاك نانو |
| naphthalenecarboxylic acid | حمض نفثالين الكربوكسيلي |
| naphthenic hydrocarbons | هيدروكربونات نفثينية |
| naphthyl | نفثيل |
| napthos | مركبات النفثا |
| narcolepsy | غفوات نومية |
| narcotic | مخدر |
| narrow molecular weight distribution | توزيع وزن جزيئي ضيق: توزيع وزن جزيئي في نطاق ضيق |
| narrow molecular weight distribution polymer; a polymer having a narrow molecular weight distribution | بوليمر ذي توزيع وزن جزيئي ضيق |
| narrow patent | براءة ضيقة |
| narrowband | نطاق ضيق |
| nascent | حديث التولد |
| national bank discount brokerage | ناشيونال بنك ديسكونت بروكاريدج |
| national economy | اقتصاد وطني |
| national petroleum refiners association | اَلتَّجَمُّعُ الْوَطَنِيُّ لِمُكَرِّرِي النَّفْطِ |
| national phase of the application | المرحلة الوطنية للطلب |
| national standards | المقاييس الوطنية |
| native | أصلي؛ طبيعي |
| native knowledge | معرفة أبناء البلد. هي المعلومات والمعارف التي تجمعت وتوافرت لدى أهل البلد |
| native people's invention | اختراع خاص بشعب أهلي |
| native refolding | إعادة طي عينة أصلية |
| nato | منظمة حلف شمال الأطلنطي |
| nato medal, with former yougoslavia barette | وسام الناتو مع شارة يوغوسلافيا السابقة |
| natrual gas liquids (ngl) | سوائل الغاز الطبيعي |
| natural bank | ركاما طبيعيا |
| natural clays | الطفلات الطبيعية |
| natural draft evaporative towers | أبراج تبخير ذات سحب طبيعي |
| natural formation | التشكيل "التكوين" الطبيعي |
| natural gas feed | تيار تغذية بالغاز الطبيعي |
| natural gas liquids (ngl) | سوائل الغاز الطبيعي |
| natural nutritive sweetener | عامل تحلية مغذ طبيعي |
| natural rubber | مطاط طبيعي |
| natural sheet silicate | سيليكات طبيعية رقاقاتية |
| natural-draft cooling tower | برج تبريد ذي سحب طبيعي |
| naturally occurring | طبيعي (أو حادث بشكل طبيعي) |
| nausea | غثيان |
| nautical mile | ميل ملاحي |
| naval station | قاعدة بحرية |
| nbc weapons | الأسلحة النووية والبيولوجية والكيميائية |
| n-buli | n- بيوتيل ليثيوم |
| n-butyl | n- بيوتيل |
| n-c8 paraffin | البارافين n-C8 |
| ncc/g | سنتيمتر مكعب عادي / جرام |
| ncci | الشركة القومية للتأمين التعاوني |
| nces | المركز القومي للإحصائيات التعليمية |
| nd | غير محدد |
| ndoc | مركز منظمة الدفاع الوطني |
| ndr | رسالة لم تصل للمرسل اليه |
| near-bit tools | أدوات قرب اللقمة |
| near-pack (near pack premium) | هدية مرافقة للسلعة |
| near-uv cd ; near-uv circular dichroism | ثنائي اللون الدائري بالأشعة فوق البنفسجية القريبة |

| | |
|---|---|
| neat dimethylsulphoxide | داي ميثيل سلفوكسيد صاف |
| neb | منقار، طرف الشيء المستدق |
| nebulizer | رشاش؛ بخاخ |
| necropsy | تشريح |
| necrosis | نخر |
| necrotizing | مميت للخلايا |
| necrotrophic | عائش على نسيج ميت |
| needed power output | قوة التشغيل اللازمة |
| needle disc | قرص إبري |
| needle latch | سقاط إبرية |
| needle valve | صمام إبرة |
| needs | احتياجات |
| nega | نيجاتيف |
| negative cells | خلايا سالبة |
| negative control | عينة مقارنة سالبة |
| negative resting membrane potential | الجهد السالب الكامن للغشاء |
| negative wave | موجة سالبة |
| negatively charged | مشحون بشحنة سالبة |
| neglect of law | عدم احترام القانون |
| negligence | إهمال |
| negligent | مهمل، متهاون |
| negotiate the staircase | تجتاز السلم - تستخدمه |
| negotiations | مفاوضات |
| negotiator | مفاوض |
| neisseria | نيسرية |
| neisseria meningitidis | نيسيريا الالتهاب السحائي |
| nelfinavir | نلفينافير |
| neomorphism | عملية تجدد التبلور |
| neon | عنصر غازي هامد عديم اللون أو الرائحة يستخدم في المصابيح الكهربائية |
| neoplasm | نمو حديث (ورم) |
| neoplasty | تصنيع، ترميم جراحي |
| neoprene | مطاط صناعي |
| neovascularization | تكون الأوعية الدموية الجديدة |
| nephralithiasis | داء الحصوة الكلوية |
| nephron | وحدة كلوية؛ كليون |
| nephropathy | أمراض الكلى بوجه عام؛ الاعتلال الكلوي |
| nephrotic syndrome | متلازمة أمراض الكلي |
| nerve injury | إصابة العصب |
| nesting material | تجهيزات مأوى |
| nest-like structure | بنية تشبه الحزمة المتشابكة |
| net energy gain | صافي مكسب الطاقة |
| net energy output | صافي مخرج طاقة |
| net lease property | عقار بإيجار صافي |
| net meeting | الاجتماع عبر الإنترنت |
| net pay | صافي الإنتاج |
| net result | نتيجة نهائية |
| nether | سفلي أو واقع تحت سطح الأرض |
| nethermost | الأسفل |
| netsky | نيتسكاي: دودة فيروسية خطيرة |
| network | يشبك، شبكة |
| network detection | اكتشاف الشبكة |
| network environment | بيئة شبكة اتصال |

| | |
|---|---|
| network failure | تعطُّل شبكة |
| network failure detection | اكتشاف إخفاق الشبكة |
| network failure recovery | العودة من عطل شبكة |
| network file system, nfs | نظام ملفات الشبكة |
| network hacking system | برنامج لاقتحام الشبكات |
| network infrastructure | البنية التحتية للشبكة |
| network intrusion prevention system | نظام منع اقتحام الشبكة |
| network licensing | ترخيص لشبكة عملاء |
| network management software | برنامج إدارة شبكة |
| network optimizability | إمكانية رفع كفاءة الشبكة إلى المستويات القصوى |
| network pc | جهاز كمبيوتر شخصي متصل بالشبكة |
| network security | أمن الشبكة |
| networked storage | مخزن مربوط بشبكة |
| networking technology | تقنية تشبيك |
| neural circuits | دوائر عصبية |
| neural implants | زراعات عصبية |
| neural tissues | أنسجة عصبية |
| neural tissues functionality | وظيفية الأنسجة العصبية |
| neural tissues stimulation | حث (تحفيز) الأنسجة العصبية |
| neuralgia | ألم عصبي |
| neurobiology | علم الأحياء العصبي |
| neuroblastoma | ورم أرومي عصبي؛ ورم الخلايا البدائية العصبية |
| neuro-chemistry | كيمياء عصبية |
| neurodegenerative disease | مرض التنكس العصبي |
| neurodermitis | الالتهاب الجلدي العصبي |
| neuro-engineering | هندسة عصبية |
| neuro-enhancement system | جهاز لدعم الأعصاب |
| neurofibroma | ورم عصبي ليفي |
| neurogenic | عصبي المنشأ |
| neuro-imaging | تصوير عصبي |
| neuroimmunological | عصبي مناعي |
| neuroleptics | مضادات الذهان |
| neurological disorder | اضطراب عصبي |
| neurologist | مختص بعلم الأعصاب |
| neurology | علم الأعصاب |
| neuro-modulation technology | تقنية تعديل الأعصاب |
| neuron | خلية عصبية |
| neuronal cabling | حزمة عصبية |
| neuronal diseases | أمراض الخلايا العصبية |
| neuronal plactisity | تقويم الأعصاب |
| neurons | أعصاب |
| neuropathic | عصبي مرضي |
| neuropathic pain | الألم العصبي |
| neuropathy | اعتلال عصبي |
| neuro-physiology | الفيسيولوجيا العصبية |
| neuropsychiatric disorder | اضطراب عصبي نفسي |
| neuro-stimulation system | جهاز لحث الأعصاب |
| neuro-technology | تقنية عصبية |
| neurotransmission | إرسال عصبي؛ نقل عصبي |
| neurotransmission plasticity | تقويم أعصاب |
| neurotransmitter | مرسل عصبي |
| neurotrauma | المرض العصبي |
| neurotrophic | مغذي عصبي |
| neurovascular | عصبي وعائي |

| | |
|---|---|
| neutral ph | رقم هيدروجيني متعادل |
| neutral red | صبغ الاحمر المتعادل |
| neutral salt | ملح متعادل |
| neutral water insoluble poly (ethyl acrylate methyl acrylate) copolymer | بوليمر مشترك من بولي (إيثيل أكريلات، ميثيل أكريلات) متعادل غير قابل للذوبان في الماء |
| neutralisation | تعادل |
| neutrality | حيادية |
| neutralize | يعادل |
| neutralized | معادَل؛ تمت معادلته |
| neutralizing potency | فعالية التعادل |
| neutrals | محايدون. تعبير يطلق على المحكمين والوسطاء والمسويين وغيرهم ممن تسند لهم مهمة الفصل البديل في النزاعات |
| neutropenia | نقص الخلايا البيض المتعادلات في الدم |
| neutrophil | خلايا متعادلة بيضاء (المتعادلات البيضاء) |
| new | جديد |
| new south wales | نيو ساوث ويلز = أستراليا |
| new technological breed | سلالة تقنية جديدة |
| new york department of education | وزارة التعليم لولاية نيويورك |
| new york mercantile exchange | بورصة نيويورك التجارية |
| newel post | قائم درابزين |
| newly born invention | اختراع حديث الولادة |
| newly invented | تم اختراعه حديثا |
| newly-purchased memory cards | بطاقات الذاكرة حديثة الشراء |
| newmorphism | تجدد التبلور |
| newness | جدة |
| newness of invention | جدة الاختراع |
| newness requirement | متطلب الجدة |
| news flash | نبأ هام مفاجئ (يقطع الإرسال العادي لإذاعته) |
| news groups | مجموعات إخبارية؛ مجموعات الأخبار |
| newscaster=broadcaster | مذيع النشرة الإخبارية |
| newsprint | ورق الصحف |
| nf | نانو فاراد (وحدة قياس السعة الكهربية) |
| n-free | الوضع المحايد لعصا صندوق التروس |
| nfs | نظام ملفات الشبكة |
| ng | نانو جرام |
| n-glycosylation | ارتباط بالجليكوزيل عند N |
| niacin | حمض نيكوتيني |
| nicotinamide | نيكوتيناميد |
| nicotinic | نيكوتينيك |
| nicotinoyl chloride hydrochloric acid | حمض نيكوتينويل كلوريد هيدروكلوريك |
| night vision | رؤية ليلية |
| night vision device | جهاز رؤية ليلية |
| night vision image intensifier | مكثف للصورة متصل بالرؤية الليلية |
| night vision technology | تقنية الرؤية الليلية |
| nikon microscope | مجهر نيكون: يستخدم بصورة أساسية لعمليات فحص الخلايا والأنسجة المجهزة على شرائح زجاجية باستخدام الضوء النافذ والمنعكس |
| nire | مكتب المعهد القومي للبيئة والموارد (علامات تجارية) |
| nitridation | نترتة |
| nitrided | منترَت: معالج بالنترات |
| nitrification | نترتة |
| nitrification | النترتة أو نترجة |
| nitrification process | عملية النترجة |
| nitrifying microorganism | كائنات حية دقيقة مشبعة بالنترات |
| nitrogen atom-coordinated boron compound represented by the following formul(ii) | مركب بورون متناسق مع ذرة نيتروجين له الصيغة (II) التالية |
| nitrogen blow | نفخ بالنيتروجين |
| nitrogen mustard | الخردل النيتروجيني |
| nitrogen purge | غاز نيتروجين منظف؛ نيتروجين في صورة غاز تنظيف |
| nitrogenated | مُنَتْرَج؛ يحتوي على نيتروجين؛ يحتوي على ذرات نيتروجين |
| nitrogenous fertilizers | أسمدة نيتروجينية |
| nitroglycerin | زيت عديم اللون شديد التفجر |
| nitrosation | إدخال مجموعة النيترو |
| nitrosylation | إدخال مجموعة نيتروسيل |
| nitrous | نيتروز |
| nk cells (natural killer cells) | الخلايا القاتلة الطبيعية |
| nl | لتر عادي |
| nl/l/h | لتر عادي/لتر/ساعة |
| n-linked-heterocycle-substituted alkyl esters of polycyclic amino alcohols | إسترات ألكيل حلقية غير متجانسة بها استبدال مرتبطة عند الموضع N |
| nll | لتر طبيعي لكل لتر |
| nm | نانو مولار |
| nm | نانو متر |
| nm3 | م3 عادي |
| nm3/s | م3 عادي / ث |
| n-methylation | إدخال مجموعة ن- ميثيل |
| nml | مل عادي |
| nmol; nanomoles | نانو مول |
| nmr | الرنين النووي المغناطيسي |
| nms | نظام إدارة الشبكة |
| nni | واجهة شبكة لشبكة |
| no broker clause | البند الخاص بعدم وجود وسطاء. بند تعاقدي يبين عدم اعتماد الطرفين في إبرام العقد وتنفيذه على وسطاء |
| no child left behind act | قانون لم نترك أي طفل |
| no commission clause | البند الخاص بعدم وجود عمولات. بند تعاقدي يبين عدم قيام الطرفين بسداد عمولات فيما يتصل بإبرام العقد وتنفيذه |
| no compound controls | العينات العيارية التي لا تحتوي على مركب |
| no fault divorce | طلاق غير مسبب |
| no fault insurance | تغطية علاجية شاملة - تغطية علاجية غير مشروطة أو غير مقيدة |

| | |
|---|---|
| no rights reserved | لا توجد حقوق محفوظة. عبارة ابتكرها مناهضو حق النشر، ويسعون لتعميم استخدامها كمقابل لاستخدام عبارة "جميع الحقوق محفوظة" التي ابتكرها المؤمنون بحق النشر |
| no third-party beneficiaries clause | البند الخاص بعدم وجود مستفيدين من الغير. بند تعاقدي يبين أن العقد لا يمنح أي حقوق للغير ولا ينطوي على منح مركز قانوني معين للغير |
| noble metal | معدن نفيس |
| nociception | حس الألم |
| nociceptive | مستقبلة الأذية |
| nociceptive pain | الألم الناجم عن ضرر جسدي |
| no-contest clause | بند عدم التحدي. بند يتضمنه اتفاق ترخيص براءة يوافق المرخص له بموجبه ألا يتحدى سلامة البراءة |
| node | عقدة |
| noise | ضوضاء؛ تشوش |
| noise reduction | تقليل التشويش |
| noisy | ضوضائي؛ مليئ بالتشوش |
| nominal | اعتباري |
| nominal number | رقم اسمي |
| non- acceleratable | غير قابل للتسريع |
| non activatable | غير قابل للتفعيل |
| non analogous art | فن غير شبيه |
| non assignable patent | براءة لا يمكن التنازل عنها |
| non belligerence | اللاحرب |
| non contentious patent | براءة غير مثيرة للنزاع |
| non controllable | لا يمكن التحكم فيه |
| non convention arbitral award | حكم تحكيم غير صادر وفقا للمعاهدة. حكم تحكيم غير صادر وفقا لمعاهدة الاعتراف بأحكام التحكيم الأجنبي |
| non ferromagnetic material | مادة غير حديدية مغناطيسية |
| non fluidic chip | شريحة غير سائلة |
| non integrated production | الإنتاج غير المتكامل: وذلك في منشأة لا يرتبط فيها إنتاج الورق أو الكرتون ارتباطا مباشرا بإنتاج اللب |
| non monetary default | إخلال غير مالي |
| non prosecutable patent | براءة لا يمكن إنشاؤها |
| non- registerable patent | براءة غير قابلة للتسجيل |
| non suability | عدم القابلية للمقاضاة. اتسام الفعل بعدم إمكانية مقاضاة فاعلة. |
| non venture-backed company | شركة ذات ظهر غير مخاطر |
| non-adjustable | غير قابل للتكيف |
| non-adsorbable | غير قابل للامتصاص |
| non-alcoholic steatohepatitis | تليف الكبد غير المرتبط بالكحول |
| non-aluminum | لا تحتوي على ألومنيوم |
| non-aluminum inorganic oxide | الأكسيد غير العضوي غير المحتوي على الألومنيوم |
| non-amidated | منزوع الأميد |
| non-analogous prior art | فن سابق غير شبيه |
| non-antibody ; non antibody | جسم غير مضاد |
| non-antibody protein scaffold | سلسلة بروتين متجاورة لجسم غير مضاد |
| non-applicable | غير قابل للتطبيق |
| non-articular inflammatory conditions | الحالات الالتهابية غير المفصلية |
| non-assignability | عدم قابلية الشيء لأن يتم التنازل عنه |
| non-assignability of patent license | عدم قابلية ترخيص البراءة لأن يتم التنازل عنه |
| non-assignable license | ترخيص لا يمكن التنازل عنه |
| non-augmentable | غير قابل للزيادة |
| non-binding arbitration | تحكيم غير ملزم |
| non-budgetary spending | إنفاق خارج الميزانية؛ إنفاق خارج نطاق الميزانية |
| noncapital spending | نفقات غير رأسمالية |
| non-challengability | عدم القابلية للتحدي |
| non-citizen nationals | المواطنون بلا جنسية |
| non-commercializable | غير قابل لأن يوضع موضع تطبيقات تجارية |
| non-commissioned officer | ضابط صف |
| non-commissioned officers | ضابط غير مكلف |
| non-commissioned offices | رتب ضباط صف الجيش |
| non-communicatable | غير قابل للاتصال |
| non-compete | عدم المنافسة |
| non-competition clause | البند الخاص بعدم التنافس. بند تعاقدي يرد في عقود تعيين الموزعين والمسوقين يتضمن الالتزام بعدم المنافسة إذ يلتزم الأصيل بعدم منافسة الوكيل في عمله |
| non-conceivable | غير قابل للتصور |
| non-conceptualizable | غير قابل أن يُبنى عنه مفهوم |
| nonconductor | مادة غير موصلة |
| non-contestability clause | بند عدم القابلية للتحدي والمعارضة |
| non-contiguous portions of the molecule | أجزاء غير متجاورة للجزيء |
| non-covalently bound | غير مرتبطة تساهميا |
| non-destructive testing / inspection | فحص غير متلف |
| non-detectable | غير قابل للرصد |
| non-displayable | غير قابل للعرض |
| non-disposable | غير قابل للتخلص منه |
| non-drivable | غير قابل للقيادة |
| non-durable | غير قابل للتحمل |
| nondurable goods | سلع مفتقرة للقدرة على الاحتمال |
| non-ejectable | غير قابل للإخراج |
| non-eliminatable | غير قابل للعزل |
| non-embeddable | غير قابل للطمر |
| non-enhanceable | غير قابل للتعزيز |
| non-entitlement government funding | التمويل الحكومي غير المدرَج |
| non-envisionable | غير قابل للاستبصار |
| non-erased | غير ممحاة |
| non-exclusive license | ترخيص غير حصري |
| non-exclusive patent license | ترخيص غير حصري لبراءة |
| non-exclusive patent licensing agreement | اتفاق بشأن ترخيص غير حصري براءة ( لبراءة ) |
| non-fat milk | لبن خال من الدهن |
| non-financible invention | اختراع غير قابل للتمويل |

non-fissile غير صفحيه
non-functionable غير قابل للقيام بالوظيفة المنوطة به
non-functional neural tissues أنسجة عصبية غير قائمة بوظيفتها
non-germlined ; non-germline من سلالة غير جرثومية
non-germlined antibody جسم مضاد من سلالة غير جرثومية
non-halide لا يحتوي على هاليد
non-hermetically crimped aluminum pan وعاء ألومنيوم متعرج (تم تعريجه) بدون الكتم بالهواء
non-hire clause البند الخاص بعدم التعيين: بند تعاقدي يتضمن الالتزام بعدم تعيين موظفين تابعين لأحد المتعاقدين
non-hodgkin lymphoma الورم الليمفاوي غير هودكين
non-human species antibody الجسم المضاد من أنواع غير بشرية؛ أجسام مضادة غير بشرية
non-hygroscopicity عدم امتصاص الرطوبة؛ عدم الاسترطاب
non-identifiable لا يمكن التعرف عليه
non-illuminatable غير قابل للإضاءة
non-imageable document مستند غير ممكن تصويره
non-industrializable غير قابل للتصنيع
non-infringable patent براءة غير قابلة للانتهاك
non-infringable technology تقنية غير قابلة للانتهاك
non-inhalable غير قابل للاستنشاق
non-integratable غير قابل للتكامل
non-invasive غير اقتحامي
noninvasive monitoring technology تقنية مراقبة غير اقتحامية
non-invasive physiological sensor جهاز إحساس فيسيولوجي غير اقتحامي
non-invasively على نحو غير اقتحامي
non-inventive worker عامل غير مبتكر
nonionic غير أيوني
non-isolatable غير قابل للعزل
non-laminate غير رقائقاتية
non-legal غير قانوني
nonlimiting غير حصري
non-locatable غير ممكن تعيين موقعه
nonmagnetic material مادة غير قابلة للمغنطيس
non-mainatainable غير قابل للإبقاء عليه
non-manufacturable غير قابل للتصنيع
non-manufacturing patentee صاحب براءة ممتنع عن تصنيعها. صاحب براءة يرفض أن يسمح بتصنيعها والاستفادة منها
non-materializable غير قابل للتحقق
nonmetal اللافلز: عنصر تعوزه خصائص المعادن
nonmetallic لا فلزي أو لا معدني
non-monitizable غير قابل أن يحول إلى نقد
non-monitizable innovation ابتكار غير قابل لأن يصبح ذا قيمة مالية
non-negotiated license ترخيص غير قابل للتفاوض
non-nucleoside hcv ns5b polymerase inhibitors المثبطات غير النيوكليوسيدية لبوليميراز NS5B لـ HCV
non-nucleoside reverse transcriptase inhibitors مثبطات غير نيوكليوسيدية لإنزيم ترانسكربتاز العكسي

nono wires تعبير يطلق على الأسلاك متناهية الصِّغَر
non-obvious invention اختراع غير بديهي
non-obvious subject matter مادة غير بديهية
non-obviousness test اختبار عدم البداهة. اختبار يتم إجراءه لقياس مدى استحقاق الاختراع أن يصدر عنه براءة وذلك من خلال تقييم مدى كون الاختراع غير بديهي
non-operable غير قابل للتشغيل
non-operatable غير قابل للتشغيل
non-optimizable غير قابل أن يحسن لأكبر مدى ممكن
non-originality عدم الأصالة
non-oxidizable غير قابل للأكسدة
non-patent eligible subject matter مادة ليست مؤهلة أن تصدر عنها براءة
non-patent literature أدبيات لا علاقة لها بالبراءات
non-patentable subject matter مادة لا يمكن أن تصدر عنها براءة
non-patented لم يصدر عنه براءة
non-patented idea فكرة لم تصدر عنها براءة
non-piracy clause بند عدم القرصنة. بند يرد في كثير من عقود الملكية الفكرية ينظم مواجهة القرصنة
non-piratable software برنامج لا يمكن قرصنته
non-pollutive غير ملوث
non-pollutive manufacturing تصنيع غير ملوث
non-positionability عدم القابلية للتموضع
non-practicing patent holder صاحب براءة غير ممارس. صاحب براءة لا يستغل براءته
non-practicing patentee صاحب براءة لا يمارس براءته
non-precedential غير سبقي. وصف يطلق على قرار أو رأي قانوني لبيان أنه لا ينطوي على أهمية خاصة تجعله يكتسب صفة السابقة التي يمكن الالتزام بها أو القياس عليها أو الاستئناس بها.
non-precedential opinion رأي غير سبقي. رأي قانوني لا يصح التعامل معه على أنه سابقة يعتد بها أو يلتزم بها أو يقاس عليها أو يستأنس بها
non-provisional غير مؤقت
non-purifiability عدم قابلية الشيء للتنقية
non-reactable غير متفاعل
non-readable code شفرة لا يمكن قراءتها
non-recognizable غير ممكن التعرف عليه
non-reducibility عدم قابلية الشيء لأن يتم وضعه موضع التنفيذ
non-reflectable غير قابل للعكس
non-registerable industrial design نموذج صناعي غير قابل للتسجيل
non-regular surface سطح غير عادي
nonrenewable energy طاقة غير متجددة
non-renewable energy sources مصادر طاقة غير متجددة
non-responders غير المستجيبين
non-retractable غير قابل للسحب
non-retrievable غير قابل للاسترجاع
non-reversable غير قابل للإرجاع

| | |
|---|---|
| non-rotatable | غير قابل للدوران، غير قابل للتعاقب |
| non-runnable software | برنامج لا يمكن تشغيله |
| non-salary budget | ميزانية العمليات خارج إطار الرواتب |
| non-serviceable | غير قابل للخدمة |
| non-sharpenable | غير قابل للشحذ |
| non-simulatable | غير قابل للمحاكاة |
| nonsmall cell lung carcinoma ; non small cell lung carcinoma ; non-small cell lung carcinoma | الورم السرطاني الذي لا يصيب الخلايا الصغيرة بالرئة |
| non-smooth surface | سطح غير ناعم |
| non-solicitation clause | البند الخاص بعدم الاستقطاب. بند تعاقدي يتضمن الالتزام بعدم السعي لاجتذاب موظفين تابعين لأحد المتعاقدين |
| non-stick submarines | غواصات ذات أسطح غير لزجة |
| non-stimulatable | غير قابل للحث (للتحفيز) |
| non-stimulatable neural tissues | أنسجة عصبية غير قابلة للحث |
| non-stop health monitoring | مراقبة صحية غير متوقفة |
| non-stop surveillance | مراقبة غير متوقفة |
| non-structurability | عدم القابلية للهيكلة |
| non-sub licensable license | ترخيص غير قابل للترخيص من الباطن |
| nonsuperimposeable ; nonsuperimposable | غير متراكب |
| non-supportable | غير قابل للدعم |
| non-touchscreenable | لا يمكن إدارته بلمس الشاشة |
| non-toxic organic products | منتجات عضوية غير سامة |
| non-trackable | غير قابل للتتبع |
| non-transactional data | البيانات غير المتعلقة بالمعاملات التجارية |
| non-transferable license | ترخيص غير قابل للتحويل |
| non-transformable | غير قابل للتحول |
| non-upgradable solutions | حلول غير قابلة للتحسين |
| non-vaporizable | غير قابل للتبخر |
| non-verifiable | غير قابل للتحقق |
| non-visible | غير مرئي |
| non-visualizable | غير قابل للرؤية |
| non-waverable license | ترخيص غير قابل للتنازل عنه |
| non-wearable | غير قابل للارتداء |
| non-wired | غير سلكي |
| non-workable | غير قابل للإعمال |
| nootropic | منشط ذهني |
| nopatent activity | نشاط غير براءاتي. نشاط غير منصب على براءة |
| norepinephrine | نور أبينفرين |
| norepinephrine (ne) | نورأبينفرين (NE) |
| norm | معيار |
| normal | عادي |
| normal catalytic cracking feedstock oil | زيت خام تغذية تقليدي للتكسير الحفزي |
| normal catalytic cracking heavy feedstock oil | زيت خام تغذية ثقيل تقليدي للتكسير الحفزي |
| normal fault | الصدع العادي |
| normal human neuronal progenitor cells | خلايا عصبية أولية بشرية طبيعية |
| normal incidence | السقوط العمودي |
| normal mode | وضع العرض العادي: مشاهده واجهه البرنامج بشكلها المعتاد |
| normal operation | تشغيل عادي |
| normal throughput of a cell | الناتج العادي |
| normal to curve | عَمُودٌ عَلَى مُنْحَنٍ |
| normal to plane | عَمُودٌ عَلَى مُسْتَوٍ |
| normal to the direction of | عمودية على اتجاه |
| normalization | تطبيع |
| normalize | يطبع، يجعل الأمر طبيعيا |
| normalize ; normalise sth to/with sth | يضبط أو يوائم كذا على كذا |
| normalized residuals | مواد متبقية عادية؛ بقايا عادية |
| normalizer | مطبع |
| normally liquid and normally solid hydrocarbons | هيدروكربونات سائلة بطبيعتها وصلبة بطبيعتها |
| normals | مستوى معياري؛ عيار؛ وسط؛ قاعدة |
| normoglycemia | سكر الدم عند المستوى الطبيعي |
| north atlantic treaty organization | منظمة حلف شمال الأطلنطي |
| north magnetic poles | أقطاب مغناطيسية شمالية |
| northern blot | بقعة نورزرن |
| northern blots | بقع نورثرن |
| north-north magnetic repulsion force | قوة التنافر المغناطيسية الشمال-الشمال |
| nose | مقدمة |
| nose of the tread of the step | الجزء المكشوف أو الجزء البارز من الجزء الأفقي العلوي من درجة السلم |
| nose wheel | عجلة المقدمة |
| nosepiece | مأنفة: قطعة من الدرع لوقاية الأنف |
| nosepiece; nose-piece | قطعة أمامية |
| nosocomial | مستوصفي؛ متعلق بالمستشفى |
| not ermetic sample pan | قنينة العينة محكمة الإغلاق |
| not insignificant reduction | تخفيض لا يُستهان به |
| notarial certificate | شهادة توثيق |
| notary | الموثق العام |
| notary public | الشهر العقاري؛ موثق عمومي؛ محرر عقود؛ الموثق العام |
| notation | ترميز |
| notch | فتحة |
| notch impact resistance | مقاومة صدمة النقر |
| notched bar impact bend test | اختبار ثني صدم قضيب مثلوم |
| notebook computer | كمبيوتر دفتري |
| notice | يلاحظ، يعلق على، إخطار، إنذار إشعار، إعلام |
| notice of agreement | إخطار بشأن عقد اتفاق |
| notice of commencement | إخطار بشأن البدء. إخطار يقوم المقاول بإرساله لرب العمل يحيطه بموجبه ببدئه العمل |
| notice of default | إخطار بشأن خلل. إخطار يخطر به متعاقد المتعاقد الآخر بحدوث خلل من جانبه، وفي بعض الأحيان يتضمن الإخطار ما يفيد دعوة الطرف المخل لإزالة الخلل خلال مدة معينة |
| notice of renewal of agreement | إخطار بشأن تجديد اتفاق |

| | |
|---|---|
| notice of termination of agreement | إخطار بشأن إنهاء اتفاق. |
| notices clause | البند الخاص بالإخطارات. بند تعاقدي يبين آلية تبادل الإخطارات والإشعارات والإعلانات الرسمية وغير الرسمية بين طرفي العقد |
| novak lo-mount carry sights | أجهزة تسديد من نوع نوفاك لو ماونت كاري |
| novel compounds iv | مركبات جديدة ذات الصيغة IV |
| novel cultured inner cell mass (cicm) | سلالات خلايا ذات كتلة خلوية داخلية مستزرعة جديدة |
| novel idea | فكرة جديدة |
| novel invention | اختراع جديد |
| novel substituted amines | أمينات جديدة بها استبدال |
| novelty assessment | تقييم الجِدَّة |
| novelty of the amended claims | الجديد في عناصر الحماية المعدلة |
| novelty requirement | متطلب الجدة |
| novelty search | البحث عن الجدة. يعد البحث عن الجدة مرحلة من مراحل إنجاز الاختراع |
| novelty test | اختبار الجدة. اختبار يتم إجراءه لقياس مدى استحقاق الاختراع أن يصدر عنه براءة وذلك من خلال تقييم مدى الجدة التي ينطوي عليها الاختراع |
| n-oxidation | إدخال الأكسجين على ذرة N |
| noxious | ضار |
| nozzle | فوهة؛ فتحة؛ ثقب |
| nozzle | فوهة، فم خرطوم |
| n-propyl | ن - بروبيل |
| nri | مثبطات إعادة امتصاص النورأدرينالين الانتقائية |
| nrt-vbr | معدل مجموعة بتات متغير لوقت غير حقيقي |
| nsaid | عقار غير ستيروديدي مضاد للالتهاب |
| nsap | نقطة وصول لخدمات الشبكة |
| nsre | اختبار المقاييس المرجعي الجديد |
| n-substituted imino | إيمينو به استبدال على ذرة N |
| nt | نيوكليوتيد |
| nta | حمض نيتريلو تراي أسيتيك |
| ntl | ليس أكثر من |
| ntp | نيوكليوسيد تراي فوسفات |
| nub | عقدة أو كتلة |
| nuclear chemistry | كيمياء نووية |
| nuclear detterence force | قوة ردع نووية |
| nuclear device | وسيلة أو سلاح |
| nuclear energy | طاقة نووية |
| nuclear fission | الانشطار النووي |
| nuclear magnetic resonance spectroscopy ("nmr") | قياس طيف الرنين المغناطيسي النووي ("NMR") |
| nuclear moderating material | مواد التهدئة النووية |
| nuclear physics | فيزياء نووية |
| nuclear power | طاقة نووية |
| nucleated | منوّاة؛ ذات نواة |
| nucleating agent | عامل تنوي |
| nucleation | تنوي: تكوين نواة |
| nuclei | نُوى |
| nucleic acid | حمض نووي |
| nucleobases | قواعد نووية |
| nucleophile | أليف النواة |
| nucleophilic | آلفة للنواة |
| nucleoside reverse transcriptase inhibitors | مثبطات نيوكليوسيدية لإنزيم ترانسكربتاز العكسي |
| Nucleosome | نيوكليوسوم |
| nucleotide | نيوكليوتيد |
| nucleus accumbens | النواة المتكئة |
| nuclide | نويدة |
| nude mouse | فأر منزوع الشعر |
| nude mouse xenograft | فأر منزوع الشعر مطعم بطعم خارجي |
| num lock | مفتاح الأرقام |
| number average degree of polymerization (dp) | المتوسط العددي لدرجة البلمرة (DP) |
| number average molecular weight; number-average molecular weight | متوسط عدد الوزن الجزيئي؛ الوزن الجزيئي بناء على متوسط العدد |
| number of interlaces | عدد التشابكات |
| number of print | عدد مرات الطباعة |
| numbering | الترقيم |
| numbers or bullets | أرقام أو علامات للتنبيه |
| numeric pad | لوحة الارقام (الجزء الخاص بالأرقام في اللوحة) |
| numerical ranges | قيم المدى العددية |
| nursery | مشتل |
| nurture | ينشئ، يرعى، تنشئة، رعاية |
| nurturing | رعاية |
| nut | صمولة |
| nut driver | مفك صمولة |
| nylon | نيلون |
| nylon thread nuts | صواميل ذات أسنان ملولبة من النايلون |

# O

| | |
|---|---|
| oao | المراصد الفلكية السيارة |
| oapi | المنظمة الأفريقية للملكية الفكرية |
| obav | التوافر الحيوي الفمي |
| obesity | السمنة |
| object | يعترض، شيء |
| object d'art film | فيلم على مستوى؛ فيلم بمثابة تحفة فنية |
| object detection | كشف الأشياء |
| object of the present invention | هدف الاختراع الحالي |
| object oriented programming (oop) language | لغة برمجة الكائنات؛ لغة البرمجة الموجَّهة بالكائنات: ظهرت الحاجة لتوحيد نظام البرمجة لدى المبرمجين لكي يكون الكود ديناميكي وسلس وله قواعد وشروط ولكي لا يخرج كل مصمم بأفكار بعيدة عن الهدف المقصود فظهر مفهوم لغة برمجة الكائنات |
| objection | اعتراض |
| objection to the drawings | اعتراض على الرسومات. اعتراض فاحص طلب البراءة على الرسومات المرفقة الذي قد يكون أحد أسبابه عدم وضوحها |
| objections | اعتراضات |
| objective invention marketability | إمكانية تسويق لاختراع محددة تحديدا موضوعيا |
| objective lens | العدسة الشيئية |
| objective or return function | دالة هدف أو عائد |
| objects of the invention | أهداف الاختراع |
| obligations | واجبات |
| oblique | منحرف؛ مائل |
| oblique angle | زاوية مائلة |
| oblique perspective | شكل منظوري مائل |
| obliterate | يبيد (المنشآت، الأماكن، المواقع إلخ) |
| obscene content detection | كشف المحتوى البذئ |
| observable | قابل للملاحظة |
| observations | ملاحظات |
| observe | يلاحظ |
| observed | ملاحظ |
| obsessive compulsion | وسواس قهري |
| obsessive compulsive disorder | اضطراب وسواسي قهري |
| obsolete invention | اختراع ذو قيمة منتهية، اختراع عفى عليه الزمن |
| obsolete technology | تقنية ما عادت ذات جدوى |
| obsolete technology infrastructure | بنية تقنية منتهية الجدوى |
| obstacle detecting sensor | جهاز إحساس كاشف للعقبات |
| obstrcution of justice | إعاقة سير العدالة |
| obtuse angle | زاوية منفرجة |
| obvious | واضح |
| obvious invention | اختراع بديهي. لا تصدر براءة عن الاختراع البديهي. |
| obviousness | وضوح |
| occlud | يعترض؛ يسد الطريق على |
| occlusion | إنسداد |
| occult blood | دم خفي أو مستتر |
| occupation forces | قوات الاحتلال |
| occupational (industrial) disease | الأمراض الصناعية المتوطنة |
| ocean energy | طاقة محيط |
| ocean thermal energy conversion | تحويل طاقة المحيط الحرارية |
| ochres | أكاسيد الحديديك |
| ocr | التعرف على الحروف الضوئية |
| octahedral | ثماني |
| octane | أوكتان |
| octane number | العدد الأوكتاني |
| ocular inflammation | التهابات العين |
| ocular lens | العدسة العينية |
| od | الكثافة البصرية |
| odbc | موصلية قاعدة البيانات المفتوحة |
| oedema | استسقاء؛ أوديما |
| oem | صانع المعدة الأصلي |
| of interest | محل الاهتمام؛ المعني؛ المقصود |
| ofdm | نظام إرسال مضاعف بتقسيم التردد العمودي- الإرسال المتعدد بالتقسيم المتعامد للتردد-الإرسال (التعاقبي) المتعدد بتقسيم التردد المتعامد- نظام الترددات المتعامدة -مضاعفة الإرسال بالتقسيم التعامدي -مضاعفة الإرسال بتقسيم التردد المتعامد: تقنية تعديل تستخدم |
| ofdma | الوصول المتعدد بتقسيم التردد المتعامِد |
| off gas/off-gas | غاز منصرف |
| off highway multiplexing technology | تقنية الإرسال المتعدد خارج الطريق السريع |
| off loading | التخلي عن حمولة |
| off loading unused patents | التخلي عن البراءات غير المستخدمة |
| off peak concentration | التركيز المنحرف عن القمة |
| off rate | معدل الاستبعاد؛ معدل التوقف |
| off rate constant | معدل فصل ثابت |
| off shore platform | منصة بحرية |
| off site paper records storage | مخزن سجلات ورقية خارج الموقع |
| offence | خروج على القانون |
| offence of contempt | جرم الإزدراء |
| offend | يأثم، يذنب |
| offended | منزعج |
| offender | خارج على القانون؛ متعد |
| offense | تعد، إزعاج، إثم، ذنب |
| offenses | تعديات |
| offensive | عدواني، هجومي |
| offensiveness | هجومية |
| office automation system | نظام جعل المكاتب أوتوماتيكية |
| officer | مسئول |

| | |
|---|---|
| officer cadet | طالب عسكري |
| offline | أثناء عدم الاتصال بالإنترنت. العكس online |
| offline analysis | بعيدا عن خط الإنتاج |
| off-line coating | طلاء الزجاج بعيداً عن خط الإنتاج: العملية التي يتم بواسطتها طلاء أي قطعة من قطع الزجاج بعيداً عن خط الإنتاج |
| offline patent auction | مزاد براءات منعقد عبر الاتصال بالشبكة |
| offline web applications | تطبيقات عنكبوتية خارج إطار الاتصال بالشبكة البينية |
| off-patent drug | دواء زالت براءته |
| off-rate ranking | فئات خارج المعدل |
| offset printing | الطباعة الملساء؛ الأوفسيت |
| offshore | بحرية |
| offshore fisheries | مصايد أعالي البحار |
| offside | تسلل |
| offsite storage | مخزن خارج الموقع |
| offspring plants | نباتات نسل |
| off-tastes | المذاقات غير المستساغة |
| off-topic | خارج عن الموضوع؛ غير متعلق بالموضوع |
| off-white solid ; offwhite solid | مادة صلبة لونها أبيض مصفر |
| ogt | مناقصة عامة مفتوحة |
| oil | يزيت، نفط |
| oil bearing formation | تكوين حاوٍ للنفط |
| oil economy | اقتصاد نفط |
| oil extraction | استخراج النفط |
| oil fix | السعي وراء البترول |
| oil leak | تسرب نفطي |
| oil pressure lifting device | جهاز إزالة ضغط نفطي |
| oil recovery | إستخلاص النفط: عندما يتم بفصله من مكونات أخرى في التكوين أو عند استخراجه من التكوين مباشرةً |
| oil sands | رمال النفط (رمال حاوية للنفط) |
| oil sands reservoir | خزان الرمال النفطية |
| oil shale | الطين الصفحي النفطي |
| oil water contact | حلقة تغذية مرتدة |
| oil water contact (owc) | تماس البترول والماء |
| oil-, organic- and wax-bleaching chemicals | مواد كيميائية زيتية وعضوية وشمعية للتبييض |
| oilfield forecasts | خطط حقل النفط |
| oilfield operations | عمليات حقل النفط؛ عمليات بحقل النفط |
| oiliholics | مدمني البترول؛ مدمني النفط |
| oiling | التلميع بالزيت |
| oily-brown | بني مزيت |
| ointment | مرهم |
| ojt | تدريب على رأس العمل |
| old world primates | رئيسيات العالم القديم |
| oleaginous | زيتية؛ زيتي |
| olefinic | أولفيني |
| olefins | أولفينات |
| oleic acid | حمض الأولييك |
| oleophobic | طارد للزيت؛ غير آلف للزيت |
| oligo | قلة- ندرة |
| oligo(dt) primed cdna | cDNA المستحث بوحدات قليلة من (dt) |
| oligomer | أوليجومر |
| oligomerisation | تكوين أوليجومرات |
| oligomictic conglomerates | مدملك وحيد الحصيات |
| oligonucleotide | أوليجو نيوكليوتيد؛ قليل النيوكليوتيد |
| oligopeptide | أوليجوببتيد |
| oligopolistic business entities | الكيانات التجارية للقلة الاحتكارية |
| oligos | قليلات الوحدات؛ وحدات الأوليجو |
| oligosaccaride | قليل السكاريد |
| olivetol | أوليفيتول |
| olivine | الأولوفين |
| olivopontocerebellar | زيتوني جسري مخيخي |
| omental | ثربي |
| on a fault | في حالة حدوث عطل |
| on rate constant | معدل وصل ثابت |
| on recognizance | بناء على تعهد |
| on the order of | في حدود؛ في مدى |
| on-bit tools | أدوات على اللقمة |
| on-board; onboard; on board | داخلي؛ محلي |
| once through ; once-through | وحيد الدورة |
| once-through steam generator | مولد بخار ماء وحيد الدورة |
| oncocytoma | ورم غدي نكفي |
| oncogenic | مكون الورم |
| one man invention | اختراع من قبل شخص واحد |
| one open disulfide bond | رابطة ثنائي كبريتيد مفتوحة واحدة |
| one part moisture cure system | نظام معالجة بالرطوبة من جزء واحد |
| one purpose invention | اختراع لغرض واحد |
| one station tablet press | مكبس أقراص سعة قرص واحد |
| one-person license | ترخيص صادر لشخص واحد |
| one-pot | بوتقة واحدة |
| one-shot tests | اختبارات المرة الواحدة |
| online | مباشر؛ في موقع خط الإنتاج؛ فوري؛ متصل بالإنترنت؛ |
| online | مباشر؛ فورا؛ أثناء الاتصال بالإنترنت |
| online auction website | موقع شبكي لعقد مزادات عبر الشبكة في حالة الاتصال. وعادة ما يتم عرض البراءات المعروضة للمزاد عبر هذه المواقع |
| online circular | نشرة دورية على الإنترنت؛ نشرة إعلانية فورية؛ إعلان فوري |
| on-line coating | طلاء الزجاج على خط الإنتاج : العملية التي يتم فيها طلاء ألواح الزجاج أثناء مرورها على خط الإنتاج |
| online gaming | القمار على الإنترنت |
| online inventor collaboration | تعاون فيما بين مخترعين تباعد بينهم مسافة |
| online patent auction | مزاد براءات منعقد خارج إطار الاتصال بالشبكة |
| online patent search | قاعدة بيانات البحث المتصل |

| | |
|---|---|
| database | |
| | بالبراءة على الخط الحيوي |
| online piracy | قرصنة مشبوكة |
| online services | شركات خدمات مباشرة |
| online visibility | كون الشيء مرئيا على الشبكة في حالة الاتصال |
| onset of flocculation | بدء الدمج |
| onshore/offshore drilling | الحفر والتنقيب في البر/الحفر والتنقيب في البحر |
| onsite paper records storage | مخزن سجلات ورقية بالموقع |
| onsite storage | مخزن بالموقع |
| oocytes | خلايا بيضية |
| oolitic limestone | الحجر الجيري البطروخي |
| oolitic texture | النسيج البطروخي |
| opec fund for international development | صندوق الأوبك للتنمية الدولية |
| open | يفتح |
| open book salary charge | رسوم غير محددة |
| open hole | ثقب مكشوف |
| open innovation | ابتكار مفتوح. مفهوم مفاده وجوب اعتماد الشركات على الابتكارات الخارجية الموجودة في السوق لدى شركات أخرى بجانب اعتمادها على الابتكارات الداخلية حتى يكون التطوير التقني حقيقيا، وأنه ليس في مستطاع الشركات اليوم الاعتماد على الابتكارات الداخلية فقط |
| open loop | حلقة مفتوحة |
| open order book | دفتر الأوامر المفتوحة |
| open session | جلسة علنية |
| open source license | ترخيص صادر وفقا لنموذج مبادرة المصدر المفتوح. ترخيص شديد المرونة ويعطي صلاحيات واسعة للمرخص له يختلف عن الترخيص التقليدي المؤسس على نظام حق النشر التقليدي، قامت بإعداده والترويج له مبادرة المصدر المفتوح |
| open source software | برامج المصدر المفتوح الحاسبية. برامج حاسبية يتم ترخيصها ترخيصا شديد المرونة يعطي المرخص له صلاحيات واسعة في التعامل مع البرنامج الحاسبي وذلك وفقا لقواعد المصدر المفتوح التي أسستها مبادرة المصدر المفتوح والتي تختلف عن قواعد الترخيص التقليدية التي تنطلق من نظام حق النشر التقليدي |
| opening | الافتتاح؛ فتحة |
| opening speech | خطبة وكيل النيابة الافتتاحية لقضية |
| opening up | الانفتاح، فتح الاقتصاد |
| open-label study ; open label study | دراسة معلومة للطرفين: دراسة العلاج بها معلوم للطبيب والمريض |
| open-label study; open label study: an open-label study is a drug clinical trial in which both the researchers and the patient know the identity of the test drug | دراسة معلومة للطرفين؛ دراسة العلاج بها معلوم للطرفين |

| | |
|---|---|
| open-loop nitrogen heat pump | مضخة حرارية للنيتروجين الذي يتدفق في الحلقة المفتوحة |
| open-source | المصدر المفتوح |
| operability | قابلية الشيء للتشغيل |
| operable | قابل للتشغيل، قابل للجراحة |
| operable to | قادر على |
| operably | بشكل فعال؛ على نحو تشغيلي [ميكانيكا؛ صناعة؛ إلخ] |
| operatable invention | اختراع قابل للتشغيل |
| operate | يشغل |
| operate in conjunction with | يعمل جنبا إلى جنب مع؛ يعمل بالاشتراك مع |
| operating | تشغيل |
| operating and indicating mechanism | آلية التشغيل والبيان |
| operating device (even referring to control device for the sake of differentiation) | وسية تشغيل |
| operating envelop | غلاف تشغيل محدود جدا |
| operating pressure | ضغط تشغيل |
| operating system | نظام تشغيل |
| operating system | نظام تشغيل |
| operation | عملية تشغيل؛ عملية؛ تشغيل |
| operation guide | دليل التشغيل |
| operation indicator | مؤشر التشغيل |
| operation library | مجموعة عملية تشغيل |
| operation robot | روبوت عمليات. روبوت يتم توظيفه في إجراء عمليات طبية |
| operation temperature | درجة حرارة التشغيل |
| operational definition | تعريف إجرائي |
| operational efficiency | فعالية عملياتية (العمليات) |
| operational optimization | تحسين العمليات للأمثل |
| operative to | يعمل على |
| operatively | بصورة فعالة؛ بشكل مؤثر |
| operatively | على نحو تشغيلي |
| operator | مشغل (بشري): (شخص) قائم بالتشغيل |
| operator | مشغل (آلي): وحدة تشغيل |
| operator | مشغل |
| opiate | مستحضر الأفيون: مسكّن يُحضر من الأفيون، مثل المورفين أو الكودين. |
| opinion | رأي |
| opioid | أفيوني المفعول؛ شبيه الأفيون |
| opioid agonist | مادة مساعدة أفيونية المفعول؛ عامل مساعد أفيوني المفعول |
| opioid analgesic | مسكن أفيوني المفعول |
| opioid controlled release matrix formualtion | صيغة قالب أفيوني المفعول ذات إطلاق مقنن (ام بالشرح: صيغة قالب ذات إطلاق مقنن تشتمل على شبيه أفيون) |
| opioid salt | ملح أفيوني المفعول |
| opportunistic enough to make hay when the sun shone | اغتنموا الفرص في الأوقات المناسبة |

| | |
|---|---|
| opposing | في الجهة المقابلة لـ |
| opposing forces | القوى المتضادة |
| opposing sidwalls protrusions | نتوءات الحوائط الجانبية المتقابلة |
| ops ; ops | عمليات |
| opsoclonus myoclonus ataxia syndrome ; opsoclonus myoclonus syndrome | متلازمة ترجرج العيون والإختلاج العضلي |
| opsoklonus | رأرأة العين |
| opsonophagocyte | خلية ملتهمة كبيرة أوبسونية |
| optic fibre | ليفة ضوئية |
| optic neuritis | التهاب العصب البصري |
| optic physics | فيزياء بصرية |
| optical | ضوئي |
| optical antipode | متقابل ضوئي |
| optical antipodes | عكسيات تقاطب ضوئية |
| optical density | الكثافة البصرية |
| optical disc | قرص ضوئي |
| optical disc and signal piracy | القرصنة على الأقراص البصرية وخدمة التلفزيون المدفوع |
| optical fiber carrier | حامل ألياف ضوئية |
| optical fire detector | كاشف حريق بصري |
| optical imaging sensing technology | تقنية التصوير البصري ذو الإحساس |
| optical instrument | أدوات نظر |
| optical isomers | أيزومرات ضوئي |
| optical lithography | الطباعة بالقوالب الضوئية |
| optical microscope | الميكروسكوب الضوئي |
| optical purity | النقاء الضوئي |
| optical rotation | الدوران الضوئي؛ تدوير ضوئي |
| optical spectra | أطياف بصرية |
| optical zoom | تكبير/تصغير بصري |
| optically | ضوئيًا |
| optics | عناصر بصرية: العناصر المكونة لجهاز وتتألف من مرايا وضوء إلخ |
| optics | علم البصريات |
| optimal | الأمثل |
| optimised manipulated variables | متغيرات المعالجة المحسنة بشكل أمثل |
| optimizabaility | رفع الكفاءة إلى المستويات القصوى |
| optimizable | قابل أن يتم تحسين أدائه لأقصى مدى ممكن |
| optimization | تحسين أداء الشيء لأقصى مدى ممكن |
| optimization software | برنامج رفع كفاءة للمستويات القصوى |
| optimization solutions | حلول لرفع الكفاءة إلى المستويات القصوى |
| optimize | يحسن أداء الشيء لأقصى مدى ممكن |
| optimized | ذو أداء تم تحسينه لأقصى مدى ممكن |
| optimizer | محسن أداء الشيء لأقصى مدى ممكن |
| option clause | بند الخيار. بند يعطي الناشر حق شراءكتاب المؤلف اللاحق أو أن يقدم عرضاً لشرائه |
| optionally substituted bicyclic, carbocyclic or heterocyclic ring system | نظام حلقي ثنائي أو كربوني أو غير متجانس به استبدال اختياري؛ نظام حلقي ثنائي الحلقات أو كربوني الحلقات أو غير متجانس الحلقات به استبدال اختياري |
| optionally substituted heteroaryl ring | حلقة أريل غير متجانسة بها استبدال اختياري |
| optionally substituted with | بها استبدال اختياري بـ |
| optometer | مبصار، أداة لقياس البصر |
| optometric | مبصاري، متعلق بالمبصارية |
| optometrist | مبصاري، متخصص في المبصارية |
| optometry | مبصارية، قياس مدى البصر بالمبصار. |
| oral | عن طريق الفم |
| oral gavage | مسبار فمي |
| oral gold | مركب الذهب الفمي |
| oral gold preparations | مستحضرات الذهب الفمية |
| order | أمر |
| order for adverse publicity | أمر بنشر اعلان مضاد |
| order of documents clause | بند ترتيب المستندات. بند تعاقدي يبين - في حالة وجود عقود مكملة للعقد المعني - مرتبة قوة المستندات والعقود في مواجهة بعضها البعض لاسيما إذا ما حصل تناقض بين بنود واردة في أحد العقود وبنود واردة في عقد آخر. ويكثر ورود هذا البند في عقود المقاولات |
| order of malta | وسام مالطة العسكري |
| ordered cascade | تسلسل مرتب |
| ordinary registration clause | بند التسجيل العادي |
| ordinate | إحْدَاثِيٌّ صادي (رأسي) |
| organic acid salts | أملاح الأحماض العضوية |
| organic amine salts | أملاح أمينية عضوية |
| organic chemistry | كيمياء عضوية |
| organic coating (sizing) | تغليف عضوي (أي تغرية) |
| organic components | عناصر عضوية |
| organic compounds | مركبات عضوية |
| organic elemental analyzer (oea) | جهاز التحليل العنصري العضوي؛ جهاز تحليل العناصر العضوية |
| organic fertilizers | أسمدة عضوية |
| organic material | مادة عضوية |
| organic mulch | مهاد عضوية من مِهاد من النُّشارة أو التبن |
| organic phase | الطور العضوي |
| organically formed sediments | صخور رسوبية عضوية النشأة |
| organics = combined organic extracts | خلاصات عضوية مجمعة؛ الطبقات العضوية المجمعة |
| organisms | كائنات حية |
| organization | منظمة |
| organization of arab petroleum exporting countries, opec | منظمةالدول العربية المصدرة للبترول |
| organization of islamic conference | منظمة المؤتمر الإسلامي |
| organization of petroleum exporting countries, opec | الدول المصدرة للبترول |
| organized intellectual property crime | الجريمة المنظمة في مجال الملكية الفكرية |
| organoaluminum compound | مركب الألومنيوم العضوي |
| organo-aluminum compounds; | مركبات الألومنيوم |

| | |
|---|---|
| organo-al compounds | العضوية |
| organoheteryl group | مجموعة عضوية غير متجانسة |
| organolead reagent | مادة تفاعل عبارة عن رصاص عضوي |
| organoleptic | منبه عضوي |
| organoleptically | من حيث التأثير العضوي |
| organometallic | عضوية فلزية |
| organothiol | ثيول عضوي |
| organothiolate | مركبات ثيولات عضوي |
| organyl group | مجموعة استبدال عضوية |
| orientations | اتجاهات؛ أوضاع |
| orientations | أوضاع |
| oriented mind | ذهن ذو وجهة |
| oriented society | مجتمع ذو وجهة |
| oriented thinking | تفكير ذو توجه |
| orifice | فوهة؛ فتحة؛ ثقب |
| original | أصيل، أصلي |
| original | أصلي، جديد، مبتكر، أصل، نسخة أصلية، مؤلف، أثر فني أصلي |
| original thought | فكرة أصيلة، فكر أصيل. تعد الفكرة الأصيلة واحدة من الأسس التي يقوم عليها صرح الاختراع |
| originality | أصالة |
| originality | الأصلية، كون الشيء أصليا، جدة، طرافة، أصالة، إبداع |
| originality of thought | أصالة الفكر ـ أصالة الفكرة |
| originate in | ينشأ في |
| o-ring; o ring seal | مانع تسريب حلقي على شكل O |
| orphan receptor | مستقبل غير محمي |
| orthoconglomerates | مدملك نقي |
| orthogonal | عمودية؛ متعامدة |
| orthogonal frequency division multiple access (ofdma) system | نظام الوصول المتعدد بتقسيم التردد المتعامد OFDMA |
| orthogonal frequency division multiplexing | نظام إرسال مضاعف بتقسيم التردد العمودي - الإرسال المتعدد بالتقسيم المتعامد للتردد - الإرسال (التعاقبي) المتعدد بتقسيم التردد المتعامد - نظام الترددات المتعامدة - مضاعفة الإرسال بالتقسيم التعامدي - مضاعفة الإرسال بتقسيم التردد المتعامد: تقنية تعديل تستخدم |
| orthogonality | تعامد |
| orthogonally multiplexed | أرسل بطريقة الإرسال التعاقبي المتعدد المتعامد |
| orthogonally protected acid | حمض محمي عموديا |
| ortholog | جينات متحدة الأصل |
| orthologous | المشابهة عند الموضع أورثو |
| orthologue | جينات تشبه في وظيفتها الأنواع المسئولة عن الطور والارتقاء |
| orthopedic problems | المشاكل المتعلقة بجراحات تقويم العظام |
| orthopedic surgery | الجراحة المتعلقة بجراحة تقويم العظام |
| orthoquartzite | الكوارتز النقي |
| orthorhombic | معينة مستقيمة |
| orthosteric | متماثل التجاسم |
| os | نظام تشغيل |
| osa | بنية النظم المفتوحة |
| osat | اختبار القبول التشغيلي للنظام |
| oscars | الأوسكار |
| oscillate | يتذبذب، يترجح |
| oscillation | ذبذبة؛ تذبذب، ترجح |
| oscillator | مذبذب |
| osi | واجهة النظم المفتوحة |
| osmium | أوزميم |
| osmolality | حالة تناضح |
| osmolarity | تناضح؛ تناضحية |
| osmolarity | درجة تناضح |
| osmosis | تناضح، أسموزية |
| osp | تجهيزات خارجية |
| osteoarthitis | التهاب عظمي مفصلي |
| osteoarthritis | التهاب المفاصل العظمي؛ الالتهاب العظمي المفصلي |
| osteoblast | نَاقِضَةُ العَظْم |
| osteomyelitis | التهاب نخاع العظم |
| osteonecrosis | تنخر العظم |
| osteopenia | قلة العظم |
| osteopetrosis | تحجر العظام |
| osteoporosis | هشاشة العظام؛ تخلل العظم؛ مسامية العظام |
| osteosarcoma | الورم السرطاني العظمي |
| other dispositions may be allowed | ترتيبات أخرى |
| otitis media | التهاب الأذن الوسطى |
| otl standards | معايير نقص قدرة التحويل |
| ouiwg | مجموعة عمل لواجهة نظام التشغيل والمستخدم |
| ounce | أونس (أوقية) |
| our agrifood value advantage | القيمة المميزة لمنتجاتنا الزراعية |
| out of court settlement | تسوية خارج المحكمة |
| out of print clauses | مادة نفاذ الكمية المطبوعة. المادة التي تبين كيفية تعامل الناشر والمؤلف عند نفاذ الكمية المطبوعة. وتختلف الاجتهادات في تحديد المقصود بنفاد الكمية المطبوعة وهل المقصود به انتهاء الكمية نهائيا أم مجرد خروج الكتاب من كتالوج الناشر. |
| outboard motor | محرك خارجي |
| outbound | متجه للخارج |
| outbreak | هجمة واسعة |
| outbred ; out-bred | مهجن خارجيا |
| outcome driven innovation | ابتكار تسوقه قاطرة المحصلة |
| outer dosage component | مكون جرعة خارجي |
| outer loop | دائرة خارجية |
| outer space related patent | براءة متصلة بالفضاء الخارجي. |
| outer support | الدعامة الخارجية |
| outermost | الأبعد للخارج |
| outernet | شبكة خارجية |
| outflank | يلتف حول العدو |
| outflow | تدفق خارج |
| outlet opening | فتحة للإخراج |
| outlet pressure | ضغط الخروج؛ الانفلات |
| outlet valve ; outlet channel | صمام خروج؛ منفذ خروج |
| out-licensing business model | نموذج تجاري يعتمد على منح التراخيص للغير |

| | |
|---|---|
| outline of submissions | مجمل الوثائق المقدمة |
| output | يخرج |
| output a, b, etc. | مخرج |
| output device | جهاز مخرجات |
| output end | طرف إخراج |
| output voltage | جهد الخرج |
| outputs | نتائج - مخرجات |
| outputted signal | الإشارة الخارجة |
| outsource | التعاقد الخارجي: يعطي العمل لمؤسسة أخرى تقوم به لضغط النفقات |
| outsourcing | توريد خارجي |
| outsourcing | تعاقد خارجي |
| ovarian cancer | سرطان المبيض |
| ovariectomized | مستأصل منه المبيض |
| over a finite time interval | على مدى فترة زمنيه محدودة |
| over time | على مدار الوقت |
| overall commingled production prediction model | نموذج تنبؤ كلي للإنتاج الممتزج |
| overbalanced conditions | ظروف ضغط أعلي |
| overbase ; over-base | قاعدة عالية |
| overbased ; over-based = highly basic | عالي القاعدة؛ عالي القاعدية |
| overburden | الغطاء الطبقي: التكوينات أعلى التكوين الهيدروكربوني |
| overburden pressure | ضغط حمل التربة |
| overburdn | طبقة ما فوق الهيدروكربون: تكوين فوق الهيدروكربون |
| overclocking | زيادة السرعة؛ كسر حاجز السرعة |
| overcook | تلف |
| overcropping | إجهاد الأرض الزراعية |
| overexpression of akt | التعبير الوراثي المفرط لـ Akt |
| overexpression of akt | والتعبير الوراثي الزائد عن Akt |
| overfiring of the turbine | الاشتعال المفرط للتوربين |
| overflow | فيض؛ تدفق (زائد) |
| overhaul | إصلاح شامل |
| overhead | حِمْل |
| overhead | وصلة علوية؛ جزء علوي |
| overlay | يوجد فوق |
| overlay | يتراكب |
| overlying | فوقي. والعكس تحتي underlying |
| overlying layer | الطبقة الفوقية |
| overlying reaction space | حيز تفاعل فوقي |
| overnight | طوال الليل |
| overreliance | اعتماد زائد |
| overreliance on technology | اعتماد زائد على التقنية |
| override | يتجاوز؛ يتخطى |
| over-thrust fold | ثنية نائمة صدعية |
| overturned fold | ثنية مقلوبة |
| ovine | خرفان |
| owned invention | اختراع مملوك لشخص ما |
| owner-operator | مالك مستغل للأرض؛ هو الذي يزرعها |
| owner's guide | دليل المستخدم |
| ownership rights | حقوق الملكية |
| owner-tenant relationship | العلاقة بين المالك والمستأجر |
| oxalate supersaturation | تشُبع مفرط بالأوكسالات |
| oxalyl bromide | بروميد أوكساليل |
| oxane | أوكسان |
| oxazolidinone | أوكسازوليدينون |
| oxidant feeder | مغذي مؤكسد |
| oxidant sparger | رشاش مادة مؤكسدة |
| oxidation zone | منطقة أكسدة |
| oxidative reforming of hydrocarbons | إعادة تشكيل الهيدروكربونات بالأكسدة |
| oxidative stress | إجهاد مؤكسد |
| oxide | أكسيد |
| oxide dispersion strengthened (ods) alloy | سبيكة مقوّاة بمشتت أكسيدي |
| oxide-dispersion-strengthened alloys | سبائك مقواة بتشتيت الأكسيد |
| oxides | أكاسيد |
| oxidizable | قابل للأكسدة |
| oxidization | أكسدة |
| oxidize | يؤكسد |
| oxidized | مؤكسد |
| oxidizing breaking agent | عامل خفض لزوجة مؤكسد |
| oximation | تكوين أوكسيم |
| oxiran | أوكسيران |
| oxiranyl | أوكسيرانيل |
| oxy | أوكسي |
| oxycodone hcl | هيدروكلوريد الأوكسي كودون |
| oxycodone n-oxide | أوكسي كودون - N - أكسيد |
| oxycodone-n-oxide (ono) test | اختبار أوكسي كودون - N - أكسيد (ONO) |
| oxygen | أكسجين |
| oxygen sensor | جهاز إحساس بالأكسجين |
| oxygenate | يمزج أو يشبع بالأكسجين (يؤكسج) |
| oxygenate | يشبع بالأكسجين |
| oxygenated water | ماء مشبع بالأوكسجين |
| oxygenates | المواد المحتوية على أكسجين |
| oxygenation | مشبع بالأكسجين |
| oxygenator | مشبع بالأكسجين |
| oxylol | أوكسيلول |
| oxynol | أوكسينول |

# P

| | |
|---|---|
| p/q-type voltage sentize channel modulators | معدلات قناة الإحساس بالفلطية من نوع P/Q |
| p110 isoform selectivity scintillation proximity binding assay | اختبار الارتباط التقريبي باستخدام الومضان الانتقائي للصورة المتماثلة p110 |
| p110a (alpha) pi3k binding assay | اختبار ارتباط إنزيم p110a (alpha) PI3K |
| pa | بيكو أمبير |
| pace | إيقاع، سرعة |
| pace of innovation | إيقاع الابتكار، سرعة الابتكار. سرعة قيام المجتمع بابتكار واختراع منتجات جديدة. ويرى منتقدو نظام الملكية الفكرية التقليدي أن البراءات تؤثر تأثيراً سلبياً في إيقاع الابتكار والاختراع |
| pacific digital cellular | النظام الرقمي الخلوي بالمحيط الهادئ |
| pacifiers for babies | مصاصة للأطفال الرضع |
| pacing | تنظيم الإيقاع القلبي |
| package insert | ملحق العبوة |
| package inserts with instructions for use | ملحقات تعبئة ذات تعليمات للمستخدم |
| packaged | مغلفة |
| packaged boiler | غلاية مغلفة |
| packages | الحزم |
| packaging | تعبئة؛ تغليف الكتب |
| packaging containers of metal | حاويات التغليف من المعدن |
| packaging containers of plastic | حاويات التغليف من البلاستيك |
| packaging machines | ماكينات التغليف |
| packaging material made of starches | مادة التغليف مصنوعة من النشا |
| packed column | عمود معبأ؛ عمود محشو |
| packed tower | برج معبأ |
| packet | كتلة (بيانات) |
| packet error rate (per). | معدل أخطاء الحِزَم |
| packet sniffer | لص (أو جاسوس ) كتل البيانات |
| packet switch node= psn | عقدة تحويل كتل البيانات |
| packet switching | تحويل كتل البيانات |
| packet switching network | شبكة محولة بالحزيمات |
| packetized ensemble protocol, pep | بروتوكول تجميع الكتل |
| packet-switched network | شبكة تحويل كتل البيانات |
| packing | حشو-تعبئة |
| packing (asbestos -) | التغليف (التغليف بالأسبستوس) |
| packing [cushioning, stuffing] materials of rubber or plastics | مواد التعبئة [التوسيد والحشو] من المطاط أو البلاستيك |
| packing [cushioning, stuffing] materials, not of rubber or plastics | مواد تعبئة [التوسيد والحشو] ليست من المطاط أو البلاستيك |
| packing density | كثافة الرص |
| packing machines | ماكينات التعبئة |
| packing paper | ورق التغليف |
| packing rope | حبال التغليف |
| packing string | خيوط التغليف |
| packing, of straw, for bottles | أغلفة الزجاجات من القش |
| packings (tin-plate -) | مواد التغليف (مواد التغليف بصاج مطلي بالقصدير) |
| pad | وحدة توهين (كهرباء)؛ حشوة؛ طبقة؛ وسادة؛ يبطن |
| padding | حشوة |
| padding materials of rubber or plastics | مواد تبطين من المطاط أو البلاستك |
| padding materials, not of rubber or plastics | مواد تبطين ليست من المطاط أو البلاستيك |
| paddings (protective -) [parts of sports suits] | مواد تبطين (مواد تبطين للحماية) [أجزاء من الملابس الرياضية] |
| paddle | محراك |
| paddles for canoes | مجاديف الزورق الفردي [زورق طويل خفيف ضيق] |
| paddy | الأرز الشعير |
| paddy field | حقول الأرز |
| padlocks | أقفال |
| pads (abdominal -) | وسادات (وسادات لتدعيم البطن) |
| pads (breast-nursing -) | وسائد (وسائد الرضاعة) |
| pads (bunion -) | اللفافات (اللفافات الخاصة بالورم الملتهب في المفصل الكبير من إبهام القدم) |
| pads (heating -), electric, for medical purposes | وسائد (وسائد للتدفئة) كهربائية للاستخدام في الأغراض الطبية |
| pads (mouse -) | وسائد (وسائد الفأرة) |
| pads (writing -) | لباد (لباد للكتابة) |
| pads [cushions] (heating -), electric | وسائد (وسائد للتدفئة) كهربائية |
| pads [pouches] for preventing pressure sores on patient bodies | وسائد [جيوب] لمنع قرح الضغط على أجساد المرضى |
| pads [stationery] | لباد [قرطاسية] |
| pads for cleaning | وسائد التنظيف |
| pads for horse saddles | وسائد سروج الأحصنة |
| page views | عدد مشاهدات الصفحة من قبل المستخدم |
| pager | جهاز استدعاء شخصي |
| paid up license | ترخيص مسدد القيمة |
| pails | دلاء |
| painful diabetic neuropathy | الاعتلال العصبي المؤلم الناتج عن مرض السكر |
| painful entrapment neuropathy | الاعتلال العصبي الانحصاري المؤلم |
| painful polyneuropathy | اعتلال الأعصاب |
| painful traumatic mononeuropathy | اعتلال العصب الأحادي المؤلم الناتج عن الإصابات |
| paint (booths of metal for spraying -) | الدهان (مقصورة من المعدن لرش الدهان) |

| | |
|---|---|
| paint (glossy platinum -) for ceramics | دهان (دهان البلاتين اللامع) الخزف |
| paint (silver -) for ceramics | دهان (دهان فضي) الخزف |
| paint (spray guns for -) | دهان (مسدسات رش الدهان) |
| paint boxes [articles for use in school] | صناديق الدهان [مواد للاستخدام في المدرسة] |
| paint spraying booths, not of metal | مقصورة رش الدهان ليست من المعدن |
| paint spraying booths, of metal | مقصورة رش الدهان مصنوعة من المعدن |
| paint stripping preparations | مستحضرات كشط الدهان |
| paintball guns [sporting apparatus] | بنادق لعبة كرة البنتابول [معدات رياضية] |
| paintballs [ammunition for paintball guns] [sporting apparatus] | لعبة كرة البنتابول [ذخائر بنادق لعبة كرة البنتابول] [معدات رياضية] |
| paintbrushes | فراشي الدهان |
| painters' brushes | فراشي الرسامين |
| painters' easels | حوامل لوحات الرسامين |
| painting machines | آلات الطلاء |
| paintings [pictures] framed or unframed | صور زيتية [صور] محاطة بأطر أو غير محاطة بأطر |
| paints | الدهانات |
| paints (agglutinants for -) | دهانات (مواد تثبيت للدهانات) |
| paints (anti-fouling -) | دهانات (دهانات مضادة لنمو الفطريات) |
| paints (bactericidal -) | دهانات (دهانات مضادة لنمو الجراثيم) |
| paints (binding preparations for -) | دهانات (مستحضرات مثبتة للدهانات) |
| paints (ceramic -) | دهانات (دهانات خزفية) |
| paints (chemical preparations for the manufacture of -) | دهانات (مستحضرات كيميائية لتصنيع الدهانات) |
| paints (enamel -) | دهانات (دهانات المينا) |
| paints (fireproof -) | دهانات (دهانات مضادة للحرائق) |
| paints (insulating -) | دهانات (دهانات عازلة) |
| paints (oils for -) | دهانات (زيوت للدهانات) |
| paints (thickeners for -) | دهانات (مواد مكثفة لقوام الدهانات) |
| paints (thinners for -) | دهانات (مواد مخففة لقوام الدهانات) |
| pair | يقرن |
| pajamas (am.) | بجامة (لباس النوم للرجال) |
| pal | خط تعديل الطور |
| palatable | سائغ |
| palette knives | سكاكين مزج [يمزج بها الرسام ألوانه] |
| palettes for painters | لوحات ألوان الرسم للرسامين |
| palinavir | بالينافير |
| palings of metal | أوتاد سياج من المعدن |
| palings, not of metal | أوتاد سياج ليست من المعدن |
| palisading, not of metal | أوتاد سياج ليست من المعدن |
| palladious chlorides | كلوريدات البلاديوس |
| palladium | البلاديوم |
| palladium catalyzed cross coupling reaction | تفاعل اقتران متبادل تم تحفيزه بالبالاديوم |
| pallet | منصة تحميل؛ منصة نقالة |
| pallets of metal (handling -) | منصات نقالة من المعدن (منصات نقالة للشحن والتعبئة) |
| pallets of metal (loading -) | منصات نقالة من المعدن (منصات نقالة للتحميل) |

| | |
|---|---|
| pallets of metal (transport -) | منصات نقالة من المعدن (منصات للنقل) |
| pallets, not of metal (loading -) | منصات نقالة ليست من المعدن (منصات نقالة للتحميل) |
| pallets, not of metal (transport -) | منصات نقالة ليست من المعدن (منصات للنقل) |
| palm kernel oil for food | زيت بذرة النخيل للاستخدام في الطعام |
| palm oil for food | زيت النخيل للاستخدام في الطعام |
| palm trees | النخيل |
| palmitic acid | حمض البلميتيك |
| palms [leaves of the palm tree] | سعف النخيل [ أوراق شجر النخيل] |
| palm-size, hand-held pcs | أجهزة الكمبيوتر الكفية بحجم كف اليد |
| palmtop | كمبيوتر محمول بحجم اليد؛ كمبيوتر محمول كفي؛ كمبيوتر كفي |
| palpitation | خفقان |
| palsy | شلل |
| pamphlets | كتيبات |
| pan | تدوير محوري |
| pan | وعاء |
| pancakes | فطائر محلاة |
| pancreatitis | التهاب البنكرياس |
| pandemic | وبائي |
| panel | هيئة، لوح |
| panel of patent arbitrators | هيئة محكمي البراءات |
| panels | هيئات، ألواح |
| panels (building -) not of metal | قطع حائطية (للبناء) ليست من المعدن |
| panels (building) | قواطيع جاهزة (قاطوع) |
| panels of metal (building -) | قطع حائطية من المعدن (للبناء) |
| panicle | السنبلة |
| p-anisidine | p-أنيسيدين |
| panniers adapted for cycles | سلال مهيأة للدراجات |
| panning shots | اللقطات الدوارة |
| panorama (bird's eye biew) | لقطة بانورامية (شاملة) |
| panoramic images | الصور شاملة الرؤية |
| pans (frying -) | أواني (أواني القلي) |
| panties (sanitary -) | سراويل تحتية للنساء (سراويل تحتية صحية) |
| pantiles | قرميد متموج متراكب |
| pantographs [drawing instruments] | أدوات للنسخ [معدات رسم] |
| pants | سراويل تحتية للرجال |
| pants (sanitary -) | سراويل تحتية (سراويل تحتية صحية) |
| pants, absorbent, for incontinents | سراويل تحتية ماصة لاستخدام مرضى السلس |
| panty liners [sanitary] | بطانة السراويل [للأغراض الصحية] |
| paper | ورقة؛ ورق |
| paper (asbestos -) | ورق (ورق الأسبستوس) |
| paper (building -) | ورق (ورق للبناء) |
| paper (electro-cardiograph -) | ورق (ورق التخطيط الكهربائية للقلب) |
| paper (insulating -) | ورق (ورق عازل) |
| paper (mothproof -) | ورق (ورق مقاوم للعثة) |
| paper (twine made of -) | ورق (خيوط مصنوعة من الورق) |

| | |
|---|---|
| paper (waxed -) | ورق (ورق شمعي) |
| paper bows | أقواس ورقية |
| paper clasps | مشابك الورق |
| paper clothing | ملابس ورقية |
| paper data storage | مخزن بيانات ورقية |
| paper engineering | الهندسة الورقية |
| paper feeder [printing] | جهاز التغذية بالورق [طباعة] |
| paper for dyeing easter eggs | ورق لصبغ بيض الفصح |
| paper for electrical capacitors | ورق المكثفات الكهربائية |
| paper for mustard plasters | ورق لاصقات الخردل |
| paper for mustard poultices | ورق كمادات الخردل |
| paper for recording machines | ورق آلات التسجيل |
| paper industry, graphit industry | صناعة الورق، صناعة الجرافيت |
| paper knives [cutters] [office requisites] | سكاكين الورق [قواطع] [لوازم مكتبية] |
| paper machines | ماكينات ورق |
| paper plates | أطباق ورقية |
| paper pulp | عجين الورق |
| paper ribbons | شرائط ورق |
| paper sheets [stationery] | صحائف الورق [قرطاسية] |
| paper shredders [for office use] | قواطع الورق [للاستخدام المكتبي] |
| paper spills for lighting | لفائف ورقية للإنارة |
| paper tapes and cards for the recordal of computer programmes | شرائط وبطاقات ورقية لتسجيل برامج الكمبيوتر |
| paperboard for building | ألواح من الورق المقوى للبناء |
| paper-clips | مشابك الورق |
| paper-faced | ذو واجهة ورقية |
| paperhanging (adhesives for -) | ورق الحائط (مواد لاصقة لورق الحائط) |
| paperless management system | نظام إدارة بلا أوراق. نظام إدارة يعتمد على إدخال المعلومات في الحواسيب عوضا عن استخدام الأوراق |
| paperless system | نظام إلكتروني |
| papermaking machines | ماكينات صنع الورق |
| papers | أوراق |
| papers (diazo -) | ورق (ورق يحتوى على الديازونيوم) |
| papers (hair curling -) | ورق (ورق تجعيد الشعر) |
| paperweights | الثقالات [أوزان توضع على الورق لمنعه من التطاير] |
| papier mâché | ورق معجن |
| papillary thyroidea carcinoma | الورم السرطاني الحليمي الدرقي |
| papilloma | ورم حليمي |
| para | بارا |
| parabasal cells | الخلايا المجاورة للقاعدة |
| parabolic or triangular temperature profile | منحنى درجة حرارة على شكل قطع مكافئ أو مثلث |
| parachute | مظلة هبوط |
| parachutes | باراشوت (مظلات) |
| paracnglomerates | مدملك طيني |
| paracrine | مفرز جار صمي: متعلق بإفراز الخلايا الصماء ذات التأثر الموضعي |
| paradigm polypeptide | عديد ببتيد نموذج |
| paraffins | بارافينات |
| paragliders | أدوات التحليق بالباراشوت |
| parainfluenza virus | فيروس شبيه الأنفلونزا |
| parallel "swing" reactors | مفاعلين متوازيين من النوع الدوار |
| parallel misalignment | سوء المحاذاة المتوازي |
| parallel port | منفذ متوازي |
| parallel propagation of signals | الانتشار المتوازي للإشارات؛ الارتحال المتوازي للإشارات؛ النقل المتوازي للإشارات |
| parallelepiped | متوازي السطوح |
| parallelepipedal | على شكل معين |
| parallel-misaligne ; parallel misaligne | يحدث سوء المحاذاة على نحو متوازي |
| parameter | متغير |
| parameterization | التعبير في صورة متغيرات |
| para-military organisations | مؤسسات شبه عسكرية |
| parasitic | طفيلي |
| parasiticides | مبيدات الفطريات |
| parasols | الشماسي |
| paratope | موقع ارتباط مولد الضد بالجسم المضاد: الجزء من الجسم المضاد المسئول عن التعرف على القمة اللاصقة |
| paratroopers = paratroops(n.pl.) parachute troops. | قوات المظلات |
| parboild rice | أرز معامل البخار |
| parchment paper | ورق البرشمان [ورق نفيس شبيه بالرق] |
| parenchymal | بارنشيمي؛ لحمي |
| parent drug and prodrug | عقار رئيسي وعقار أولي |
| parent molecular ion | الأيون الجزيئي الأبوي |
| parental | أبوي؛ رئيسي |
| parental genotypes | أنماط جينية أبوية |
| parental lines | سلالات أبوية؛ السلالات الأم |
| parental negligence | إهمال أبوي |
| parenteral | عن غير طريق القناة الهضمية (غير معوي) (حقنًا مثلاً) |
| paresis | شلل خفيف |
| parietal | جدارية |
| paring irons [hand tools] | حدائد التقليم [عُدد يدوية] |
| paring knives | سكاكين التقليم |
| paring machines | آلات التقليم |
| park meter | عداد مواقف السيارات |
| parkas | البرْكة [سترة فرائية ذات قلنسوة تُلبس في مناطق القطب الشمالي] |
| parking bicycles (installations, not of metal, for -) | إيقاف الدراجات (تجهيزات ليست من المعدن لإيقاف الدراجات) |
| parking meter | جهاز قياس زمن التوقف |
| parkinsonism | الشلل الرعاش |
| parkinson's disease | داء باركنسون |
| parlimantary sub-committee | لجنة برلمانية فرعية |
| parlimant's standig committee | اللجنة البرلمانية الدائمة |
| parlor games | ألعاب منزلية |

| | |
|---|---|
| parlour games | ألعاب منزلية |
| parquet floor boards | ألواح أرضية الباركيه |
| parquet floor wax | شمع أرضية الباركيه |
| parquet flooring | أرضية الباركيه |
| parquet wax-polishers, electric | أدوات كهربائية لصقل الباركيه بالشمع |
| parralel flow band-tunnel dryere | جهاز تجفيف نفقي شريطي ذو تدفق متوازي |
| parsing a signal | توزيع إشارة |
| parsing a text | تحليل نص |
| part time inventor | مخترع يستغرق الاختراع جزءا من وقته |
| partial cut-through view | منظر قطع جزئي |
| partial delete | حذف جزئي |
| partial exclusivity | حصرية جزئية |
| partial response maximum likelihood (prml) | أقصى احتمال للاستجابة الجزئية |
| partial view | منظر جزئي |
| partially de-glycosylated | مرتبط بالجليكوزيل جزئيا |
| particle | جسيم |
| particle accelerator | جهاز تسريع الجسيمات (مسارعات) |
| particle physics | فيزياء الجسيمات |
| particle size | حجم جسيمي؛ حجم جسيمات؛ حجم دقائقي |
| particles | جسيمات |
| particular crystallographic surfaces | أسطح بلورية محددة |
| particulate | دقائقية |
| particulate material | مادة دقائقية |
| parties appointed arbitrators | المحكمون المعيونون من قبل الأطراف |
| partition | يقسّم؛ يجزئ |
| partitions of metal | فواصل من المعدن |
| partitions, not of metal | فواصل ليست من المعدن |
| partner | شريك |
| partnership | شركة تضامن |
| partnership limited by share company | شركة توصية بالأسهم |
| part-time farming | زراعة لبعض الوقت |
| party organ (mouthpiece) | صحيفة ناطقة بلسان الحزب |
| party-appointed arbitrator | محكم معين من قبل طرف |
| party-directed mediation | وساطة يوجهها الأطراف بأنفسهم. |
| pass filter ; pass-filter | يرشح بالتمرير |
| passage | مجرى |
| passementerie | الزركشة القيطانية |
| passes | مسارات |
| passion | شغف |
| passion for invention | الشغف بالاختراع |
| passive energy source | مصدر طاقة سلبي. مثل الهواء المضغوط |
| passive immunity | مناعة منفعلة |
| passphrase ; pass phrase | عبارة مرور |
| passport holders | حافظات جوازات السفر |
| password folders | إمكانية تخصيص إسم مستخدم وكلمة مرور سرية لحماية محتويات أي مجلد فرعي |
| password hacking software | برنامج لاقتحام كلمات المرور |
| password recovery | استعادة كلمة السر |
| password recovery software | برنامج لاستعادة كلمات المرور |
| pasta | الباستا (نوع من المكرونة) |

| | |
|---|---|
| paste | معجون؛ عجين لصق؛ يلصق |
| paste (almond -) | عجين (عجين اللوز) |
| paste (cake -) | عجين (عجين الكعك) |
| paste (silver -) | عجين (عجين الفضة) |
| paste jewellery [costume jewelry (am.)] | مجوهرات من الزجاج البراق [مجوهرات للملابس] |
| pastels [crayons] | أقلام التلوين [أقلام ملوّنة] |
| pastes (farinaceous food -) | عجين (عجين الأطعمة النشوية) |
| pastes (liver -) | عجين (عجين لحم الكبد) |
| pastes for razor strops | عجين لشاحذ أمواس الحلاقة |
| pasteuriser | جهاز بسترة |
| pasteurized milk | البسترة |
| pastill | باستيليا |
| pastilles (fumigating -) | كرات التبخير (كرات تبخير لإزالة الالتهاب بالتعرض للبخار) |
| pastilles [confectionery] | أقراص محلاة [ حلوى ] |
| pastilles for effervescing beverages | أقراص محلاة للمشروبات الفوارة |
| pastilles for pharmaceutical purposes | أقراص محلاة للاستخدام في الأغراض الصيدلانية |
| pastries | معجنات |
| pastry | الفطائر |
| pastry cutters | قطاعات الفطائر |
| pasty | فطيرة اللحم |
| patch | القطفة |
| patch clamp electrophysiology | الفيسيولوجيا الكهربائية لمشبك قطفة |
| patch clamp technique | تقنية تعليق القطفة |
| patch pipette | مِمَصّ القطفة |
| patches (adhesive rubber -) for repairing inner tubes | رقع (رقع لاصقة من المطاط) لإصلاح الأنابيب الداخلية |
| patches (heat adhesive -) for decoration of textile articles [haberdashery] | رقع (رقع لاصقة بالحرارة) لتزيين الأقمشة [خردوات] |
| patches (heat adhesive -) for repairing textile articles | رقع (رقع لاصقة بالحرارة) لإصلاح الأقمشة |
| pâté (liver -) | فطائر (فطائر من لحم الكبد) |
| pâté [pastries] | فطائر [معجنات] |
| patelet | صفيحة دموية |
| patent | يسجل براءة، براءة |
| patent abstract | ملخص البراءة التجريدي |
| patent acquisition strategy | إستراتيجية استحواذ على براءات |
| patent action | إجراء قانوني بشأن براءة، دعوى بشأن براءة |
| patent activation | تفعيل براءة |
| patent acts | مراسيم براءات |
| patent advisor | مستشار براءات |
| patent advocate | محامي براءات |
| patent agency | مكتب براءات الإختراع |
| patent agent | وكيل براءات |
| patent ambush | كمين براءات. تعبير يطلق على قيام موظف في هيئة وضع معايير برائتية بإخفاء معلومات عن براءة يمتلكها أو تمتلكها شركته أو هي منظورة أو ينوي طلب تسجيلها عند وضع معيار مما يجعل الجهات التي تقوم بتطبيق المعيار عرضة للاتهام |

| | |
|---|---|
| | بانتهاك البراءة |
| patent analytics | تحليلات البراءات |
| patent analytics services | خدمات تحليل البراءات |
| patent analytics training services | خدمات التدريب على تحليل البراءات |
| patent and copyright clause | بند حق النشر والبراءات. البند 1 القسم 8 من الدستور الأمريكي التي تمكن الكونغرس من تطوير العلم المفيد والآداب من خلال منح حقوق حصرية مؤقتة لهم بإزاء اكتشافاتهم وكتاباتهم |
| patent application | طلب براءة الاختراع |
| patent application drafting | صياغة طلب براءة، تحرير طلب براءة |
| patent application filing | إيداع طلب البراءة |
| patent application fraud | احتيال متصل بطلب البراءة |
| patent application grant | موافقة على طلب براءة |
| patent application reviewer | مراجع طلب براءات |
| patent application title | عنوان طلب البراءة. العنوان العام الذي يعطيه طالب البراءة لطلبه |
| patent arbitration rules | قواعد التحكيم في حقل البراءات |
| patent assets | أصول براءاتية |
| patent assignability | قابلية البراءة للتنازل |
| patent assignee | الطرف الذي تم التنازل عن البراءة لصالحه |
| patent assignment | تنازل عن براءة |
| patent assignment agreement | اتفاق بشأن التنازل عن براءة |
| patent associate | مساعد براءات |
| patent association | جمعية براءات |
| patent attorney | وكيل براءات |
| patent attorney malpractice | تقصير مهني من قبل وكيل براءات |
| patent attorney's advice | مشورة وكيل براءات |
| patent auction | مزاد براءات |
| patent audit | تدقيق براءاتي |
| patent audit checklist | قائمة المهام اللازمة لإجراء تدقيق متصل بالبراءات |
| patent auditor | مدقق براءات |
| patent award | يصدر حكما، يمنح جائزة، حُكم، قرار، جائزة |
| patent awardability | القابلية لاستصدار حكم أو موافقة أو قرار تم تقديم طلب بشأنه |
| patent awareness | وعي البراءات |
| patent bar | نقابة (خبراء البراءات) البراءاتيين |
| patent blog | مدونة براءات |
| patent blogger | مدون براءات |
| patent broker | وسيط براءات |
| patent brokerage | وساطة براءات |
| patent busting project | مشروع القبض على البراءات. مشروع دشنته Electronic Frontier Foundation لمواجهة البراءات غير الشرعية الزائفة المتصلة بمجال البرامج الحاسبية والشبكة البينية بحسبانها تؤثر سلباً في حرية التعبير. |
| patent candidate | مرشح لبراءة. اختراع مرشح أن يكون محلاً لبراءة. |
| patent claim | ادعاء خاص ببراءة |
| patent claim validity | سلامة إدعاء البراءة |
| patent claims | دعاوى البراءة |
| patent client | عميل للبراءة |
| patent collection | تجميع براءات |
| patent commercial potentialities | إمكانيات البراءة التجارية |
| patent commercialization | جعل البراءة ذات طبيعة تجارية |
| patent commercialization measurement | قياس إمكانية جعل البراءة ذات طبيعة تجارية |
| patent competitiveness | تنافسية البراءة. قدرة البراءة على التنافس |
| patent consolidation | توحيد البراءات. تجميع براءات ذات صلة ببعضها |
| patent coordinator | منسق براءات |
| patent counsel | مستشار (محامي) براءات |
| patent creation | ابتكار براءة ابتكارات خلاقا |
| patent crime | جريمة براءات |
| patent crisis | أزمة براءات |
| patent cross-licensing agreement | اتفاق بشأن ترخيص متقابل لبراءات |
| patent data provider | مقدم خدمة التزويد ببيانات براءات |
| patent data services | خدمات بيانات البراءات |
| patent dependent claims | دعاوى براءاتية تابعة |
| patent description | وصف البراءة |
| patent destruction | تدمير براءة |
| patent detective | مستقصي براءات، مفتش براءات تحري براءات |
| patent dilution | إضعاف البراءة. جعل البراءة ذات قيمة أقل. |
| patent dispute | نزاع بشأن براءات |
| patent dispute administration | إدارة نزاعات براءات |
| patent dispute resolution lawyer | محامي مختص بحل نزاعات البراءات |
| patent documents | مستندات البراءة |
| patent documents interpretation | تفسير مستندات البراءة |
| patent drafting | صائغ طلبات البراءات |
| patent drafting and prosecution practice | ممارسة صياغة طلبات البراءات وإنشائها |
| patent drafting fees | أتعاب صياغة طلبات البراءات |
| patent drafting firm | مؤسسة صياغة براءات |
| patent drafting services | خدمات صياغة طلبات البراءات |
| patent draftsman | صائغ طلب البراءة |
| patent drawing cervices provider | مقدم خدمة إعداد رسومات البراءات |
| patent drawing services | خدمات إعداد رسومات البراءات |
| patent drawings | رسومات براءة |
| patent drawings correction | تصحيح رسومات البراءة |
| patent drawings design | تصميم رسومات البراءة |
| patent due diligence | مراجعة واجبة بشأن البراءات، عناية واجبة بشأن البراءات. تقييم وضع البراءات ذات الصلة بالنشاط التجاري بما في ذلك البراءات المملوكة بغية الوقوف على عناصر القوة والضعف والهشاشة. ويتم القيام بالمراجعة |

| | |
|---|---|
| | الواجبة في مناسبات مختلفة أبرزها عند اتخاذ قرار تجاري مهم بالنسبة للشركة مثل دمجها أو الاستحواذ عليها |
| patent due diligence checklist | قائمة المهام اللازمة لإجراء مراجعة واجبة متصلة بالبراءات |
| patent effectiveness | فعالية البراءة |
| patent eligibility | الأهلية لاستصدار براءة |
| patent eligibility assessment | تقييم أهلية المادة لاستصدار براءة عنها |
| patent eligibility of a process | أهلية طريقة لاستصدار براءة عنها |
| patent enablement | تعبير يطلق على وجوب كون مستندات البراءة من الوضوح بحيث تمكن الغير من تشغيل الاختراع |
| patent enforceability | قابلية البراءة للإنفاذ |
| patent engineer | مهندس براءات |
| patent engineering | هندسة براءات |
| patent ethics | أخلاقيات البراءات |
| patent evaluation | تقييم البراءة |
| patent examination | فحص براءة |
| patent examination report | تقرير بحث بشأن براءة |
| patent examiner | فاحص براءة |
| patent exclusive licensing agreement | اتفاق بشأن ترخيص حصري لبراءة |
| patent executive | تنفيذي براءات. مدير تنفيذي في مجال البراءات |
| patent expiration | انقضاء أجل البراءة |
| patent exploitability assessment | تقييم إمكانية استغلال البراءة |
| patent family | عائلة براءات |
| patent feasibility | جدوى البراءة |
| patent firm | مؤسسة براءات |
| patent forms | نماذج براءات. الأوراق النموذجية التي يتوجب ملؤها لاستصدار براءة. |
| patent fraud | الاحتيال المتصل بالبراءات |
| patent funding | تمويل براءة |
| patent funding referral services | خدمات الإحالة إلى جهات تمويل براءات |
| patent gallery | معرض براءات |
| patent gap | فجوة برائتية. وجود فارق في عدد ونوعية البراءات بين فئتين تحليليتين. |
| patent governance | حوكمة البراءات |
| patent grant | موافقة على براءة |
| patent grant certificate | شهادة منح البراءة |
| patent grantee | الطرف الممنوح البراءة |
| patent granting procedure | إجراء منح البراءة |
| patent grants | موافقات لإصدار براءات |
| patent guru | مرشد براءات. خبير براءات يقدم النصح الفني للغير. |
| patent holder | صاحب براءة |
| patent holding company | شركة حاملة الحق في البراءات. شركة تؤسس خصيصا لكي تمتلك وتدير وترخص براءات للغير |
| patent illustrations | توضيحي |
| patent illustrator | مختص برسم الرسوم التوضيحية للبراءات |
| patent improvement feasibility | جدوى تحسين براءة |
| patent industry | صناعة البراءات |
| patent ineligible subject matter | مادة غير مؤهلة أن تصدر عنها براءة |
| patent information analysis | تحليل معلومات البراءة |
| patent information services | خدمات معلومات البراءات |
| patent infringement | انتهاك براءة |
| patent infringement analysis | تحليل انتهاكات البراءات |
| patent infringement award | حكم تعويض لانتهاك براءة |
| patent infringement damages | تعويضات عن انتهاك براءة |
| patent infringement damages award | جائزة معطاة لبراءة |
| patent infringement insurance | تأمين ضد انتهاك البراءة |
| patent infringement lawsuit | دعوى قانونية بشأن انتهاك براءة |
| patent infringement offender | متعد منتهك لبراءة |
| patent infringement offenses | تعديات انتهاك براءات |
| patent infringement test | اختبار للتحقق من حصول انتهاك لبراءة |
| patent infringer | منتهك براءات |
| patent infringibility | قابلية البراءة للانتهاك |
| patent intensive industry | صناعة ذات حضور كثيف للبراءات فيها |
| patent interference | تعبير يطلق على نزاع قضائي بين ملاك براءات على الأولوية |
| patent invalidation | إبطال براءة |
| patent issuability | قابلية البراءة للصدور |
| patent know-how | دراية الكيفية في مجال البراءات |
| patent landscaping | تعبير يطلق على البحوث التي تتم فيما يتصل بمعرفة البراءات الصادرة ذات الصلة بالاختراع أو بخط الاختراعات والابتكارات المزمع السير فيه |
| patent landscaping studies | تعبير يطلق على الدراسات التي تتم فيما يتصل بمعرفة البراءات الصادرة ذات الصلة بالاختراع أو بخط الاختراعات والابتكارات المزمع السير فيه |
| patent law | قانون براءات |
| patent law firm | شركة قانونية متخصصة في مجال براءات الإختراع |
| patent law firm | مؤسسة قانونية للملكية الفكرية |
| patent law professional | خبير قانون براءات |
| patent lawyer | محامي براءات |
| patent lease agreement | اتفاق لتأجير براءة. اتفاق ينظم قيام مالك البراءة بتأجيرها للغير |
| patent legislation | تشريع بشأن البراءات |
| patent licensability | قابلية براءة للترخيص، القيمة التي يمكن الحصول عليها من ترخيص براءة |
| patent licensability evaluation | تقييم قابلية براءة للترخيص |
| patent license | ترخيص براءة |
| patent license agreement | اتفاق بشأن رخصة براءة |
| patent license evaluation | تقييم رخصة براءة |
| patent license valuation | تقييم ترخيص براءة |
| patent license value | قيمة ترخيص البراءة |
| patent licenses management | إدارة تراخيص البراءات |
| patent licensing | ترخيص البراءات |
| patent licensing agreement | اتفاق بشأن ترخيص براءة |

| | |
|---|---|
| patent licensing services | خدمات ترخيص البراءات |
| patent licensing strategy | إستراتيجية ترخيص براءات |
| patent literacy | الإلمام بالبراءات |
| patent literature | أدبيات براءات |
| patent litigation | تقاضٍ بشأن براءة |
| patent litigation lawyer | محامٍي مختص بالتقاضي المتصل بالبراءات |
| patent litigation strategy | إستراتيجية التقاضي في قضية براءات |
| patent litigator | مختص بالنزاعات القضائية المتعلقة بالبراءات |
| patent lobbying | استمالة فيما يتصل بسياسات البراءات |
| patent locator | معين البراءات |
| patent malpractice | تقصير مهني في مجال البراءات |
| patent malpractice suit | دعوى بشأن تقصير مهني في ممارسة أعمال البراءات |
| patent management | إدارة البراءات |
| patent manager | مدير براءات |
| patent mapping | رسم خريطة للبراءة. تحديد وضع البراءة قبل السعي لاستصدارها من خلال إجراء بحث بشأن المجال الذي ستصدر فيه ومن ثم بيان موقعها المستقبلي |
| patent market | سوق البراءات |
| patent market needs | احتياجات سوق البراءات |
| patent marketability evaluation | تقييم قابلية براءة للتسويق |
| patent mining | تعبير يطلق على البحث في مجال البيانات |
| patent misuse | إساءة استعمال براءة |
| patent misuse doctrine | مبدأ إساءة استخدام البراءة |
| patent monetization | جعل البراءة ذات عائد نقدي |
| patent monetization business model | نموذج تجاري لجعل البراءات ذات عائد نقدي |
| patent monetization market | سوق جعل البراءات ذات عائد نقدي |
| patent negotiator | مفاوض بشأن البراءات |
| patent novelty assessment | تقييم جدة البراءة |
| patent originality | أصلة البراءة |
| patent papers | أوراق البراءة |
| patent pending algorithm | خوارزمية (لوغاريتم) ذات براءة معلقة |
| patent pending process | عملية ذات براءة معلقة |
| patent pending product | منتج له طلب براءة منظور |
| patent pending testing process | عملية اختبار ذات براءة معلقة |
| patent pirate | قرصان براءات |
| patent policy | سياسة البراءات |
| patent policy matters | مسائل تتعلق بسياسات البراءات |
| patent policy players | القائمون بالأدوار فيما يتصل بسياسات البراءات |
| patent pool | مجمع براءات |
| patent pooling | تأسيس مجمع براءات، تجميع براءات |
| patent portfolio | محفظة براءات. مجموعة براءات مملوكة لشخص أو لشركة. |
| patent portfolio assessment | تقييم محفظة براءات |
| patent portfolio audit | تدقيق محفظة براءات |
| patent portfolio evaluation | تقييم محفظة براءات |
| patent portfolio license | ترخيص لمحفظة براءات |
| patent portfolio management | إدارة محافظ البراءات |
| patent portfolio manager | مدير محفظة براءات |
| patent portfolio monetization | جعل محفظة البراءات ذات عائد نقدي |
| patent portfolio value | قيمة محفظة براءات |
| patent potentials | إمكانيات البراءة |
| patent practice | ممارسة البراءات |
| patent practitioner | ممارس براءات |
| patent preparation | تحضير البراءة |
| patent proceeds | متحصلات براءة |
| patent procurement | شراء براءة |
| patent professional | خبير براءات |
| patent profile | تعريف موجز بالبراءة |
| patent profile services | خدمات توفير التعريفات الموجزة للبراءات |
| patent promoter | مروج براءات |
| patent prosecutability | قابلية البراءة للإنشاء، إمكانية إنشاء البراءة |
| patent prosecution | إنشاء البراءة. عملية استصدار البراءة منذ تقديم طلب البراءة حتى صدورها |
| patent prosecution lawyer | محامي مختص بإنشاء البراءات |
| patent protection strategy | إستراتيجية الدفاع عن البراءة. مجمل الخطط التي تعتمدها شركة للدفاع عن البراءات التي تمتلكها أو المرخصة لها في مواجهة أي هجوم يتوخى النيل منها |
| patent purchase and sale agreement | اتفاق بشأن شراءة براءة وبيعها |
| patent reexamination | إعادة فحص براءة |
| patent reform | إصلاح براءاتي |
| patent register | سجل براءات |
| patent registration expertise | خبرة تسجيل البراءات |
| patent reissue | إعادة إصدار براءة. إعادة إصدار براءة تم هجرانها. |
| patent reliant company | شركة تعتمد على البراءات |
| patent restrictions | قيود البراءة |
| patent reviewer | مراجع براءات |
| patent rights | حقوق البراءة، الحقوق المنبثقة عن البراءة |
| patent rivalry | تنافس حول براءة |
| patent scientist | عالم براءات |
| patent scope | نطاق البراءة |
| patent search | بحث متصل ببراءة |
| patent search analytics | تحليلات بحوث البراءات |
| patent search analytics services | خدمات تحليل بحوث البراءات |
| patent search database | قاعدة بيانات البحث المتصل بالبراءة |
| patent search engine | محرك بحث للبراءات |
| patent search expert | خبير بحوث براءات |

| | |
|---|---|
| patent search provider | مقدمة خدمة البحث المتصل بالبراءات |
| patent search services | خدمات البحث عن البراءات، خدمات بحوث البراءات |
| patent secrets | أسرار البراءة |
| patent security agreement | اتفاق بشأن منح الحق في براءة كضمان لدين |
| patent seeker | الراغب في البراءة |
| patent service provider | مقدم خدمات براءات |
| patent services | خدمات براءات |
| patent settlement | تسوية بشأن براءات. تسوية بشأن نزاع يدور حول براءات |
| patent settlement agreement | اتفاق تسوية بشأن براءات |
| patent sharks | أسماك قرش براءاتية. تعبير يطلق على شركات مليئة تقوم بالاستحواذ على البراءات لاسيما البراءات التي تمتلكها شركات وقعت في إفلاس والذين يضعون أنفسهم في موضع الضحية التي انتهكت حقوقها البراءاتية سعيا للحصول على تعويضات ضخمة |
| patent society | جمعية براءات |
| patent specification | تحديد اسم البراءة المعنية |
| patent specification | مواصفات البراءة |
| patent strategist | إستراتيجي براءات |
| patent strategy | إستراتيجية براءات |
| patent strategy alignment | ضبط وضعية لإستراتيجية البراءات |
| patent suit | دعوى براءة |
| patent swap agreement | اتفاق بشأن تبادل براءات |
| patent swap deal | صفقة تبادل براءات. |
| patent system | نظام البراءات |
| patent territoriality | إقليمية البراءة |
| patent theft | سرقة براءات |
| patent thicket | دغل براءات. حالة من تشابك البراءات تقوم جهة مالكة لبراءة بتصميمها بغية منع منافس من تصميم براءة مشابهة |
| patent transfer | تحويل براءة، نقل البراءة |
| patent transfer agreement | اتفاق بشأن تحويل ملكية براءة |
| patent transferability | قابلية البراءة للتحويل |
| patent troll | تعبير يطلق على صاحب حق في براءة ينفذ البراءات لكي يستهدف ـ على نحو استغلالي ـ منتهك مزعوم وليس لاستخدامها استخداما اعتياديا |
| patent troll tracker | تعبير يطلق على من يتعقب صاحبَ الحق في براءةٍ الذي يُنَفذ البراءة لكي يستهدف ـ على نحو استغلالي ـ منتهكا مزعوما وليس لاستخدامها استخداما اعتياديا ويسعى إلى كشفه على الملأ |
| patent usability | قابلية البراءة للاستعمال |
| patent usability test | اختبار قابلية البراءة للاستعمال |
| patent validation | تثبيت شرعية البراءة |
| patent validation service provider | مقدم خدمة تثبيت شرعية البراءة |
| patent validation services | مقدم خدمة تثبيت شرعية البراءة |
| patent validity | سريان البراءة، شرعية البراءة |
| patent valuation | تقييم براءة |
| patent valuation services | خدمات تثمين البراءات |
| patent's commercial value | قيمة البراءة التجارية |
| patent's market value | قيمة البراءة السوقية |
| patent's salability | قابلية البراءة للبيع |
| patentability | إمكانية الحصول على براءة، قابلية الشيء أن تصدر عنه براءة |
| patentability opinion | رأي بشأن القابلية للبراءة |
| patentability test | اختبار القابلية لاكتساب براءة. اختبار يتم إجراءه لقياس مدى استحقاق الاختراع أن يصدر عنه براءة |
| patentable | قابل أن يصدر عنه براءة |
| patentable idea generation | توليد أفكار يمكن أن يصدر عنها براءات |
| patentable invention | اختراع يمكن أن تصدر عنه براءة |
| patentable process | عملية قابلة أن يصدر عنها براءة |
| patentable subject matter | مادة قابلة أن يصدر عنها براءة |
| patent-based acquisition | استحواذ مؤسس على وضع البراءات. قيام شركة بالاستحواذ على شركة أخرى مع كون باعث الاستحواذ هو البراءات المملوكة للشركة التي ترغب الشركة المستحوذة في تملكها |
| patent-based business | عمل تجاري مرتكز على البراءات |
| patent-based business model | نموذج تجارى مؤسس على البراءات. نموذج تجاري لشركة أبرز أسسه تملك الشركة براءات، ربما لترخيصها |
| patent-based company | شركة مؤسسة على براءات |
| patent-based organization | منظومة مرتكزة على البراءات |
| patent-cross licensing | ترخيص متقابل لبراءات |
| patent-driven company | شركة تقودها البراءات. شركة تعتمد في مسيرتها الصناعية والتجارية وتموضعها الإستراتيجي على البراءات. |
| patented | صادر عنه براءة |
| patented algorithm | خوارزمية (لوغاريتم) صدرت عنها براءة |
| patented drug | دواء صادرة عنه براءة |
| patented idea | فكرة صدرت عنها براءة |
| patented idea | فكرة صدار عنها براءة |
| patented invention | اختراع صدرت عنه براءة |
| patented process | عملية صادر عنها براءة |
| patentee | صاحب البراءة |
| patentee's lawyer | محامي صاحب البراءة |
| patentee's monopoly power | سلطة صاحب البراءة الاحتكارية |
| patentee's power | سلطة صاحب البراءة |
| patentee-alleged infringer relationship | علاقة الحاصل على البراءة بالمنتهك المحتمل |
| patentee-licensee relationship | علاقة الحاصل على البراءة بالحاصل على الترخيص |
| patentee-patent attorney relationship | علاقة الحاصل على البراءة ب,وكيل البراءات |
| patent-eligible subject matter | مادة مؤهلة أن تصدر عنها براءة |
| patent-focused website | موقع شبكي مهتم بالبراءات |

| | |
|---|---|
| patenting | إصدار براءة، العمل على إصدار براءة |
| patenting activity | نشاط إصدار البراءات |
| patenting an indigenous medicine | إصدار براءة عن دواء محلي. القيام باستخراج براءة موضوعها دواء محلي، وهو أمر غير مشروع ويعد شكلاً من أشكال انتهاك حقوق الملكية الفكرية الخاصة بالشعوب التقليدية والأصلية |
| patenting behavior | السلوك المتصل بإصدار البراءات |
| patenting forms of life | منح براءات عن أشكال الحياة. منح براءات عن التطويرات الوراثية والجينية لبعض المخلوقات |
| patent-institution | مؤسسة براءات. مؤسسة لها دور في مجال البراءات أو في وضع سياسات وقوانين البراءات موضع التنفيذ |
| patent-intensive company | شركة تمتلك براءات كثيرة |
| patent-intensivedeveloped economy | اقتصاد نام ذو حضور كثيف للبراءات فيه |
| patent-less society | مجتمع بلا براءات. يدعو بعض المناهضين لفكرة البراءات جعل المجتمع بلا براءات لفترة محدودة لتجربة الوضع بلا براءات |
| patentologist | عالم براءات |
| patentology | علم البراءات |
| patent-pending drug disposal method | طريقة للتخلص من الأدوية ذات براءة معلقة |
| patent-pending method | طريقة ذات براءة معلقة |
| patent-pending technology | تقنية بانتظار براءة |
| patent-related arbitration proceedings | إجراءات تحكيم تتصل ببراءات |
| patents | براءات |
| patent's industrializability | قابلية البراءة للتصنيع |
| patent's useful life | حياة البراءة التي تكون مفيدة خلالها. لكل براءة عمر افتراضي، وعندما تبلغ البراءة أرذل العمر فإنها تفقد الكثير من قيمتها السوقية |
| pathogen | ممرض |
| pathogenesis | منشأ وتولد المرض؛ نشأة وتطور مرض |
| pathologist | متخصص في علم الأمراض |
| pathology | علم الأمراض |
| pathophysiological | متعلق بفسيولوجيا الأمراض |
| pathophysiology studies | دراسات فسيولوجيا الأمراض |
| pathway | مسار |
| patrol boat | زورق داورية |
| pattern | نمط |
| pattern of land use | نمط استخدام الأرض |
| patterned glass | زجاج مزخرف (المشكل) أو منقوش: زجاج نصف شفاف يتم إنتاجه بعملية الدلفنة (الدرفلة)، وعادة كلما كانت الزخرفة عميقة يكون الزجاج أكثر عتامة ونشراً للضوء |
| patterns | أنماط |
| patterns for dressmaking | نماذج خياطة ملابس النساء |
| patterns for making clothes | نماذج صنع الملابس |
| paving (luminous -) | حجارة تعبيد (حجارة تعبيد مضيئة) |
| paving blocks of metal | كتل رصف من المعدن |
| paving blocks, not of metal | كتل رصف ليست من المعدن |
| paving slabs, not of metal | بلاط الرصف ليس من المعدن |
| paw | قدم |
| pay out | يدفع (مالا) |
| pay out | يرخي (حبلا) |
| pay zone ; payzone | منطقة إنتاج؛ منطقة عطاء: منطقة غنية بالمعادن إلخ |
| payload | حمل بأجر؛ حمل آجر: حمولة يُدفع عنها أجر |
| payload | حمل أساسي: هو الجزء من القالب الذي يحوي معلومات قادمة من الطبقات العليا |
| payload commander | منسق التجارب العلمية على متن المكوك الفضائي |
| payment clause | البند المحدد لسعر العقد |
| paypal | باي بال: طريقة باي بول للدفع الإلكتروني على الإنترنت |
| pay-tv piracy | قرصنة التلفزة مسددة القيمة |
| pb | خط الأساس للمنتج |
| pc | كمبيوتر شخصي |
| pc card slots | فتحات/شقوق بطاقة كمبيوتر شخصي |
| pc card/ pcmcia card | بطاقة كمبيوتر شخصي/بطاقة PCMCIA: نوع من الملحقات الصغير تتيح لك إمكانية توصيل هاتف محمول رقمي ملائم مع هاتف شخصي محمول لإرسال واستقبال الفاكس والملفات الرقمية |
| pci | بيكو كوري pCi = 10-9 كوري |
| pcr | المعدل الذروي للخلية |
| pcr | جهاز تفاعل البوليميريز المتسلسل: يستخدم في عمليات بلمرة أجزاء من الأحماض النووية لغرض استنساخ الجينات وتحليلها التي هي أساس علم الهندسة الوراثية والتقنية الحيوية والوراثة الجزيئية. |
| pcr (polymerase chain reaction) | تفاعل سلسلة إنزيم بوليمراز |
| pct | معاهدة التعاون الدولي بشأن البراءات |
| pct filing | إيداع طلب براءة في ظل معاهدة التعاون بشأن البراءات. |
| pct. | نسبة |
| pd(0) | البالاديوم (صفر) |
| pda | المساعد الرقمي الشخصي: نظام تنظيم شخصي يتيح لك إمكانية تخزين المعلومات واستخدام برامج كمبيوتر بسيطة تعرف أيضا بكمبيوتر مصغر |
| pdf | ملف بيانات شخصية |
| pdf-format manual | دليل بتنسيق PDF |
| pdm | نموذج بيانات فعلية |
| pdr | مراجعة التصميم الأولي |
| peach | خوخ |
| peak | قمة |
| peak concentration | تركيز القمة |
| peak of the tail current response | قمة الاستجابة للتيار الطرفي |

| | |
|---|---|
| peak percent area ; peak area percent | النسبة المئوية لمنطقة الذروة |
| peak plasma concentration | أقصى تركيز في البلازما |
| peaks (cap -) | حواف ناتئة (حواف ناتئة للقبعات) |
| peanut butter | زبد الفول السوداني |
| peanut cake for animals | كعك الفول السوداني لطعام الحيوانات |
| peanut confectionery | حلوى الفول السوداني |
| peanut meal for animals | مجروش الفول السوداني لطعام الحيوانات |
| peanut milk [soft drink] | لبن الفول السوداني [شراب غير كحولي] |
| peanuts [fruits] | الفول السوداني [فاكهة] |
| peanuts, processed | الفول السوداني، معالج |
| pearier | ماكينة تلميع |
| pearls [jewellery, jewelry (am.)] | لؤلؤ [مجوهرات] |
| pearls made of ambroid [pressed amber] | لؤلؤ من الكهرمان المضغوط [كهرمان مضغوط] |
| peas, fresh | بازلاء طازجة |
| peas, preserved | بازلاء محفوظة |
| peasant | فلاح؛ يملك قطعة أرض صغيرة |
| peat | خُث (نبات) |
| peat (blocks of -) [fuel] | خُث (كتل من الخث )[وقود] |
| peat (litter -) | خُث (خُث القش) |
| peat [fertiliser] | خُث [سماد] |
| peat [fuel] | خُث [ وقود ] |
| peat briquettes [fuel] | قوالب من الفحم الخثي [وقود] |
| peat pots for horticulture | قدور الخث للاستخدام في فلاحة البساتين |
| pectin | بكتين |
| peculiarities | صفات |
| pecuniary right | حق مالي |
| pedal drives for sewing machines | دواسات ماكينات الخياطة |
| pedals for cycles | دواسات الدراجات |
| pedals for musical instruments | دواسات الآلات الموسيقية |
| pedestals (flower-pot -) | قواعد (قواعد أصيص الزهور) |
| pediatrics | طب الأطفال |
| pedicure sets | معدات الباديكير (للعناية بالقدم) |
| pedigree breeding | تربية الأنساب |
| pedometer | جهاز قياس مسافة السير |
| peel (fruit -) | قشرة (قشرة ثمار الفاكهة) |
| peeling machines | آلات التقشير |
| peephole | ثقب مراقبة |
| peepholes [magnifying lenses] for doors | ثقوب الباب [عدسات مكبرة] |
| peer device | جهاز تناظري |
| pegs for musical instruments | أوتاد الآلات الموسيقية |
| pegs of metal | مشاجب من المعدن |
| pegs, not of metal (tent -) | أوتاد ليست من المعدن (أوتاد الخيم) |
| pegs, not of metal [pins] | مشاجب ليست من المعدن [دبابيس] |
| pegylate | يضيف إليه بولي إيثيلين جليكول |
| pegylated | مضاف إليه بولي إيثيلين جليكول؛ مرتبط به؛ معالَج به |
| pelamis machines | آلات بيلاميس |
| pelerines | بلرين [وشاح نسوى طويل الأطراف] |
| pelisses | البليس [معطف أو سترة طويلة من الفراء] |
| pellet | يحصل عليه في صورة كريات |
| pelletic texture | نسيج العقد الطينية الجيرية |
| pelletizing processes | التقطيع على هيئة مواد طافية |
| pellets | حبيبات |
| pelts | جلود الحيوانات غير المدبوغة |
| pelvic | حوض |
| pemphigoid | شبيه الفقاع |
| pemphigus | الفقاع |
| pemphigus vulgaris | الفقاع الشائع |
| pen | قلم |
| pen cases | علب الأقلام |
| pen clips | مشابك الأقلام |
| pen wipers | ممسحة الأقلام |
| penal code | قانون العقوبات |
| penal servitude (for life) | أشغال شاقة (مؤبدة)؛ السجن المؤبد مع الأشغال الشاقة |
| penalitive | عقابي |
| penalize | يحدد عقاب المقصر |
| penalty | جزاء |
| pencil holders | مثبتات أقلام الرصاص |
| pencil lead holders | حوامل أطراف أقلام الرصاص |
| pencil leads | أطراف أقلام الرصاص |
| pencil sharpeners [electric or non-electric] | برايات أقلام الرصاص [كهربائية أو غير كهربائية] |
| pencil sharpening machines [electric or non-electric] | آلات برى أقلام الرصاص [كهربائية أو غير كهربائية] |
| pencils | الأقلام الرصاص |
| pencils (cosmetic -) | أقلام (أقلام التجميل) |
| pencils (eyebrow -) | أقلام (أقلام الحواجب) |
| pendant group | مجموعة مثبتة على مادة حاملة |
| pendants | دلايات (مجوهرات) |
| pending official action | إجراء رسمي معلق |
| pending patent | براءة منظورة |
| pendulums [clock- and watchmaking] | بندول الساعة [صناعة ساعات الحائط وساعات اليد] |
| penecontemporanous dolomitization | الدلمته المصاحبة |
| penetrability | القابلية للاختراق |
| penetrants | مواد نافذة |
| penetrate | يخترق |
| penetration | اختراق |
| penetration depth | عمق الاختراق |
| penholders | حوامل الأقلام |
| penknives | مطواة الجيب |
| pens (electronic -) [visual display units] | أقلام (أقلام إلكترونية) [وحدات عرض مرئي] |
| pens [office requisites] | أقلام [ لوازم مكتبية] |
| penstock pipes [not of metal] | مواسير المياه [ليست من المعدن] |
| penstock pipes [of metal] | مواسير المياه [من المعدن] |

| | |
|---|---|
| pentachloride phosphorous | خامس كلوريد الفسفوروز |
| pentamer | بنتامر: وحدة بنائية خماسية |
| pentanoyl | بنتانويل |
| pentavalent | خماسية التكافؤ |
| pentose | بنتوز |
| pentyl | بنتيل |
| penultimate | قبل الأخير |
| peoples' knowledge | المعرفه الخاصه بالشعوب |
| pepper | فلفل |
| pepper mills other than hand-operated | مطاحن الفلفل بخلاف المدارة باليد |
| pepper mills, hand-operated | مطاحن الفلفل, تدار باليد |
| pepper pots of precious metal | علب الفلفل من المعادن النفيسة |
| pepper pots, not of precious metal | مبهرة ليست من المعادن النفيسة [علب الفلفل] |
| peppermint | نعناع بستاني |
| peppermint liqueurs | مشروبات مسكرة من النعناع الفلفلي |
| peppermint sweets | حلوى النعناع الفلفلي |
| peppers [plants] | الفلفل [نبات] |
| peppers [seasonings] | الفلفل [توابل] |
| pepsin-like | شبيه بالببسين |
| pepsins | الببسين |
| peptibody | الجسم الببتيدي |
| peptibody binding to hek 293 cells | ارتباط الجسم الببتيدي بخلايا HEK 293 |
| peptic ulcer | قرحة هضمية |
| peptide amide hydrogen exchange method | طريقة تبادل الببتيد أميد هيدروجين |
| peptide bond | رابطة عديد ببتيد |
| peptide mimetics / peptidomimetics | محاكيات الببتيد؛ شبيهات الببتيد |
| peptization | المعالجة بالببتيد |
| peptizing | ببتيد |
| peptoids | أشباه الببتيدات |
| peptones | الببتون |
| per os | عن طريق الفم |
| per se | بذاته؛ بمفرده؛ بنفسه؛ على حدة |
| per unit area over time | لكل وحدة مساحة على مدار الزمن |
| perambulator covers (fitted -) | أغطية عربات الأطفال (أغطية مهيأة لعربات الأطفال) |
| perborate of soda | فوق بورات الصودا |
| percarbonate | فوق كربونات |
| percent identity | النسبة المئوية للتطابق |
| percent minority | الأقلية المئوية |
| percent point | نقطة في المئة |
| percent sequence identity | النسبة المئوية للتطابق (بين المتواليات) |
| percentile | مقياس النسبة المئوية |
| perchlorate | فوق الكلورات |
| percolate water | ماء مترشح |
| percolators (coffee -), electric | أجهزة ترشيح كهربائية (أجهزة ترشيح القهوة) |
| percolators (coffee -), non-electric | أجهزة ترشيح غير كهربائية (أجهزة ترشيح القهوة) |
| percussion caps [toys] | كبسولات القدح في البندقية [ألعاب] |
| percussion caps other than toys | كبسولات القدح في البندقية بخلاف الألعاب |
| percutaneously | عن طريق الجلد |
| perfluorinated | معالجة بفوق الفلور |
| perforant path | مسار ثاقب |
| perforated | مثقوبة |
| perforated cards for jacquard looms | بطاقات مثقبة في نول الجاكارد |
| perforated music rolls | قوائم النوتة الموسيقية مثقبة |
| perforated plate | لوح مثقب |
| perforated, whole-cell patch clamp recording | تسجيل مثقَّب لمشبك قطعة خلية كاملة |
| perforating tools [hand tools] | أدوات تثقيب [عُدد يدوية] |
| perform | يجري؛ ينفذ |
| perform a drilling operation | يجري عملية حفر |
| perform processing | يجري المعالجة |
| perform selected processes consecutively | يجري العمليات المحددة على التوالي |
| performance | أداء |
| performance assessment | تقيم الأداء |
| performance driven innovation | ابتكار تقوده قاطرة وضع الأداء. جهد ابتكاري غايته تحسين الأداء |
| perfume burners | مواقد العطور |
| perfume sprayers | إسبراي عطري |
| perfume vaporizers | أدوات تبخير العطور |
| perfumery | عطور |
| perfumes | عطور |
| perfusion | إرواء |
| perhaloalkoxy | بيرهالو ألكوكسي |
| pericarditis | التهاب التأمور |
| pericardium | التأمور |
| pericholangitis | التهاب ما حول القنوات المرارية |
| peridontitis | التهاب دواعم الأسنان |
| perimenopausal | قُرب انقطاع الدورة الشهرية |
| perimenopausal women | النساء اللاتي اقتربن من انقطاع الدورة الشهرية |
| perimeter | محيط |
| perineural | حول العصب (محيط بالعصب) |
| periodic table ; periodic table of the elements | الجدول الدوري للعناصر |
| periodically | دوريًا |
| periodicals | نشرات دورية |
| periodontal disease | مرض دواعم السن |
| periodontitis | التهاب الغشاء الحول السني |
| periods of production upsets | فترات اضطراب الإنتاج |
| perioperative pain | الألم في الفترة المحيطة بالجراحة |
| peripheral | طرفي |
| peripheral arterial occlusive disease | مرض انسداد الشرايين المحيطية |
| peripheral blood (pb) neutrophils | كرات الدم البيضاء متعادلة الصبغة بالدم المحيطي |
| peripheral bus | موصل عمومي محيطي |
| peripheral device | جهاز طرفي |
| peripheral devices (computer -) | أجهزة ملحقة (أجهزة ملحقة بالحاسبات الآلية) |
| peripheral nervous system | جهاز عصبي محيطي |
| peripheral neuroectodermal | الأورام العصبية المتعلقة بالأدمة |

tumors الظاهرة المحيطية
periscopes أجهزة البيريسكوب [مناظير أفقية]
perish يتلف
perishable قابل للتلف
perishable goods سلع قابلة للتلف
peristalsis تمعج؛ الحركة الدودية للأمعاء
peritoneal متعلق بالغشاء البريتوني
peritoneal dialysis غسيل البريتوني: إزالة الفضلات من الدم بواسطة تمرير سوائل في الغشاء البريتوني حيث يعمل كفلتر
peritonitis التهاب البريتون
perivenous حول الوريد
perjury الحنث باليمين
perl لغة البرمجة (بيرل)
permalloy material مادة من سبيكة عالية الإنفاذية المغناطيسية
permanent income دخل دائم
permanent magnet مغناطيس دائم
permanent storage device وحدة تخزين دائمة
permanent waving (neutralizers for-) التموج الدائم (مواد معادلة للتموج الدائم)
permeability إنفاذية
permeable rock صخرة منفذة
permeate(n) محلول قابل للنفاذ (مادة نافذة)
permeation promoter محفز نفاذي
permutation to the embodiment of the invention صورة بديلة
pernicious anemia فقر الدم الوبيلي
peroneal متعلق بعظم الشظية
peroxidase substrate مادة خاضعة لإنزيم بيروكسيداز
peroxide فوق أكسيد؛ بيروكسيد
peroxide فوق أكسيد (بيروكسيد)
peroxisome جسم أكسدة؛ جسيم أكسدة
perpendicular to متعامد على؛ أو عمودي على
perpetual license ترخيص دائم
perry عصير الأجاص
persilylated محتوي على بيرسيل
persistent vegetative state حالة مستمرة من غياب الوعي
person شخص
person skilled in the art شخص ذو مهارة في التقنية
person skilled in the field شخص ماهر في الحقل
personal demand items بنود طلبات شخصية
personal jurisdiction الخضوع للسلطة القضائية؛ التبعية القضائية
personal knowledge management إدارة المعرفة الشخصية
personal property ملكي شخصي
personal robbery نشل
personal robot روبوت شخصي
personal stereos أجهزة استريو شخصية
personalizable device جهاز قابل للتعديل حسب الحاجة الشخصية
personalize يضفي طابعا شخصيا؛ يخصص
personnel and material الأفراد والمعدات
personnel security أمن الأفراد
perspective منظور، زاوية النظر في الشيء
perspective ; perspective view شكل منظوري؛ رسم منظوري
perspective balance التوازن المنظور
perspective distortion التشويه المنظور
perspective view شكل منظوري
persuasive precedent سابقة مقنعة
persulfate; persulphate فوق كبريتات
persulphate فوق كبريتات
persulphuric acid حمض فوق الكبريتيك
perturbation اضطراب؛ تشوش
pertussis السعال الديكي
pertussis toxin سم السعال الديكي
pervaporation تبخر خارج الغشاء
pessaries كعك الرحم (لولب) [أدوات توضع في الرحم للعلاج أو لمنع الحمل]
pest control السيطرة على الآفات
pesticide industry صناعة المبيدات الحشرية
pesticides مبيدات الآفات
pesticides مبيدات الحشرات
pestles for pounding يد الهاون للاستخدام في السحق
pests الآفات
pet حيوان منزلي أليف
pet cushions وسائد للحيوانات الأليفة
pet food طعام للحيوانات الأليفة
petit mal صرع صغير
petit-beurre biscuits بسكويت بيتي بير (بالزبد)
petition تظلم (قانون)
petits fours [cakes] كعك البيتي فور
petrochemicals industries صناعات البتروكيماويات
petrol بترول
petrol burners مواقد البنزين
petrol gauges مقاييس البنزين
petrol pumps for service stations مضخات البنزين للاستخدام في محطات الخدمة
petrolatum فازلين
petroleum [raw or refined] البترول [خام أو منقى]
petroleum dispersants مواد تشتيت البترول
petroleum ether إيثر بترولي
petroleum feedstocks خامات تغذية بترولية
petroleum industries الصناعات البترولية
petroleum jelly الفازلين
petromin وزارة البترول والتعدين
pets (aromatic sand for -) [litter] حيوانات منزلية (رمل عطري للحيوانات المنزلية) [تبن الحيوانات]
pets (cages for household -) حيوانات منزلية أليفة (أقفاص للحيوانات المنزلية)
pets (clothing for -) حيوانات منزلية أليفة (ملابس للحيوانات المنزلية)
pets (litter boxes [trays] for -) حيوانات منزلية أليفة (صناديق القش [صواني] للحيوانات المنزلية الأليفة)
pets (sanded paper for -) [litter] حيوانات منزلية أليفة (ورق رملي للحيوانات المنزلية) [تبن الحيوانات]
pets (shampoos for -) حيوانات منزلية (شامبو للحيوانات المنزلية الأليفة)
petticoats تنورة

| | |
|---|---|
| petty patent | براءة بسيطة |
| pewterware | أواني بيوترية |
| pfe | معدة مقدمة من قبل المشتري |
| pfi | معلومات مقدمة من قبل المشتري |
| pfs | برامج حاسب مقدمة من قبل المشتري |
| pfu = plague forming units | وحدات مكونة للويحات |
| ph | الرقم الهيدروجيني |
| ph adjuster | معدّل (وسط ضبط) الرقم الهيدروجيني |
| ph buffer | محلول منظم للرقم الهيدروجيني |
| ph buffering agents | عوامل منظمة للرقم الهيدروجيني |
| pha | راصة دموية نباتية |
| phage display libraries | مجموعات إظهار الخلايا الملتهمة |
| phage(mid) display libraries | مجموعات إظهار الخلايا الملتهمة (الفاجميد) |
| phagemid | فاجميد |
| phagocytosis | الالتهام الخلوي |
| phagosome | جسم التهامي حالّ |
| phanerogams | نباتات زهرية |
| phantom limb pain | ألم الطرف الشبحي |
| pharmaceutical | مستحضر صيدلي |
| pharmaceutical grades | الفئات الصيدلانية |
| pharmaceutical packaging materials | مواد التعبئة الصيدلانية |
| pharmaceutical preparations | مستحضرات صيدلانية |
| pharmaceutical preparations for treating dandruff | مستحضرات صيدلانية لمعالجة قشر الشعر |
| pharmaceutically acceptable salt of an opioid analgesic | ملح مقبول صيدلانيا من مسكن أفيوني المفعول |
| pharmaceutically active | نشط صيدلانيا |
| pharmacodynamic | ديناميكي دوائي |
| pharmacodynamic half-life | العمر النصفي للتأثير الدوائي |
| pharmacokinetic | دوائي حركي |
| pharmacokinetics | علم الحركة الدوائية: يُعنى بالخواص الحركية الدوائية للعقاقير |
| pharmacological | دوائي |
| pharmacological activity | فعالية دوائية |
| pharmacologically active | فعال دوائياً |
| pharmacology | علم الأدوية؛ خصائص دوائية |
| pharmacopeia | دستور الأدوية |
| pharmacore | أساس صيدلاني (أساس يتم تأسيس العقار عليه) |
| pharyngeal inflammation | الالتهاب البلعومي |
| phase diagram | شكل الطور |
| phase diagram | مخطط الطور |
| phase envelopes | الظروف الطورية |
| phase shift keyed modulation systems | نظم التضمين للإزاحة الطورية؛ نظم التضمين بمفتاح إزاحة الطور |
| phase-change random access memory (pram) | ذاكرة الوصول العشوائية متغيرة المراحل |
| phasing | طور؛ مطاورة: نظّم على أطوار |
| phenol | فينول |
| phenol red | فينول أحمر |
| phenol red-free | خال من الفينول الأحمر؛ خال من أحمر فينول؛ خال من حمرة الفينول |
| phenol-aldehyde resole | الفينول-ألدهيد ريزول |
| phenolic resin | راتنج فينولي |
| phenotype | نمط ظاهري |
| phenoxymethyl | فينوكسي ميثيل |
| phenyl para substituted with | مجموعة فينيل بها استبدال في الموضع بارا بـ |
| phenyl-thio-benzylamines | مركبات فينيل-ثيو-بنزيل أمين |
| pheochromocytoma | ورم الأعصاب السمبتاوية القاتمة |
| phials (drop counting -), for medical purposes | قوارير (قوارير لعدّ القطرات) للاستخدام في الأغراض الطبية |
| philosophy | فلسفة |
| phishers and pharmers | اللصوص الإلكترونيين |
| phishing | السرقة الإلكترونية: الاحتيال المالي على الإنترنت/ فن الاحتيال على الحسابات الائتمانية على الإنترنت |
| phloem | لحاء |
| phobia | خوف مرضي عصبي-رعب-رهبة |
| phone dialer | برنامج الهاتف |
| phoneme | فونمية، صوت |
| phonemic | فونيمي، صوتي |
| phonetic | صوتي أو لفظي |
| phonetician | أصواتي |
| phonetics | علم تمثيل أو تصوير الأصوات |
| phonic | صوتي |
| phonics | علم الصوت |
| phonily | علي نحو زائف أو مزور |
| phoniness | زيف؛ زيوفة |
| phonogram | تسجيل صوتي، فونوغرام |
| phonograph | حاكي، فونوغراف |
| phonograph records (compositions for the manufacture of -) | أسطوانات الفونوغراف (مركبات لتصنيع أسطوانات الفونوغراف) |
| phonograph records (renovating preparations for -) | أسطوانات الفونوغراف (مستحضرات تجديد أسطوانات الفونوغراف) |
| phonographic | فونوغرافي، يتعلق برسم الكلمات |
| phonography | رسم صوتي |
| phonolite | فونوليت: صخر بركاني |
| phonologic | فونولوجي، متعلق بعلم الأصوات الكلامية |
| phonologist | فونولوجي: عالم الأصوات الكلامية |
| phonology | فونولوجيا: علم الأصوات الكلامية |
| phonoreception | سماع |
| phosgene | فوسجين: غاز عديم اللون كريه الرائحة كان يحضر أصلا بالاستعانة بأشعة الشمس. |
| phosphane | فوسفان |
| phosphanyl | فوسفانيل |
| phosphatase | إنزيم فوسفاتاز |
| phosphatase | فوسفاتاز |
| phosphate | فوسفات |
| phosphate buffer | محلول فوسفات منظم |
| phosphate buffered saline (pbs) | محلول ملحي منظم بالفوسفات |
| phosphate fertilizers | أسمدة الفوسفات |
| phosphate-glycerol group presenting bodies | أجسام تُعطي مجموعة فوسفات-جليسرول |
| phosphates [fertilisers] | فوسفات [أسمدة] |
| phosphatide | فوسفاتيد |
| phosphatidylcholine | فوسفاتيديل كولين |

| | |
|---|---|
| phosphatidylcholines | مركبات فوسفاتيديل كولين |
| phosphatidylinositol | فوسفاتيديل إينوسيتول |
| phosphine | فوسفين |
| phosphine ligands | مركبات الفوسفين الترابطية |
| phosphino | فوسفينو |
| phosphodiestarase | إنزيم فوسفو داي إستراز |
| phosphodiester | فوسفو داي إستر |
| phosphoinositide 3-kinases (pi3k) | إنزيمات فوسفو إينوسيتيد 3- كيناز |
| phospholipid | شحمي فسفوري |
| phosphon | فوسفون |
| phosphonamido | فوسفوناميد |
| phosphonate esters can be cleaved under strong acidic conditions | إحداث انقسام بإسترات الفوسفونات في ظروف حمضية قوية |
| phosphoramidate | فوسفورأميدات |
| phosphorescent | ذو بريق فسفوري |
| phosphorescent materials | مواد فوسفورية؛ مواد ذات بريق فوسفوري |
| phosphoric acid | حمض الفوسفوريك |
| phosphorinan | فوسفورينان |
| phosphorodithioate | فوسفورودايثيوات |
| phosphorothioate | فوسفوروثيوات |
| phosphorus | فوسفور |
| phosphorylated | معالج بالفسفرة |
| phosphorylation | فسفرة |
| photo | صورة |
| photo recovery software | برنامج لاستعادة صورة |
| photo view mode | وضع عرض الصورة |
| photocopiers (toner cartridges [filled] for printers and -) | ناسخات فوتوغرافية (خراطيش الحبر [مملوءة] في الطابعات والناسخات الضوئية) |
| photocopiers [photographic, electrostatic, thermic] | ناسخات فوتوغرافية [فوتوغرافية، كهروستاتية؛ حرارية] |
| photocopy machine | آلة تصوير |
| photodynamic | ديناميكي ضوئي |
| photoelectric | كهروضوئي |
| photograph stands | قواعد الصور الفوتوغرافية |
| photographic developers | مظهرات فوتوغرافية |
| photographic emulsions | مستحلبات تصوير فوتوغرافي |
| photographic paper | ورق فوتوغرافي |
| photographic prints (drying apparatus for -) | مطبوعات فوتوغرافية (أجهزة تجفيف النسخ الفوتوغرافية) |
| photographic prints (glazing apparatus for -) | مطبوعات فوتوغرافية (أجهزة تزجيج المطبوعات الفوتوغرافية) |
| photographic sensitizers | محسات فوتوغرافية |
| photographic transparencies (centering apparatus for -) | شرائح فوتوغرافية شفافة (أجهزة تثبيت الشرائح الفوتوغرافية الشفافة في المركز) |
| photographic transparencies (frames for -) | شرائح فوتوغرافية شفافة (أطر للشرائح الفوتوغرافية الشفافة) |
| photographs | صور فوتوغرافية |
| photographs (apparatus for mounting -) | صور فوتوغرافية (أجهزة تركيب صور فوتوغرافية) |
| photography (chemical preparations for use in -) | تصوير فوتوغرافي (مستحضرات كيميائية للاستخدام في التصوير الفوتوغرافي) |
| photography (reducing agents for use in -) | تصوير فوتوغرافي (عوامل مختزلة للاستخدام في التصوير الفوتوغرافي) |
| photolithography | الحفر الضوئي؛ طباعة الصفائح الضوئية؛ الطباعة الحجرية التصويرية |
| photolysis | تحلل ضوئي |
| photometer | جهاز قياس ضوئي |
| photometric paper | ورق قياس الضوء |
| photomicrograph | صورة مجهرية |
| photomorphogenesis | الشكل الضوئي |
| photomovie | مشاهد فيلم |
| photomovie scenes | مشهد فيلم مصور |
| photon | فوتون (وحدة القوى الضوئية) |
| photoperiodism | الدورية الضوئية |
| photosensitive plates | ألواح حساسة للضوء |
| photosensitizers | عوامل حساسية تجاه الضوء؛ محسسات للضوء |
| photosynthesis | التمثيل الضوئي أو التخليق الضوئي التمثيل الضوئي أو التخليق الضوئي |
| photosynthetic bacteria | البكتريا الممثلة للضوء: بكتيريا التمثيل الضوئي: بكتيريا منتجة تمارس البناء الضوئي |
| phototelegraphy apparatus | جهاز إرسال الصور تلغرافياً |
| photovoltaic | الألواح الضوئية |
| photovoltaic cells | خلايا فلطية ضوئية |
| photovoltaic cells | الخلايا الفولتية الضوئية؛ الخلايا الفولتضوئية |
| photovoltaic panels | الألواح الضوئية |
| photovoltaic power plant | نبات الطاقة الكهربيضوئية |
| php with cache | لغة البرمجة (بي أتش بي) الجديدة والقوية مع تقنية الضغط والتسريع |
| phraseology and terminology | التعبيرات والمصطلحات |
| phreatic level | المستوى الباطني |
| phthalo blue and hansa yellow | أزرق فثالو وأصفر هانسا |
| phthatlic acid | حامض الفثاليك |
| phylectenulosis | الالتهاب الفقاعي في العين |
| phylloxera (chemical preparations for treating -) | الفلكسر [نوع من قمل النبات] (مستحضرات كيميائية لمعالجة الفلكسر) |
| phylum | شعبة |
| physical | موجود؛ قائم |
| physical and juridical persons | الأشخاص الطبيعيون والمعنويون /الاعتباريون |
| physical chemistry | كيمياء فيزيائية |
| physical distance of the water sweep | المسافة الطبيعية للاكتساح المائي |
| physical exercise apparatus | أجهزة الرياضة البدنية |
| physical exercises (machines for -) | تمرينات بدنية (آلات التمرينات البدنية) |
| physical machine | آلة مادية |
| physical security | الأمن المادي |
| physical solvent | مذيب طبيعي |
| physical stress | الإجهاد البدني |

| | |
|---|---|
| physician | طبيب |
| physicist | فيزيائي |
| physicochemical | كيميائي طبيعي |
| physics (apparatus and instruments for -) | الفيزياء (أجهزة ومعدات للفيزياء) |
| physiologically active | نشط فسيولوجيا |
| physiology | الفيسيولوجيا. علم وظائف الأعضاء |
| physiotherapy apparatus | جهاز العلاج الطبيعي |
| physisorbed | ممتز فيزيائياً |
| physisorption | امتزاز فيزيائي |
| phytochrome | صبغ نباتي |
| phytoplankton | عوالق نباتية |
| phytosanitary certificate | شهادة صحية نباتية |
| phytosanitary inspection certificate | شهادة صحية زراعية؛ شهادة تفتيش نباتي؛ شهادة الخلو من الآفات الزراعية |
| pi-acid catalysts | محفزات pi-حمض |
| piano keyboards | ألواح مفاتيح البيانو |
| piano keys | مفاتيح البيانو |
| piano strings | أوتار البيانو |
| pianos | البيانو |
| piccalilli | المخلل |
| pick up | نصف نقل , بيك أب |
| pickaxes | مِعول |
| pickhammers | مطارق نقر |
| pickles | المخلل |
| picks (ear -) | الخِلال (خِلال الأذن) |
| picks [hand tools] | مِعول [عُدد يدوية] |
| picks for stringed instruments | ريش للاستخدام في الآلات الموسيقية الوترية |
| picnic baskets (fitted -) [including dishes] | سلال الرحلات (سلال مهيأة للرحلات) [تشمل الأطباق] |
| picolinoyl chloride | كلوريد بيكولينويل |
| picot [lace] | عراوي زينية [مخرّمات] |
| picric acid | حمض البكريك |
| picture frame brackets | حوامل إطاريه للصور |
| picture frames | أطر الصور |
| picture frames (moldings [mouldings] for -) | أطر الصور (حُلى لأطر الصور) |
| picture interference | تداخل بالصورة |
| picture transfer protocol (ptp) | بروتوكول نقل الصور القياسي |
| pictures | صور |
| pie servers | أواني تقديم الفطائر |
| pie type slice | شريحة من نوع (على شكل) قرص |
| piercing apparatus (ear -) | جهاز ثقب (جهاز ثقب الأذن) |
| pies | فطائر |
| pies (meat -) | فطائر (فطائر اللحم) |
| piezoelectric | كهروضغطي؛ كهربائي ضغطي |
| piezoelectric accelerometers | مقاييس سرعة كهروضغطية |
| piezoelectric nano wires | أسلاك كهروإجهادية نانوية |
| pig bristles | هُلب الخنازير |
| pig iron | حديد زهر |
| piggy banks, not of metal | الحصالات ليست من المعدن (على شكل خنزير) |
| pigment | خضاب؛ صبغة |
| pigment extender | عامل تمديد للخضاب |
| pigments [in paints field] | خضابات [في مجال الدهانات] |
| pigsties | زرائب الخنازير |
| pile | ركيزة أساس |
| pilings of metal | ركائز من المعدن |
| pilings, not of metal | ركائز ليست من المعدن |
| pillared clay | طفل على هيئة أعمدة |
| pillars of metal for buildings | دعائم من المعدن للاستخدام في المباني |
| pillow shams | أكياس وسادات مزخرفة |
| pillowcases | أكياس وسادات |
| pillows | وسادات |
| pillows (soporific -) for insomnia | وسادات (وسادات منومة) لمعالجة الأرق |
| pills | حبوب |
| pilot | دليلي |
| pilot | طيار |
| pilot | دليل |
| pilot identification information | معلومات تعريف دليلية |
| pilot officer | ملازم طيار |
| pilot plant | محطة تجريبية |
| pilot reaction | تفاعل تجريبي |
| pilot signal | إشارة دليلية |
| pilot signals | إشارات تحكم |
| pilot signals and beacon signals | إشارات تحكم وإشارات إرشاد لاسلكية |
| pilot valve | تعبير يطلق على صمام يتحكم في تدفق محدود ذي ضغط عالٍ |
| pilot-scale reaction | تفاعل تجريبي (دليلي مصغر) |
| pilot-scale reactor | مفاعل تجريبي |
| pilot-scale studies | دراسات رائدة |
| pin | رقم تعريف شخصي؛ مسمار |
| pin cushions | وسائد الدبابيس |
| pin punches | أدوات نزع المسامير |
| pince-nez | النظارات الأنفية |
| pince-nez cases | حافظات النظارات الأنفية |
| pince-nez chains | سلاسل النظارات الأنفية |
| pince-nez cords | حبال النظارات الأنفية |
| pince-nez mountings | حاملات النظارات الأنفية |
| pincer movement | حركة كماشة |
| pincers | كماشات |
| pincers (castrating -) | ملاقط (ملاقط خصي) |
| pincers ; nippers | كَمَّاشَةٌ: أداة بمقبضين قصيرين، وفكين على محور، لمسك الأشياء. |
| pinch belt | حزام ضغط |
| pinched grains, weevily grains | حبوب ضامرة؛ حبوب مسوسة |
| pine cones | ثمر الصنوبر |
| pinocytosis | الإرتشاف الخلوي؛ امتصاص السوائل الخلوية: أي أن الخلايا تشرب هذه السوائل |
| pins (cotter -) | مسامير (مسامير وتدية) |
| pins (ornamental -) | دبابيس (دبابيس زينة) |
| pins (tie -) | دبابيس (دبابيس رابطات العنق) |
| pins [hardware] | دبابيس [خردوات] |
| pins [jewellery, jewelry (am.)] | البروش [مجوهرات] |

| | |
|---|---|
| pins [other than jewellery, jewelry (am.)] | دبابيس [بخلاف المجوهرات] |
| pins for artificial teeth | مسامير للاستخدام في الأسنان الاصطناعية |
| pins for wheels, etc. | مسامير العجلات.. الخ |
| pins of metal (cooking -) | أواني من المعدن (أواني الطهي) |
| pins, not of metal [pegs] | دبابيس ليست من المعدن [مشاجب] |
| pipa [chinese guitars] | بيبا [جيتار صيني] |
| pipe cleaners [for tobacco pipes] | أدوات تنظيف الغليون [لتنظيف غليون التدخين] |
| pipe gaskets | أطواق منع التسريب في الأنابيب |
| pipe jackets, not of metal | أغلفة الأنابيب ليست من المعدن |
| pipe line cocks [spigots] | محابس خط الأنابيب [صنابير] |
| pipe muffs of metal | جلبة الأنبوبة من المعدن |
| pipe muffs, not of metal | جلبة الأنبوبة ليست من المعدن |
| pipe or cable clips of plastics | مشابك الأنابيب أو الكبلات من البلاستيك |
| pipe racks [for tobacco pipes] | حوامل الغليون (لغليون التدخين) |
| pipeline | خط أنابيب |
| pipeline investigation device | جهاز فحص الأنابيب |
| pipelines (manifolds of metal for -) | خطوط الأنابيب (مشعبات من المعدن لخطوط الأنابيب) |
| piperazin | ببرازين |
| piperidin | ببريدين |
| piperidyl | ببريديل |
| pipes (clips of metal for -) | أنابيب (مشابك من المعدن للأنابيب) |
| pipes (drain -) not of metal | أنابيب (أنابيب الصرف) ليست من المعدن |
| pipes (gutter -) not of metal | أنابيب (أنابيب الميزاب) ليست من المعدن |
| pipes (joint packings for -) | أنابيب (حشوة وصل للأنابيب) |
| pipes (junctions for -), not of metal | أنابيب (وصلات الأنابيب) ليست من المعدن |
| pipes (penstock -) [not of metal] | أنابيب (أنابيب البربخ) [ليست من المعدن] |
| pipes (penstock -) [of metal] | مواسير (مواسير ماء) [من المعدن] |
| pipes (reinforcing materials of metal for -) | أنابيب (مواد تقوية الأنابيب من المعدن) |
| pipes (reinforcing materials, not of metal for -) | أنابيب (مواد تقوية الأنابيب ليست من المعدن) |
| pipes (rigid -) not of metal [building] | أنابيب (أنابيب قاسية) ليست من المعدن [للبناء] |
| pipes (tobacco -) | غليون (غليون التدخين) |
| pipes (water--) not of metal | أنابيب (أنابيب الماء) ليست من المعدن |
| pipes [parts of sanitary installations] | أنابيب [أجزاء من تركيبات صحية] |
| pipes of metal | أنابيب من المعدن |
| pipes of metal, for central heating installations | أنابيب من المعدن لتركيبات التدفئة المركزية |
| pipette into | ينقل بممص إلى |
| pipettes | الممص (سحاحات للمعمل) |
| pipettes [wine-tasters] | مصاصات [أدوات لتذوق الخمور] |
| pipettte | يمتص |
| pipework | أنابيب |
| pipework of metal | أنابيب من المعدن |
| piping | أنابيب؛ شبكة أنابيب |
| piping system | شبكة أنابيب |
| piquette | شراب البيكيت |
| piracy | قرصنة |
| piracy agreement | اتفاق قرصنة |
| piracy clause | البند المتعلق بالقرصنه |
| pirate | يقرصن، قرصان |
| pirate dvds | أقراص دي في دي المسروقة |
| pirated | مقرصن |
| pirated drug | دواء مقرصن |
| pirated idea | فكرة مقرصنة |
| pirated patent | براءة مقرصنة |
| pirated software | برنامج مقرصن |
| pistols (caps for -) [toys] | مسدسات (كبسولات من المتفجرات للمسدسات) [ألعاب] |
| pistols (toy -) | مسدسات (مسدسات للعب) |
| pistols [arms] | مسدسات [أسلحة] |
| piston | مكبس؛ كباس؛ بيستون |
| piston pump | مضخة بكباس |
| piston pump | مضخة بمكبس |
| piston segments | فلقات الكباس |
| pistons for cylinders | مكابس الأسطوانات |
| pistons for engines | مكابس المحركات |
| pit | حفرة الوحل |
| pitch | زِفْت؛ قار؛ قَطِران؛ قير |
| pitch mark repair tools [golf accessories] | عُدد إصلاح حفر الجولف [كماليات الجولف] |
| pitchers, not of precious metal | أباريق ليست من المعادن النفيسة |
| pitching | خطران؛ ترجُّح |
| pitons of metal [mountaineering equipment] | أوتاد الصخور من المعدن [معدات تسلق الجبال] |
| pivot | محور |
| pivotal | محور |
| pivotal attachments | وصلات محورية |
| pivotal axis | محور الارتكاز |
| pivotal irrigation | ري محوري |
| pivoted | متمحور |
| pivoting | التمحور |
| pivoting amplitude | سعة الدوران الارتكازي |
| pivots about hinge | تتمحور البوابة حول مفصلة |
| pixel | بكسل: أصغر عناصر الصورة وهو على شكل نقطة او مستطيل صغير. |
| pizza cutters [non-electric] | أدوات قطع البيتزا [غير كهربائية] |
| pizzas | البيتزا |
| pka | ثابت التأين Pka |
| pl | خط الطور |
| placards of paper or cardboard | إعلانات من الورق أو الورق المقوى |
| placards of wood or plastics | لوحات إعلانات من الخشب أو البلاستيك |

| | |
|---|---|
| place mats [not of paper] | قواعد أواني المائدة [ليست من الورق] |
| place mats of paper | قواعد أواني المائدة من الورق |
| place under sequestration | يضع تحت الحراسة |
| placebo | دواء إرضائي: علاج وهمي خال من المادة الفعالة |
| placental | سخدي |
| plagiarism | انتحال عمل فكري |
| plain asphalt | أسفلت عادي |
| plain circles | دوائر مظللة؛ دوائر سادة |
| plaintiff | مدّعٍي؛ جانب الادعاء |
| plaited hair | شعر مجدول |
| plaited straw [except matting] | قش مجدول [بخلاف تصنيع الحصير] |
| plaits (straw -) | جدائل (جدائل من القش) |
| plan | مسقط أفقي |
| plan diagram | مخطط أفقي |
| plan view | مسقط أفقي |
| planar | مستوي؛ مستوٍ |
| planar to planar bearing system | نظام المحمل المستوي-إلى-المستوي |
| plane irons | أسلحة السحج |
| plane tables [surveying instruments] | الألواح المستوية [معدات المسح] |
| planes | مسحاج |
| planimeter | جهاز قياس السطوح |
| planing machines | مسحاج آلي |
| planks [wood for building] | ألواح خشبية غليظة [أخشاب البناء] |
| plant | وحدة تصنيع؛ مصنع؛ وحدة صناعية؛ وحدة؛ محطة؛ يزرع، نبات |
| plant diseases | أمراض النبات |
| plant fibers [fibres] (edible -) [non-nutritive] | ألياف نباتية (ألياف نباتية معدة للأكل) [غير مغذية] |
| plant growth regulating preparations | مستحضرات تنظيم نمو النبات |
| plant parasite killing apparatus | جهاز القضاء على الطفيليات النباتية |
| plant patent | براءة تمنح لاختراع نوع جديد من النباتات. |
| plant seeds | بذور النبات |
| plants | نباتات |
| plants (preparations for destroying noxious -) | نباتات (مستحضرات للقضاء على النباتات الضارة) |
| plants, dried, for decoration | نباتات زينة مجففة |
| plants:factories, workshops, production tools, equipment | المضانع، الورش، أدوات الإنتاج، المعدات |
| plaque calcification | تكلس اللويحات |
| plaques (decorative wall -) [furniture] not of textile | لوحات (لوحات تزين جداريه) [أثاث] ليست من القماش |
| plasma (blood -) | بلازما (بلازما الدم) |
| plasma concentration of the active substance | تركيز المادة الفعالة في البلازما |
| plasma concentration-time profile | منحنى التركيز – الزمن في البلازما |
| plasma display panel pdp ; plasma flat panel display pdp | شاشة بلازما؛ شاشة عرض بلازما مسطحة |
| plasma physics | فيزياء البلازما |
| plasmapheresis | استخراج (استخلاص) البلازما |
| plasmid | بلازميد |
| plasmocytoma | ورم البلازماويات |
| plaster | جص؛ ملاط؛ طين البناء؛ لزقة؛ لصوق |
| plaster (insulating -) | لاصق (لاصق عازل) |
| plaster bandages for orthopaedic purposes | أربطة لاصقة للاستخدام في أغراض تقويم العظام |
| plaster of paris | جص باريس |
| plasterboard | لوح جصي |
| plasterer | مبيض |
| plasters | لاصق للاستخدام في الأغراض الطبية |
| plasters (mustard -) | لاصق (لاصق الخردل) |
| plastic antibodies | أجسام مضادة لدائنية |
| plastic bushing | جلبة بلاستيكية |
| plastic cling film, extensible, for palletization | شريط لاصق من البلاستيك قابل للتمدد للاستخدام في النقل على منصة نقالة |
| plastic deformation | تشوه لدن |
| plastic fibers [fibres] for textile use | ألياف بلاستيكية للاستخدام في النسيج |
| plastic fibers [fibres], not for textile use | ألياف بلاستيكية ليست للاستخدام في النسيج |
| plastic file | مبرد اللدائن |
| plastic film for wrapping | شريط بلاستيكي للاستخدام في التغليف |
| plastic film other than for wrapping | شريط بلاستيكي ليس للاستخدام في التغليف |
| plastic material [substitute for fabrics] | مادة بلاستيكية [بديلة للأقمشة] |
| plastic sheeting | أغطية بلاستيكية |
| plasticise; plasticize | يلدّن |
| plasticiser | ملدن |
| plasticity | مرونة؛ اللدونة |
| plasticizer | ملدن؛ مادة مكسبة لليونة |
| plastics (dispersions of -) | بلاستيك (مشتتات البلاستيك) |
| plastics for modelling | بلاستيك للتشكيل |
| plastics, unprocessed | بلاستيك غير معالج |
| plastisols | بلاستيسول [مادة تتكون من خليط من راتنج ومواد حافظة اللدّانة] |
| plate column | عمود صفائحي |
| plate glass [raw material] | بلور للمرايا والنوافذ الكبيرة [مادة خام] |
| plate glass [windows], for building | بلور للمرايا والنوافذ الكبيرة [نوافذ] للاستخدام في البناء |
| plate racks | أرفف حمل الأواني |
| plate spring | نابض مسطح |
| plate structures | الهياكل المسطحة |
| plate warmers | مدفئ الأطباق |
| plateau | مستوى مستقر نسبيا: مستوى مستوي أو منبسط |
| plateau-like form | صورة شبه مستقرة |
| plated articles [precious metal plating] | مواد مطلية [طلاء بالمعادن النفيسة] |
| platelet | صفيحة دموية |
| platelet adhesion | التصاق الصفائح الدموية |

| | |
|---|---|
| plates (carriers for dark -) [photography] | ألواح (حوامل للألواح الداكنة) |
| plates (hot -) | أطباق (أطباق ساخنة) |
| plates (paper -) | أطباق (أطباق ورقية) |
| plates (photosensitive -) | ألواح (ألواح حساسة للضوء) |
| plates (printing -) | ألواح (طباعة) |
| plates (registration -) of metal | لوحات (لوحات تسجيل) من المعدن |
| plates (sensitized photographic -) | ألواح (ألواح فوتوغرافية حساسة) |
| plates are coated by incubation | تم وضع العينات في الأطباق ووضعها في حضانة |
| plates for addressing machines (address -) | لوحات آلات عمل العناوين (لوحات لآلات عمل العناوين) |
| plates for batteries | ألواح البطاريات |
| plates for offset printing (sensitized -) | ألواح طباعة الأوفست (ألواح حساسة للاستخدام في طباعة الأوفست) |
| plates to prevent milk boiling over | أطباق لمنع فوران اللبن الحليب عند الغلي |
| plates, not of metal (registration -) | لوحات ليست من المعدن (لوحات تسجيل) |
| plate-type structures | الهياكل المسطحة: الهياكل البنائية ذات النمط السطحي |
| platform mounting on the receiver | المنصة الموجودة على المستقبل |
| platforms (firing -) | منصات (منصات إطلاق النار) |
| platforms, prefabricated, not of metal | منصات سابقة التصنيع ليست من المعدن |
| platforms, prefabricated, of metal | منصات سابقة التصنيع من المعدن |
| platinum | بلاتين |
| platinum [metal] | البلاتين [معدن] |
| platinum paint (glossy -) for ceramics | طلاء بلاتيني (طلاء بلاتيني لامع) للخزفيات |
| platoon | فصيلة |
| play | يلعب، يقوم بدور، يمثل، حركة، لعبة |
| play (between teeth, gaps, etc.) | خلوص (بين الأسنان، الفجوات، إلخ) |
| play (vcr) | يشغل "فيديو" |
| play balloons | مناطيد للعب |
| play sound | يشغل الصوت |
| playback | التشغيل؛ يشغل |
| playback pause | الإيقاف المؤقت للتشغيل |
| playback time | الفترة الزمنية للتشغيل |
| playback zoom | التكبير للتشغيل |
| player | مشغل؛ قائم بدور، فاعل |
| players | القائمون بالأدوار |
| playing a movie | تشغيل فيلم |
| playing back/searching images | تشغيل/البحث عن الصور |
| playing balls | كرات اللعب |
| playing cards | ورق اللعب |
| playing/pausing/stopping | تشغيل/إيقاف مؤقت/توقف |
| playlist | قائمة التشغيل |
| playpens for babies | حظائر نقالة للعب الأطفال |
| plcs | ورقة مراقبة التعبئة والتشغيله |
| plead the 5th | يرفض الإجابة باللجوء إلى التعديل الدستوري الخامس |
| pleading | المرافعة |
| pleading law | قانون المرافعات |
| pleated | منثني |
| plectrums | ريشة العازف |
| plekstrin homology (ph) regions | نواحي تجانس بليكسترين (PH) |
| pleural effusion | انسكاب بلوري |
| pleurectomy | بتر جزء من البلورا |
| pleuritis | التهاب البلورا |
| plexus | شبكة |
| pliers | الزردية |
| pliers; (long-nose pliers; long-handles pliers) | زرادية: كماشة صغيرة الرأس طويلة المقبضين لمسك الأشياء، وثني وقطع الأسلاك |
| pliers bits | رؤس الكماشات والزرديات (التي تضم الفكين الحديديين اللذين تمسك بهما الأشياء) |
| plo | مكتب معلومات عامة |
| ploidy | ازدواجية |
| plot | منحنى |
| plotter | جهاز رسم منحنيات أو خطوط بيانية |
| ploughs | محاريث |
| ploughshares | أنصال المحراث |
| plt | معاهدة قانون البراءات |
| plug | يوصل بمصدر الكهرباء، قابس، سدادة |
| plug valve | صمام مقبسي |
| plug flow | تدفق كتلي؛ تدفق دفعي |
| pluggability | قابل للوصل بالقبس |
| pluggable | قابلية الشيء للوصل بالقبس |
| plugged | موصل بالقابس الكهربائي |
| plugging | كبح المحفز |
| plug-like flow | تدفق شبه كتلي |
| plugs (detonating -) | طلقات (طلقات متفجرة) |
| plugs of metal | مقابس من المعدن |
| plugs of metal (wall -) | مقابس من المعدن (مقابس الجدار من المعدن) |
| plugs, sockets and other contacts [electric connections] | مقابس ودوايات وتوصيلات أخرى [توصيلات كهربائية] |
| plum | برقوق (فواكه) |
| plumb bob | شاقول |
| plumb bobs | ثقل الفادن [الرصاصة التي بطرف خيط الفادن] |
| plumb lines | خيوط الفادن |
| plunger | كباس |
| plunger pistons | مكابس غاطسة |
| plungers for clearing blocked drains | مغاطس لتصفية انسداد المياه المنصرفة |
| plural data bits | أرقام ثنائية للبيانات المجمعة |
| plurality of oilfield events | مجموعة من حالات حقل النفط |
| plurality of sets of | وفرة (أو عدد ) من مجموعات من |
| pluripotent | وافرة القوة |
| plush toys | ألعاب مصنوعة من البلش (المخمل) |

| | |
|---|---|
| plutonium | البلوتونيوم |
| plywood | أبلكاج |
| pm | مدير مشروع؛ صيانة وقائية |
| pm; pmol; pmole | بيكو مول |
| pmcs | فحوصات وخدمات الصيانة الوقائية |
| pme | عنصر المهمة الرئيسي |
| pmo | مكتب إدارة المشروع |
| pmr | مراجعة إدارة المشروع |
| pneumatic | بالهواء المضغوط (تعمل بالهواء المضغوط) |
| pneumatic circuit | دائرة هوائية |
| pneumatic conveying system | نظام نقل بالهواء المضغوط |
| pneumatic door openers and closers [parts of machines] | أدوات تعمل بضغط الهواء لفتح وغلق الأبواب [أجزاء من آلات] |
| pneumatic hammers | مطارق تعمل بضغط الهواء |
| pneumatic tires [tyres] | إطارات تعمل بضغط الهواء |
| pneumatic transporters | وسائل نقل تعمل بضغط الهواء |
| pneumatic tube conveyors | ناقلات أنبوبية تعمل بضغط الهواء |
| pneumatically | بالهواء المضغوط |
| pneumicoccus | المكورات الرئوية |
| pneumococcus | مكورة رئوية |
| pneumoconiosis | السحار الرئوي |
| pneumonectomy | استئصال الرئة |
| pneumonia | التهاب الرئة |
| pneumonitis | التهاب رئوي |
| pnni | واجهة شبكة لشبكة خاص |
| po | عبر الفم |
| poc | نقطة الاتصال |
| pocket | تجويف |
| pocket calculators | حاسبات الجيب |
| pocket lamps (batteries for -) | مصابيح الجيب (بطاريات لمصابيح الجيب) |
| pocket searchlights | كشافات النور للجيب |
| pocket squares | مناديل الجيب للزينة |
| pocket torches, electric | كشافات كهربائية للجيب |
| pocket wallets | محافظ الجيب |
| pocket warmers | مدفئات الجيب |
| pockets for clothing | جيوب الملابس |
| pod | قائم |
| point advantage | أفضلية نقاط |
| point loads | أحمال نقطية (موضعية) |
| point mutation | طفرة نيوكليوتيد واحد |
| point of attachement | نقطة ارتباط |
| point of sale terminal | وحدة نقطة بيع |
| point products | منتجات نقطية |
| pointer-based snapshots | لقطات المؤشر |
| pointers (chart -), non-electronic | مؤشرات (مؤشرات الرسم البياني) غير إلكترونية |
| pointers (light-emitting electronic -) | مؤشرات (مؤشرات ضوئية إلكترونية) |
| pointing device | جهاز تأشير |
| pointing device | جهاز إشارة |
| pointless discovery | اكتشاف لا قيمة له |
| pointless invention | اختراع غير ذي قيمة |
| pointless invention | اختراع عديم المعنى |
| pointless patent claims | دعاوى برائية غير ذات قيمة محددة |
| points (railway -) | نقاط (نقاط سكة حديد) |
| points of incidence | نقاط السقوط |
| point-to-point link | وصلة بين نقطتين |
| poisons | سموم |
| poistion (in) | يضع (في) |
| pol | وقود وزيوت وشحوم |
| polar compound | مركب قطبي |
| polar solvent | مذيب مستقطب؛ مذيب قطبي الجزيئات؛ مذيب متقاطب |
| polarimeter | جهاز قياس الاستقطاب |
| polarization | استقطاب |
| poles of metal | أعمدة من المعدن |
| poles of metal, for electric lines | أعمدة الخطوط الكهربائية من المعدن |
| poles, not of metal | أعمدة ليست من المعدن |
| poles, not of metal, for electric power lines | أعمدة خطوط القدرة الكهربائية ليست من المعدن |
| police batons | هراوات رجال الشرطة |
| police post | كمين للشرطة |
| police state | دولة بوليسية |
| policy | سياسة، لائحة |
| polio (poliomyelitis) | شلل الأطفال |
| polish | صقل |
| polish for furniture and flooring | مواد تلميع الأثاث والأرضيات |
| polish removing substances | مواد إزالة اللمعة |
| polished wired glass | زجاج مصقول المقوى بالأسلاك: يتم إنتاج الزجاج المصقول الشفاف المقوى بالأسلاك بجلي وصقل الزجاج المزخرف المقوى بأسلاك |
| polishes (denture -) | مواد تلميع (مواد تلميع الأسنان) |
| polish-filter | يرشح باستخدام مرشح متوسط الثقوب |
| polishing (machines and apparatus for -) [electric] | صقل (آلات وأجهزة للصقل) [كهربائية] |
| polishing apparatus and machines, for household purposes, non-electric | أجهزة وآلات غير كهربائية للصقل للاستخدام في الأغراض المنزلية |
| polishing creams | كريمات التلميع |
| polishing gloves | قفازات صقل |
| polishing irons [glazing tools] | أدوات صقل حديدية [عُدد للتزجيج] |
| polishing leather | جلود صقل |
| polishing materials [for making shiny] [except preparations, paper and stone] | مواد صقل [للتلميع] فيما عدا مستحضرات, وورق وأحجار] |
| polishing paper | ورق صقل |
| polishing preparations | مستحضرات صقل |
| polishing rouge | أحمر الصقل |
| polishing step | خطوة إنهاء |
| polishing stones | أحجار صقل |
| polishing wax | شمع الصقل |
| poll ; survey | استطلاع للرأي |
| pollen [raw material] | لقاح [مادة خام] |
| pollen prepared as foodstuff | لقاح معدّ للاستخدام كطعام |
| polling stations | مراكز الاقتراع |

| | |
|---|---|
| pollution control device | جهاز تحكم في التلوث |
| pollution reduction device | جهاز خفض التلوث |
| pollutive material | مادة ملوثة |
| polonium | البولونيوم [عنصر فلزي] |
| poly | متعدد |
| poly- styrenic block | كتلة بولي ستيرينية |
| polyacetals | مركبات بولي أسيتال |
| poly-acid ester | إستر حمض متعدد |
| polyacrylamide | بولي أكريل أميد |
| polyadenylation | تذييل بعديد الأدينيلات |
| polyalkoxy | بولي ألكوكسي |
| polyarthritis | الالتهاب المفصلي المتعدد |
| polycarboxylic acid polymers | بوليمرات الأحماض عديدة الكربوكسيل |
| polychondritits | التهاب غضروفي متعدد |
| polycondensation | تكثيف متعدد |
| polycyanoacrylates | مركبات بولي سيانو أكريلات |
| polycystic | عديد الحويصلات |
| polycystic ovary syndrome | متلازمة المبيض عديد الحويصلات (متلازمة تكيس المبايض) |
| polydihydropyrans | مركبات بولي داي هيدروبيران |
| polyepsilon caprolactone | بولي إبسيلون كابرولاكتون |
| polyester amides | أميدات البوليستر |
| polyester pellets | كريات البوليستر |
| polyesters | مركبات بوليستر |
| polyetherester amides | أميدات إستر البولي إيثر |
| polyetheresters | إسترات البولي إيثر |
| polyethylene glycol (peg) | بولي إيثيلين جليكول |
| polyethylene terephthalate | البولي إيثيلين تريفثالات |
| polyethylene terephthalate copolymer | بوليمر بولي إيثيلين تريفثالات مشترك |
| polyethyleneglycol | بولي إيثيلين جليكول |
| polyethylenenaphthalate | البولي إيثيلين نفثالات |
| polygenic | متعدد الجينات |
| polyglycolic acid | حمض عديد السكريات |
| polygon | مضلع |
| polyhedral | متعدد الوجوه؛ كثير السطوح |
| polyhydric alcohol | كُحُولٌ عَدِيد الهيدروكسيل |
| polyhydroxy butyric acid | حمض بولي هيدروكسي بيوتيريك |
| polyketones | بولي كيتون |
| polylactic acid | حمض عديد اللاكتيك؛ حمض البولي لاكتيك |
| polymer end groups | مجموعات البوليمر النهائية |
| polymer slurry | ملاط بوليمري |
| polymeric | بوليمري |
| polymeric matrix ; polymer matrix | شبكة بوليمرية؛ نسيج بوليمري شبكي؛ قالب بوليمري؛ كتلة بوليمرية؛ حامل بوليمري |
| polymeric melt | مصهور بوليمري |
| polymeric pellets | كريات البوليمر |
| polymerisation installations | تركيبات بلمرة |
| polymerizable ethylenically unsaturated monomers | مونومرات غير مشبعة إيثيلينياً قابلة للبلمرة |
| polymerization | بلمرة |
| polymictic conglomerates | مدملك متنوع الحصيات |
| polymorph | متعدد الأشكال |
| polymorphic | متعدد الأشكال |
| polymorphism | تعدد الأشكال |
| polymorphism | تعدد التشكل المعدني |
| polymorphism of the gene | تعدد الأشكال للجين |
| polymorphonuclear | متعدد أشكال النوى |
| polymyalgia | تعدد الآلام العضلية |
| polymyositis | الالتهاب العضلي المتعدد |
| polyneuropathy | اعتلال أعصاب عديدة |
| polynomial | متعددة الحدود |
| poly-ol | عديد الهيدروكسيل |
| polyolefin | البولي أوليفينات |
| polyolefins | بولي أولفين |
| polyols | كحوليات عديدة الهيدروكسيل |
| polyoma | توارم |
| polyorthoesters | إسترات بولي أورثو |
| polyoxy | بولي أوكسي |
| polyoxycations of aluminum | إدخال مجموعة بولي أوكسي كاتيونات للألومنيوم |
| polypeptide | بولي ببتيد |
| polyphonic ring tones | نغمات إيقاعية: هي أنواع متطورة من نغمات الهاتف التي تستخدم نغمات متعددة بدلا من نغمات واحدة حيث تصدر أكثر من نغمة في وقت واحد محدثة صوتا أوركستري متعددا وبالإمكان تنزيل هذه النغمات على بعض الأجهزة. |
| polyposis | داء البوليب |
| polyprotein | عديد بروتين |
| polysaccharides | عديد السكريات |
| polyster polymer or copolymer | بوليمر البوليستر أو بوليمر البوليستر المشترك |
| polystyrenes | بولي ستيرين |
| polythelene | بولي إثيلين |
| polyunsaturated | المحتوي على العديد من مناطق عدم التشبع |
| pomades for medical purposes | مراهم للاستخدام في الأغراض الطبية |
| ponderal recuperation | استعادة الوزن |
| pontoon bridges | كباري عائمة؛ براطيم |
| pontoons | زوارق مسطحة |
| pool | مجموعة؛ تجميع؛ يجمع؛ مجمع أشياء؛ بركة؛ حوض |
| pooled fractions | الأجزاء المجمعة |
| pooled supernatants | المواد الطافية المتجمعة |
| pooling | تجميع |
| pooling ideas | تجميع الأفكار |
| pools (swimming -) [metal structures] | أحواض (أحواض سباحة) [هياكل معدنية] |
| pools (swimming -) [play articles] | أحواض (أحواض سباحة) [مواد للعب] |
| pools (swimming -) [structures, not of metal] | أحواض (أحواض سباحة) [هياكل ليست من المعدن] |
| poor cell penetration | ضعف نفاذها إلى الخلايا |
| poor examination/performance | ضعيف، رديئ المستوى |
| poor visibility | رؤية ضعيفة |
| popcorn | الفشار |

| | |
|---|---|
| popular resistence | المقاومة الشعبية |
| populate | يجمع |
| populating the frame | إشغال الإطار |
| population | مجموعة |
| pop-up menue | قائمة منبثقة |
| porcelain | الصيني |
| porcelain for dental prostheses | بورسلين للاستخدام في جراحة الأسنان التعويضية |
| porcelain fused metal (pfm) dental prosthesis | لتركيبة أسنان من معدن ملتحم بالبورسلين PEM أو تركيبة نصفها معدن نصفها بورسلين |
| porcelain ware | آنية من البورسلين |
| porches of metal [building] | شرفات من المعدن [مباني] |
| porches, not of metal, for building | شرفات المباني ليست من المعدن |
| pore pressure | ضغط مسامي؛ ضغط خلالي |
| pore size distribution | توزيع حجم مسام |
| pore wall surface | سطح جدار مسامي |
| pores per inch | مسام في البوصة |
| pork | لحم الخنزير |
| porosimetry | مقياس المسامية |
| porosity | مسامية |
| porous | مسامي |
| porro prism | منشور بورو |
| port forwarding | خاصية port forwarding |
| portability | قابلية النقل |
| portable | متنقل؛ محمول: يمكن حمله |
| portable device | جهاز يمكن حمله |
| portable electric screw driver | مِفَكّ براغي كَهْرَبَائِيّ مُتَنَقِّل |
| portable photosynthesis system | جهاز التمثيل الضوئي: يستخدم لقياس الفروقات بين معدل التمثيل الضوئي للأجناس المختلفة للنباتات والفروق بين معدلات الأصناف لنفس الجنس النباتي مما يتيح امكانية اختيار الأصناف ذات المعدلات العالية للتمثيل تحت الظروف القاسية كالجفاف |
| portable telephones | هواتف محمولة |
| portal | بوابة؛ مدخل |
| portfire | مشعل |
| portfolio | محفظة، حزمة |
| portfolio assessment | تقييم محفظة |
| portfolio development | التطوير الاستثماري |
| portfolio license | ترخيص لمحفظة |
| portfolio management | إدارة محفظة |
| portfolio management services | خدمات إدارة المحافظ الاستثمارية |
| portfolio value | قيمة محفظة |
| portfolios | الحقائب التعليمية |
| portholes | كوات في جانب السفينة أو الطائرة |
| portion | جزء |
| portland cement | أسمنت بورتلاندي |
| portrait | صورة شخصية |
| portraits | صور وجوه أشخاص |
| posit | الموقع |
| position | وضع؛ موضع؛ يموضع |

| | |
|---|---|
| position locator device | جهاز تعيين الموضع |
| position signals | إشارت موضع |
| positionability | قابلية الشيء للتموضع |
| positionable | قابل لتحديد الوضع (بشكل انتقائي) |
| positionable | قابل للتموضع |
| positioned | متموضع |
| positioner | محدد الموضع |
| positioning | وضع أو تحديد وضع |
| positioning | تموضع |
| positioning device | جهاز تموضع |
| positioning system | نظام تموضع |
| positive and negative symptoms | الأعراض الإيجابية والسلبية |
| positive cells | خلايا موجبة |
| positive control | عينة مقارنة موجبة |
| positive control experiment | تجربة مقارنة إيجابية (للتأكد من صحة تجارب أخرى) |
| positive ions/linear mode | الأيونات الموجبة/الوضع الخطي |
| positive sense | مظهر إيجابي |
| positron emission tomography | تصوير مقطعي بالإصدار البوزيتروني |
| posix | واجهة نظام تشغيل متنقل |
| possessing the combined effect | تظهر التأثير المشترك |
| possession order | أمر حيازة |
| possible embodiments of the inventions | تجسيدات ممكنة للاختراع |
| post capillary resistance | ما بعد مقاومة الشعيرات |
| post hoc responders | المستجيبون اللاحقون |
| post translational | ما بعد التحول |
| postage stamp meter | جهاز قياس طوابع البريد |
| postage stamps | طوابع البريد |
| postcards | بطاقات بريدية |
| post-compound | بعد إعطاء المركب |
| postcontacted | متلامس لاحقا |
| post-depositional dolomitization | الدلمتة المتأخرة |
| post-depositional structures | بنيات بعد الترسيب |
| post-employment inventions | اختراعات ما بعد الوظيفة. الاختراعات التي يخترعها الموظف بعد انتهاء وظيفته، والتي لا تدخل ضمن الاختراعات التي عادة ما يتنازل عنها الموظف لرب العمل عند توقيعه على عقد العمل |
| postencephalitic | عقب التهاب الدماغ |
| posterior | خلفي |
| posters | ملصقات |
| post-flow side | جانب خروج التدفق من المفاعل |
| postherpetic neuralgia | الألم العصبي الذي يعقب الإصابة بالحلاء (مرض جلدي وعائي مخاطي) |
| post-hoc analysis | مغالطة منطقية |
| post-hoc; post hoc | لاحق |
| postmastectomy syndrome | متلازمة ما بعد استئصال الثدي |
| postmenopausal | بعد انقطاع الدورة الشهرية |
| postmenopausal women | النساء اللاتي في سن بعد انقطاع |

| | |
|---|---|
| | الدورة الشهرية؛ النساء بعد انقطاع الطمث |
| postmortem | تشريح الجثة |
| posts of metal | دعائم من المعدن |
| posts of metal for electric lines | دعائم الخطوط الكهربائية من المعدن |
| posts, not of metal | دعائم ليست من المعدن |
| posts, not of metal, for electric power lines | دعائم خطوط القدرة الكهربائية ليست من المعدن |
| postsurgical pain syndromes | متلازمات الألم التالي للعمليات الجراحية |
| postthoracotomy syndrome | متلازمة ما بعد شق الصدر |
| post-translational (posttranslational) mechaniscms | آليات ما بعد التحول |
| pot | وعاء |
| pot elements | أوعية |
| pot hooks of metal | مساكات القدور من المعدن |
| pot lids | أغطية القدور |
| pot tending machines | ماكينات إمالة الأوعية |
| potash | بوتاس |
| potash water | ماء البوتاس |
| potassic fertilizers | أسمدة البوتاسيوم |
| potassium | بوتاسيوم |
| potassium dioxalate | ثاني أوكسالات البوتاسيوم |
| potassium phosphate tribasic | فوسفات البوتاسيوم ثلاثية القواعد |
| potassium phthalimide | بوتاسيوم فثاليميد |
| potassium salts | أملاح البوتاسيوم |
| potato chips | رقاقات البطاطس (البطاطا) |
| potato crisps | رقاقات البطاطس (البطاطا) |
| potato flakes | رقاقات البطاطس (البطاطا) |
| potato flour for food | دقيق البطاطس (البطاطا) للاستخدام في الطعام |
| potato fritters | فطائر البطاطس (البطاطا) المجهزة للقلي |
| potatoes, fresh | بطاطس (بطاطا) طازجة |
| potential camelizing substitutions | استبدالات جَمَلِيَّة ممكنة |
| potential difference | فرق جهد |
| potential infringer | منتهك محتمل |
| potential licensee | ترخيص محتمل |
| potential patent | براءة محتملة |
| potential patent infringement | انتهاك براءة محتمل |
| potential patent licensees | مرخص لهم محتملون لاستخدام البراءات |
| potential patent rights | حقوق براءة محتملة |
| potential patentability | إمكانية محتملة لصدور براءة |
| potential steric hindrance | إعاقة فراغية محتملة |
| potentialities | إمكانيات |
| potentiality | إمكانية |
| potentially infringible patent | براءة من المحتمل أن تكون موضع انتهاك |
| potentially patentable idea | فكرة من المحتمل أن تصدر عنها براءة |
| potentially relevant prior art | فن سابق من المحتمل أن يكون ذا صلة |
| potentials | إمكانيات، احتمالات كامنة |
| potentiate | يدعم؛ يعزز |
| potentiation | تدعيم - تعزيز |
| potentiometric | متعلق بمقياس فرق الجهد |
| potentiostat | مثبت الجهد |
| potpourris [fragrances] | عطور [مزيج من أوراق الورد المجففة مع شئ من التوابل يحفظ في وعاء رغبة في ريحه الطيب] |
| pots | قدور |
| pots (flower -) | قدور (قدور الزهور) |
| pots (peat -) for horticulture | قدور (قدور الخث) للاستخدام في أعمال البساتين |
| pots, not of precious metal | قدور ليست من المعادن النفيسة |
| potters' clay | طين الخزافين |
| potters' wheels | عجلات الخزافين |
| pottery | أواني فخارية |
| potting soil | تربة القدور |
| pouches (cartridge -) | جراب (جراب الخراطيش) |
| pouches (disposable sterilization -) | أكياس (أكياس التعقيم للاستخدام لمرة واحدة ) |
| pouches (tobacco -) | أكياس (أكياس التبغ) |
| pouches, of leather, for packaging | أكياس من الجلد للتغليف |
| poultices | كمادات |
| poultices (mustard -) | كمادات (كمادات الخردل) |
| poultry for breeding | دواجن التربية |
| poultry rings | أطواق الدواجن |
| poultry, live | دواجن حية |
| poultry, not live | لحوم دواجن غير حية |
| pound | رطل |
| pounds per square inch gauge (psig) | رطل لكل بوصة مربعة (بالعداد) |
| pounds-force | بثقل الرطل |
| pour point | نقطة الانصباب |
| pour-point depressant | خافض نقطة الانصباب |
| povidone | بروفيدون |
| powder (aluminium -) for painters, artists and decorators | مسحوق (مسحوق الألومنيوم) لاستخدام عمال الدهان والفنانين وعمال الديكور |
| powder (bronze -) [paint] | مسحوق (مسحوق البرونز) [دهان] |
| powder (cake -) | مسحوق (مسحوق الكعك) |
| powder (make-up -) | مسحوق (مسحوق التجميل) |
| powder compacts of precious metal | علب مسحوق تجميل صغيرة من المعادن النفيسة |
| powder compacts, not of precious metal | علب مسحوق تجميل صغيرة ليست من المعادن النفيسة |
| powder form (metals in -) for painters, decorators, printers and artists | شكل مسحوق (معادن على شكل مسحوق) لاستخدام عمال الدهان وعمال الديكور وعمال الطباعة والفنانين |
| powder horns | قرون البارود |
| powder metallurgy | ميتالوريجية المساحيق |
| powder of cantharides | مسحوق الذراح [مسحوق الخنفس الأسباني المجفف] |
| powder puffs | المذرات [قطيفات صغيرة لتجميل الوجه بالمساحيق] |

| | |
|---|---|
| powder x-ray diffraction patterns ; x-ray powder diffraction patterns | أنماط حيود الأشعة السينية في المسحوق؛ أنماط حيود أشعة X في المسحوق |
| powdered crystalline silicon | مسحوق السيليكون المتبلر |
| powdered eggs | مسحوق البيض |
| powdered glass for decoration | مسحوق الزجاج للاستخدام في الزينة |
| powders (explosive -) | مساحيق (مساحيق متفجرة) |
| powders (silvering -) | مساحيق (مساحيق تفضيض) |
| powders for effervescing beverages | مساحيق المشروبات الفوارة |
| powders for ice cream | مساحيق الأيس كريم |
| power | يمد بالطاقة، يمد بالقدرة، يشغل، قوة، قدرة، سلطة، طاقة |
| power button | زرار تغذية كهربائية |
| power cable | كبل التغذية الكهربائية |
| power control for a transmission without error detection coding | تحكم القدرة لإرسال بدون شفرة كشف الأخطاء |
| power density | كثافة قدرة |
| power equalization | توازن القوى |
| power hammers | مطارق آلية |
| power in numbers | القوة العددية |
| power loom | نول آلي أو ميكانيكي |
| power of attorney | توكيل رسمي |
| power of procuration | تفويض رسمي |
| power output | مخرج قوة تشغيل |
| power pack | وحدة الطاقة |
| power physics | فيزياء القدرة |
| power plant | وحدة توليد القدرة |
| power plant (also powerplant) | وحدة الطاقة |
| power steering fluid | مائع للمقود الآلي |
| power tailgates (am.) [parts of land vehicles] | أرفف آلية [أجزاء من مركبات أرضية] |
| power transmission belt | سير ناقل الحركة |
| power transmission belt arrangement | ترتيبة السير ناقل الحركة |
| powerable | قابل للشحن |
| powerablility | قابلية الشيء للشحن |
| powered | مشحون، مُشغل، مدعوم |
| powered air cylinder | اسطوانة هواء تعمل بالطاقة |
| powerplant | محطة توليد طاقة |
| powertrain | مولد طاقة |
| powwow organizers | منظمو الندوات |
| ppb | جزء في البليون |
| ppg | رطل لكل جالون |
| ppi | جزء في البوصة |
| ppm | جزء في المليون |
| ppm | صفحة في الدقيقة |
| ppmv | جزء في المليون بالحجم |
| ppmw | جزء في المليون بالوزن |
| ppo | مكتب المشروع التابع لمشتري |
| pps | جدول الأسعار والسداد |
| ppt | جزء في الألف |
| pr | مسؤوليات المشتري |
| pr | العلاقات العامة |

| | |
|---|---|
| practicable use of an invention | استعمال ممكن لاختراع |
| practical jokes [novelties] | المداعبات العملية [ألعاب مبتكرة] |
| practice | يمارس، ممارس |
| practice of the invention | التطبيق العملي للاختراع |
| practitioner | ممارس |
| pralines | البرالين [حلوى اللوز أو الجوز] |
| prams [baby carriages] | عربات الأطفال |
| praseodymium | البريزيوديميوم [عنصر فلزي] |
| prawns [not live] | القريدس [الروبيان] [غير حي] |
| pre- | أولي؛ مسبق؛ تحضيري |
| pre licensing patent due diligence | مراجعة واجبة بشأن البراءات سابقة على منح ترخيص. تقييم وضع البراءات ذات الصلة قبل منح الترخيص |
| pre se | بحد ذاتها؛ بنفسها؛ بمفردها |
| pre technology transfer patent due diligence | مراجعة واجبة بشأن البراءات السابقة على نقل التقنية. تقييم وضع البراءات ذات الصلة قبل القيام بنقل التقنية |
| pre-algebra | بدايات علم الجبر |
| preamble | ديباجة؛ مقدمة الدستور أو وثيقة برلمانية |
| pre-b-cell | سَلاَئِفُ الخَلاَيا B (سَلاَئِفُ اللِّمْفاوِيَّات B) |
| pre-beta cells (pre beta-lymphocytes) | سَلاَئِفُ الخَلاَيا بيتا (سَلاَئِفُ اللِّمْفاوِيَّات بيتا) |
| pre-cast | الخرسانة الجاهزة |
| precedent | سابقة |
| precedential | سبق |
| precedential opinion | رأي سبقي يصح التعامل معه على أنه سابقة |
| preceding invention | اختراع سابق |
| precious metals (salts of -) for industrial purposes | معادن نفيسة (أملاح المعادن النفيسة) للاستخدام في الأغراض الصناعية |
| precious metals, unwrought or semi-wrought | معادن نفيسة، مشغولة أو شبه مشغولة |
| precious stones | أحجار كريمة |
| precipitate | راسب؛ المترسب |
| precipitate | يرسب أو يترسب |
| precipitation hardening | التصليب بالترسيب |
| precision and scale | خصائص العدد والقيمة |
| precision balances | موازين دقيقة |
| precision measuring apparatus | جهاز قياس دقيق |
| precision screwdriver | مفك للثقب |
| pre-cleaning | التنظيف المبدئي |
| preclinical | قبل الفحص السريري- ما قبل الفحص الكلينكي |
| pre-coat filter | فلتر أولي |
| precognition | تحقيق تمهيدي |
| pre-compound | قبل إعطاء المركب |
| precompression | ضغط متقدم |
| precontacted | متلامس مسبقا |
| pre-contacting pot | دورق تلامس أولي |
| precursors | مادة منتجة (لغيرها) |
| precut | قبل القطع |

| | |
|---|---|
| pre-depositional structures | بنيات قبل الترسيب |
| predicate offence | جريمة أصلية |
| predict | يتنبأ |
| predictable inventability | قابلية للاختراع مستشرفة |
| prednisone | بريدنيزون |
| predominately | بشكل سائد؛ على نحو سائد |
| preemployment invention | اختراع سابق على شغل وظيفة |
| pre-employment inventions | اختراعات ما قبل الوظيفة. الاختراعات التي يخترعها الموظف قبل استلامه وظيفته. وفي بعض الأحيان يقوم الموظف بتزويد رب العمل بصور لهذه الاختراعات لتوضيح سجله الاختراعي لاسيما وأن الغالب أن يتنازل الموظف عن الاختراعات التي يخترعها خلال عمله لصالح رب العمل |
| pre-employment screening | اختبارات ما قبل التوظيف |
| preemptive analgesia | التسكين التداخلي |
| preference shares | أسهم الأفضلية أو الأسهم المتميزة |
| preferences | تفضيلات |
| preferred embodiment | التجسد المفضل. التجسد الذي يفضله المخترع للاختراع |
| preferred embodiments of the invention | التجسدات المفضلة للاختراع. التجسدات المثلى من بين التجسدات العديدة المتاحة فيما يتصل باختراع معين |
| preferred embodiments of the invention | التجسيدات المفضلة للاختراع |
| preferred hydrodynamic sizes | الأحجام الهيدروديناميكية المفضلة |
| prefrontal cortex | القشرة الجبهية الأمامية |
| pregnancy (chemical preparations for the diagnosis of -) | الحمل (مستحضرات كيميائية لتشخيص الحمل) |
| pre-hearing conference | اجتماع ما قبل الجلسة |
| pre-installed cgi scripts | برامج (بيرل) أدوات مساعدة للمواقع مدمجة بالموقع وجاهزة للعمل مجاناً |
| pre-ipo | مساهمة قبل الاكتتاب (العام) |
| premature aging syndrome known as hutchinson-gilford progeria syndrome (hgps) | متلازمة الشيخوخة المبكرة المعروفة باسم متلازمة هتشينسون-جيلفورد بروجيريا (HGPS) |
| premature labor | ولادة مبتسرة |
| premature release | الإفراج قبل نهاية المدة |
| prematurely aged | مصاب بشيخوخة مبكرة |
| premeditated murder | قتل عمد مع سبق الإصرار والترصد |
| premenopausal | ما قبل انقطاع الدورة الشهرية |
| premenopausal women | النساء اللاتي في سن قبل انقطاع الدورة الشهرية |
| premiere screening | العرض الأول (للفيلم) |
| pre-milled window | فتحة مسبقة |
| premium | قسط |
| premium | علاوة |
| premium gasoline | بنزين ممتاز |
| premium location | موقع متميز |
| pre-mix mouse airpouch assay | اختبار خلط أولي لجيب هوائي فأري |
| prepaid cards | البطاقات المسبوقة الدفع؛ المسبقة الدفع؛ المدفوعة مقدما |
| preparation | تحضير أو مستحضر |
| preparation | إعداد، تحضير |
| preparation of patent disclosure | إعداد الإفصاح عن البراءة |
| preparation of phosphonate 1,3-propandiol cyclic esters | تحضير إسترات فوسفونات حلقية لمركب 1؛ 3 - بروبان دايول |
| preparative | تحضيري |
| preparative chromatography | كروماتوجراف تحضيري |
| prepare | يعد |
| preparing the camcorder | إعداد كاميرا الفيديو |
| pre-patent licensing | ترخيص سابق على صدور البراءة. ترخيص الاختراع قبل إتمام الحصول على البراءة. |
| pre-pay service ; pay-as-you-go service | خدمة الدفع المسبق أو الدفع مقدما: مصطلح يستخدم في حالة عدم وجود عقد أو خدمات رسوم إيجار حيث تشتري قسائم رصيد مقدما لتنفيذ المكالمات. |
| prepolymer | بوليمر مسبق |
| pre-polymer | بوليمر أولي |
| preproglucagon | الجزيء المنتج للجلوكاجون |
| presbycusis | ضعف السمع لدى كبار السن |
| pre-scan herg tail current amplitude >150 pa | مقدار (أو سعة أحسن) التيار الطرفي لـ hERG قبل الفحص> 150 بيكو أمبير |
| pre-scan seal resistance | مقاومة مانع التسرب قبل الفحص |
| prescription | وصفة طبية |
| present arms | سلام سلاح |
| presents | المستند الحاضر (في القانون) |
| preseparator | وحدة الفصل المسبق |
| preservation of masonry (oil for the -) | حفظ الأبنية (زيت حفظ الأبنية) |
| preservatives | المواد الحافظة |
| preservatives (brickwork -), except paints and oils | مواد حافظة (مواد حافظة لبنية الطوب) فيما عدا الدهانات والزيوت |
| preservatives (cement -), except paints and oils | مواد حافظة (مواد حافظة للأسمنت) فيما عدا الدهانات والزيوت |
| preservatives (concrete -), except paints and oils | مواد حافظة (مواد حافظة للخرسانة) فيما عدا الدهانات والزيوت |
| preservatives (flower -) | مواد حافظة (مواد حافظة للزهور) |
| preservatives (masonry -), except paints and oils | مواد حافظة (مواد حافظة للبناء) فيما عدا الدهانات والزيوت |
| preservatives (wood -) | مواد حافظة (مواد حافظة للأخشاب) |
| preservatives for leather [oils and greases] | مواد حفظ الجلود [زيوت ومواد تشحيم] |
| preservatives for leather [polishes] | مواد حافظة للجلود [مواد تلميع] |

| | |
|---|---|
| preservatives for pharmaceutical preparations | مواد حافظة للمستحضرات الصيدلانية |
| preservatives for tiles, except paints and oils | مواد حماية القرميد (البلاط)، فيما عدا الدهانات والزيوت |
| preserve tins | علب الحفظ |
| preserving (salt for -), other than for foodstuffs | حفظ (أملاح حفظ) بخلاف للاستخدام في الأطعمة |
| preserving boxes of metal | علب الحفظ من المعدن |
| preserving foodstuffs (chemical substances for -) | حفظ الأطعمة (مواد كيميائية لحفظ الأطعمة) |
| preserving foodstuffs (salt for -) | حفظ الأطعمة (أملاح حفظ الأطعمة) |
| presiding arbitrator | المحكم الذي يترأس التحكيم |
| presoaking | نقع أولي |
| press | مكبس |
| press fit | توافق بالكبس |
| press preview | معاينة الضغط |
| press roll | دلفين كبس [مع الفولاذ إلخ] |
| press roll | اسطوانة كبس [تشكيل طباعي إلخ] |
| presses | مكابس |
| presses (garlic -) [kitchen utensils] | مكابس (مكابس الثوم) [أدوات المطبخ] |
| presses (smoothing -) | مكابس (مكابس تنعيم) |
| presses (trouser -) | مكابس (قطع كي السراويل) |
| presses (wine -) | مكابس (مكابس الخمور) |
| presses [machines for industrial purposes] | مكابس [ماكينات للاستخدام في الأغراض الصناعية] |
| presses and rollers | مكابس ودرافيل |
| pressing machines [to make satin-like] | ماكينات كبس [لصنع الأقمشة المشابهة للحرير المصقول] |
| pressure | يضغط، ضغط |
| pressure bulidup | زيادة الضغط |
| pressure control valves | صمام للتحكم في الضغط |
| pressure cookers [autoclaves], electric | قدور طهي كهربية بالضغط [أجهزة طهي بالبخار عالي الضغط] |
| pressure cookers [autoclaves], non-electric | قدور طهي غير كهربائية بالضغط [أجهزة طهي بالبخار عالي الضغط] |
| pressure cooking saucepans, electric | قدور كهربائية للطهي بالضغط |
| pressure deflection | حرف الضغط |
| pressure depletion | هبوط الضغط |
| pressure drawdown | نقص الضغط |
| pressure drop | تسليط الضغط؛ فرق الضغط |
| pressure filter | مرشح ضغطي |
| pressure filteration | ترشيح ضغطي |
| pressure gauge | جهاز قياس الضغط |
| pressure head | مقدمة ضغط؛ رأس ضغط: دَفعة صغيرة من الضغط |
| pressure in vehicle tires [tyres] (automatic indicators of low -) | الضغط في إطارات المركبات (مؤشرات أتوماتيكية للضغط المنخفض في إطارات المركبات) |
| pressure indicator plugs for valves | سدادات مبينة للضغط في الصمامات |
| pressure indicators | مؤشرات الضغط |
| pressure measuring | جهاز قياس الضغط |

| | |
|---|---|
| apparatus | |
| pressure reducer | خافض للضغط |
| pressure reducers [parts of machines] | مخفضات الضغط [أجزاء من ماكينات] |
| pressure regulators [parts of machines] | منظمات الضغط [أجزاء من ماكينات] |
| pressure release element | عنصر تخفيف ضغط (وهو عنصر يعمل على تخفيف أو إزالة الضغط عن شيء ما مثل خزان .... إلخ) |
| pressure relief | تفريج الضغط |
| pressure sensor | جهاز إحساس بالضغط |
| pressure sensors | أجهزة إحساس بالضغط |
| pressure swing absorber (psa) | وحدة ماصة متأرجحة الضغط؛ وحدة ماصة بتأرجح الضغط |
| pressure swing adsorption (psa) unit | وحدة امتزاز متأرجحة الضغط |
| pressure valves [parts of machines] | صمامات الضغط [أجزاء من ماكينات] |
| pressure vessel | وعاء ضغطي؛ وعاء ضغط |
| pressure water tanks | صهاريج ضغط المياه |
| pressure-biasing mechanisms and methods | آليات وطرق توجيه ضغط |
| pressure-fit attachments | وصلات مواءمة ضغط |
| pressure-fit; pressure fit | مواءمة ضغط |
| pressures | قيم ضغط |
| pressure-sensitive adhesive flexible, finite carriers; pressure-sensitive adhesive flexible finite carriers | مواد حاملة مرنة محدودة من نوع اللاصق الحساس للضغط |
| pressurization | زيادة الضغط (في نظام أو حيز ما إلخ) |
| pressurization system | نظام الضغط |
| pressurize | يزيد الضغط (في نظام أو حيز ما إلخ)؛ يكيف الضغط |
| pressurized air supply | مصدر إمداد بالهواء المضغوط |
| pressurized water | ماء مضغوط |
| pressurizer | مكيف للضغط |
| preterm delivery | بينما الولادة المبكرة |
| pre-term labor | مخاض مبكر |
| prev. | السابق |
| prevention software | برنامج منع |
| prevention system | نظام للمنع |
| preview images | معاينة الصور |
| preview mode | وضع المعاينة |
| price restrictive patent licenses | تراخيص براءات تقييدية السعر |
| prilling tower | برج تحبيب |
| primary | أولي؛ أساسي |
| primary amine | أمين أولي |
| primary and metastatic brain tumours | أورام الدماغ الأولية والثانوية |
| primary biliary cirrhosis | التشمع الصفراوي الأولي |
| primary color filter | مرشح الألوان الأساسية |
| primary colour | اللون الأساسي |
| primary energy | طاقة أولية |
| primary fuel feeder | مغذي وقود أساسي |
| primary hydroxyl group | مجموعة هيدروكسيل ابتدائية |

| | |
|---|---|
| primary key | مفتاح أساسي |
| primary recovery method | طريقة الاستخلاص الأولى |
| primary sclerosing cholangitis | التهاب قناة الصفراء المصلّب الأولي |
| primary storage | مخزن أساسي |
| primary structure | إنشاء رئيسي |
| primate | رئيسيات |
| primatized | متوافقة مع الرئيسيات |
| primer | بادئ؛ مادة بطانية |
| primer layer | طبقة بطانة |
| primers | أساسات (بطانة) الدهان |
| priming | حث |
| priming | تعزيز؛ حث |
| priming irons [hand tools] | قطع حديدية للتسوية قبل الدهان [عُدد يدوية] |
| primings [fuses] | كبسولات الإشعال [صمامات الإشعال] |
| principal registry of the family division | مكتب التسجيل الرئيسي لشعبة شئون الأسرة |
| principle | مكون؛ عنصر |
| principle of original horizontality | أساس أصل الأفقية |
| print | يطبع |
| print clauses | البند المتعلق بالمطبوعات |
| print order | ترتيب الطباعة |
| printed circuit board (pcb) | اللوحة المطبوعة: لوحة إلكترونية..لوحة الدوائر المطبوعة |
| printed circuits | دوائر مطبوعة |
| printed matter | مطبوعات |
| printed publications | منشورات مطبوعة |
| printed timetables | جداول مطبوعة |
| printer and layout settings | إعدادات الطابعة والمخطط |
| printer indicator | مؤشر الطابعة |
| printer setup utility | أداة إعداد الطابعة المساعدة |
| printers and photocopiers (toner cartridges [filled] for -) | طابعات وناسخات ( خراطيش الحبر [مملوءة] في الطابعات والناسخات الضوئية) |
| printers' blankets of textile | أغطية الطابعات من القماش |
| printers' blankets, not of textile | أغطية الطابعات ليست من القماش |
| printers for use with computers | طابعات للاستخدام مع الحاسبات الآلية |
| printers' pastes [ink] | عجين للطابعات [حبر] |
| printers' reglets | رقاقات خشبية للتوسيع بين السطور |
| printing blocks | أكليشيهات [الراسمات] |
| printing compositions [ink] | تركيبات الطباعة [حبر] |
| printing cylinders | أسطوانات الطباعة |
| printing indexes | فهارس الطباعة |
| printing ink | حبر الطباعة |
| printing machines | آلات الطباعة |
| printing machines for use on sheet metal | آلات الطباعة للاستخدام على الألواح المعدنية |
| printing pictures | طباعة الصور |
| printing plates | أكليشيهات [الراسمات] |
| printing plates (sensitized -) for offset | أكليشيهات (أكليشيهات حساسة) للاستخدام في طباعة الأوفست |
| printing press | مطبعة [الصحف] |

| | |
|---|---|
| printing presses | المطابع |
| printing rollers for machines | بكر الطابعة للاستخدام في الآلات |
| printing sets, portable [office requisites] | معدات الطباعة المحمولة [لوازم مكتبية] |
| printing type | حروف الطباعة |
| printing with print order settings | الطباعة باستخدام إعدادات ترتيب الطباعة |
| prints [engravings] | نسخ مطبوعة [أكليشيهات] |
| prior art | الفن السابق |
| prior art | الفن السابق |
| prior art references | الإحالات للفن السابق |
| prior art search | بحث متصل بالفن السابق |
| prior art search services | خدمات البحث عن الفن السابق |
| prior invention | اختراع سابق |
| prior work | عمل سابق |
| priority | أسبقية |
| priority award | حكم بحصول انتهاك لبراءة |
| priority inventions | اختراعات ذات أولوية. اختراعات ذات أهمية تجعلها تحظى بأولوية |
| priority needs | الاحتياجات ذات الأولوية |
| priority technology areas | مجالات ذات أولوية من مجالات التقنية |
| prism | منشور |
| prism dye-terminator sequencing kits | أطقم عمل متواليات باستخدام المنشور وإنهاء الصبغة |
| prisms [optics] | منشورات زجاجية [بصريات] |
| prisoners of war (pows) | أسرى الحرب |
| privacy legal disclaimer | إخلاء المسئولية القانونية بشأن الخصوصية |
| privacy notice | إشعار بشأن الخصوصية. بيان غرضه الحث على احترام الخصوصية. يرد في المواقع الشبكية وفي شبكات العمل الداخلية |
| private patent practice | ممارسة العمل في البراءات على نحو مستقل |
| private placement | اكتتاب خاص |
| privatization | خصخصة |
| privileges | الامتيازات |
| prize ribbons | أوشحة الجوائز |
| pro- (prefix) | أولي (pro-drug) "prodopaminergic") ("product |
| pro- (prefix) | معزز لكذا (pro-inflammatory drug) |
| pro bono publico | خدمات المصلحة العامة |
| pro patent lobby | تجمع استمالة مؤيد للبراءات |
| pro-apoptotic bax gene | جين Bax المعزز للموت المبرمج |
| proarrhythmia ; pro-arrhythmia | الاضطرابات المعزَّزة عدم انتظام إيقاع القلب |
| probabilistic chips | شرائح احتمالية |
| probability density function | دالة الكثافة الاحتمالية |
| probability distribution | توزيع الاحتمالات |
| probability distribution function | دالة التوزيع الاحتمالي |
| probability factor | عامل احتمالية |
| probability of error conditioned on non-erased codewords | احتمال الخطأ المتوقف على كلمات مشفرة غير ممحاة |

| | |
|---|---|
| probe | مسبار؛ مجس |
| probe | يختبر [كمبيوتر وبرمجة ويب] |
| probe dna | حمض DNA مسباري |
| probe message | رسالة اختبار [كمبيوتر وبرمجة ويب] |
| probe or sensor | مسبار أو جهاز استشعار |
| probe port | منفذ اختبار [كمبيوتر وبرمجة ويب] |
| probiotics | الكائنات الحية المفيدة: مثل البكتيريا أو الخميرة النافعة |
| problem | مشكلة |
| problem focused thinking | تفكير متركز حول المشكلة. تفكير لا يستطيع الفكاك من أسر المشكلة |
| problem of "appropriability" of innovation | مشكلة السيطرة على الابتكار. مشكلة مفادها مواجهة الشركات والنشاطات الصغر والمبتدئة تحدياً مفاده عدم التيقن من إمكانية السيطرة على الاختراعات التي يتسنى لها اختراعها من خلال تسجيلها كبراءات، وبالتالي عدم القدرة على جني أرباح من استغلالها بسبب كلفة التعامل مع نظام البراءات في بعض الأحيان وعدم الإحاطة الكاملة بنظام البراءات في أحيان أخرى |
| problem-based learning | التعليم القائم على المشكلة |
| procedure | طريقة، إجراء |
| proceed | يواصل |
| proceeding | إجراءات |
| proceedings | إجراءات |
| proceedings code ; procedures law | قانون المرافعات |
| proceeds | متحصلات |
| process | يعالج، طريقة، عملية |
| process chamber | غرفة العمليات |
| process chart | مخطط عمليات؛ مخطط صندوقي لسير عملية |
| process control | التحكم في العمليات |
| process control block | حجب التحكم في العملية |
| process diagram | مخطط عمليات |
| process diagram ; process scheme | مخطط عمليات؛ مخطط صندوقي لسير عملية |
| process flow diagram | مخطط سير عمليات |
| process fluid | مائع العمليات |
| process gas | غاز العمليات |
| process improvement invention | اختراع تحسين طريقة |
| process server | محضر (محكمة) |
| process train | سلسلة العملية |
| process virtual machine | آلة عملية افتراضية |
| processed | مُعالج |
| processing | معالجة شيء |
| processing device | جهاز معالجة |
| processing system | نظام معالجة |
| processor | معالج |
| processor [central processing units] | معالج؛ جهاز المعالجة [وحدات معالجة المركزية] |
| proctitis | التهاب الشرج أو المستقيم |
| proctocolectomy | استئصال المستقيم والقولون |
| proctocolitis | التهاب المستقيم والقولون |
| proctoscope | منظار المستقيم |
| procurable patent | براءة يمكن شراؤها |
| procure | يشتري |
| procurement | شراء |
| prodopaminergic product | منتج دوباميني أوّلي |
| prodrug ; pro-drug | عقار أولي |
| produce | ينتج، منتج |
| produced waterfeed | تيار التغذية بالماء الناتج |
| producer gas | غاز المولدات |
| producibility | قابلية الشيء للإنتاج |
| producible | قابل للإنتاج |
| product | منتج |
| product analysis | تحليل المنتج |
| product commercialization | جعل المنتج ذا طبيعة تجارية |
| product deconstruction | تفكيك المنتج |
| product gas | الغاز المنتج |
| product improvement invention | اختراع تحسين منتج. |
| product merchandisability | قابلية المنتج للترويج كسلعة والمتاجرة بها |
| product search | بحث عن منتج |
| product separation/solvent recycle | فصل المنتج وإعادة تدوير المذيب |
| product silicone | السيليكون المنتج |
| production | إنتاج |
| production | إنتاج |
| production capacity | قدرة إنتاجية |
| production car | سيارة إنتاج |
| production choke valve | صمام اختناق إنتاج |
| production function | دالة الإنتاج |
| production manifold (header) conduits | قناة مشعب إنتاج (علوية) |
| production optimisation" | تحسين إنتاج عمليات الآبار للأمثل |
| production predictions | توقعات الإنتاج |
| production scheduling software | برنامج لجدولة الإنتاج |
| production sectors, assembly, finishing, packing, printin, dyeing | أقسام الإنتاج، التجميع، التشطيب، التغليف، الطباعة، الصباغة |
| production string | عمود الإنتاج |
| production string of tubing | عمود أنابيب الإنتاج |
| production tubing or casing in well | أنبوب إنتاج أو أنبوب تغليف |
| production universe real time optimisation (pu rto) | تحسين الإنتاج العالمي في الزمن الفعلي للمستوى الأمثل؛ أمثلية الإنتاج العالمي في الزمن الفعلي |
| production-driven country | بلد يقوده الإنتاج |
| productions | نواتج |
| productions requirements | مستلزمات الإنتاج |
| productive efficiency | فعالية منتجة. تعبير يطلق على وضع يتسم فيه الاقتصاد بتحقيق فعالية كبيرة في توظيف موارده إذ ينتج أكبر قدر ممكن من المخرجات بأقل قدر ممكن من المدخلات |
| productivity growth | نمو الإنتاجية |
| products | نواتج: مثل نواتج الطور الغازي؛ التيار السائل؛ إلخ |

| | |
|---|---|
| products | منتجات |
| professional | خبير، محترف |
| professional inventor | مخترع محترف |
| professional negligence | إهمال مهني |
| profile | خاصية (والجمع: خصائص)؛ صورة؛ هيئة (عقار إلخ)؛ منحنى؛ خط بياني؛ يعرف تعريفا موجزا، تعريف موجز |
| profile server | خادم مجموعة البيانات |
| profiling | جمع البيانات الشخصية الخاصة بالآخرين: بناء التشكيلات الجانبية للآخرين |
| profiling | خصائص؛ ملامح؛ سمات |
| profit | يربح، ربح |
| profitability | قابلية الشيء لتحقيق ربح |
| profitable idea | فكرة مربحة |
| prognosis | توقعات سير المرض |
| prognostic assay | اختبار تحذيري |
| program | يبرمج، برنامج |
| program ae indicator | مؤشر (وضع التصوير) |
| program selector | محدد البرنامج |
| programmable circuit | دائرة قابلة للبرمجة |
| programmable logic devices (plds) | أجهزة برمجة المنطق PLDs |
| programmable network infrastructure | بنية تحتية للشبكة قابلة للبرمجة |
| programmable robot | روبوت قابل للبرمجة |
| programmable system | نظام قابل للبرمجة |
| programming interface | واجهة برمجية |
| programs (computer -) [downloadable software] | برامج (برامج الكمبيوتر) [برامج قابلة للتنزيل (للتحميل)] |
| programs (computer game-) | برامج (برامج ألعاب الكمبيوتر) |
| programs (computer operating -) recorded | برامج (برامج تشغيل الكمبيوتر) مسجلة |
| progress | يتقدم |
| progress bar | شريط التقدم |
| progress clause | بند التطوير، البند 1 القسم 8 من الدستور الأمريكي التي تمكن الكونغرس من تطوير العلم المفيد والآداب من خلال منح حقوق حصرية مؤقتة لهم بإزاء اكتشافاتهم وكتاباتهم |
| progressive | متقدم؛ مضطرد |
| progressive multifocal leukoencephalopathy (pml) | اعتلال مادة الدماغ البيضاء عديد البؤر المتقدم |
| pro-inflammatory ; proinflammatory | معزز للالتهاب |
| project | يبرز |
| project | يختط، يتصور، خطة، مشروع |
| project management software | برنامج إدارة مشاريع |
| project scheduling software | برنامج لجدولة المشروعات |
| projected beam | حزمة مسلطة؛ حزمة مسقطة |
| projectile | قذيفة، قذاف، دافع |
| projectiles [weapons] | قذائف [أسلحة] |
| projecting films | عرض الأفلام |
| projection | بروز |
| projection | إسقاط، اختاط، فكرة متصورة، تقدير احتمالات مستقبلية |
| projection apparatus | جهاز الإسقاط |
| projection of a fault surface | إبراز سطح صدعي |
| projection screens | شاشات الإسقاط |
| projectionist | مراقب التليسينما |
| projective | ناتئ، إبرازي |
| projector | شاشة عرض سينمائية؛ جهاز عرض؛ مسلاط |
| projector lamps | مصابيح الإسقاط |
| prokaryotes | الخلايا ذات التنوي المبكر |
| prokaryotic | بدائي النواة |
| proliferative | متكاثر؛ متشعب |
| proliferator | مسبب تكاثر |
| prolyl cis/trans isomerization | أزمرة بروليل سيس/ترانس |
| promethium | البروميثيوم |
| promiscuity | اقتران |
| promotable invention | اختراع قابل للترويج |
| promote | يرقي (إلى الأحدث)؛ ينشر؛ يروج؛ يرقي |
| promoter | محفز؛ مروج |
| promoters | مروجون |
| promotion | ترويج |
| promotion company | شركة ترويج |
| promotion event | حدث ترويجي أو دعائي |
| promotor | معزز |
| prompting | حث برسالة |
| proof-of-concept malware | فيروس إعادة كتابة ملفات نظام التشغيل: برنامج حاقد يقوم بإعادة كتابة ملفات نظام التشغيل |
| proofs | الأدلة |
| pro-oxidant | معزز للأكسدة |
| propagate | ينشر أو ينتشر |
| propagation direction and an energy distribution | باتجاه انتشار وتوزيع طاقة |
| propanamid | بروبان أميد |
| propane precooled mixed refrigerant (c3mr) | مادة تبريد (غازية) مختلطة مبردة مسبقًا بالبروبان |
| propane recovery methods and configurations | طرق وتصميمات لاستخلاص البروبان |
| propanoate | بروبانوات |
| pro-patent society | مجتمع مقرٌ لفكرة البراءات |
| propel | يدفع، يحث |
| propellant | دافع، مسير |
| propellant ; propellent | مادة دافعة؛ مادة دفعية؛ مادة دفع (مثل وقود الدفع) |
| propeller | داسر؛ دافع؛ رفاص (في الهواء/الماء) |
| propeller airplanes | طائرات دفع |
| proper | سليم، صحيح |
| properties of hardened concrete | الخواص الرئيسية للخرسانة المتصلدة |
| property | خاصية، خاصة، صفة مميزة، ملك، ملكية |
| property infringement | انتهاك ملكية |
| property modifying agent | عامل تعديل خاصية |
| property right | حق بإزاء ملك، حق ملكية |
| property tax | ضريبة الممتلكات |
| property wealth | ثروة الملكية |

| | |
|---|---|
| prophylactic | واقية |
| prophylaxis | الوقاية |
| propionamide | بروبيوناميد |
| propolis [bee glue] for human consumption | العِكبر [شمع النحل] للاستهلاك الآدمي |
| proportion | يجعل تناسبياً |
| proportional to | بالتناسب مع؛ تناسبيا مع |
| proppant particles | جسيمات حشو دعمي |
| proppants | مواد حشو دعمي |
| propping agent | عامل حشو دعمي |
| proprietary know-how | دراية كيفية ممتلكة. |
| props of metal | دعائم من المعدن |
| props, not of metal | دعائم ليست من المعدن |
| propulsion | دفع |
| propulsion | دفع، تسيير |
| propulsion mechanisms for land vehicles | آليات الدفع في المركبات الأرضية |
| propulsion mechanisms other than for land vehicles | آليات الدفع بخلاف المستخدمة في المركبات الأرضية |
| propulsive | دفعي، تسييري |
| propylene selectivity of the catalyst | انتقائية المحفز تجاه البروبيلين |
| propyl-paraben | بروبيل-بارين |
| prosecutability | القابلية للإنشاء، القابلية للمحاكمة |
| prosecutable patent | براءة يمكن إنشاؤها |
| prosecute | يواصل، يتابع حتى النهاية، يقوم بـ يحاكم، يقاضي |
| prosecution | محاكمة، مقاضاة، جهة الادعاء، إقامة |
| prosecutor | وكيل النيابة |
| prospective patent client | عميل متوقع للبراءة |
| prostaglandin | بروستاجلاندين |
| prostatitis | التهاب البروستاتة |
| prostheses | أعضاء بديلة (بديلة عن أعضاء مفقودة من الجسم) |
| prostheses (hair -) | بدائل اصطناعية (بدائل اصطناعية للشعر) |
| prostheses (intraocular -) [lenses] for surgical implantation | بدائل اصطناعية (بدائل اصطناعية للمقلة) [عدسات] في عمليات الزرع الجراحية |
| prosthesis | جراحة ترقيعية |
| prosthetic group | مجموعة استبدالية |
| prosthetic joint failure | قصور المفصل الاستبدالي |
| prosthetics | جراحة ترقيعية، أعضاء اصطناعية |
| prosthetics laboratories | مختبرات الجراحة الاصطناعية |
| prosthodontics | طب أسنان ترقيعي |
| prosthodontist | أخصائي بطب الأسنان الترقيعي |
| protable driver | مفك متنقل؛ مفك محمول |
| protactinium | البروتكتنيوم |
| protease | بروتياز |
| protease inhibitors | مثبطات البروتياز |
| protect | يحمي |
| protect mark | علامة الحماية |
| protect off | يوقف تشغيل الحماية |
| protect on | يشغل الحماية |
| protect switch | مفتاح حماية |
| protected image mark | علامة الصورة المحمية |
| protecting groups | مجموعات حامية؛ مجموعات حماية |
| protecting images | حماية الصور |
| protecting photo files | حماية ملفات الصور |
| protection devices against x-rays [roentgen rays] | أجهزة الحماية من أشعة إكس [أشعة رونتجن] |
| protection devices for personal use against accidents | أجهزة الحماية للاستخدام الشخصي ضد الحوادث |
| protectionism | حماية المنتجات المحلية |
| protective coat | معطف واق |
| protective coating | طبقة خارجية واقية |
| protective coatings | مواد طلاء حامية |
| protective gases for welding | غازات الوقاية من اللحام |
| protective helmets | خوذات الوقاية |
| protective helmets for sports | خوذات الوقاية للاستخدام في الألعاب الرياضية |
| protective masks | أقنعة واقية |
| protective paddings [parts of sports suits] | وسائد واقية [أجزاء من الحُلل الرياضية] |
| protective payee | مدبّر المدفوعات - متولّي الشؤون المالية للغير |
| protective preparations for metals | مستحضرات واقية للمعادن |
| protective suits for aviators | حُلل واقية لقائدي الطائرات |
| protector (voltage surge -) | جهاز الوقاية (جهاز الوقاية من التغير المفاجئ في الفولت) |
| protein [raw material] | البروتين [مادة خام] |
| protein for animal consumption | البروتين للاستهلاك الحيواني |
| protein for human consumption | البروتين للاستهلاك الآدمي |
| protein refolding | إعادة طي البروتين |
| protein scaffold | سلسلة بروتين متجاورة؛ جزء رئيسي لبروتين |
| protein scaffolds for antibody mimics | سلاسل البروتين المتجاورة لنماذج محاكاة جسم مضاد |
| protein toxin | توكسين البروتين |
| protein tyrosine kinase | كيناز تيروسين البروتين |
| proteins from the extracellular matrix | بروتينات من الكتلة خارج الخلايا |
| proteins misfold and accumulate as insoluble inclusion bodies | أجسام اشتمال غير قابلة للذوبان |
| protein-tyrosine phosphatase | إنزيم بروتين-تيروسين فوسفاتاز |
| proteinuria | البول البروتيني |
| proteolysis | تحليل محدود للبروتين |
| proteolytic | حال للبروتين |
| proteomics | علم البروتينات والأنزيمات |
| protfolios | الحقائب |
| protic | بروتوني |
| protogenic | مولد (مانح) للبروتونات |
| protomer ; proto-mer | وحدة بروتين |
| proton pump inhibitor | مثبط لمضخة البروتون |
| protonatable | يمكنه منح بروتونات؛ يمكنه إضافة بروتونات |
| protoplast | خلية غير نوعية -( حسب المراجع: جبلة مجردة) |
| protoquartzite | الكوارتز الأولى |

| | |
|---|---|
| prototype | نموذج أولي |
| prototype | نموذج أول |
| protozoan infection | العدوى بالكائنات أحادية الخلية |
| protracted war | حرب مطولة |
| protractors [measuring instruments] | المنقلة [أدوات قياس الزوايا] |
| protuberance | نتوء |
| provenance | مكان النشأة |
| provide for | يوفر؛ يمد بـ |
| provide sheen to the tablet | إضافة سطح لامع للقرص |
| provide zonal isolation for the life of the well. | يوفر عزل للمنطقة طوال عمر البئر |
| provided with a lock | مزودة بقفل |
| provider | مقدم، مزود |
| provisional | مؤقت |
| proviso that | بشرط أن |
| provisos | شروط |
| provoking environment | بيئة مثيرة، بيئة مستفزة |
| proxemic manifestations | مظاهر القرب المكاني |
| proximal end | طرف قريب |
| proximity effect | تأثير التقاربية: تأثير المجال المغناطيسي لموصل |
| proximity sensors | أجهزة إحساس بالقرب. أجهزة إحساس بالأشياء المحيطة دون لمسها |
| proxy | خادم بروكسي |
| proxy measures | إجراءات بالوكالة |
| prune | برقوق (خوخ أخضر مجفف)؛ قراصيا |
| pruning knives | سكاكين التقليم |
| pruning scissors | مقصات التقليم |
| pruning shears | مقص تقليم |
| pruritis | حكة |
| prussiates | البروسيات [ملح السيانيد] |
| ps | بوليمر مدعم |
| ps/2 port | منفذ PS/2 |
| pseudoazurin | أزورين زائف |
| pseudo-isothermal conditions | ظروف تماثل حراري كاذب |
| pseudomembranous | غشائي كاذب |
| pseudomonas aeruginosa | الزائفة الزنجارية |
| pseudorandom | عشوائية زائفة |
| pseudo-random number | رقم عشوائي زائف |
| pseudo-random number (pn) sequences | تسلسلات مختلفة لرقم عشوائي زائف PN |
| psi | رطل لكل بوصة مربعة |
| psi ( pounds per square inch ) | أرطال لكل بوصة مربعة |
| psia | رطل/بوصة مربعة مطلق |
| psig | رطل لكل بوصة مربعة بالمقياس |
| psoriasis | الصدفية |
| psoriatic arthritis | التهاب المفاصل الناتج عن الإصابة بالصدفية |
| pstn | الشبكة العامة لتحويل التليفونات |
| psychiatric disorder | اضطراب نفسي |
| psychographics | علم النفس التجاري أو التسويقي |
| psychological warfare | الحرب النفسية |
| psychopharmacology | علم الأدوية النفسية |
| psychosis | اضطراب نفسي |
| psychotropic | منبه عقلي |

| | |
|---|---|
| ptilosis | السحار الريشي |
| p-to-p | من قمة إلى قمة |
| ptpn22 expression | التعبير الوراثي عن PTPN22 |
| ptz camera; pan tilt zoom camera; pan-tilt-zoom camera | كاميرا PTZ: كاميرا تدوير وإمالة وتقريب الصورة |
| public knowledge | معارف عامة. |
| public money | المال العام |
| public notary | الشهر العقاري |
| public prosecutor | المدعي العام |
| public prosecutor general | النائب العام |
| public sector industries | صناعات القطاع العام |
| publication | نشرة |
| publications (electronic -) [downloadable] | منشورات (منشورات إلكترونية) [قابلة للتنزيل] |
| publications (printed -) | منشورات (منشورات مطبوعة)؛ مؤلفات |
| publicly accessible patent database | قاعدة بيانات عامة يمكن الوصول إليها |
| publicly disclosed invention | اختراع مفصح عنه على الملأ |
| publicly undisclosed invention | اختراع غير مفصح عنه على الملأ |
| published patent | براءة منشورة |
| published patent documents | مستندات براءة منشورة |
| publishers licensing society | جمعية ترخيص النشر التي أسست بالمملكة المتحدة عام 1980 لحماية وتعزيز حقوق المؤلفين في جميع التخصصات و ضمان الحصول على السداد العادل للاستخدامات المختلفة لعملهم |
| publishing industry | صناعة النشر |
| pudding (black -) [blood sausage] | نقانق (نقانق داكنة اللون) [سجق يحتوى على كمية كبيرة من الدم] |
| puddings | خلائط طينية |
| puddings | البودنج: حلوى تعد من دقيق أو أرز أو تابيوكا |
| puddling machines | آلات تسويط الحديد |
| pulley | بكرة |
| pulleys | بَكَرات |
| pulleys (adhesive bands for -) | بكرات (أشرطة لاصقة للبكرات) |
| pulleys [parts of machines] | بكرات [أجزاء من آلات] |
| pulleys of metal [other than for machines] | بكرات من المعدن [بخلاف الآلات] |
| pulleys of plastics for blinds | بكرات من البلاستيك للستائر |
| pull-out | ملحق يُنزع من مجلة |
| pullovers | البلوفر (كنزة صوفية) |
| pull-proof ; pull proof | بروفة؛ نسخة تجريبية |
| pulmonary | رئوي |
| pulmonary hypertension | ارتفاع ضغط الدم الرئوي |
| pulmonary sarcoidosis | اللحمانية التنفسية |
| pulp (fruit -) | لب (لب الفاكهة) |
| pulp (paper -) | عجين (عجين ورقية) |
| pulp (wood -) | لب (لب الأخشاب) |
| pulping | فصل الألياف الخام أو المسترجعة: عملية تحويل الألياف الخام أو المسترجعة إلى لب يتم إستخدامه في صناعة الورق بأقل عمليات معالجة تالية ممكنة |

| | |
|---|---|
| pulse spun | دوران نبضي حول مركز |
| pulse width modulation | تضمين بعرض النبضات |
| pulse-chase experiments | تجارب تعقب النبض |
| pulsed neutron log inflow analysis | تحليل الدفق الداخل بتسجيل أداء النيوترونات النبضية |
| pulsed neutron logging run | دورة تسجيل النيوترونات النبضية |
| pulsing | إرسال نبضة من ... |
| pulsing neutrons | نيوترونات نبضية |
| pulverant | قابل للسحق الدقيق |
| pulverisers (sewage -) | آلات السحق (آلات سحق نفايات المجاري) |
| pulverisers [machines] | آلات السحق [ماكينات] |
| pulverize | طحن |
| pulverizer | مطحنة |
| pulverulent | سهل التفتت |
| pumice stone | الحجر الخفاف |
| pump | يضخ، مضخة |
| pump around loop | حلقة حول مضخة |
| pump diaphragms | أغشية المضخات |
| pumper | مضخة |
| pumping | ضخ |
| pumping action | فعل الضخ |
| pumps (air -) [vehicle accessories] | مضخات (مضخات الهواء) [كماليات المركبات] |
| pumps (hand -) | مضخات (مضخات يدوية) |
| pumps (vacuum -) [machines] | مضخات (مضخات تفريغ) [ماكينات] |
| pumps [machines] | مضخات [ماكينات] |
| pumps [parts of machines, engines or motors] | مضخات [أجزاء من ماكينات أو محركات أو موتورات] |
| pumps for bicycles, cycles | مضخات الدراجات |
| pumps for heating installations | مضخات تركيبات التدفئة |
| pumps for medical purposes | مضخات للاستخدام في الأغراض الطبية |
| punch pliers [hand tools] | زرديات تخريم [عُدد يدوية] |
| punch rings [knuckle dusters] | حلقات مخرمة [قطع معدنية تكسى بها الأصابع في الملاكمة] |
| punches [hand tools] | خرامات [عُدد يدوية] |
| punches [office requisites] | خرامات [لوازم مكتبية] |
| punches for punching machines | خرامات ماكينات التثقيب |
| punching bags | أكياس التدريب على الملاكمة |
| punching machines | آلات تخريم |
| punishment | عقوبة |
| punitive damages | تعويضات عقابية |
| puppets | دُمى متحركة |
| pupura | فرفرية |
| purchase agreement | اتفاق شراء |
| pure enantiomeric form | صورة نقية من ناحية التشاكل |
| purgatives | أدوية الإسهال |
| purge | ينظف؛ يطهر؛ ينقي |
| purge gas | غاز تنظيف |
| purgeable patent misuse | إساءة استعمال براءة من الممكن إزالتها |
| purged | مطهر |
| purging | تنظيف [لتنظيف أنبوب، مرشح إلخ ومنع انسدادها] |
| purging gas | غاز تنظيف |
| purifiable | قابل للتنقية |
| purifiable material | مادة قابلة للتطهير |
| purification | تنقية |
| purification installations for sewage | تركيبات تنقية مياه المجاري |
| purification of gas (preparations for the -) | تنقية الغاز (مستحضرات لتنقية الغاز) |
| purification preparations | مستحضرات التنقية |
| purification process | عملية تنقية |
| purified by biotage | بيوتاج |
| purified sodium aluminate pregnant solution | محلول مشبع بألومينات الصوديوم المنقاة |
| purified water | ماء منقى |
| purifying chemicals (oil- -) | مواد كيميائية للتنقية (مواد كيميائية لتنقية الزيت) |
| purifying chemicals (water- -) | مواد كيميائية للتنقية (مواد كيميائية لتنقية الماء) |
| purlin | رافدة أفقية |
| purpose | غاية |
| purposeless invention | اختراع لا غاية له |
| purses | محافظ (حقائب النقود) |
| purses of precious metal | حقائب النقود من المعادن النفيسة |
| purses, not of precious metal | حقائب النقود ليست من المعادن النفيسة |
| push button | زر ضاغط |
| push buttons for bells | أزرار الضغط للأجراس |
| pushbutton | زر ضغط، زر كبس |
| pushchair covers | أغطية المقاعد المتحركة |
| pushchair hoods | أغطية الرأس في المقاعد المتحركة |
| pushchairs | المقاعد المتحركة |
| push-fit capsules | كبسولات الدفع المشترك |
| putative | مظنونة؛ مفترضة؛ مزعومة |
| putting an invention into production | وضع الاختراع موضع الإنتاج |
| putty (glaziers' -) | معجون (معجون مركّب الزجاج) |
| p-value | قيمة P |
| pvr | الفيديو الرقمي |
| pxrd | حيود الأشعة السينية في المسحوق |
| pyjamas | البيجاما |
| pyran | بيران |
| pyrethrum powder | مسحوق البيرثرم |
| pyrex glass | زجاج بيركس |
| pyrexia | حمى |
| pyridylidene | بيريديليدين |
| pyrogallic acid | حمض بيروجللي |
| pyrogen-free water | ماء خال من مسببات الحمة |
| pyroligneous acid [wood vinegar] | حمض بيرولجيني [خل الأخشاب] |
| pyrolize | يحلل بالحرارة العالية |
| pyrolysis | انحلال حراري |
| pyrometer | البيرومتر [جهاز قياس درجة الحرارة المرتفعة] |
| pyrophoric (fuel) | تلقائي الاشتعال |
| pyrophoric metals | معادن تلقائية الإشعال |
| pyrophoric substances | مواد تلقائية الإشعال |

| | |
|---|---|
| pyrotechnic products | منتجات صناعة الصواريخ والألعاب النارية والمقذوفات |
| pyroxylin | بيروكسيلين [قطن البارود] |
| pyrrolidone | بيروليدون |

# Q

| | |
|---|---|
| q | رباعي |
| q.d.s | أربع مرات يوميًا |
| q.s ph 4.0 | الكمية الكافية للوصول إلى الرقم الهيدروجيني 4.0 |
| q.s. ad | الكمية الكافية للحصول على |
| q2h | كل ساعتين |
| qa | توكيد الجودة |
| qap | خطة توكيد الجودة |
| qd | مرة في اليوم |
| qh | كل ساعة |
| qid | أربع مرات في اليوم |
| ql | طبقاً للحاجة |
| qn | كل ليلة |
| qod | مرة كل يومين |
| qos | جودة الخدمة |
| qow | مرة كل أسبوعين |
| qp | طبقاً للرغبة |
| qs. | كمية كافية |
| qtl locus | موقع صفات كمية QTL |
| qtr | استبدال نص في صف انتظار |
| qty | الكمية |
| quadrature amplitude modulation (qam) | تضمين سعة الموجة الرباعية؛ تضمين الذروة المتعامد (QAM)؛ تضمين السعة الرباعي |
| quadrature phase shift keying | مفاتيح تناوب الطور |
| quadrolobe | شكل رباعي الفصوص |
| qualified legal opinion | رأي قانوني مسبب |
| qualitative evaluation of a patent | تقييم كيفي لبراءة. تقييم جوانب الضعف والقوة لبراءة |
| qualitative physics | فيزياء نوعية |
| quality | الجودة |
| quality control, quality assurance | ضبط الجودة؛ تأكيد الجودة |
| quality factor | عامل جودة |
| quality magazine | مجلة رفيعة المستوى |
| quality of education | جودة التعليم |
| quant | ضليع في الرياضيات |
| quant. | ناتج كمّي |
| quanta | الكميّات |
| quantico | كوانتيكو |
| quantifiable | قابل للقياس |
| quantifications | القياس |
| quantified | محدّد |
| quantifier | المحدّد للكمية |
| quantify | يحدّد |
| quantifying | التحديد |
| quantile | قسامات متساوية |
| quantitative | كمّي |
| quantitative physics | فيزياء كمية |
| quantitatively | بشكل كمّي |
| quantitativeness | الكمّيّة |
| quantity | الكمية |
| quantity indicators | مؤشرات الكمية |
| quantity of produced, consumed and flared of natural gas | كمية الغاز الطبيعي المنتج والمستهلك والمحروق |
| quantization | التقسيم الى كمّيّات -التقسيم الكمي -تكمية |
| quantize | يثبت الكمية؛ يقسم إلى كميات صغيرة |
| quantizer | المقسّم الى كميات صغيرة |
| quantizers | المقسّمون الى كميات صغيرة |
| quantum | كمية؛ كمّ |
| quantum energy | طاقة الكمية |
| quantum energy healing | العلاج بالطاقة الكمية |
| quantum numbers | أعداد الكم |
| quantum physics | فيزياء الكم |
| quarantine | المحجر الصحي |
| quarantined | محجور |
| quarantines | المحاجر الصحية |
| quarantining | الحجر |
| quarriesl | محجر |
| quartermaster | ضابط الإمداد والتموين |
| quarternize | يحوّل إلى الصورة الرباعية |
| quarto type | من نوع كوارتو |
| quartz | كوارتز |
| quartz glass | زجاج الكوارتز |
| quartz lamps | مصابيح الكوارتز |
| quartz pebbleconglomerates | مدملكات الكوارتز الحصوي |
| quartz sand | رمل مرويّ |
| quartzarenite | الكوارتز أرينايت |
| quassia for medical purposes | الكواسيا [خشب المر] للاستخدام في الأغراض الطبية |
| quaternary ammonium salts | أملاح أمونيوم رباعية |
| quaternized amidoamine surfactants | مخفضات التوتر السطحي من الأميدو أمين المحوّل إلى الصورة الرباعية |
| quebracho | الكبراش |
| queen's bench division | المحكمة العليا؛ قسم المحكمة الملكية |
| queen's counsel | محامي ملكي |
| quench | يخمد |
| querry | يستعلم عن |
| questionable originality | أصالة موضع تساؤل |
| questionable patentability | إمكانيةٌ موضعُ تساؤلٍ لصدور براءة |
| questionable technology | تقنية مثيرة للتساؤل |
| questioned patent originality | أصالة لبراءة موضع تساؤل |
| quiches | فطائر الكسترد غير سكرية |
| quicklime | جير حي |
| quiescent culture chamber | غرفة استزراع ساكنة |
| quiescent period | فترة خمود؛ همود؛ سكون |
| quillaia bark for washing | لحاء شجر الكوليا للاستخدام في الغسيل |
| quilts | الألحفه |

| | |
|---|---|
| quinazoline | كينازولين |
| quinine | الكينين |
| quinolyl | كينوليل |
| quinquina | الكينكين |
| quit movie edit task | إنهاء مهمة تحرير الأفلام |
| quoits | لعبة قذف الحلقات (حدوة الحصان) |
| qw | مرة في الأسبوع |
| qwerty | طريقة ترتيب الأحرف على لوحة مفاتيح الكمبيوتر |

# R

| | |
|---|---|
| rabbit anti-human ige | الأرنبي غير البشري IgE |
| rabbit polyclonal il-17 neutralising antibodies | الأجسام المضادة المعادلة لـ IL-17 عديدة النسائل الأرنبية |
| rac | راسيمي |
| racemic forms | الصور الراسيمية |
| racemic mixtures | الخلائط الراسيمية |
| racemiform | عنقودي الشكل |
| racemisation: racemization | مراسمة؛ تكوين خليط راسيمي |
| racemose | عنقودي الشكل |
| racial vilification laws | قوانين تجريم الازدراء العنصري |
| radar installations | منشآت الرادار |
| radar surveillance | المسح الرداري |
| radial | كعبري؛ مرتبط بالعظم الكعبري |
| radial block copolymers | بوليمرات مشتركة كتلية قطرية |
| radial symmetry | التماثل الشعاعي [في الخلايا الشمسية] |
| radial temprature gradient | تدرج درجة الحرارة القطري |
| radial tree | تفرع قطري |
| radiance | إشعاعية، تألق، بهاء |
| radiant flux | تدفق إشعاعي |
| radiate | يشع |
| radiation | إشعاع |
| radiation heating | تسخين إشعاعي |
| radiation physics | فيزياء الإشعاع |
| radiation therapy | علاج بالإشعاع؛ علاج بالأشعة |
| radiator | مشع |
| radical | شق |
| radical innovation | ابتكار جذري |
| radiculopathy | اعتلال جذور الأعصاب؛ اعتلال الجذور |
| radio receiver | مستقبل راديو |
| radio transmitter | جهاز إرسال لاسلكي |
| radioactive | نشيط إشعاعيا |
| radioactive labels | علامات مشعة |
| radioactive materials | مواد مشعة |
| radioactivity | نشاط إشعاعي |
| radioautograph | إشعاع ذاتي |
| radioautography | التصوير الإشعاعي الذاتي |
| radiobiology | علم الأحياء الإشعاعي |
| radiobroadcast | يذيع بالراديو، بث إذاعي |
| radiochemical | كيميائي إشعاعي |
| radiochemistry | كيمياء إشعاعية |
| radioelement | عنصر مشع |
| radio-frequency identification | تعريف موجة الراديو |
| radiograph | الصورة المشعاعية |
| radiography | التصوير بالأشعة |
| radioimmunoassay | اختبار المناعة المشع |
| radioisotopes | نظائر مشعة |

| | |
|---|---|
| radiolabeled | معلّم بالإشعاع؛ مرقم إشعاعيًا |
| radiolabeled antigen-binding assay (ria) | اختبار ربط بمولد ضد معلّم بالإشعاع |
| radio-labeled compound | مركب معلّم بالإشعاع |
| radiolabeled ligands | مركبات ترابطية مشعة |
| radioligand | مركب ترابطي مشع |
| radiolocation | تحديد الموقع بالرادار |
| radiologic technologist | تقني الأشعة. الطبيب الذي يقوم بإعطاء مريض الورم جرعات من الأشعة لمواجهة الخلايا السرطانية |
| radiological | خاص بالطب الإشاعي أو بالاشعاع النووي |
| radiology | الطب الإشاعي |
| radiolucent | منفذ للأشعة |
| radiometric scintillation proximity assay | اختبار تقاربية ومضان إشعاعية |
| radiophone | التليفون أو الهاتف اللاسلكي |
| radius | نصف قطر |
| raid | مصفوفة متكررة من أقراص مستقلة |
| railway crossing | تقاطع سكك حديدية |
| railway junction | تفريعة سكة حديد |
| ram | ذاكرة الوصول العشوائي |
| ram shear devices | أجهزة قص ضاغطة |
| raman spectroscopy ("raman") | قياس طيف رامان ("رامان") |
| ramp down | يخفض |
| ramp rate | معدل انخفاض |
| ramp up | يرفع؛ يزيد |
| ramp-heat | زيادة تدريجية في درجة الحرارة |
| random access memory (ram) | ذاكرة توصل عشوائي |
| random and nondiscriminatory terms | عبارة لنوع من الترخيص يستخدم في عمليات اعتماد المستويات القياسية في حقل ما. عندما تنضم الشركة لهيئة المستويات القياسية توافق الشركات سلفا أنها إذا حصلت على براءة بإزاء تقنية ما تصبح جوهرية وشديدة الأهمية للمستوى القياسي فإنها ستسمح للجهات الأخرى التي تسعى لتطبيق المستوى القياسي باستخدام تلك البراءات وأن يكون المقابل المادي لذلك الاستخدام معقولا. ويسهم هذا النمط من الترخيص في إيجاد حالة من التنافسية بين الشركات التي تصنع منتجات تسهم في تطبيق مستويات قياسية |
| random blood glucose | تحليل السكر العشوائي |
| random copolymers | بوليمرات مشتركة عشوائية |
| random play indicator | مؤشر التشغيل العشوائي |
| randomised double blind crossover study | دراسة عشوائية تبادلية مجهولة للطرفين. انظر أيضا blind clinical trial وdouble-blind clinical trial |
| randomized complete block design | تصميم الوحدات العشوائية الكاملة |
| raney nickle | نيكل راني |
| range | مدى؛ نطاق؛ مرمى البندقية |

| | |
|---|---|
| rankings | تصنيفات |
| ranks of air force officers | رتب ضباط القوات الجوية |
| ranks of naval officers | رتب ضباط البحرية |
| ranks of tubes | صفوف الأنابيب |
| rank-sum test | اختبار كامل للدرجة |
| rapidly-progressing glomerulonephritis | التهاب كبيبات الكلى المتطور بسرعة |
| rappelling static rope | حبل إنقاذ للهبوط في الكهوف |
| rare earth-containing cations | كاتيونات محتوية على عناصر أرضية نادرة |
| rare earths | أكاسيد عناصر الأتربة النادرة |
| ras gene | جين راس |
| rasin | راتنج |
| raster scanning | مسح بخطوط متوازية |
| rat | الجرذ |
| rat anti-mouse antibody | جسم مضاد لفأر من جرذ؛ جسم مضاد جرذي لفأر |
| ratcheted | مزوَّد بسقاطة |
| rate card | بطاقة أسعار ومواصفات الإعلان |
| rate determining step = rate limiting step | خطوة تحديد/تقييد سرعة التفاعل |
| ratify | يصدق على الحكم |
| ratio of hydrogen to the crude feed | نسبة الهيدروجين إلى تيار التغذية الخام |
| rations | التعيينات |
| raw cotton, cotton wool | قطن خام |
| raw data | معطيات أولية |
| raw data: unhandled data | بيانات خام: بيانات غير معالجة |
| raw earth | خام أرضي |
| raw gum or partly processed | صمغ خام أومعالج جزئياً |
| raw idea | فكرة خام |
| raw materials | المواد الخام |
| raw of jute | برم الجوت |
| raw water | ماء غير معالج |
| ray path | مسار الشعاع |
| raynaud syndrome | متلازمة راينود |
| rayon | رايون |
| rbj | آر بي جي: رشاش آر بي جي |
| rbl-er51 calcium signalling assay | إصدار إشارات الكالسيوم في خلايا -RBL ER51 |
| r-configuration | الصورة R |
| reach (%) | نسبة عدد الزوار للموقع |
| react | يؤثر في، يفاعل، يستجيب |
| reactable material | مادة متفاعلة |
| reactance | مفاعلة |
| reactant | المادة المتفاعلة؛ مفاعل |
| reaction | رد فعل، رجعة، ارتكاس، تفاعل |
| reaction kinetics | الخواص الحركية للتفاعل؛ حركيات التفاعل |
| reaction product | منتج ناجم عن تفاعل |
| reaction schemes | مخططات التفاعل |
| reactivate | يعيد تنشيط |
| reactive | تفاعلي، متفاعل، رجعي، ارتكاسي، مفاعل |
| reactive cyclic sulfites or sulfates | الكبريتيت أو الكبريتات الحلقية التفاعلية |
| reactive oxygen species (ros) | أنواع الأكسجين التفاعلي |
| reactivity | نشاط تفاعلي |
| reactor | مفاعل؛ مفاعل نووي |
| reactor feedstock | خام تغذية المفاعل |
| reactors | مفاعل إعادة تشكيل بالأكسدة؛ مفاعل إعادة التشكيل المؤكسد |
| read only storage (ros) | وحدة تخزين للقراءة فقط |
| readable | قابل للقراءة؛ جهاز نقل البيانات |
| reader | قارئ، معيد، مدرس يقرأ الموضوعات للطلاب، مِقرأة |
| reading | قراءة |
| reading frame | إطار القراءة |
| read-plate | يقرأ |
| ready-to-wear clothes industry | صناعة الملابس الجاهزة |
| reagent | مادة تفاعل؛ مادة كاشفة |
| real estate | قطاع |
| real field-of-view | مجال رؤية حقيقي |
| real number term and an imaginary number term | حَدّ يكون عبارة عن عدد حقيقي، وحَدّ يكون عبارة عن رقم تخيلي |
| real property | عقار |
| real world | العالم الحقيقي |
| re-aligned patent strategy | إستراتيجية براءات تم إجراء محاذاة لها |
| real-image zoom | تكبير على مستوى الصورة |
| reality | واقع، حقيقة |
| reality technology | تقنية الواقع |
| real-time clock (rtc) battery | بطارية (RTC) ساعة الوقت الحقيقي |
| real-time detection | كشف فوري |
| real-time energy metering | قياس طاقة فوري |
| real-time locator | معين فوري للموضع |
| real-time operating system | نظام تشغيل فوري |
| real-time sensing device | جهاز إحساس فوري |
| rear admiral | عميد بحري |
| rear power take-off | وحدة الدفع الخلفية |
| rear seat bench of the car | المقعد الطويل الخلفي للسيارة |
| rear-engined | مُزود بمحرك خلفي |
| reasonable doubt | شك معقول؛ شك في محله؛ شك منطقي |
| reasonable notice | إخطار معقول. إخطار مرسل من قبل أحد المتعاقدين للآخر خلال مدة زمنية معقولة وكافية |
| reasonable utilization of traditional knowledge | توظيف معقول للمعرفة التقليدية |
| reasoned arbitral award | حكم تحكيم مُسبب |
| reasons for the judgement | حيثيات الحكم |
| reassume | يستعيد |
| reboilers | مراجل إعادة غلي |
| rebuttal | تفنيد |
| rec mode std play | تشغيل قياسي وضع التسجيل |
| rec search | بحث خلال التسجيل |
| recapture a position | يستعيد (مكان استراتيجي) |
| receiprocating motion | حركة ترددية |
| receivability provisions | أحكام قبول الدعوى |
| receive | يستقبل |
| receive - deliver (gas mixture) | استلام - تسليم (الخليط الغازي) |

| | |
|---|---|
| received codewords | كلمات مشفرة مستقبلة |
| received signal quality (snr) | جودة الإشارة المستقبَلة |
| receiver | جهاز استقبال؛ مستقبل؛ مستلم، مستقبل الإشارات، مستقبل البث |
| receiver card | بطاقة المستقبل |
| recent introduction of digital broadcasting | والاستخدام الحديث للبث الرقمي |
| receptacle | مقبس؛ وعاء |
| receptacle bore | ثقب استقبال |
| receptor antagonistic effects | تأثيرات مضادة على المستقبل |
| receptor tyrosine kinase | إنزيم كيناز التيروسين المستقبل |
| receptor tyrosine kinase inhibitors | كمثبطات لمستقبل كيناز التيروسين |
| recess | تجويف |
| recessed slot | شق مجوف |
| recessive | متنح |
| recessive mutation | طفرة متنحية |
| recharger | معيد الشحن |
| recharging | إعادة الشحن |
| recipient antibody | الجسم المضاد المستقبل |
| reciprocal | متبادل |
| reciprocating compressor | ضاغط ترددي الكباس |
| recirculation pump | مضخة المنتجات المعادة التدوير |
| recital | عرض؛ مقدمة؛ مدخل؛ تقديم؛ تمهيد |
| recognised borders | حدود معترف بها |
| recognition | التعرف إلى |
| recognition device | جهاز تعرف |
| recognizability | إمكانية التعرف على الشيء |
| recognizable | يمكن التعرف عليه |
| recognize ; recognise | يتعرف على |
| recognizer | متعرف على |
| recoilless weapons | أسلحة عديمة الارتداد |
| recombinant | ناتج عودة الارتباط الجيني؛ معاود الارتباط الجيني |
| recombinant dna technology | تقنية DNA الناتج عن عودة الارتباط الجيني |
| recombinant virus | فيروس ناتج عن عودة الارتباط الجيني |
| recombinantly | بشكل ناتج عن عودة الارتباط الجيني |
| recombination | عودة الارتباط الجيني؛ توافق |
| re-conditionable photocopy machine | آلة تصوير قابلة لإعادة التهيئة |
| reconnaissance mission | مهمة استطلاعية |
| reconnaissance plane | طائرة استطلاع |
| reconnoitre | يستطلع |
| reconsider the case | يعيد محاكمة |
| reconstituted | معادة الصياغة |
| record management solutions | حلول إدارة السجلات |
| record pause mode | وضع الإيقاف المؤقت للتسجيل |
| record review | معاينة التسجيل |
| record/standby indicator | مؤشر التسجيل/الاستعداد |
| recording a movie | تسجيل فيلم |
| recording from the tape on a memory card | التسجيل من الشريط إلى بطاقة الذاكرة |
| recording mode | وضع التسجيل |
| recording panoramic images | تسجيل الصور شاملة الرؤية |
| recording programs | برامج التسجيل |

| | |
|---|---|
| recording reminder | تذكير التسجيل |
| recording still images | تسجيل الصور الثابتة |
| recording time | مدة التسجيل |
| records storage | مخزن سجلات |
| recover | يسترد؛ يستعيد (بيانات)؛ يتعافى |
| recover (compounds etc.) | يستخلص (مركبات إلخ) |
| recover (data etc.) | يسترد (بيانات إلخ) |
| recover (oil etc.) | يستخلص (النفط إلخ) |
| recovery | استرداد، استعادة، تعاف |
| recovery (mining) | استخلاص أو استخراج |
| recovery software | برنامج للاستعادة، برنامج للإصلاح |
| recovery time objective | هدف وقت الاسترجاع |
| recruit | مستجد |
| recruitment | تجنيد؛ استدعاء |
| recrystallization | عملية إعادة التبلور |
| rectal | عن طريق المستقيم |
| rectangular gating period | فترة الإمرار الانتقائي |
| rectangular key | خابور مستطيل الشكل |
| rectoverso printing | الطباعة على الوجهين |
| rectum carcinoma | الورم السرطاني بالمستقيم |
| recurrent parent x non-recurrent parent | أب راجع × أب غير راجع |
| recycle | يدور |
| recycle paper pulping | استخلاص الألياف من الورق المعاد تدويره |
| recycle-oriented society | مجتمع ذو وجهة لإعادة التدوير |
| recycling | إعادة تدوير |
| red eye correction | تصحيح تأثير العين الحمراء |
| red iron oxide | أكسيد الحديد الأحمر |
| rededication | اعادة الافتتاح اعادة التدشين |
| red-eye reduction mode | وضع تقليل العين الحمراء |
| red-lining | ارتكاب تجاوزات عنصرية |
| redox | تفاعل اختزال وأكسدة |
| redox agents | عوامل اختزال وأكسدة |
| redox potential | جهد الأكسدة و الاختزال |
| redox reagents | مواد تفاعل مختزلة مؤكسدة؛ مواد كاشفة مختزلة مؤكسدة |
| redox refolding of igg1 | إعادة طي IgG1 في ظل تفاعل اختزال مؤكسد |
| reduce recompressor inlet temperature | يخفض درجة حرارة الدخول لوسيلة إعادة الضغط |
| reduced energy consumption | توفير منخفض للطاقة |
| reduced light chain | سلسلة خفيفة مختزلة |
| reduced seismic data output record | سجل مخرجات بيانات زلزالية مخفضة |
| reduced-set bit-reversal operator | مُشغِّل عكس الرقم الثنائي ذي مجموعة مخفضة |
| reducible | قابل لأن يتم وضعه في موضع معين |
| reducible to practice | ممكنٌ وضعه موضع الممارسة |
| reducing agent | عامل اختزال |
| reducing gas | غاز مختزل |
| reducing sugar | سُكَّرٌ مُختزلٌ |
| reducing the higher possible amount of organic compounds to the liquid | اختزال الكمية المحتملة العالية للمركبات العضوية إلى الحالة السائلة |

| | |
|---|---|
| State | |
| reductase | إنزيم الرديكتاز (إنزيم مختزل) |
| reduction | اختزال |
| reduction of allyl double bond | اختزال الرابطة المزدوجة للأليل |
| reduction/oxidation coupling reagent | مادة تفاعل إقران مختزلة مؤكسدة |
| reduction/oxidization agents | عوامل اختزال وأكسدة |
| reductive alkylation | ألكلة اختزالية؛ معالجة اختزالية بالألكيل |
| reductive amination | أمْيَنة اختزالية؛ معالجة اختزالية بالأمين |
| redundancy | تسريح العمالة أو الموظفين |
| reed switch | مفتاح ذو ريشة |
| reef rocks | الصخور الشعابية |
| reel | بكرة |
| reel off the spool | فك من على البكرة |
| re-engineering | إعادة هندسة |
| reexamination | إعادة مناقشة الشاهد؛ إعادة فحص |
| reexamine | يعيد الفحص |
| ref | المرجع |
| reference data | بيانات المرجع |
| reference electrode | إلكترود مرجعي |
| reference sth | يرجع إلى؛ يشير إلى |
| references | إحالات |
| referendum | استفتاء |
| referential integrity | التكامل المرجعي |
| referred pain | تسميع الألم |
| refine | يكرر، ينقي، يهذب، يصقل |
| refined oil | زَيْتٌ مكرر؛ زيت التكرير |
| refinement | تنقيح |
| refinement | تكرير، تنقية، تصفية، تجويد |
| refinery | عملية تكرير؛ مصفاة تكرير |
| refinery feedstock | خام تغذية التكرير؛ خام تغذية لعملية تكرير |
| refinery gas | غَازُ تكرير |
| refinery processes | عمليات تكرير |
| refining | تصفية؛ تنقية؛ التقوية: عملية المعالجة الميكانيكية للألياف لتقويتها |
| reflect | يعكس، ينعكس، يفكر |
| reflectability | قابلية الشيء للانعكاس |
| reflectable object | شيء قابل للعكس |
| reflectable vest | صدرة قابلة للانعكاس |
| reflectance; reflection coefficient, reflection factor | معامل الانعكاس |
| reflection | عكس، انعكاس، التواء، عضو ملتو |
| reflection index (for light) | معامل انعكاس (الضوء) |
| reflection physics | فيزياء العكس |
| reflectional | انعكاسي، ناشيء عن الانعكاس |
| reflective | عاكس، انعكاسي |
| reflector | عاكس |
| reflex | لا إرادي، ضوء أو حرارة أو لون منعكس،صورة منعكسة، منحن، ملتوٍ |
| reflex sympathetic dystrophy | سوء التغذية الانعكاسي الودي |
| reflow | ينجزر، ينحسر، جزر |
| reflux | ارتجاع؛ تيار ارتجاع |

| | |
|---|---|
| reflux rate | معدل الارتجاع |
| refluxing | ارتجاعي |
| refold | يعيد طي |
| refolding | إعادة طي |
| reform | يصلح، إصلاح |
| reformate | نواتج إعادة التشكيل |
| reformate line | خط ناتج إعادة تشكيل |
| reformer | وحدة إعادة تشكيل |
| reforming unit | وحدة إعادة تشكيل كيميائي |
| reforming zone | منطقة إعادة تشكيل |
| refracted into; refracted towards | يتم انكساره نحو |
| refractive index | معامل الانكسار |
| refractometer | مقياس الانكسار |
| refractories | حراريات |
| refractory | حراري |
| refractory | مضادة للحرارة الشديدة |
| refractory industry | صناعة الحراريات |
| refractory material | مادة حرارية |
| refractory oxide | أكسيد حراري |
| refrigerant | مبرِّد (بالغاز)؛ مادة تبريد (بالغاز)؛ تيار تبريد (بالغاز) |
| refrigeration | عملية تبريد (بالغاز) |
| refueling drogue assembly | تجميعة مرساة لإعادة التزود بالوقود |
| regenerant | مادة تنشيط |
| regenerated catalyst | محفز مجدَّد |
| regeneration | تنشيط (لمادة داخل تفاعل) |
| regenerative | منشط |
| regenerator | وسيلة تجديد |
| regimen | نظم علاج |
| regiment | مدرعة/ كتيبة مدفعية |
| regio isomers | أيزومرات نطاقية |
| regiochemistry | كيمياء نطاقية؛ خواص الكيمياء النطاقية |
| regioisomer | أيزومر نطاقي |
| region | منطقة (هـوراثية) |
| regional | نطاقي؛ منطقي (متعلق بمنطقة) (في أسماء الأمراض الطبية) |
| regional enteritis | التهاب الأمعاء المنطقي |
| regional musculoskeletal strain | الإجهاد العضلي الهيكلي الموضعي |
| region-wide | في مختلف أنحاء المنطقة |
| regioselectivity | انتقائية مكانية |
| register | يسجل، مسجل، سجل |
| registerable industrial design | نموذج صناعي قابل للتسجيل |
| registerable patent | براءة قابلة للتسجيل |
| registered education savings plan | برنامج الادخار للتعليم؛ برنامج التوفير للتعليم |
| registered patent | براءة مسجلة |
| registered patent agent | وكيل براءات مسجل |
| registration clause | البند المتعلق بالتسجيل |
| registration expertise | خبرة في مجال التسجيل |
| regn.no: 5986 wk | رقم التسجيل |
| regular / irregular polygon | مضلع منتظم / غير منتظم |
| regular bit reversal operation | عملية عكس الرقم الثنائي المنتظمة |

| | |
|---|---|
| regular surface | سطح عادي |
| regulate | ينظم |
| regulations | اللوائح |
| regulator | منظم |
| rehabilitate | يعيد تأهيل |
| rehabilitation | إعادة تأهيل |
| reinforcement | تدعيم؛ تسليح؛ حديد التسليح |
| reinforcement of (tensions) | إذكاء، تأجيج (التوترات) |
| reinventability | القابلية لإعادة الاختراع |
| reinventable | قابل لإعادة الاختراع |
| reinvtion | إعادة الاختراع |
| reissue | يعيد الإصدار |
| reiter's syndrome | متلازمة ريتر |
| reject | يزيل؛ يتخلص من؛ يطرد؛ يرفض (عضواً إلخ) |
| rejected patent application | طلب براءة مرفوض |
| rel | نسبي |
| rel int | الكثافة النسبية (في صورة حيود الأشعة السينية في المسحوق XRPD) |
| rel vol | حجم نسبي |
| related applications | الطلبات ذات الصلة |
| related applications | تطبيقات ذات صلة. تطبيقات ذات صلة بالاختراع موضوع طلب البراءة، وهو ما يتوجب ذكره في طلب البراءة |
| related art | الفن ذو العلاقة |
| related art search | بحث متصل بالفن ذو العلاقة |
| related invention | اختراع ذو صلة |
| related patent | براءة ذات صلة |
| related prior art | فن سابق ذو علاقة |
| relational database management system (rdbms) | نظام إدارة قواعدالبيانات الارتباطية |
| relationship | علاقة |
| relative | نسبي |
| relative humidity | الرطوبة النسبية |
| relative permeability | النفاذية النسبية |
| relative proportions of a conformation of a protien | النسب النسبية لهيئة بروتين |
| relative to | بالنسبة لـ |
| relative transmission power levels | مستويات قوة إرسال نسبية |
| relative volatilities | نسب قابلية التطاير النسبية |
| relax period | فترة الاسترخاء |
| relaxant | متعلق بالإرخاء |
| relaxed diameter (mm) | القطر أثناء فترة الاسترخاء (مم) |
| relay | مرحِّل |
| releasably | على نحو قابل للتحرير؛ بصورة قابلة للتحرير |
| release | يحرِّر؛ يعتق (في مجال الصناعة والآلات)؛ يطلق (في مجال الكيمياء) |
| release for health reasons | الإفراج الصحي: الإفراج لأسباب صحية |
| release on bail | يفرج بكفالة |
| relevant patent documents | مستندات براءة ذات صلة |
| relevant prior art | فن سابق ذو صلة |
| reliability | موثوقية |
| reliability function | دالة موثوق فيها |

| | |
|---|---|
| reliable patent search | بحث براءتي يعول عليه |
| reliable sources | مصادر موثوق بها |
| relief map | خريطة مجسمة |
| relief printing | الطباعة النافرة؛ الطباعة البارزة |
| relief valve | صمام تصريف |
| religh waves | موجات ريلاي |
| remaining recording time | وقت التسجيل المتبقي |
| remaking the keyboard. | إعادة تكوين لوحة المفاتيح |
| remote armament solutions | حلول للتسليح عن بعد |
| remote computer | كمبيوتر متصل عن بعد |
| remote control switch | مِفْتَاحٌ لِلتَّحَكُّمِ مِنْ بُعْدٍ |
| remote control technology | تقنية تحكم عن بعد |
| remote robot operation | عملية تتم بواسطة روبوت بعيد |
| remote sensor | وحدة الاستشعار عن بعد |
| remote sensor mode | وضع وحدة الاستشعار عن بُعد |
| removable flow balancing means | وسيلة موازنة تدفق قابلة للإزالة |
| removing the cassette | إخراج الشريط |
| renal carcinoma | الورم السرطاني الكلوي |
| renal colic | المغص الكلوي |
| renal fibrosis | التليف الكلوي |
| rename | يعيد تسمية |
| renewable electricity | كهرباء متجددة |
| renewable energy | طاقة متجددة |
| renewable energy source | مصدر طاقة متجددة |
| renewable energy technology | تقنية طاقة متجددة |
| renewed patent | براءة مجددة |
| rent | إيجار |
| rental value (of farmland) | القيمة الإيجارية (للأرض الزراعية) |
| repair clause | بند الإصلاح |
| repair parts | قطع غيار |
| repaired dna | الحمض النووي DNA المصحَّح أو المُصلَح أو المرمَّم |
| repeat infringer | منتهك كرر الانتهاك |
| repeat patent infringement offender | متعد منتهك لبراءة أكثر من مرة |
| repeating pentadecameric helical fibre | ألياف حلزونية متكررة بنتاديكاميرية |
| repellent | نسيج صاد للماء |
| repeller | طارد |
| reperfusion | إعادة الارتواء |
| reperfusion injury | الإصابات الناتجة عن معاودة التروية |
| repertoire | سجل |
| repetitive motion pain | ألم الحركة التكراري |
| replace | يستبدل |
| replacement | استبدال |
| replacement | إحلال شيء محل آخر، بديل |
| replacement of one carboxylic group hydrogen | استبدال ذرة هيدروجين واحدة بمجموعة كربوكسيلي |
| replacement therapy | علاج بديل |
| replenishing the evaporator | استبدال المبخر: إمكانية استعواض المبخِّر: أي إزالته وإحلال غيره محله |
| replication | نسخ؛ تناسخ-تكرار |
| replicon | نسخة |

| | |
|---|---|
| repol | تقرير طارئ عن الاحتياج لكميات ضخمة من الوقود |
| repolarization | إعادة القطبية |
| report | يذكر، يصف، يفيد؛ يبلغ، يرفع تقريرا، تقرير، محضر |
| report as | يعبر عنه في صورة |
| report to sb | يعطي إفادة لـ أو يعمل تحت إشراف |
| reporter | مرسل |
| reporter gene | جين مرشد؛ جين مراسل- جين دال؛ مرشد؛ كاشف |
| reporting | إعداد تقرير (أو إرسال تقرير)؛ إبلاغ |
| repose | سكون؛ سكينة |
| repower | يعيد الشحن |
| repowerability | القابلية لإعادة الشحن |
| repowerable | قابل لإعادة الشحن |
| represent | يعبر عن |
| representation | تمثيل |
| representations and warranties clause | البند الخاص بالتعهدات والإقرارات |
| representative of | ممثّل لـ |
| repressor | كابت |
| reproccessability | إمكانية إعادة المعالجة |
| reproccessable | قابل لإعادة المعالجة |
| reprocess | يعيد المعالجة |
| reprogrammed stem cells | خلايا سلالية معادة برمجتها |
| re-pulp | يعيد عجن |
| repulsive magnetic forces of opposite magnet faces | قوى التنافر المغناطيسية للأسطح المغناطيسية المتقابلة |
| request | يطلب، طلب |
| request for an ex parte reexamination | طلب لإجراء إعادة فحص عن براءة من طرف واحد |
| request for examination | طلب لإجراء فحص . طلب يقدمه مقدم طلب البراءة لكي يتم البدء في فحص البراءة، وهو طلب تشترط قوانين بعض البلدان تقديمه في حين لا تشترط قوانين بلدان أخرى تقديمه |
| request for patent search | طلب لإجراء بحث عن براءة |
| request for reexamination | طلب لإجراء إعادة فحص عن براءة |
| request to reexamine a patent | طلب لإعادة فحص براءة |
| require | يتطلب |
| requirement | متطلب |
| requirements | متطلبات |
| requisition compensation | تعويض المصادرة |
| reruns | العروض المرئية المعادة |
| rescue robot | روبوت إنقاذ |
| research based industry | صناعة مؤسسة على البحث |
| research scientist | عالم بحوث |
| research stage | مرحلة البحث |
| research-driven company | شركة يسوقها البحث |
| research-driven organization | منظومة يقودها البحث |
| resection of the intestine | الاستئصال الجزئي للأمعاء |
| reservability | قابلية الشيء للتخزين |
| reservable | قابل للتخزين |
| reserve | يخزن، احتياطي، يحفظ، ذخيرة، قوات احتياط |
| reserve officer | ضباط احتياط |
| reserved | محفوظ، متحفظ |
| reservoir | خزان؛ صهريج؛ مستودع؛ احتياطي |
| reservoir pressure-volume-temperature fluid characteristics | خصائص المائع المخزون من حيث الضغط-الحجم-درجة الحرارة |
| reservoir rock | صخر خازن للزيت |
| reset | يعيد ضبط |
| reset the battery | يعيد إعداد البطارية |
| resetting | إعادة ضبط |
| resetting blade | نصل إعادة الضبط |
| resetting gems | إعادة ترصيع الجواهر |
| resid | الزيت المتبقي |
| resid pitch | قار متبقي |
| residence time | زمن الاحتجاز؛ زمن بقاء |
| residential strata title | حق ملكية وحدة سكنية |
| residential use | في نفس الموقع |
| residual fabricating stresses | الإجهادات المتبقاة |
| residual stress | إجهاد متخلف |
| residue | مادة متبقية؛ وحدة بنائية |
| residue gas | الغاز المتبقي |
| residue gas compression | ضغط الغاز المتبقي |
| residuum | متخلفات |
| resilience | ارتداد؛ مرونة |
| resilient | مرن |
| resin | راتنج |
| resist | يقاوم |
| resistant | مقاوم |
| resistence to authorities | مقاومة السلطات |
| resistibility | المقاومية |
| resistible | مقاوم، ممكن مقاومته |
| resistive | مقاوم، مقاومي |
| resistive imaging | تصوير مقاوم |
| resistivity | مقاومة نوعية؛ المقاومية. القدرة على المقاومة |
| resistless | عديم المقاومة |
| resistor | مقاوم |
| resize | يعيد ضبط حجم الشيء |
| resizer | مُعيد ضبط حجم الشيء |
| resizing photos | تغيير حجم الصور |
| reslove | يحلل |
| resolution | انحلال؛ حل؛ تحليل؛ درجة وضوح الشاشة؛ صفاء، قرار، تصميم، ثبات |
| resolution of a symptome | تلاشي أحد الأعراض |
| resolve | يحل؛ يفصل؛ يفك؛ يذيب |
| resolved failure | تعطّل تم حله |
| resolvent | مذيب |
| resolving racemates into the optical antipodes | حل الراسيمات إلى نقائض ضوئية |
| resonance | رنين |
| resonance physics | فيزياء الرنين |
| resonant | رنان، مُرجِع |
| resonant energy | طاقة مدوية |
| resonant frequency | تردد ذو رنين |
| resonate | يرن، يُرجع الصدى |

| | |
|---|---|
| resonator | مرنان |
| resorption | ارتشاف |
| resource conflicts | تعارض الموارد |
| resource-efficient solutions | حلول ذات فعالية مواردتية |
| resourceful mind | ذهن واسع الموارد |
| resource-rich investment environment | بيئة استثمار غنية بالموارد |
| resource-wasting consumer gadgets | أدوات استهلاكية مضيعة للموارد |
| resource-wasting invention | اختراع مضيع للموارد |
| respective | خاص بـ؛ مناظر |
| respectively | بالترتيب؛ على التوالي |
| respiratory syncytial virus | الفيروس التنفسي الخلوي؛ فيروس الالتهاب الرئوي |
| respiratory tract | أمراض القناة التنفسية |
| respiratory viral infection caused by human rhinovirus (hrv) | عدوى فيروسية في الجهاز التنفسي ناتجة عن فيروس أنفي في البشر |
| respondent | مطعون ضده |
| respondent's appointed arbitrator | المحكم المعين من قبل المُحتَكَم ضده |
| response to b-cell depletion therapy with rituximab | الاستجابة لعلاج نضوب خلايا B باستخدام الريتوكسيماب |
| response units (ru). | وحدة استجابة |
| responsibility | مسئوليه |
| rest | يرقّد |
| rest and recreation - r&r | الراحة والترويح |
| restart | يعيد التشغيل |
| restenosis | معاودة التضيق |
| restitution | إسترداد التعويض |
| restless leg syndrome (rls) | متلازمة الرجل القلقه: الرغبه الملحة بتحريك او هزّ القدم |
| restore | يرمم |
| restrict | يقيد |
| restricted patentee's power | سلطة مقيدة لصاحب البراءة |
| restricted practice | ممارسة محدودة/مقيدة |
| restriction | قيد |
| restriction enzyme | إنزيم القيد |
| restriction enzyme digestion | اهتضام الإنزيم التقييدي؛ اهتضام الإنزيم المقيّد |
| restriction fragment length polymorphism (rflp) markers | واسمات تعدد شكل طول شظية تقييد |
| restriction site | موقع تقييد |
| restrictions | قيود |
| restrictive patent laws | قوانين براءات مقيد، قانون براءات ذو طابع تقييدي |
| restrictor | وسيلة تقييد |
| restructuring of the industrial sector | إعادة تنظيم الهيكل الصناعي |
| retail-vendor relationship | علاقة بائع التجزئة بالبائع |
| retainer ; retaining means | وسيلة احتجاز |
| retainer fee | أتعاب الاستبقاء. أتعاب استبقاء المستشارين لمدة معينة. |
| retainership agreement | عقد توكيل |
| retaining wall | جدار محتجز |
| retention | إمساك |
| retention time | زمن احتجاز؛ زمن استبقاء |
| reticular | شبكي |
| reticulate | مكسو بشبكة، سبكي الشكل، ذو ألياف متشابكة |
| reticulation | تشابك، شبكة |
| reticulocyte | خلية شبكية |
| retinal degeneration | تنكس الشبكية؛ ضمور الشبكية |
| retinoblastoma | ورم خلايا الشبكية البدائية |
| retinoids | شبيهات بالراتنج |
| retinopathy | اعتلال الشبكية |
| retired officer | ضابط متقاعد |
| retract | يكمش، يضم، يسحب، يتراجع |
| retractability | قابلية الشيء للسحب |
| retractable | قابل للسحب |
| retractable landing gear | عدة حط منسحبة |
| retractive index | معامل الانكسـار |
| re-treatment ; retreatment | إعادة العلاج: إعادة إعطاء العلاج |
| retribution | قصاص |
| retrievability | قابلية الشيء للاسترجاع |
| retrievable | قابل للاسترجاع |
| retrieval system | نظام استرجاع |
| retrieve | يسترجع |
| retriever | مسترجع |
| retrofit | يعيد مواءمة |
| retrofittable | قابل لإعادة المواءمة؛ قابلة للتعديل الرجعي |
| retrograde | تراجعي؛ تقهقري: عكسي؛ في اتجاه عكسي |
| retro-inverso isomer | أيزومر قهقري عكسي |
| retroorbit | خلف الحجاج |
| retroviral/retroviruses | فيروس النسخ العكسي/فيروسات النسخ العكسي |
| retrovirus | فيروس قهقري؛ فيروس ارتجاعي |
| retry | يعيد المحاولة |
| return date | تاريخ العودة |
| return line | خط عودة |
| return means | وسيلة إرجاع |
| returning to a pre-marked position | الرجوع للوضع الذي تم تحديده مسبقًا |
| reuptake | إعادة امتصاص؛ استرجاع؛ استرداد؛ يعيد امتصاص |
| revascularization | إعادة التوعية الدموية |
| revenue generating patent | براءة مدرة للدخل |
| reverse | يعكس |
| reverse feedback | تغذية عكسية |
| reverse link | وصلة عكسية |
| reverse or thrust fault | الصدع العكسي |
| reverse osmosis | تناضح عكسي |
| reverse sequence | متوالية عكسية |
| reverse transcriptase | إنزيم ترانسكربتاز العكسي |
| reversed phase | ذو طور عكسي |
| reverse-link power control algorithm | حساب تحكم القدرة في الوصلة العكسية |
| reverse-phase column chromatography | عمود كروموتوجراف بطور منعكس |
| reversible | عكوسة |
| reversible water shift reactions | تفاعلات إزاحة مياه عكسية |

| | |
|---|---|
| review | يعاين؛ يراجع؛ يفحص بعناية؛ مراجعة |
| review paper | ورقة علمية |
| reviewer | مراجع |
| revived patent | براءة تم إحياؤها. براءة تم تفعيلها بعد تعرضها لما منع تفعيلها مثل هجرانها من قبل صاحبها. |
| revoacable license | ترخيص قابل للرجوع فيه |
| revoked license | ترخيص تم الرجوع عن منحه |
| revoked patent | براءة منقوضة، براءة تم الرجوع عن منحها. |
| revolution | ثورة |
| revolutionary improvement | تحسين ثوري |
| revolutionary invention | اختراع ثوري |
| revolutionary patent | براءة ثورية |
| revolutionizing | تثوير |
| rewire | يعيد التسليك، يجهز بأسلاك جديدة |
| rewiring | إعادة التسليك، يجهز بأسلاك جديدة |
| rf | تردد لاسلكي؛ عامل الإحتجاز |
| rflp | واسمات تعدد شكل طول شظية تقييد |
| rfp | طلب تقديم عرض |
| rgb | أحمر وأخضر وأزرق: الألوان الأساسية |
| rh | رطوبة نسبية: تقاس بالنسبة المئوية (%) |
| rhabdomyosarcoma | الورم السرطاني العضلي المخطط |
| rheological properties of the paint | خصائص انسياب الدهان |
| rheology | علم الانسياب |
| rheometer | ريومتر |
| rhesus | الرِّيص (قرد هندي صغير) |
| rheumatic disease | المرض الروماتيزمي |
| rheumatoid | روماتويد |
| rheumatoid arthritis | التهاب المفاصل الروماتويدي |
| rheumatoid arthritis (ra) | التهاب المفاصل شبه الروماتزمي |
| rhf chamber furnaces | أفران حرارية |
| rhinitis | التهاب الأنف |
| rhinorrhea | زكام |
| rhodium | الرديوم |
| rhomic dodecahedron | ذو اثنا عشر وجها معيني |
| rhyolite | ريوليت |
| rib | ضلع |
| ribble | قصل بذور الكتان |
| rice mills | مضارب الأرز |
| rice strach | نشا الأرز |
| richter scale | مقياس ريختر |
| ridge | سلسلة جبال |
| ridge | نُتُوء |
| riding the boards | فحص أو تفحص أو معاينة لوحات الإعلانات |
| rifle barrel | ماسورة البندقية |
| rig | منصة الحفر؛ جهاز الحفر |
| rigged elections | انتخابات مزورة أو تم التلاعب فيها |
| right | حق، يمين |
| right angle | زاوية قائمة |
| right lateral abdomen | الجانب الأيمن للبطن |
| right to a patent | الحق في البراءة |
| right triangle | مثلث قائم الزاوية |
| rights | حقوق |
| rights clause | بند ينص على حقوق كل الأطراف |
| rights project | مشروع الحقوق |
| ring | حلقة |
| ring surface | سطح حلقي |
| ring system | نظام حلقي |
| ring-closing metathesis ; ring-closure metathesis | تفاعل إبدال إغلاق الحلقة |
| rinsate | الماء الملوث بالمبيد |
| riot | أعمل شغب |
| rip | ينسخ صوت أو صورة (من قرص مدمج) إلى ملف (كمبيوتر) |
| riser | أنبوب صاعد؛ ماسورة صاعدة؛ مفاعل صاعد؛ مفاعل علوي؛ قائم الدرجة: الجزء القائم من درجة السُّلَّم |
| risk assessment report | تقرير تقييم المخاطر |
| risk-weighted | تتضمن مخاطر |
| ritonavir | ريتونافير |
| rival | ينافس، يزاحم، يضارع، يتنافس، متنافس، مزاحم، ند |
| rival inventor | مخترع منافس |
| rivalry | تنافس، منافسة |
| rivet | مسمار برشام |
| rj11 modem port | منفذ مودم RJ11 |
| rma | الاعتمادية وإمكانية الصيانة والمتاحية |
| rms | المتوسط التربيعي؛ متوسط الجذر التربيعي |
| ro | تناضح عكسي |
| roadblocking | بث متزامن؛ تزامن بث الآعلان |
| roadside bomb | قنبلة على جانب الطريق |
| roadster | رودستر |
| roaming | خدمة التجوال: استخدام هاتف المحمول في شبكات أخرى غير تلك التي تدفع لها إيجار خطك الهاتفي -عادة خارج البلد التي تقيم فيه. جميع الشبكات بالمملكة المتحدة تقدم خدمة التجوال. عدد الدول التي يمكنك التجوال فيها يعتمد على عدد اتفاقيات التجوال التي توقعها الشبكة |
| roasting | تحميص |
| robber | لص (بنوك؛ محال) |
| robot | روبوت |
| robot awareness | وعي الروبوت. درجة إحاطة الروبوت بما يدور حوله |
| robot failure | تعطُّل روبوت |
| robot locomotion | دراسات كيفية تزويد الروبوت بأنظمة تمكنه من التحرك. |
| robot operation | عملية تتم بواسطة روبوت |
| robot surgeon | جراح روبوتي |
| robot system | نظام روبوتي |
| robot's faculties | قدرات الروبوت |
| robot's sensors | أجهزة إحساس الروبوت |
| robot's traversability | قابلية الروبوت على التحرك جيئة وذهابا |
| robot-aided | بمعونة الروبوت |
| robot-assisted | بمساعدة الروبوت |
| robotic | روبوتي |
| robotic decision making | صناعة القرار الروبوتي |

| | |
|---|---|
| robotic device | جهاز روبوتي |
| robotic espionage system | نظام تجسس روبوتي |
| robotic mechanism | آلية روبوتية |
| robotic surgery | جراحة روبوتية |
| robotic surgery simulators | مُحاكوا جراحة روبوتيون |
| robotic system | نظام روبوتي |
| robotic technologist | تقني روبوتات |
| robotic welding technology | تقنية لحم روبوتي |
| robotics | روبوتية |
| robotization | تحويل الشيء إلى روبوت |
| robotization of industry | تحويل الصناعة إلى الحالة الروبوتية |
| robotization of mining operations | تحويل عمليات التنجيم إلى الحالة الروبوتية |
| robotized operation | عملية تم جعلها روبوتية |
| robot-mediated | بواسطة الروبوت |
| robot-robot awareness | وعي الروبوت بالروبوت. درجة إحاطة الروبوت بالروبوت المجاور |
| robtize | يحول الشيء إلى روبوت |
| robust standard errors | الأخطاء القياسية الثابتة |
| rock salt | الملح الصخري |
| rocket artillery | مدفعية صاروخية |
| rocket engine | محرك صاروخي |
| rockwool | صوف صخري |
| rod | قضيب |
| rod mill | مطحنة قضيبية |
| rod portions | أجزاء قضيب |
| rod pump | مضخة قضيبية |
| roe | بطارخ |
| roles | الأدوار |
| roll | بكرة أم أسطوانة |
| roll reduction | تقليل الحجم باللف: تقليل حجم (أنبوب إلخ) باللف |
| roll(er) feed | تغذية بالأسطوانات الدوارة |
| rollator | مَشّاءة |
| rollback segments (rbs) | إدارة مقاطع إلغاء التعديلات |
| rolle (roller) mill | ماكينة دلفنة |
| rolled glass | زجاج السحب أو زجاج الرولات: وينتج هذا النوع من الزجاج عن طريق صب الزجاج المصهور على مجموعة من الاسطوانات (Rollers)، وعن طريق الضغط والتمرير بين الأسطوانات يتم تشكيله حسب السماكة المطلوبة، ثم ينقل الزجاج إلى غرفة التلدين (annealing) وبعد التلدين يسحب الزج |
| rolled steel | صلب مدلفن |
| roller | بكرة |
| roller blind | ستارة حصيرة؛ ستارة لفافة |
| roller door | بَابُ حَصِيرَةٍ |
| rolling | عُطوف |
| rollover | ضغط آني للمفاتيح (كمبيوتر) |
| rolls and extensions | تحويلات بنكية بينية وتأخيرات |
| roll-up doors | أبواب منزلقة نحو الأعلى |
| rom | ذاكرة القراءة فقط |
| root avulsions | اقتلاعات الجذر |
| root ball | طين الجذور - مدر الجذور |
| root mean squared (rms) | جذرمتوسط مربع الانحراف |
| deviation ; root-mean-square deviation | |
| root mean-square value | قيمة متوسط الجذر التربيعي |
| root spiralling | التفاف الجذور |
| rootkits | الأدوات الخفية |
| root-solving method | طريقة حل باستخدام الجذور |
| rootstock | فسيلة جذرية |
| rope making | صناعة الحبال |
| rope yarn | خيط غزل الحبال |
| ropping an enlarged photo file | قص ملف صورة تم تكبيره |
| rotary airlocks and blow pots | محابس الهواء الدوارة وأوعية نفخ. |
| rotary drum | إسطوانة دوارة |
| rotary evaporation | تبخير دوراني |
| rotary knife | سكين دوار |
| rotary plate | لوح دوار |
| rotary swivel | رأس دوار |
| rotary table | صِينِيَّةٌ دَوَّارَةٌ |
| rotatability | قابلية الشيء للدوران |
| rotatable | قابل للدروان |
| rotatable | قابل للدوران، قابل للتعاقب |
| rotatable building structure | هيكل المبنى الدوار؛ هيكل المبنى القابل للدوران |
| rotatable perfusable culture chamber | غرفة استزراع؛ غرفة مزرعة |
| rotate | تدوير (أو دوران حسب النص)؛ يدور، يتعاقب |
| rotating a photo file | تدوير ملف صورة |
| rotating coating drum | وعاء تغليف اسطواني دوار |
| rotating prilling bucket | وعاء تحبيب دوار |
| rotating shaft | عمود التدوير؛ عمود الإدارة |
| rotation | دوران، تعاقب |
| rotational | دوراني، تعاقبي |
| rotational faults | الصدوع الدورانية |
| rotational motion | حركة دورانية |
| rotational shaft | عمود دوران |
| rotational symmetry | تماثل دوراني |
| rotator | مُدور |
| rotavapor | مبخر دوار |
| rotor | عضو دوار |
| rotorcraft | طائرة ذات أجنحة دوَّارة |
| rotovap | روتوفاب |
| rough-press paper | ورقة ضغط شديد |
| round | دفعة طلقات |
| round key | خابور مستدير |
| round robin | عريضة احتجاجية |
| route of administration | طريق الإعطاء؛ مسار الإعطاء |
| router | جهاز توجيه |
| routine vacatur | إبطال حُكم |
| routing | توجيه |
| row id | معرف الصف |
| row triggers | أوامر الصفوف |
| royalty | إتاوة. |
| royalty agreement | اتفاق بشأن سداد إتاوة |
| royalty bearing license | ترخيص مدر للأتاوة |
| royalty-bearing products | منتجات حاملة للإتاوة |
| royalty-free license | ترخيص بلا أتاوة |

| | |
|---|---|
| rp-hplc | كروماتوجراف السائل مرتفع الأداء في الطور المنعكس |
| rp-hplc purification | التنقية باستخدام RP-HPLC |
| rpm | دورة في الدقيقة |
| rss | قارئ الأخبار |
| rt | درجة حرارة الغرفة |
| rt-vbr | معدل بت متغير في الزمن الحقيقي |
| ru | وحدة استجابة |
| rubber fibers | ألياف المطاط؛ |
| rubberised coir | ألياف جوز الهند المعاملة بالمطاط |
| rubber industry | صناعة الكاوتشوك |
| rubella | الحصبة الألمانية |
| rubella arthritis | التهاب المفاصل الناتج عن الحصبة الألمانية |
| rudaceous rocks | بالصخور الحصوية |
| rudder | دفّة |
| rule | يحكم، يقضي، قاعدة |
| rule of law | سياة أو حكم القانون |
| rules | قواعد |
| rumble robot | روبوت مدمدم |
| run | دورة معالجة |
| run (through) | يتم مد (كبل إلخ) (خلال) |
| run of press (rop) | في أي موقع تختاره الصحيفة |
| run of schedule (ros) | البث في أي وقت؛ البث حسب خيار المحطة |
| runnable software | برنامج يمكن تشغيله |
| running buffer minus dimethylsulphoxide | المحلول المنظم المستخدم ناقص داي ميثيل سلفوكسيد |
| runs into | يمتد إلى |
| runway | مَدرج: ممر هبوط الطائرات |
| rupture | تمزق |
| rural industries | صناعات ريفية |
| rural innovation | ابتكار ريفي |
| rush the scene of the crime / accident | يهرع إلى مكان الجريمة / الحادث |
| ruthenium | روثنيوم |

# S

| | |
|---|---|
| sabouraud agar | آجار سابورو |
| saccharin sodium | سكرين الصوديوم |
| saccharomyces | الفطور السكرية |
| sachette | زرور (كيس زرور) |
| sacrifice (an animal) | يتخلص من (يذبح) (الحيوان) |
| sacrificial anode system | نظام مصعد التضحية |
| sacrificial render | طبقة تبطين ذوابة |
| saddle key | خابور راكب |
| safety gates | بوابات الأمان |
| safety glass | زجاج سلامة: الزجاج الذي لا ينكسر أو ينكسر بأمان عندما يختبر طبقاً للمواصفة BS 6206 كما أنه يحمي الأشخاص الذين يتعرضون للاصطدام به بشكل مفاجئ من الجروح الحادة والعميقة |
| safety negligence | إهمال أمني |
| safety outcome measures | قياسات نتيجة السلامة |
| safety valve | صمام أمان |
| safflower | العصفر |
| sag | ارتخاء |
| saga | أفلام المغامرات |
| salability | قابلية الشيء للبيع |
| salable | قابل للبيع |
| salable idea | فكرة قابلة للبيع |
| salable idea generation | توليد أفكار قابلة للبيع |
| salable intangibles | أمور غير ملموسة يمكن بيعها |
| salable patent | براءة قابلة للبيع |
| sale | يبيع، بيع، تخفيض |
| sales channel | قناة مبيعات |
| salicylic acid | حمض السلسليك |
| salimeter | المملاح، مقياس الملوحة في سائل |
| salina | الملاحة |
| saline | مالح، ملحي، ملح معدني، محلول مالح |
| salivary gland carcinoma | الورم السرطاني بالغدة اللعابية |
| salix | الصفصاف |
| salt dome | قبة ملحية |
| salt face | سطح ملحي |
| salt out | يفصل بالتمليح |
| salt-forming counter-ions such as sodium | الأيونات المعاكسة المكونة للملح مثل الصوديوم |
| salting-out; salting out | الفصل بالتمليح |
| salts of alkaline metals | فلزات قلوية (أملاح الفلزات القلوية) |
| salvage | انقاذي |
| salvage receptor | مستقبل علاج إنقاذي |
| salves | مراهم؛ دهانات |
| same desktop's replacement hard disk | قرص صلب استبدال سطح المكتب نفسه |
| same order of magnitude | بنفس المقدار؛ بنفس نسبة أو حجم المقدار |
| sample injection | حقن العينة |
| sampling of liquid metal | أخذ عينات من معدن سائل |
| san | شبكة منطقة التخزين |
| san-attached | المرتبطة بتكنولوجيا SAN |
| san-based | التي أساسها تكنولوجيا SAN |
| sanctioned decisions | قرارات مدعمة بعقوبات |
| sand oil | زيت رمال |
| sandblasting | سفع بالرمال |
| sander | ماكينة سنفرة رملية |
| sander | المرملة، أداة لذر الرمل |
| sandiness | الرملانية، كون الشيء رمليا والقرار لكم. |
| sandstone | الحجر الرملي |
| sandwich | يُقحِم |
| sandwich | يقحم |
| sandwich (shaped) | ساندويتش (على شكل الطيات) |
| sandwiched | مقحَم؛ متضمَّن |
| sandy | ترابي، محتو على تراب |
| san-enabled | الممكّنة بتكنولوجيا SAN |
| san-enabled backups | النسخ الاحتياطي المزود بتكنولوجيا SAN |
| sanitary napkin | فوطة صحية (للنساء) |
| sanity | التمتع بالقوى العقلية |
| sapheous vein | الوريد الصافن |
| saponification | مركب السابونين |
| sapper | فرد في سلاح المهندسين |
| sapropelite | بالصخور الوحلية العضوية |
| saquinavir | ساكوينافير |
| sar | معدل الامتصاص المحدد: وحدة معيارية لقياس مستوى التعرض لطاقة التردد اللاسلكي الصادرة من الهواتف المحمولة مقاسا بالوات للكيلوجرام الواحد القيمة القصوى التي أوصت بها المجموعة الأوروبية هي 2 وات / كيلوجرام |
| sarbanes-oxley | قانون ساربينز-أوكسلي؛ أو تشريع ساربينز-أوكسلي |
| sarcoidosis | لحمانية |
| sarcoma | ساركوما؛ ورم سرطاني بالأنسجة الضامة |
| sat | مُشبَّع |
| sat (scholastic aptitude test) | اختبار القدرات الدراسي |
| sat. aq | مائي مشبع |
| satchel | حقيبة مدرسية |
| sat'd | قياسي |
| satellite | تابع |
| satellite computer | كمبيوتر ستالايت |
| satellite tv piracy | قرصنة تلفزة الأقمار الصناعية |
| satirical comedy | الكوميديا الساخرة |
| saturated aqueous sodium hydrogencarbonate solution | محلول بيكربونات صوديوم مائي مشبع |
| save energy (energy saving) | توفير طاقة |
| save-all | نظام استرجاع الألياف: جهاز يستخدم في استعادة الألياف والمواد المالئة من المياه البيضاء |

| | |
|---|---|
| | ويعمل عادة على الترشيح، الترسيب، التلبيد أو الطفو |
| saving technology | تقنية المحافظة |
| savory | لاذع |
| saw | منشار |
| saw blade | نصل منشاري؛ نصل مشرشر كالمنشار |
| saw dust | نشارة الخشب |
| sbr | معدل البتات الاحصائية |
| sbws | هيكل تفاصيل أعمال المقاول من الباطن |
| sc; s.c. | تحت الجلد (مثل إعطاء عقار تحت الجلد) |
| scaffold | سلسلة جزيئات متجاورة (وبخاصة: سلسلة بروتين متجاورة) |
| scaffold | سقالة |
| scalable to a size that can be utilized in a commercial process | قابل للزيادة إلى حجم يمكن استخدامه في عملية تجارية |
| scalar values | قيم عددية |
| scale | قشرة؛ مقياس الرسم |
| scaled | متدرج؛ مقاس |
| scaledown | خفض بنسبة معينة |
| scaler | وحدة مقياسية |
| scaleup | رفع بنسبة معينة |
| scaling | تقشير |
| scams | رسائل الاحتيال؛ رسائل الاحتيال المخادعة؛ الخدع |
| scan | يمسح ضوئيا، يفحص بدقة، ينعم النظر |
| scan sth | يمسح ضوئيا |
| scan sth over sth | يحرك كذا ليمسح كذا ضوئيا |
| scanable | قابل للمسح |
| scanable document | مستند قابل للمسح للضوئي |
| scanner | ماسح ضوئي، فاحص |
| scanner and camera wizard | معالج الماسحة الضوئية والكاميرا |
| scanning | مسح ضوئي |
| scanning electron microscope (sem) | الميكروسكوب الإلكتروني الماسح |
| scanning electron microscopy | القياس المجهري الإلكتروني الماسح |
| scanning transmission electron microscopy | القياس المجهري الإلكتروني بالمسح النافذ |
| scar | واسمات منطقة مكربة تتميز بمتواليات |
| scarlet beans | فاصوليا حمراء |
| scatter | يبعثر، يتفرق، يبدد، تبعثر |
| scatter attenuation tomography | التصوير المقطعي عن طريق اضمحلال التشتت |
| scatter buying | شراء الشتات؛ شراء البقايا؛ شراء بقايا الفترات الإعلانية؛ الشراء الفصلي؛ الشراء الربع سنوي |
| scattered light | ضوء متفرق |
| scattering | بعثرة |
| scb | تفرع سلسلة قصيرة |
| sccr | حقوق التأليف والحقوق المجاورة |
| scelroderma | تصلب الجلد |
| scenario (screenplay) | سيناريو |
| scene editing | تحرير مشهد |
| scene index | فهرس المشاهد |
| scene mode (ae) | وضع المشهد (AE) |
| scenes | مصور |
| scf | قدم معيارى مكعب |
| scfh | قدم مكعب في الساعة |
| schedulable task system | نظام مهام قابل للجدولة |
| scheduler | وحدة جدولة |
| scheduling software | برنامج جدولة |
| scheduling system | نظام جدولة |
| schema | مخطط قاعدة بيانات |
| schematic | تخطيطي |
| schematic = schematic diagram | مخطط؛ رسم تخطيطي |
| schematic cut-out view of a detail of the apparatus | منظر تخطيطي مقتطع لإحدى تفصيلات الجهاز |
| schematic depiction | رسم تخطيطي |
| schematic diagram | مخطط؛ رسم تخطيطي |
| schematic drawing | رسم تخطيطي |
| schematic illustration | رسم تخطيطي |
| schematic of clipping | مخطط للقص |
| schematic partially cross | شكل تخطيطي لمقطع عرضي جزئي |
| schematic view | مخطط |
| schematic view, partially in cross-section | مخطط، في صورة مقطع عرضي جزئي |
| schematically | رسم تخطيطي |
| scheme | مخطط؛ نظام |
| schiff | شِف |
| schistosome | البلهارسيا |
| schizo-affective disorder | الاضطراب النفسي العاطفي الفصامي |
| schizophrenia | انفصام الشخصية |
| school districts | المناطق التعيمية |
| school dropout/discontinuation | انقطاع عن الدراسة؛ انقطاع عن المدرسة |
| school effects | تأثيرات مدرسية |
| school finance | تمويل المدارس |
| school invention | اختراع مدرسي |
| school performance and efficiency | الكفاءة والأداء المدرسي |
| school-level | مدارس |
| schwanoma | ورم غمد العصب |
| sciences | علوم |
| sciences-driven company | شرطة تسوقها العلوم |
| scientific know-how | دراية الكيفية العلمية |
| scientist | عالم |
| sci-fi robot | روبوت الخيال العلمي. |
| scintillation counter | عداد الومضات |
| scintillation proximity assay (spa) | اختبار تقاربية ومضان |
| scintillation vial | قارورة ومضية |
| scintillography | كروماتوجراف ومضات |
| scissors ; pair of scissors | مقص |
| scleredema | الأوديما التصلبية |
| scleritis | التهاب الصلبة |
| scleroderma | تصلب الجلد |
| sclerosing | متصلب |
| scn | إشعار بتغيير المواصفات |
| scooping up | تجريف الأراضي الزراعية |
| scope | مجال؛ نطاق |
| scope of the invention | مجال الاختراع |

| | |
|---|---|
| scops | أضواء منتشرة |
| score | قيمة مسجلة |
| score | مجموع نقاط (نقاط) |
| scored | متحزز |
| scoring matrix | مصفوفة تسجيل |
| scott schedule | نموذج سكوت أو جدول سكوت |
| scr | معدل الخلية المتواصل |
| scramble | يشفر |
| scrambling | تشفير |
| scrape | يقشر |
| scrapie | داء الأعصاب المميت |
| scratch | يحفر، ينبش، يك، يخربش؛ محو |
| scratchy | شائك، كثير الشوك، مخربش، منجز بعجلة |
| screen | مصفاة؛ شبكة ترشيح؛ منخل، غربال |
| screen displays | شاشات العرض |
| screen displays during playback | عروض الشاشة أثناء التشغيل |
| screen flickers | ارتعاش الشاشة |
| screen for | 1. يفحص 2. يفرز |
| screen for myostatin binding | فرز للوقوف على مدى ارتباط الميوستاتين |
| screen mesh sizes | أحجام المش للمصفاة |
| screen panel | ألواح فاصلة |
| screen printing | الطباعة المسامية |
| screen test | اختبار تمثيل، لصلاحية ممثل على الشاشة |
| screening assays | اختبارات الفحص |
| screening means | وسيلة حاجبة |
| screening searches | بحوث الفحص |
| screenout | حاجز |
| screensaver | شاشة توقف |
| screenwriter | كاتب سينمائي |
| screw | يربط بلولب، يسد بلولب، يبرم، برغي، لولب؛ مسمار لولبي: بالعربية الفصيحة اسمه "بُرْغي" والجمع "بَرَاغي" |
| screw connection | وصلة ملولبة |
| screwable | قابل للبرم |
| screw-cap vial | قارورة ذات غطاء بأسنان ملولبة |
| screwdriver | مفك براغي؛ مفك لوالِب |
| screwdriver bits | قطع مفكات (الرؤوس الحديدية للمفكات) |
| screwdriver blade | شفرة مفك براغي |
| screwdriver set | مجموعة مفكات؛ طقم مفكات |
| scriber | المخطاط. شوكة يخدش بها الخشب أو المعدن المعد للقطع |
| scrifulous rhinitis | التهاب الأنف السلي |
| scriptwriter | كاتب سيناريو |
| scroll bar | شريط التمرير |
| scroll mode | وضع التمرير |
| scrub column (scrubbing tower) | عمود تنقية بالغسل (برج تنقية بالغسل) |
| scrubber | جهاز غسل الغاز |
| scsi | واجهة نظم الحاسبات الصغيرة |
| sd | انحراف معياري |
| sdd | وصف تصميم النظام |
| sdh | تدرج رقمي متزامن |
| sdp | خطة تطوير البرنامج؛ إجراءات تشغيل قياسية |
| sdr | مراجعة تصميم النظام |
| sdrl | قوائم متطلبات بيانات المقاول من الباطن |
| sds polyacrylamide gel electrophoresis | تحليل الإشراد الكهربائي لهلام كبريتات دوديكل الصوديوم-بولي أكريل أميد |
| sds-page ; sds page | تحليل الإشراد الكهربائي لهلام كبريتات دوديكل الصوديوم-بولي أكريل أميد |
| sds-page analysis of the protein | تحليل الإشراد الكهربائي للبروتين باستخدام PAGE -SDS |
| sdvt | اختبار التحقق من تصميم النظام |
| se | خطأ قياسي |
| sea bed | قاع البحر |
| seal | مانع تسرب؛ مانع تسريب؛ سداد محكم؛ مانع تسرب؛ وسيلة إحكام إغلاق (مانع للتسريب) |
| seal | يحكم إغلاق |
| seal against | يمنع تسريب |
| seal off | يغلق (بإحكام) |
| seal ring | حلقة مانعة للتسريب؛ حَلَقَة محكمة الغلق |
| sealant | مادة مانعة للتسرب |
| sealed | مغلق بإحكام؛ تم إحكام إغلاقه |
| sealed body of liquid | جسم مانع لتسرب سائل |
| sealed plastic jars | أوعية بلاستيكية محكمة الغلق |
| sealed tube reactor | مفاعل أنبوب مغلق بإحكام |
| seal-fix | تثبيت بحيث لا يُحدِث تسريب |
| sealing | منع تسرب |
| sealing packer | حشوة مانعة للتسريب |
| seam roll stand | حامل بكرة لحام حرفي |
| seams | وصلات اللحام |
| seaplane | طائرة بحرية |
| search | يبحث، بحث |
| search engine | محرك بحث؛ آلة بحث |
| search engine optimization | رفع كفاءة محرك البحث إلى المستويات القصوى |
| search optimization software | برنامج رفع كفاءة محرك البحث إلى المستويات القصوى |
| searchable | قابل للبحث |
| searchable patent database | قاعدة بيانات براءات يمكن البحث فيها |
| searcher | باحث |
| searches | بحوث |
| seasonal affective disorder | الاضطرابات العاطفية الموسمية |
| seat | مرتكز؛ مقعد؛ قاعدة؛ قاعدة سيستقر عليها أو فيها شيء |
| seating | ارتكاز |
| seating nipple | فوهة تثبيت |
| seaweed ; rockweed | طحلب بحري؛ طحلب صخري؛ الطحلب: عشب نباتي ضار |
| seborrheic | ناتج عن الطفح الدهني أو الزهامي |
| sec(s) | ثانية (ثوان) |
| secam | لون متتابع بذاكرة |
| second fuel line | خط وقود ثاني |
| second fuel tank | خزان وقود ثاني |

| | |
|---|---|
| second lieutenant | ملازم ثان بحري |
| second lieutenant (2 lt) | ملازم ثان |
| second oxidant line | خط مؤكسد ثاني |
| secondary button | زر ثانوي |
| secondary porosity | مسامية ثانوية |
| secondary recovery method | طريقة الاستخلاص الثانية |
| secondary role | دور ثانوي |
| second-in-chief | قائد ثان |
| secret | سر |
| secret invention | اختراع سري |
| secret invention design | تصميم سري لاختراع |
| secret know-how | دراية كيفية سرية |
| secret license agreement | اتفاق ترخيص سري |
| secretary of offense | وزير خارجية الجنايات |
| secretive | سري |
| secrets | أسرار |
| section | جماعة |
| section (of a gas turbine, of a generator, etc.) | مقطع |
| sectional | مقطعي |
| sectional end view | منظر طرفي مقطعي |
| sectional view | منظر مقطعي |
| sectioned | تم التقسيم إلى شرائح (كيمياء وفزياء) |
| sectioning device | جهاز تقسيم إلى شرائح |
| sector | قطاع |
| secure | آمن |
| secure (to) | يثبت أو يربط بكذا |
| secure communications | يؤمن الاتصالات |
| secure usage | استعمال آمن |
| securitization | تحويل القروض إلى أوراق مالية |
| security | أمن، جهة أمن |
| security agreement | اتفاق أمني |
| security awareness | وعي الأمن. درجة الإلمام بالشئون الأمنية |
| security detail | طاقم الحراسة |
| security glass | زجاج أمان: الزجاج الذي يعطي الوقاية، حتى مستوى معين، من الهجمات |
| security lock slot | شق قفل أمان |
| security risk | خطر على الأمن |
| security sensors | أجهزة إحساس خاصة بالأمن |
| security software | برنامج للأمن |
| sedative | مسكن |
| sedimentary deposits | القرارات الرسوبية |
| sedimentary rocks | الصخور الرسوبية |
| sediment-hydrate system | نظام ناتج ترسيب-هيدرات |
| sedition | تحريض على) الفتنة |
| see | بيئة هندسة البرامج |
| seed | بلورة مستخدمة لبدء التبلور؛ ينثر أنوية تبلر؛ يزرع (خلايا إلخ) |
| seed crystal | نواة تبلر؛ بلورة بذرية؛ بلورة بدء التبلور |
| seeded solution | محلول تبلر |
| seedling | الشتلة (البادرة)؛ بادرة؛ شتلة |
| seeing i to i | الاجتماع وجهًا لوجه |
| seek | ينشد، يقصد، يرغب في، يسعى |
| seeker | راغب |
| see-through tech | تقنية الرؤية النافذة |
| segment | جزء؛ قطعة |
| segmented and collimated detector arrays | مصفوفات جهاز كشف قطعي أو مرتب على التوازي |
| segmented scatter detector array 14 | مصفوفة كشف تشتت قطعية 14 |
| seismic | زلزالي |
| seismic reflection | انعكاس رجفي |
| seismic trace | مسار زلزالي |
| seismic truck | شاحنة تسجيل الزلازل؛ شاحنة زلزالية |
| seismograph | سيزموجراف |
| seizure | نوبة |
| select | يحدد؛ يختار |
| select & transfer | يحدد وينقل |
| select an image and print | يحدد صورة ويطبعها |
| select the save image type | يحدد نوع صورة الحفظ |
| selecting images for transfer (transfer order) | تحديد الصور لنقلها (ترتيب النقل) |
| selecting the card mix effect | تحديد تأثير مزج البطاقة |
| selecting the drive mode | تحديد وضع التشغيل |
| selecting the focusing point | تحديد إعداد ضبط البؤرة |
| selecting the image quality/size | تحديد جودة/حجم الصورة |
| selecting the metering method | تحديد طريقة ضبط كثافة الإضاءة |
| selection frame | إطار التحديد |
| selectively | انتقائيا |
| selectivity | انتقائية |
| selectivity and species cross-reactivity of antibodies | التفاعلية المتبادلة للأجسام المضادة المحسنة من حيث الانتقاء والأنواع |
| selectivity to | الانتقائية نحو |
| selector valve | صمام انتقاء |
| self aligning | ذاتي المحاذاة |
| self alignment | محاذاة ذاتية |
| self contained seismic sensor | مستشعر زلزالي مكتفي ذاتيا |
| self executing judgement | حكم بنفاذ معجل |
| self-anchored | ذاتي الارتكاز |
| self-assembled monolayers | طبقات أحادية ذاتية التجمع |
| self-cleaning glass-house coating | طلاء بيوت زجاجية ذاتي التنظيف |
| self-diagnosis display | شاشة التشخيص الذاتي |
| selfed plants = inbred | نباتات مهجنة داخليا |
| self-fertilization / self-pollination | تلقيح ذاتي |
| self-generating nitrogen unit | وحدة نيتروجين ذات توليد ذاتي |
| selfing | تلقيح ذاتي |
| self-opacification property in latex | الإعتام الذاتي في المادة اللثية |
| self-priming pump | مضخة ذاتية التحضير |
| self-propelled gun | مدفع ذاتي الحركة |
| self-serve backup tools | أدوات نسخ واسترجاع النسخ الاحتياطية بواسطة مدير الموقع (المستخدم) مباشرة |
| self-timer | المُوَقِّت الذاتي |
| self-timer lamp | مصباح المُوَقِّت الذاتي |
| sem | ميكروسكوب إلكتروني ماسح؛ الأخطاء المعيارية للمتوسط |
| sem adduct | ناتج إضافة SEM |
| semantic | متصل بمعنى الكلمة، لفظي |

| | |
|---|---|
| semantics | علم دلالات الألفاظ وتطورها |
| semaphore | علامة الوصول لموارد النظام |
| semi conducting material | مادة شبه موصلة |
| semi-autonomous robot | روبوت شبه ذاتي |
| semiconductor device | جهاز من أشباه الموصلات |
| semiconductor substrate | ركيزة شبه موصلة |
| semi-finished products | منتجات شبه منتهية التصنيع |
| semi-matt | شبه متلبد |
| seminoma | الورم المنوي |
| semi-obsolete technology | تقنية شبه منتهية الجدوى |
| semi-skim milk | لبن نصف دسم |
| senator | عضو مجلس الشيوخ |
| senescence | شيخوخة |
| senile cataract | المياه البيضاء لدى كبار السن |
| senior head gardener | رئيس البستانيين؛ كبير البستانيين |
| sense | غير مضاد لاتجاه النسخ: غير مضاد للتعبير الجيني |
| sense | حاسة، يحس |
| sense of inequality | مَنْحَى الْمُتَبَايِنَةِ |
| sense or antisense | غير مضادة لاتجاه النسخ أو مضادة لاتجاه النسخ (غير مضادة للتعبير الجيني أو مضادة للتعبير الجيني) |
| sensed | محسوس به، مُستشعَر |
| sensible heat | حرارة محسوسة |
| sensing | إحساس، استشعار |
| sensing device | جهاز إحساس |
| sensitise | يجعله حساسا تجاه |
| sensitizers | عوامل زيادة الحساسية: العوامل التي تزيد الحساسية تجاه |
| sensor | مستشع؛ جهاز استشعار؛ جهاز إحساس |
| sensor casing | غلاف استشعار |
| sensor package | حزمة استشعار |
| sensoric neuropathy and achalasia | اعتلال الأعصاب الحسي وتعذر الارتخاء |
| sensors | أجهزة إحساس |
| sensors system | نظام أجهزة إحساس |
| sensory device | جهاز إحساسي |
| sensory discrimination | تمييز استشعاري |
| sensory input | مدخل استشعاري |
| sensory panel | هيئة من الذواقة |
| sensory substitution | استبدال إحساسي |
| sentence | يفصلح منطوق الحكم |
| separated difference | فرق معزول |
| separated milk | لبن فرز (منزوع الدهن) |
| separator | فراز |
| separator tower | برج فصل |
| sepcified | محدد |
| sepia | بني داكن |
| sepsis | إنتان؛ تعفّن؛ تقيح (الدم) |
| septic shock | الصدمة الناتجة عن التسمم الدموي الداخلي |
| septicemia | التسمم الدموي |
| septum | حاجز؛ غشاء فاصل |
| septum cap | غطاء ذو حاجز |
| seq id no | المتوالية رقم؛ المتوالية ذات رقم التعريف |
| sequelae | مراحل تالية |
| sequence | متوالية |
| sequence | يسلسل، تسلسل، مسلسل، متتالية |
| sequence characterized amplified region (scar) markers | واسمات منطقة مكبرة تتميز بوجود متواليات |
| sequence diagram | مخطط التتابع |
| sequence homology | تجانس المتوالية |
| sequence id number | المتوالية رقم؛ المتوالية ذات رقم التعريف |
| sequence identifier | محدد المتوالية |
| sequence identity | تطابق المتواليات؛ تطابق بين المتواليات |
| sequence motif | تتابع تنظيمي لمتوالية |
| sequence of amino acid | متوالية حمض أميني |
| sequencer | تسلسل |
| sequencing | جعل الشيء متسلسلا |
| sequential innovations | ابتكارات تتابعية. ابتكارات تنطلق من نفس الفرضيات التقنية الكبرى وتعد في مجملها متكاملة |
| sequential quadratic programme | برنامج متسلسل من الدرجة الثانية |
| sequentially | على التتابع؛ بطريقة تتابعية |
| sequentially rearranged | مرتبة بطريقة تتابعية |
| sequestrants | منحيات |
| sequestration | الحراسة |
| sequestration | عزل |
| sergent (sgt) | رقيب |
| sergent major (sm) | رقيب أول |
| serial | مسلسل |
| serial autocorrelation | ارتباط ذاتي تسلسلي |
| serial dilution | تخفيف على التسلسل؛ تخفيف تسلسلي؛ تخفيف متسلسل |
| serial no. | رقم مسلسل؛ رقم تسلسلي |
| serial number | رقم |
| serial port | منفذ تسلسلي |
| serially diluted | تم تخفيفها تسلسليا |
| series | مسلسل من حلقات منفصلة |
| series flow ; series-flow | تدفق متوال |
| serigraph printing | الطباعة المسطحة والمستوية |
| serine protease | بروتياز السيرين |
| serine proteinase | بروتيناز السيرين |
| seroconversion | انقلاب تفاعلية المصل |
| serogroups | مجموعات مصلية |
| serology | علم الأمصال |
| seronegative | السلبي للمصل |
| seronegativity | سلبية المصل |
| seropositivity | إيجابية المصل |
| serotonin (5-ht) | سيروتونين (HT-5) |
| serotype | نمط مصلي |
| serum | مصل |
| serum albumen; serum albumin | ألبومين المصل |
| server computer | كمبيوتر خادم: جهاز كمبيوتر يعمل كوحدة خدمة؛ خادم؛ وحدة خدمة |
| service initiation protocol proximity | خادم بروكسي يستخدم بروتوكول بدء |
| server | خدمة |
| services | خدمات |
| servicing the debt | خدمة الدين |
| serving base station | المحطة القاعدية الخادمة |

serving sector قطاع خدمة
servo مدعِّم؛ مؤازر
servomechanisms والأليات المدعِّمة
sesquihydrate هيدرات ثلاثية النصف؛ هيدرات واحد ونصف
session دورة تحاور
set مجموعة؛ طقم؛ يضبط؛ يقوم بإعداد
set designer مصمم الديكور
set gypsum جبس جامد
set point نقطة ضبط
set-screw مِسْمَارٌ ملولب جامد؛ برغي تثبيت؛ مسمار تثبيت ملولب
setpoint نقطة ضبط
sets of artificial teeth طقم أسنان صناعية
settable قابل للتصلب
setting إعداد
setting digital effects ضبط التأثيرات الرقمية
setting the dpof (digital print order format) function ضبط وظيفة DPOF (تنسيق ترتيب الطباعة الرقمي)
setting the equaliser ضبط الموازن
setting the iso speed (sensitivity) ضبط سرعة ISO (حساسية)
setting the macro mode ضبط Macro Mode (وضع الماكرو)
setting the metering method ضبط أسلوب القياس
setting the multi shot ضبط اللقطة المتعددة
setting the photo quality ضبط جودة الصورة
setting the photo size ضبط حجم الصورة
setting the repeated play ضبط التشغيل المتكرر
setting the self timer ضبط الموقت الذاتي
setting the slideshow ضبط عرض الشرائح
setting the time zone/daylight saving time إعداد المنطقة الزمنية/التوقيت الصيفي
setting the video out ضبط مخرج الفيديو
setting the viewing options ضبط خيارات العرض
setting the wind cut ضبط وظيفة حجب صوت الرياح
settle يسوي، يجري تسوية
settleable patent dispute نزاع بشأن براءات قابل للتسوية
settlement تسوية
settler حوض ترسيب
settling legs سيقات ترسيب
set-top box الجهاز المستقبل للتلفاز الرقمي: جهاز صغير يتم توصيله بجهاز التليفزيون بالمنزل، ويسمح للتليفزيون بالاتصال بشبكة الإنترنت.
seven-domain trans¬membrane receptors مستقبلات النطاقات السبع عبر الغشائية
sever aging تعتيق قاسي
severability استقلالية النصوص
severability clause البند الخاص بقابلية بقية بنود العقد للبقاء سارية. بند تعاقدي يبين أنه في حالة ثبوت انعدام أثر بند من بنود العقد فإن بقية بنوده تظل سارية
several polyesters بوليسترات عديدة
sewage مجاري
sewarag الصرف الصحي
sewer بالوعة المجاري: ماسورة الصرف الصحي: بالوعة
sex steroid precursor مادة منتجة للستيرويدات الجنسية
sfe معدة مزودة من قبل المقاول من الباطن؛ كروماتوجراف مائع فوق حرج
shaded area المنطقة المظللة
shaft عمود دوران؛ قصبة، قضيب، عمود
shaft work الشغل الناتج عن عمود التدوير
shake يهز
shake يهتز، يترنح، يهز، المخفوق اللبني، تمايل
shake free منع الاهتزاز
shaker جهاز هزاز
shaker أداة للرج، الهزاز
shaking incubator جهاز حضانة هزاز: يستخدم لتحضين العينات الموجودة في أنابيب أو كؤوس مخروطية عند درجات حرارة مختلفة.
shaking water bath حمام مائى هزاز: يستخدم لتحضين العينات عند درجات حرارة مختلفة لعمليات الهضم باستخدام الأنزيمات المختلفة.
shale الطين الصفحي
shale oil النفط الصخري
shape memory alloy سبيكة تحتفظ بشكلها: سبيكة ذاكرة الشكل؛ سبيكة ذاكرة للشكل
shaped catalyst support المادة الحاملة المشكَّلة للمحفز: مادة حاملة للمحفز تم تشكيلها (لتأخذ شكل أسطواني إلخ)
sharable know-how دراية للكيفية يمكن إشراك الآخرين في الإحاطة بها
share-alike license ترخيص للمشاركة. ترخيص لاستعمال عمل فكري وفق أحد نماذج تراخيص منظمة العموم المبدع
share-cropper مزارع بالمشاركة في المحصول
share-cropping نظام المشاركة في المحصول؛ مزارعة
share-cropping tenancy الإيجار بالمشاركة؛ بالمزارعة
share-cropping tenant مستأجر بالمشاركة في المحصول
shared invention اختراع مشترك
shared sql pool مجمع SQL المشترك
shari'a infringement انتهاك الشريعة. تجاوز الضوابط الشرعية.
sharing agreement اتفاق مشترك
sharing pool صندوق مشترك
sharing your videos مشاركة ملفات الفيديو
sharp يرفع درجة النغم، حاد، ماض، صارم
sharp syndrome متلازمة شارب
sharpen يجعل الشيء حادا، يشحذ
sharpenability قابلية الشيء للشحذ
sharpenable قابل للشحذ
sharpener شاحذ
sharpening device جهاز شاحذ (بري)
sharpness درجة الوضوح
sharpness indicator مؤشر درجة الوضوح

| | |
|---|---|
| shear blender | ماكينة ثني |
| shear failure | فشل القص |
| shear strength | مقاومة القص |
| shear stress | إجهاد القص |
| shear traction | شد القص |
| shear wall | جدار مقاوم للقص |
| shear waves | أمواج مستعرضة |
| shearing | قص |
| sheath | غمد (في المجال الطبي) |
| shedding of c-met extracellular domain | إزاقة نطاق c-Met خارج الخلايا |
| sheet | رقاقة |
| sheet glass | ألواح زجاج: زجاج شفاف يتم إنتاجه بعملية السحب المسطح، وله أسطح بإنهاء حراري طبيعي. وبسبب عدم استواء وتوازى سطح الزجاج من الجهتين بصورة تامة فإنه لا يسمح بالرؤية الواضحة والانعكاس الصافي |
| sheet pile | ركيزة مستعرضة |
| shelf life/shelf-life | عمر التخزين (العمر التخزيني) |
| shelf screamers (shelf talkers) | إعلان رفي؛ دعاية رفية؛ لافتة رف |
| shelf-ready commodities | سلع جاهزة للعرض؛ سلع جاهزة للتسويق |
| shell | قشرة؛ غلاف |
| shell a postion | يقصف موقع العدو |
| shell and tube heat exchanger | مبادل حراري أنبوبي غلافي؛ مبادل حراري مكون من أنبوب وغلاف |
| shell bank | بنك اعتباري |
| shell gasification process | عملية التحويل إلى غاز في غلاف |
| shell jackets | سترات قصيرة ضيقة |
| shell material | مادة غلاف |
| shellac | اللك |
| shelters | ملاجئ |
| sheriff | الشريف؛ المأمور |
| shield | درع |
| shift | إزاحة |
| shift reaction | تفاعل إزاحة |
| ship-building industry | صناعة السفن |
| shock loading | تحميل فجائي |
| shock wave | موجة الصدمة |
| shockwave | موجة صدمية |
| shoe adaptor | محول الغلاف الخارجي |
| shoot ( film ; lens) | يصور فيلما |
| shoot on-location | يصور مشهدا خارجيا |
| shooting date | تاريخ الالتقاط |
| shooting range | ميدان ضرب النار |
| shooting training | تدريب ضرب النار |
| shop truck | شاحنة ورشة |
| short chain branch | تفرع قصير السلسلة |
| short term repopulating hematopoietic stem cells "st-hsc" | خلايا جذعية مكونة للدم ذات إعادة تجميع قصير الأجل |
| short time durations | فترات زمنية قصيرة |
| short timer | موقت قصير المدى |
| short-cuircuit; disrupt | يعطل |
| shortcut buttons | أزرار الاختصارات |
| short-term lease | عقد إيجار قصير الأجل |
| shoulder belts | أحزمة كتف |
| shoulder launched missile | صاروخ كتف |
| shoulder strap | حزام الكتف |
| shoulder-bed effects | تأثيرات الطبقات أعلى وأسفل خزان |
| shoulder-fired anti-aircraft missiles | صواريخ محمولة مضادة للطائرات |
| shovel | جاروف |
| shrink | ينكمش |
| shrink timer | موقت تنازلي |
| shrinkable | قابل للانكماش |
| shrinks | الاطباء النفسيون |
| shrink-wrap license | ترخيص نزع الغلاف. ترخيص غير قابلة للتفاوض توضع داخل غلاف بعض المنتجات الحاسبية ويعد مجرد نزع الغلاف موافقة على الترخيص |
| shroud | غطاء |
| shuffle | يعيد توزيع |
| shuffle play | لتشغيل الملفات الموجوده بقائمه Now Playing بشكل عشوائي. |
| shuffling | إعادة توزيع |
| shunt | يوصل على التوازي (كهرباء، جهد إلخ)؛ يحول (شبكات سكة حديد إلخ) |
| shut | يغلق، يوصد، يلحم المعادن، إغلاق |
| shutdown button | زرار إيقاف التشغيل |
| shutter | الغالق |
| shutter | يغلق بمصراع، يزود بمصاريع، مصراع |
| shutter doors | أبواب إغلاق؛ أبوبا مغلاق |
| shutter speed | سرعة الغالق |
| shuttering | شدات: هياكل (شدات) خشبية للأعمال الإنشائية الخرسانية |
| shuttering | وسيلة إغلاق |
| shuttle | مكوك |
| shuttleless loom | نول بدون مكوك |
| sialidated | محتوي على مجموعة سيالايل |
| sickle cell anemia | أنيميا الخلايا المنجلية |
| side arms | أسلحة بيضاء |
| side chain protected amino acid | أحماض أمينو محمية لسلسلة جانبية |
| side elevation | مسقط جانبي |
| side elevation, partially in cross section | مسقط جانبي؛ في صورة مقطع عرضي جزئي |
| side face | وجه جانبي |
| side view | مسقط جانبي |
| sidecar | عربة جانبية |
| siderite | السيدرايت |
| siderosis | السحار الحديدي |
| sideward | جانبي |
| sieve tube | أنبوب غربالي |
| sieving | نخل؛ غربلة |
| sif | خاصية التمييز الإنتقائي |
| sight | ناشنكاة |
| sigmoid | سيني |

| | |
|---|---|
| sigmoidoscopy | فحص منظاري للقولون |
| signal | يشير، إشارة |
| signal conditioner | وسيلة تكييف إشارة |
| signal containing noise | إشارة محتوية على تشويش |
| signal corps | سلاح الإشارة |
| signal interference | تداخل الإشارات |
| signal transduction | عمليات نقل الإشارة |
| signaling | إعطاء إشارة |
| signaling pathway components | مكونات مسار إصدار إشارات |
| signaling process | عملية إصدار إشارات - إرسال إشارات - انتقال إشارات |
| signalize | يميز، يجعل الشيء ذا ميزة بارزة، يبلغ بالإشارات |
| signalling | إصدار إشارات - إرسال إشارات - انتقال إشارات |
| signalling (also 'signalling device, mechanism, etc.') | إصدار إشارة (أو إشارة) |
| signalman | فرد الإشارة |
| signals | إشارات |
| signature | مُمَيِّز؛ متميز |
| signature tag | علامة التوقيع: علامات للخصائص الشكلية أو الظاهرية |
| significance level | مستوى الدلالة |
| significant | ذو دلالة إحصائية؛ كبير |
| significant prior art | تقنية سابقة كبيرة (مهم) |
| significant quantity of propane | كمية كبيرة |
| significant results | نتائج ذات دلالة |
| sign-in pages | صفحات تسجيل |
| silane cross-linked polymer composition | تركيبة بوليمر مرتبطة تبادليًا بالسيلان |
| silent film | فيلم صامت |
| silica flash column | عمود سيليكا وميضي |
| silica gel | جل السيليكا |
| silica gel chromatography | كروماتوجراف جل السيليكا |
| silica gel plug | طبقة من جل سيليكا |
| silica sol | محلول سيليكا غرواني |
| silicate / fused silica glass | سيليكات/زجاج سيليكا مدمج |
| siliceous rocks | صخور رسوبية كيميائية سيليسيه |
| silicification | عملية الستلكن |
| silicoaluminophosphates (sapo), | سيليكو ألومينو فوسفات |
| silicon chip | شريحة سيليكون |
| silicon powder accumulating and takeoff mechanism | آلية تجميع وسحب مسحوق السليكون |
| silicon steel | فولاذ سيليكوني |
| silicon valley | وادي السيليكون |
| silicosis | السحار الرملي |
| silk-screen = screen-printing, silk-screen process | طباعة السلك سكرين؛ طباعة حريرية |
| silkscreen printing | طباعة السلكسكرين |
| silo | سلوة |
| siltstone | حجر الغرين |
| silvered glass | زجاج مفضض (المغطى بالفضة): وينتج من عملية ترسيب طبقة من الفضة على الزجاج، وتتم حماية الفضة بطلائها، كما هو الحال عند صناعة المرايا |
| sim | وحدة تعريف المشترك: البطاقة الذكية المستخدمة في الهواتف الرقمية وتشتمل على تعريف المستخدم للوصول للشبكة واستقبال المكالمات وتخزين المعلومات الشخصية مثل سجل الهاتف ورسائل التي تم استلامها |
| similar patent litigation | تقاضٍ بشأن براءات متشابهة |
| similarity requirement | متطلب التشابه |
| simple screw thread | أسنان بسيطة لمسمار ملولب |
| simple, yet sophisticated (web) hosting | خدمة استضافة مواقع الويب تتمتع بالبساطة وكثرة المزايا في نفس الوقت |
| simulatability | قابلية الشيء للمحاكاة |
| simulatable | قابل للمحاكاة |
| simulate | يحاكي |
| simulated and gridded earth formation' | تكوين أرضي شبكي محاكى |
| simulation | محاكاة |
| simulator | محاكٍ؛ برنامج محاكاة |
| single | فردي |
| single bond | رابطة أحادية |
| single carrier qam systems | نظم QAM بموجة حاملة مفردة |
| single crystal x-ray diffraction data | بيانات حيود الأشعة السينية في المسحوق لعينة وحيدة البلورة |
| single node microwave oven | فرن موجات دقيقة ذو عقدة واحدة |
| single nucleotide polymorphism (snp) markers | واسمات تعدد شكل نيوكليوتيد فردي |
| single pass mode | وضع مرور فردي |
| single stranded ; single-stranded sequence | متوالية وحيدة الجديلة؛ ذو جديلة واحدة؛ أحادي الجديلة |
| single value | قيمة فردية |
| single-nucleotide polymorphism (snp) ; single-nucleotide polymorphism (snp) | النيوكليوتيد المفرد متعدد الأشكال |
| single-track schedule | نظام الجدول الثابت |
| single-walled tube | أنبوب ذي جدار مفرد |
| singular and plural clause | البند الخاص بالجمع والمفرد. بند تعاقدي يبين أن صيغ المفرد والجمع المعتمدة بالعقد يتوجب أن يفهم منها أن المفرد يعني الجمع والعكس إلا إذا تم النص على غير ذلك صراحة |
| sinonasal natural killer | القاتل الطبيعي للجيوب الأنفية |
| sinuous | متعرج |
| sinusitis | التهاب الجيوب |
| sinusoidal | جيبي |
| sio2 | سيليكا |
| sip | بروتوكول بدء الجلسة: عبارة عن بروتوكول للإشارات الهاتفية المرتبطة ببروتوكولات الانترنت، والتي تستخدم في بدء، وتعديل، وإنهاء مكالمات الهواتف من نوع VOIP. |
| siphoning | غسل |
| sitchback design | تصميم الرجوع الخلفي |
| site | يختار الموقع، موقع |

| | |
|---|---|
| site-based management | الإدارة القائمة على الموقع |
| site-directed | موجه نحو موقع محدد |
| sites of glycosylation | مواقع الارتباط بالجليكوزيل |
| sits | المواصفات الفنية لواجهة الخدمات |
| situate (in) | يضع (في) |
| size exclusion column | عمود استبعاد الحجم |
| size-reduced | مصغر الحجم |
| sizing screen | غربال تصنيف |
| sjogren syndrome | متلازمة شوجرين |
| skeleton | مخطط |
| sketch | يخط رسوما تخطيطية مجملة |
| sketches | رسوم تخطيطية مجملة |
| skew | متعرج |
| skid | زلاقة؛ مزلقة |
| skid mount | يُركب بالانزلاق |
| skilled worker | عامل ماهر |
| skills | مهارات |
| skim milk | لبن مقشود؛ لبن فرز (منزوع الدهن) |
| skimmed milk | منزوع الدسم |
| skin | غشاء |
| skin detail function | وظيفة تفاصيل البشرة |
| skin effect | ظاهرة سطحية |
| skin factor | معامل القشرة |
| skin of the wellbore | قشرة حفرة البئر: القشرة حول حفرة البئر |
| skin ulcers | تقرحات الجلد |
| skipping scenes | تخطي مشاهد |
| skirmishes | مناوشات |
| skylight filter | مرشح ضوء السماء |
| sl | لتر قياسي |
| slack | سروال فضفاض |
| slag | خبث |
| slag cotton, smoothness | قطن معدني؛ نعومة القطن |
| slag wool fiber | صوف الخبث المعدني |
| slaked lime | جير مطفأ |
| slander | التشهير |
| slate | نوعية |
| slate type tablet pc | جهاز كميوتر شخصي مسطح ذو لوحات متصلة |
| slave robot | روبوت خادم |
| sleen | طحال |
| sleep | السكون |
| sleep apnea disorders | اضطرابات انقطاع النفس أثناء النوم |
| sleep disruptions | اضطرابات النوم |
| sleep mode | وضع السكون |
| sleeve | جلبة (تكون ذات شكل حلقي) أو كم (يكون ذي شكل أسطواني) |
| slick line; slickline | خط انزلاق: مثل سلك ميكانيكي |
| slide | مزلاق |
| slide hybridization oven | فرن لتهجين الشرائح: يستخدم في عمليات الدنترة والتهجين في الموضع عند درجات حرارة مختلفة للأحماض النووية |
| slide show | عرض شرائح |
| slide switch | مفتاح منزلق |
| slide valve | صمام انزلاقي |

| | |
|---|---|
| sliding guide | وسيلة توجيه منزلقة |
| slip | انزلاق |
| slip additive | مادة إضافة تزليق |
| slip hanger | وسيلة تعليق منزلقة |
| slip ring | حلقة انزلاق |
| slips | عوازل |
| slipstream | هواء مزاح |
| sloat defense battery | بطارية دفاع سلوت |
| sloat radar station | محطة رادار سلوت |
| slop | مواد ملوثة |
| slop oil | نفط ملوث |
| slope | (في المنحنيات) ميل |
| slot index | معامل الفتحة |
| slot machine | ماكينة شقبية |
| slots | شقوق طولية {في عمود حفر بئر} (أو فتحات) |
| slow motion | الحركة البطيئة |
| sludge | راسب طيني؛ حمأ |
| slug | كتلة معدنية |
| slug flow | تدفق كتلي |
| slug flow regime | نظام التدفق المتتابع |
| slump test | اختبار كزازة |
| slurry | ملاط؛ مستعلق؛ رَوْبَة؛ عجين؛ رديغ |
| slurry | يعرّض لتفاعل ملاط |
| slurry reaction | تفاعل ملاط |
| slurry wash | يغسل من الملاط |
| sm3 | متر مكعب قياسي |
| small business liaison section | مكتب اتصال الأعمال الصغيرة |
| small cell lung cancer (sclc) | السرطان الذي يصيب الخلايا الصغيرة بالرئة |
| small intestine | أمعاء دقيقة |
| small molecule | جزيء صغير |
| smaller industries | صناعات صغيرة |
| small-molecule | جزيئية صغيرة |
| smart building technology | تقنية الأبنية الذكية |
| smart cards | بطاقات ذكية |
| smart eyeglass | نظارات ذكية |
| smartcard | كارت إلكتروني |
| smartmedia indicator | مؤشر smartmedia |
| smartmedia slot | فتحة smartmedia |
| smears | شوائب |
| smelt | صهر |
| smok screen | ستارة دخان |
| smok, star, penetrative, incendiary shell | دانة دخان؛ مضيئة؛ خارقة؛ حارقة |
| smoke detector | كاشف دخان |
| smoke point | نقطة الإدخان |
| smoke sensors | أجهزة إحساس بالدخان |
| smooth paper | ورقة مرنة |
| smooth surface | سطح ناعم |
| sms | `رسائل الجوال القصيرة: هي عبارة عن خدمة رسائل في اتجاهين تقدم في كافة الشبكات ويمكن إرسال رسائل من 160 حرف / رقم فيما بين الهواتف عبر أي من الشبكات |

| | |
|---|---|
| | ويمكن إرسال رسائل أطول بواسطة بعض الهواتف اليدوية |
| smuggle | يهرب |
| snap | إطباقي |
| snap freeze; snap-freeze | تجميد بسرعة |
| snap-copy snapshots | لقطات النسخة الصغيرة |
| snap-frozen; snap frozen | تجميد بسرعة |
| sniff | يكتشف |
| sniper ; marksman | قناص: ضارب ماهر |
| snit | لحظة غضب؛ حالة هيجان؛ خلاف حاد؛ شقاق |
| snmp | بروتوكول إدارة الشبكة المقياس |
| snoring | شخير |
| snri | مثبطات إعادة امتصاص السيروتونين والنورأدرينالين |
| snug fit | توافق احتضاني محكم |
| soak section | مقطع النقع |
| soc | شريحة، أو شرائح، أو مجموعة شرائح |
| so-called controlling and signalling mechanism | ما يسمَّى بآلية التحكم والإشارة |
| so-called power mechanism | ما يسمى بآلية القدرة |
| social empowerment | تمكين اجتماعي |
| social needs driven innovation | ابتكار تسوقه الحاجات الاجتماعية |
| social responsibility | مسئولية اجتماعية |
| socialist international, si, vienna | الاشتراكية الدولية، فيينا |
| socially useful invention | اختراع مفيد اجتماعيا |
| society | مجتمع، جمعية |
| socket | مقبس |
| socket drive member | عضو تدوير مقبس |
| socket wrench | مفتاح مقبس |
| soda ash | كربونات الصوديوم اللامائية؛ رماد الصودا |
| soda lime glass | زجاج جير الصودا |
| sodium bicarbonate | بيكربونات الصوديوم |
| sodium borohydride | بوروهيدريد صوديوم |
| sodium dihydrogen phosphate | أحادي فوسفات الصوديوم |
| sodium dodecyl sulfate-polyacrylamide gel electrophoresis nalysis | تحليل الإشراد الكهربائي لهلام كبريتات دوديكل الصوديوم متعددالأكريلامايد (SDS-PAGE) |
| sodium hydrogen carbonate | بيكربونات الصوديوم |
| sodium hydrogencarbonate ; sodium hdyrogen carbonat | بيكربونات الصوديوم |
| sodium hypochlorite | هيبوكلوريت الصوديوم |
| sodium monohydrogen phosphate | ثنائي فوسفات الصوديوم |
| sodium pyrosulphite | بيرو كبريتيت الصوديوم |
| sodium salt mono hydrate | أحادي هيدرات ملح الصوديوم |
| sodium salt sesqui hydrate | هيدرات ثلاثية النصف لملح الصوديوم |
| sodium sulphate | كبريتات الصوديوم |
| sodium sulphide | كبريتيد الصوديوم |
| sodium sulphite | كبريتيت الصوديوم |
| sodium thiomethoxide | ثيو ميثوكسيد الصوديوم |
| sodium thiosulfate | ثيو كبريتات الصوديوم |
| sodium triacetoxyborohydride | تراي أسيتوكسي بوروهيدريد الصوديوم |
| sodium-chemisorption surface area | مساحة سطح الامتزاز الكيميائي للصوديوم" أو S.A.Na |
| sofonates | أملاح السلفونات |
| soft | رخوة (مع الأقراص) |
| soft drinkds | مشروبات غير كحولية |
| soft gelatin capsules | كبسولات جيلاتين رخوة |
| soft handoff | التبادل السلس |
| soft hand-off | تحويل سلس |
| softener | وحدة إزالة العسر |
| softener clarifier underflow | التيار الناتج عن وحدة ترويق مادة إزالة العسر |
| softening temprature | درجة حرارة ليونة |
| softkey | زر Softkey: أحد أزرار الهاتف المحمول يغير وظيفته حسب المهمة التي تنفذها من الجهاز ووظيفته الحالية المعروضة باستخدام كلمة مفتاحية فوق الزر الموجود في شاشة الجهاز مباشرة تساعد في تسهيل استخدام الهواتف المحمولة ويزيد من سرعة التنقل في القوائم |
| soft-shell mobile phone | هاتف محمول ذو غطاء |
| software | برنامج |
| software anti-tamper technology | حماية البرامج ضد العبث |
| software designer | مصمم برامج حاسوبية |
| software failure | تعطُّل برنامج |
| software investments | استثمارات في البرامج |
| software optimizability | إمكانية رفع كفاءة البرنامج إلى المستويات القصوى |
| software patent crisis | أزمة براءات البرامج الحاسبية. رفض بعض البلدان منح براءات عن برمجيات حاسبية |
| software phone | هاتف إنترنت |
| software solutions | حلول برامجية |
| software system | نظام برمجي |
| software upgradability | قابلية البرنامج للتحسين |
| soil | التربة |
| soil classification | تصنيف التربة |
| soil components | عناصر التربة |
| soil consolidation and liquefaction | انزلاق التربة وانضمامها |
| soil development | نمو التربة |
| soil erosion | إنجراف التربة |
| soil fertility | خصوبة التربة |
| soil fungi | فطريات التربة |
| soil layers | طبقات الأرض |
| soil mictobiology | علم الأحياء المجهرية للتربة |
| soil nutrients | المواد الغذائية للتربة |
| soil productivity | إنتاجية التربة |
| soil properties | خصائص التربة |
| soil salinity, | ملوحة التربة |
| sol gel | جل محلول غرواني |
| solar cell | خلية شمسية |

| | |
|---|---|
| solar cells | خلايا شمسية |
| solar energy | طاقة شمسية |
| solar energy generating system | نظم توليد الطاقة الشمسية |
| solar hot water | ماء شمسي ساخن |
| solar photovoltaic power plant | نبات الطاقة الشمسية الضوئية |
| solar power | طاقة شمسية |
| solar thermal collectors | مجمع حراري شمسي |
| solar thermal power | طاقة شمسية حرارية |
| solder | لحام |
| solder | يلحم |
| solder sucker | شفاط: يستخدم من أجل إزالة القصدير من على الPCB |
| soldering iron | الكاوي؛ كاوية لحام: يستخدم لتذويب القصدير من أجل تثبيت العناصر الإلكترونية على اللوحة المطبوعة (printed circuit board PCB) |
| sole arbitrator | محكم وحيد |
| sole inventorship | اختراعية منفردة |
| sole mediator | وسيط وحيد |
| solenoid valve | صمام الملف اللولبي |
| sol-gel | جل محلول غرواني |
| solicitor | محامي (عام) |
| solid | صلب؛ مصمت؛ مادة صلبة |
| solid angle | الزاوية المجسمة؛ الزاوية الصلدة |
| solid bed adsorber | طبقة المادة المازة الصلبة |
| solid bed adsorption | امتزاز على طبقة صلبة |
| solid cylinder | أسطوانة مصمتة |
| solid line | خط متصل |
| solid oral extended release pharmaceutical dosage form | صورة الجرعة الصيدلانية الفمية الصلبة ذات الإطلاق الممتد |
| solid oxide fuel cell | خلايا وقود الأكسيد الصلب |
| solid solution hardening | التصليب بإذابة المواد الصلبة |
| solid state physics | فيزياء الحالة الصلبة |
| solid stating is used to both raise inherent viscosity and remove acetaldehyde | التحويل إلى الحالة الصلبة |
| solid stating process reactor | مفاعل عملية تحويل إلى حالة صلبة |
| solid waste | نفايات صلبة |
| solidfy | يصلب |
| solid-phase peptide synthesis (spps) | تخليق ببتيد في الطور الصلب |
| solid-state | ذات الحالة الصلبة |
| solitary confinement | الحبس الانفرادي |
| soln | محلول |
| solubilizer | مادة مذيبة؛ مذيب |
| solubilizing agent | عامل إذابة |
| soluble | قابل للذوبان؛ ذواب |
| soluble material | مادة قابلة للذوبان |
| solublizing | ذواب |
| solute | مذاب |
| solute | مادة مذابة |
| solution | حل |
| solution ph | الرقم الهيدروجيني للمحلول |
| solution phase reagents | مواد تفاعل موجودة في طور المحلول |
| solution retardant | مؤخر محلول |
| solution's upgradability | قابلية الحل للتحسين |
| solution-focused thinking | تفكير متركز حول الفعل |
| solutions | حل، محلول، المحاليل |
| solvate | ذوابة |
| solvated | مذاب: في صورة مذابة (منذاب) |
| solvent | مذيب |
| solvent deasphalting unit | وحدة نزع الأسفلت باستخدام مذيب (بمذيب) |
| solvolysis | الانحلال بالتفاعل مع مذيب؛ "الحلحلة" |
| somatic | جسدي |
| somatosensory | حسي جسدي |
| sonar sensor | جهاز استشعار راداري |
| sonde | مسبار |
| sonet | شبكة ضوئية متزامنة |
| sonic log | سجل سبر صوتي |
| sonication (sonicate; sonicated ) | بالتعرض لموجات صوتية أو التعريض لموجات صوتية |
| sor | مراجعة تصميم النظام |
| sorbent | مادة ماصة |
| sorbitol | سوربيتول |
| sorption and desorpion | عب ومج (ماء؛ سائل؛ إلخ) |
| sort code | كود البنك |
| sortie | طلعة جوية |
| sound amplifier | مضخم صوت |
| sound assembler | مجمع صوت |
| sound assembly | تجمع صوت |
| sound conditioner | مهيء صوت |
| sound deadening | مخافتة الصوت |
| sound energy | طاقة صوتية |
| sound enhancement | دعم الصوت |
| sound normalizer | مطبع صوت |
| sound recognition device | جهاز التعرف على الصوت |
| sound waves | موجات صوتية |
| sound waves physics | فيزياء الموجات الصوتية |
| sounding | سبر الأعماق |
| sour gas | غاز كبريتي |
| sour gas plant | محطة معالجة غاز كبريتي |
| source | مصدر، منبع |
| source ipaddr | عنوان IP المصدر |
| sources | مصادر |
| south magnetic poles | أقطاب مغناطيسية جنوبية. انظر North poles magnetic |
| southeast asian treaty organization, seato | منظمة حلل جنوب شرق آسيا |
| southern blot | بقعة سزرن |
| sow | قائمة الأعمال |
| spa bath | مغطس ينابيع المياه العذبة |
| space | حيز |
| space | يباعد |
| space group | مجموعة فراغية |
| space heating | تسخين فضائي |
| space recalamation | تجميع مساحة |
| space related invention | اختراع ذو صلة بالفضاء |
| space robot | روبوت فضاء |
| space velocity | السرعة الفراغية |

| | |
|---|---|
| space warfare technology | تقنية حرب الفضاء |
| spacecraft | مَركبة فضائية |
| spaced-apart ; spaced apart | متباعدة (عن بعضها البعض) |
| spacer | مباعدة |
| spacer arms | أذرع فاصلة |
| space-time | الزمن الفراغي |
| spacing | المسافة الفاصلة |
| spaghetti jungle | شبكة تمويه |
| spallation | تشظي |
| spalling resistance | مقاومة التقشر |
| spam | السبام: يسمى أيضا البريد المزعج، البريد غير المرغوب فيه، البريد الإلكتروني غير المعتمد |
| spam filter system | نظام تنقية البريد الوارد والتخلص من الرسائل المزعجة قبل وصولها إليكم |
| spammer | شخص يرسل بريد إليكتروني غير مرغوب فيه |
| spammers | مرسِل السبام؛ مرسل البريد المزعج |
| span | باع؛ شبر |
| span | يمتد (لمسافة معينة) |
| spanner | مِفْتَاحُ رَبْطٍ |
| spar | عضد |
| spasmolytic | مزيل للتقلص |
| spe paper | ورقة عمل في المؤتمر التقني لجمعية مهندسي البترول SPE |
| speaker | سماعة |
| speakerphone | سماعة أذن |
| spearhead | رأس الحربة |
| spec out | يقدم |
| special agent | عميل خاص |
| special forces | القوات الخاصة |
| special tribunal | محكمة خاصة. محكمة تتأسس وتنعقد للنظر في قضية معينة |
| speciation | تحديد نوع؛ تشكل نوع جديد |
| speciation plot | منحنى تحديد النوع |
| specific absorption rate | معدل الامتصاص النوعي |
| specific activity | نشاط إشعاعي نوعي |
| specific analytes | نواتج التحلل النوعية |
| specific binding agent | عامل ربط نوعي |
| specific energy consumption | الاستهلاك النوعي للطاقة |
| specific gravity | الوزن النوعي؛ الكثافة النسبية؛ الثقل النوعي |
| specific water consumption | الاستهلاك النوعي للماء: كمية المياه العذبة المستخدمة خلال الإنتاج (سواء كانت مياه سطحية أو جوفية) وتكون مأخوذة من مصدر خارجي |
| specifically bind sth | يرتبط نوعيا بـ |
| specifically tailored for | يتم إنشاؤه خصيصا لـ |
| specification | مواصفات |
| specification of the invention | وصف الاختراع |
| specificity | نوعية |
| specified | محدد؛ معين |
| specify | يحدد |
| spectrofluorimeter | مقياس الطيف التألقي |
| spectroheliscope | مقياس الطيف الشمسي |
| spectrometer | مقياس الطيف |
| spectrophometrically | على نحو طيفي شكلي |
| spectrophotometer | مقياس الطيف الضوئي؛ فوتومتر طيفي |
| spectrophotometric | مرتبط بمقياس الطيف الضوئي |
| spectroscope | مقياس الطيف |
| spectroscopic | مقياسي طيفي |
| spectroscopy | قياس طيفي |
| spectrum | طيف |
| spectrum technology | تقنية مد نطاق |
| specular reflection | انعكاس منتظم |
| speech connections/ telecommunications | اتصالات صوتية |
| speech recognition | التعرف إلى الكلام |
| speech recognition device | جهاز التعرف على الكلام |
| speech-enabled software | برامج صوتية |
| spent anodes | أنودات مستهلكة / مستنفدة |
| spent compound | مركب مستنفد أو مستهلك |
| spent zone of adsorbent | المنطقة المستهلكة أو المستنفدة |
| spheres | أشكال كروية؛ كريات |
| spheronized powder | مسحوق تم تحويله إلى كريات |
| spiked profile | مخطط القمة (وفقًا للسياق) |
| spin | يغزل، ينسج، يدور بسرعة، يهبط لولبيا بسرعة، غزل، دوران سريع |
| spin column | عمود تدويم |
| spinal | شوكي |
| spinal cord | الحبل الشوكي |
| spinal cord injury | إصابة الحبل الشوكي |
| spinal cord transaction | القطع المستعرض للحبل الشوكي |
| spinal stenosis | التضيُّق الشوكي |
| spinel | بلخش |
| spinet | خام بلُوري معدني |
| spinner | وسيلة دوارة |
| spinner | مُدَوِّر، جاعل الشيء يدور دورانا سريعا |
| spinning; weaving | الغزل؛ النسيج |
| spinning cup sequenator | متتبع كأس الغزل |
| spinocerbellar | شوكي مخيخي |
| spin-off | انبثاق |
| spinout | زيادة سرعة الانزلاق |
| spirit | روح، روحية |
| spirit of the invention | فحوى الاختراع؛ روح الاختراع |
| spirofused ring systems | أنظمة حلقية ملتحمة مع مجموعة سبيرو |
| spiro-ring system | نظام حلقي ملتحم مع مجموعة سبيرو |
| spleen | الطحال |
| splenic | طحالي |
| splenocyte | خلية طحالية |
| splice acceptor site | موقع مستقبل الجدل |
| spline fault tracking | تعقب الصدوع المخدَّدَة |
| split run | نشـر مزدوج أو متواز؛ نشـر مُقارَن؛ نشـر متعدد للمقارنة |
| split-mirror snapshots | لقطات عكس التجزئة |
| splitter | وسيلة تقسيم؛ وسيلة تجزئة |
| splt | معاهدة قانون البراءات الموضوعي |
| spoke | قضيب شعاعي |
| spondyl | فقرة |
| spondylitis | التهاب الفقرات |
| spongiform encephalopathy (tse) | اعتلال دماغي اسفنجي |
| sponsored inventor | مخترع مدعوم من قبل راعٍ |

| | |
|---|---|
| sponsorship | رعاية إعلانية |
| spontaneous morphological, chemical and structural changes | تغيرات شكلية وكيميائية وبنائية عفوية |
| spool wound | ذو لفات حلزونية |
| spore | بوغة (كائن حي دقيق) |
| sport utility vehicle | سيارة ترفيهية رياضية؛ سيارة رياضية SUV |
| sports | رياضة |
| sports anthropological aspects | المظاهر الإنتروبولوجية للأنشطة الرياضية |
| spot | يحدد الموقع، يسم بنقطة، ينقط، بقعة، وصمة، يضع في نقاط، يحدد موضعا |
| spot cotton | قطن بضاعة حاضرة |
| spotable | قابل لأن يُلتقط بالعين أو بغير العين |
| spot-check | يختبر اختبارا بلا تمعن |
| spotlight | أضواء مسلطة |
| spotter | مُحدد الموقع، مراقب، مزيل بقع، مُموضع، واضع الشيء في موضعه |
| spotting | تحديد الموقع |
| spotting device | جهاز تحديد الموقع |
| spotting technology | تقنية تحديد الموقع الدقيق |
| spotty | منقط، متفاوت الجودة |
| sprains or fracture | الالتواءات أو التمزقات |
| spray | رشاش؛ رذاذ |
| spray dryer | مجفف بالرش |
| spray gum | مادة صمغية رذاذية |
| spray gun | مسدس الرذ |
| spray pump | مضخة رش |
| spread | مدى الانتشار |
| spread spectrum | طيف انتشار |
| spread spectrum | تقنية الطيف المنتشر |
| spreadsheet | جدول بيانات |
| spread-spectrum + n. | بتقنية الطيف المنتشر |
| spring onion / onion | بصل أخضر؛ بصل عادي |
| spring seat | قاعدة نابضة |
| spring-loaded pivot arm | ذراع محوري محمل على نابض |
| springs | ينابيع |
| sprinkle irrigation | ري بالرش |
| sprocket gear | ترس مسنَّن |
| sps | مواصفة منتجات البرامج |
| spun | تدوير |
| spunbond; spunbonded | مترابط (وصف قماش غير مغزول) |
| spunlace; spun-lace | تشابكي (وصف قماش غير مغزول) |
| sputter-deposited | مرسَّب بالرش |
| sputtering | رش؛ لفظ |
| sputum | بصاق |
| spyglase | المنظار، النضارة المقربة |
| spyware detection system | نظام اكتشاف أدوات التجسس |
| spyware detecton | اكتشاف حِزم البرمجيات التجسسية على الشبكة البينية. |
| sq m | أمتار مربعة |
| sqauatty | خفيف و عريض، قصير وثخين |
| sql | لغة الاستفسار المهيكلة |
| squadron | سرية مدرعات |
| squadron leader | رائد طيار |
| squamous | حرشفي |
| square inch | بوصة مربعة |
| square root | الجذر التربيعي |
| squarish | مربعاني. مربع بعض الشيء. |
| squash | يسحق، يحرص، شيء لين سهل سحقه |
| squashy | شيء لين سهل سحقه، سبخ، مستنقعي |
| squeegee | المسحة المطاطية. ممسحة مطاطية صغيرة ذات مقبض |
| squeeze bottle | الزجاجة المنضغطة. زجاجة لدائنية تستخرج محتوياتها بالضغط |
| srr | مراجعة متطلبات النظام |
| srs | مواصفة متطلبات البرامج |
| ss | مواصفة النظام الفرعي |
| ssh/telnet access | وصول آمن لنظام تشغيل الموقع عبر نافذة تلينت مشفرة لأعمال المحترفين بأمان |
| ssi | مدخول ضمان إضافي |
| ssr | مراجعة مواصفة البرنامج؛ واسمات تابعة دقيقة |
| ssr markers | واسمات تابعة دقيقة |
| ssri | مثبطات إعادة امتصاص السيروتونين الانتقائية |
| sss | مواصفة النظام / النظام الفرعي |
| sstp | خطة انتقالية دعم النظام |
| ssu | وحدة دعم النظام |
| stabilisation | ثبات |
| stabilized | مثبتة |
| stabilizer | مُوازِن؛ مثبت |
| stabilizing agents | عوامل التثبيت؛ العوامل المثبتة |
| stable brain chemistry | كيمياء دماغ مستقرة |
| stack | يرص |
| stack gas | غاز منصرف؛ غاز المدخنة |
| stacked bed reactor | مفاعل طبقة مجمعة |
| stacked configuration | تجهيزة بطبقة متراصة |
| stacking | رص؛ تراص |
| staff | موظفين |
| staff officer | ضابط أركان حرب |
| stage | يخرج إخراجا مسرحيا، مرحلة، درجة، منصة، مسرح |
| stage of an inverted, phase-contrast microscope | منصة ميكروسكوب طوري تبايني |
| stagger | يضع، يرتب |
| stain | صبغ |
| stained | مبقعة |
| staining | صبغ |
| staining buffer | محلول صبغي منظم |
| stainless | مقاوم للصدأ |
| stainless steel | صلب مقاوم للصدأ |
| stainless steel "load and lock" column | عمود "تحميل وإقفال" من الصلب المقاوم للصدأ |
| stair stringers | عوارض ارتكاز درجات السلم |
| staircase = stairway | السلم؛ بيت الدرج؛ الدرج |
| stairwell | بئر الدرج؛ بئر السلم |
| stakeholder analysis | تحليل أصحاب المصلحة |

| | |
|---|---|
| stakeholders | أصحاب المصلحة؛أصحاب الشأن؛ اللاعبون في هذا المجال |
| stalactites | رواسب الهوابط |
| stalagmites | رواسب الصواعد |
| stalk fibers (stem fibers) | ألياف السيقان |
| stall(ing) speed | سرعة الانهيار |
| stamp | يَرُض، يسحق، يضرب شيء بأخمص قدميه، مسحقة، ختم، علامة، طبعة، صفة مميزة،طابع بريدي |
| stamping | تشكيل بالختم |
| stamping film | طبقة رقيقة مشكلة بالختم |
| stanchion | عمود؛ دعامة |
| stand | يتركه ليستقر |
| stand at room temprature | يتركه ليستقر عند درجة حرارة الغرفة |
| standard | مقياس، قياسي، غير استثنائي |
| standard deviation | الانحراف العياري |
| standard error of the mean (sem) | الخطأ المعياري للمتوسط |
| standard fisher-indolization conditions | ظروف فيشر القياسية لإدخال مجموعة إندول |
| standardization | التقييس، التوحيد القياسي |
| standardize | يقيس، يضع مقاييس موحدة، يوحد مقاييس؛ يجعل الشيء مطابقا لقياس معين |
| standardized z-score | درجات معيارية زائية موحدة القياس |
| standards | مقاييس |
| standards-dependent industry | صناعة معتمدة على المستويات القياسية |
| standards-driven industry | صناعة تقودها المستويات القياسية |
| standarisation | التوحيد (القياسي) |
| standby air conditioning | تكييف هواء في وضع الاستعداد |
| standby time | زمن الجاهزية للتشغيل: عدد الساعات التي يمكن لبطارية مشحونة تماما أن تشغل الهاتف المحمول دون تنفيذ أو استقبال المكالمات وعندما يتم تشغيل الطاقة يتم استخدامها بشكل مستمر لتوصيل الجهاز بالخلية المحلية لكي تعرف الشبكة موقعك وتقوم بتوصيلك عندما تستقبل مكالمة |
| stand-in = double | دوبلير |
| standing call | مكالمة مستقلة |
| standing committee | لجنة دائمة |
| standing valve | صمام ثابت |
| stand-off weapon | سلاح للقتال بمنأى |
| stannanes | قصديرات؛ أملاح حمض القصدير |
| stannous salts | أملاح قصديرية |
| staphylococcus aureus | المكورة العنقودية البرتقالية |
| star in | يقوم بالبطولة |
| stardom | النجومية |
| starlet | ممثلة ناشئة؛ نجمة ناشئة |
| start | يبدأ |
| start codon | رامزة بدء جينية |
| start page | صفحة البداية: الصفحة التي تبدأ عندها الاستعرض |
| starter/helper motor | محرك الابتداء/المساعد |
| starting material | مادة البدء |
| start-up voltage | جهد بدء التشغيل |
| state agency | وكالة حكومية تابعة لولاية |
| state audit institution (sai) | ديوان المحاسبة |
| state commissioners authority | هيئة مفوضي الدولة |
| state diagram | مخطط حالة - رسم بياني لحالة |
| state litigation authority | هيئة قضايا الدولة |
| state machine | جهاز حالة |
| state of aggregate | حالة التجمع |
| state of the art | الحالة الراهنة المعروفة في المجال؛ ما هو معروف في المجال: كل ما ظهر من اختراعات في المجال حتى الآن |
| state security investigation | مباحث أمن الدولة |
| stateful | خاص أو متعلق بالحالة |
| statement regarding federally sponsored research or development | بيان بشأن البحث أو التطوير برعاية فيدرالية |
| statement triggers | أوامر الجمل البرمجية |
| static investment | الاستثمار الراكد |
| static poisson's ratio | نسبة بويسون الاستاتيكية |
| static pressure | الضغط الاستاتيكي |
| static support bed technology | الطبقة الحاملة الثابتة |
| static young's modulus | معامل يونج الاستاتيكي |
| static, mobile, active defence | دفاع ثابت؛ متحرك؛ نشط. |
| statins | مركبات ستاتين |
| station car | ستيشن |
| stationary | ثابت |
| stationary exercise bicycles | الدراجات الثابتة المخصصة للتمرينات الرياضية |
| stationary robot | روبوت ماكث |
| statistically significant | له دلالة إحصائيا |
| stator | عضو ساكن |
| stator | الساكن: الجزء الساكن من محرك أو آلة |
| status light | نور الحالة |
| statute and rule | القانون وقرار المحكمة |
| statutory exclusivity | حصرية بنص القانون |
| stave | عارضة |
| stay of execution | وقف التنفيذ |
| stay wire | سلك تثبيت؛ سلك دعم |
| std or std | قياسي |
| steady improvement of technology | التطور ثابت الخطى للتقنية |
| steady-state ; steady state | حالة الاستقرار؛ حالة مستقرة |
| steam | بخار: المقصود بخار ماء |
| steam assisted gravity drainage | تصريف بفعل الجاذبية بمساعدة البخار |
| steam assisted gravity drainage heavy oil recovery process | عملية استعادة نفط ثقيل متصرف بفعل الجاذبية بمساعدة البخار |
| steam blower | مُفجر بُخاري |
| steam cracking | التكسير بالبخار |
| steam drum | اسطوانة تجميع بخار الماء |

| | |
|---|---|
| steam ejector | مخرج البخار |
| steam flooding | الحقن بالبخار؛ الغمر بالبخار |
| steam methane reforming (smr) | إعادة تشكيل الميثان بالبخار |
| steam methane reforming unit | وحدة إعادة تشكيل الميثان ببخار الماء |
| steam reformation | إعادة تشكيل البخار |
| steam reformed (converted) ; steam-reformed (converted) | إعادة تشكيل (تحويل) بالبخار |
| steam reforming process | إعادة تشكيل بالبخار |
| steam soaking | نقع أو تشريب بخاري |
| steaming | تبخير |
| stearate | ستيارات |
| stearic exclusion reactions | تفاعلات الاستبعاد بالإعاقة |
| stearyl methacrylate | ميث أكريلات ستياريل |
| stearylamine | ستياريل أمين |
| steato- | شحم؛ دهن |
| steel alloy | سبيكة فولاذية |
| steel anchor rods | قضبان الإرساء الفولاذية |
| steel mill | مصنع الصلب |
| steel shell | غلاف من الصلب |
| steely | فولاذي، صلب أو قوي كالفولاذ |
| stellular | نجمي الشكل. شبيه بنجم صغير |
| stem cell | خلية جذعية |
| stem cell technology | تقنية الخلايا الجذعية |
| stem cells | خلايا مدورية |
| stemless | عديم الساق |
| step | يخطو، درجة، إجراء |
| step down resistivity profile | منحنى مقاومية خفْض |
| step up resistivity profiles | منحنى مقاومية رفع |
| stepper (stepping) motor | محرك خطوي |
| step-van | شاحنة أحادية الهيكل |
| stepwise | تدريجي |
| stereisomers | متجاسمات |
| stereo- | تجاسمي |
| stereocenter | مركز تجاسم |
| stereocenters | مراكز تجاسمية |
| stereochemisrty | كيمياء فراغية (الخواص الكيميائية الفراغية) |
| stereochemistry | كيمياء الجوامد |
| stereogenic | تجاسمي |
| stereogenic centres | مراكز فراغية المنشأ |
| stereoisomeres | المتجاسمات؛ الأيزومرات الفراغية |
| stereoisomeric forms | صور أيزومرات تجاسمية |
| stereoisomic | تجاسمي؛ متعلق بالمتجاسمات |
| stereospecific | ذو نوعية تجاسمية أو خصوصية فراغية |
| stereospecificity | نوعية تجاسمية أو خصوصية فراغية |
| steric | فراغي |
| steric hinderance | إعاقة تجسمية |
| sterically | فراغيا: حسب الترتيب الفراغي للذرات في الجزيء |
| sterically hindered amine | الأمين المعاق فراغياً |
| sterile | معقم |
| sterilization | تعقيم |
| sterilize | يعقم |
| sterilized milk | لبن معقم |
| sterilizer | معقم |
| sternotomy | شق القص |
| sterocenter | مركز تجاسمي |
| sterochemistry | الكيمياء الفراغية |
| steroid | ستيرويد |
| stetched seam | لحام نقطي |
| stickies | اللواصق : المواد التى تلتصق ببعضها البعض، مثل الملوثات اللاصقة في الورق المسترجع |
| stickness | لزوجة، تدبق |
| sticky | لزجة |
| stiff | متيبس، صلب |
| stiffen | يصلب، ييبس، يتصلب، يتيبس |
| stiffener | مقوية |
| stiff-man syndrome | متلازمة الرجل المتيبس |
| still | يسكن، يهدئ، ثابت، ساكن، غير متحرك |
| still images | الصور الثابتة |
| still life painting | لوحات طبيعة صامتة |
| stilling well | بئر معايرة |
| stimulant | حاث، محفز، منبه، مثير |
| stimulatable | قابل للحث |
| stimulate | يحث |
| stimulation | استثارة؛ تنبيه |
| stimulation | استثارة |
| stimulation | حث، تحفيز، تنبيه، إثارة |
| stimulator | حاث، محفز |
| stimuli | عوامل حاثة، محفزات |
| stinger | إبرة |
| stinger port | فتحة إبرة |
| stir | يقلب |
| stirred and nitrogen-flushed suspension | معلق تم تقليبه تم غسله بالنيتروجين من |
| stirred solution | محلول سبق تقليبه |
| stirring | تقليب |
| stitched seam | غرزة ملتحمة |
| stldd | وثيقة تصميم عالية المستوى لنظام |
| stm | وحدة نمطية لنقل متزامن |
| stochastic modelling | صياغة النماذج الاحتمالية |
| stock concentration | تركيز التخزين |
| stock control system | نظام التحكم بالبواقي |
| stock plates | أطباق التخزين |
| stock solution | محلول خام |
| stock substrate | ركيزة تخزين |
| stock tank = storage tank | صهريج تخزين |
| stockpile | المخزون (الاحتياطي) |
| stoichiometric | متكافئ العناصر |
| stoichiometric solvates | ذوابات متكافئة |
| stoichiometry | كمية متكافئة - اتحاد عناصر |
| stol | إقلاع وحط قصير |
| stolen idea | فكرة مسروقة |
| stolen inventive concept | مفهوم اختراعي مسروق |
| stolen knowledge | معرفة مسروقة |
| stop codon | رامز الإنهاء |
| stop valve | صمام إيقاف |
| stopple | سدادة، يسد بسدادة |
| storability | القابلية للتخزين |

| | |
|---|---|
| storable | قابل للتخزين |
| storage | مخزن |
| storage buffer | محلول تخزين منظم |
| storage device | جهاز تخزين |
| storage of water | مخزون الماء |
| storage software | برنامج للتخزين |
| storage system | نظام تخزين |
| storage system | نظام تخزين |
| store | يخزن، محل |
| storer | مخزن |
| storing | تخزين |
| storing system | نظام تخزين |
| stow-and-go seating | مقاعد طي وتخزين |
| stp | ظروف الضغط والحرارة القياسية؛ الظروف القياسية للضغط ودرجة الحرارة |
| straddle | يمتد عبر |
| stragtegist | إستراتيجي |
| straight | مستقيم |
| straight run | التقطير المباشر |
| straight run naphtha | نفثا التقطير المباشر؛ نفثا ناتجة عن التقطير المباشر |
| straight run vacuum gas oil | نفط غاز التقطير المباشر تحت ضغط منخفض |
| straight-chained or branched | قد تكون ذات سلسلة مستقيمة (خطية) أو متفرعة |
| straightening | تقويم |
| straightening machine | آلة جعل الشيء مستقيما |
| straightening member | عضو استعدال |
| straight-run | ناتج عن التقطير المباشر |
| strain | سلالة |
| strain | إجهاد؛ انفعال {صناعة وميكانيكا وبترول}؛ يشد، يمط، يعصر، يصفي، يتصفى |
| strain couple | يقرن بواسطة الإجهاد |
| strain gauges ; starin gages | مقاييس انفعال |
| strain on | الإجهاد على |
| strain-controlled tensile machine | آلة شد متحكم فيها بالإجهاد |
| strained | مشدود |
| strainer | مصفاة؛ أداة شد، أداة مط |
| strain-hardening | تصليد بالانفعال |
| strand | سلسلة |
| stranded or remote natural gas | غاز طبيعي نائي أو بعيد |
| strands | جدائل؛ جديلة |
| strap | حزام |
| strap eyelet | فتحة تركيب الحزام |
| strata and community schemes division | مشاريع الأبنية السكنية والتجارية(ستراتا). |
| strategic alignment | ضبط وضعية استراتيجي |
| strategic alignment of intellectual capital | ضبط وضعية استراتيجي لرأس المال الفكري |
| strategize | يضع إستراتيجية |
| strategy | إستراتيجية |
| strategy officer | مدير الإستراتيجيات |
| stratified hazard ratio | نسبة الخطورة المتدرجة |
| stratum corneum | الطبقة المتقرنة (للجلد) |

| | |
|---|---|
| stream | تيار؛ يجري، يتدفق، يتموج، نهير، سيل، تيار، دفق، مورد متجدد باستمرار، موكب متصل، مجرى |
| streamer | شريط |
| strenght | شدة؛ قوة؛ متانة؛ مقاومة (حسب النص) |
| strength plates | ألواح تقوية |
| strengthen security | يشدد الحراسة |
| streptococcus pneumoniae | مكورة الالتهاب الرئوي السبحية |
| stress | إجهاد |
| stress crack | تشقق إجهادي |
| stress proteins | بروتينات الإجهاد |
| stress urinary incontinence | سلس البول الإجهادي |
| stressor | مجهد؛ عامل محدث للإجهاد |
| stretch | يمدد؛ يفرد |
| striaghtener | مقوم |
| strickle | المسواة. أداة لإزالة الفائض |
| stride | خطوة |
| striker fired action | إطلاق النار بطاقة آلية الضرب |
| striking plate | مِصَدّ لِسَانِ القُفْل: صَفِيحَةُ حِمَايَةِ مِصَدّ لِسَانِ القُفْلِ |
| string | عمود حفر؛ عمود أنابيب؛ سلسلة أنابيب حفر |
| string of tubing | عمود الأنابيب |
| stringed | مدّ بما يشكل سلسلة |
| stringent security measures | إجراءات أمن مشددة |
| stringer | مقوية |
| stripe | يخطط، يقلم، ضاربة، جلدة، تخطيط، تقليم |
| stripped down versions | نسخ مصغرة (تحمل السمات الأساسية فقط) (من البرامج إلخ) |
| stripper | ماكينة فرك؛ وسيلة نزع؛ وسيلة فصل |
| stripping gas | غاز نزع؛ غاز فصل |
| stroke | السكتة الدماغية |
| stroke engine | محرك شوطي |
| stromal | سدّي؛ سدوي: متعلق بالنسيج الضام الأساسي لعضو، خلية، بنية إلخ |
| stromatoporoids | الاستروماتوبورايد |
| strong suddenly turning on light detector | كاشف ضوء قوي يضاء فجأة |
| strongpoints | نقط حصينة |
| strongyloidiasis | داء الاسطوانيات |
| strouhal number | رقم ستراوهال |
| structurability | قابلية الشيء للهيكلة |
| structurable | قابل للهيكلة |
| structural | إنشائي؛ بنائي؛ بنيوي |
| structural formula | الصيغة البنائية |
| structurally and functinally | بنائيا ووظيفيا |
| structure | بنية؛ الصيغة البنائية؛ هيكل؛ يهيكل |
| structure collapse temprature | درجة حرارة انهيار البنية |
| structure of folders and files | بنية المجلدات والملفات |
| structure on | يبني على؛ يرتكز على |
| structured | مُهَيكل |
| structured finance | التمويل المنظم |
| structured programming | برمجة بنيوية |
| structures | إنشاءات |

| | |
|---|---|
| stu | وحدة التدريب على النظام |
| stubborn resistence | مقاومة عنيفة |
| stucco | جبس |
| studies | دراسات |
| stud-partition construction | بناء مقسم إلى أجزاء بالأخشاب |
| stuffed animals | حيوانات محنطة للزينة |
| stuffed birds | طيور محنطة |
| stump pain | ألم الجدعة (بقية العضو المبتور) |
| stun bomb | قنبلة صدمية |
| stylus | مؤشر أو إبرة (كمبيوتر) |
| suability | القابلية للمقاضاة |
| sub | مشترك؛ وصلة |
| sub judice | أمام القاضي |
| sub nom. (sub nomine) | باسم |
| sub saharan africa | النصف الجنوبي من القارة الأفريقية |
| subacute | حاد نوعا |
| subacute sclerosing panencephalitis | التهاب الدماغ الشامل المصلّب دون الحاد |
| sub-ambient | أقل من درجة الحرارة المحيطة |
| subband | نطاق فرعي |
| sub-branch | تفريعة |
| subcarrier frequency | تردد الموجة الحاملة الفرعية |
| subclavian | تحت الترقوة |
| subclone | نسيلة فرعية |
| sub-compact vehicle | مركبة شبه مكتنزة |
| subcontract | عقد فرعي؛ عقد من الباطن |
| subcontractor | مقاول فرعي؛ مقاول من الباطن |
| subcooling | تبريد إضافي |
| sub-critical | في المجال تحت الحرج |
| subcutaneous | تحت الجلد |
| subcutaneous emphysema | إمفزيما تحت جلدية |
| sub-doses | جرعات فرعية |
| subdural | تحت الأم الجافية |
| subendocardial | تحت غشاء القلب الداخلي |
| subfamily | فصيلة |
| subgreywacke | تحت جريواكي |
| subject | مريض |
| subject application | الطلب المقدَّم |
| subject disposition | توزيع المرضى |
| subject global impression | الانطباع العام للمريض |
| subject mater | موضوع (الدراسة)؛ مادة، موضوع |
| subject notice | إعلان (دعوى في القانون) |
| subject to be treated | الحالة الخاضعة للعلاج؛ الحالة المراد علاجها |
| subjects who have treatment success | حققوا [ نجاحا علاجيا؛ أو معالجة ناجحة (نجاحا في المعالجة) [إلخ] |
| sub-licensable license | ترخيص قابل للترخيص من الباطن |
| sub-license agreement | اتفاق بشأن ترخيص من الباطن. اتفاق ينظم قيام طرف حاصل على ترخيص لاستخدام حق ما بترخيص ذلك الحق بدوره للغير |
| sublimation point | نقطة التسامي |
| sublingual | تحت اللسان |
| sublingual tablets | أقراص تحت اللسان |
| sub-machine gun | رشاش قصير؛ مسدس رشاش |

| | |
|---|---|
| sub-maximal concentrations | تحت قصوى |
| submerged | مغمور بالماء، غارق |
| submergible | قابل للغمر |
| submerse | يغمر |
| submersed | مغمور بالماء، نام تحت الماء |
| submersible | مغمور بالماء |
| submicromolar | لها تركيز أقل من الميكرو مولار |
| submicromolar antagonists | المضادات التي لها تركيز أقل من 1 ميكرو مولار |
| submicron | بحجم دون الميكرون |
| submicron particles | جسيمات بحجم دون الميكرون |
| suboptimal | شبه مُثلى |
| sub-optimum field conditions | ظروف عمل اقل مما هو مفروض |
| subpleural | تحت البلورا |
| subsea | عمق مغمور |
| subsequences (single: subsequence) | متواليات فرعية |
| subsequent invention | اختراع لاحق |
| subsequent inventor | مخترع لاحق |
| subsequent patent | براءة لاحقة |
| subsequent reaction | تفاعل تالي |
| subset or superset of the examples | مجموعة فرعية أو شاملة من الأمثلة |
| subsidiary | شركة تابعة |
| subsonic | اقل من سرعة الصوت |
| subsonic speed | سرعة دون الصوت |
| substance withdrawal | انسحاب مادة |
| substantial amount | قدر كبير |
| substantially | إلى حد كبير؛ بشكل كبير |
| substechiometric quantity | كمية أقل من المفروضة طبقاً للمعادلة الكيميائية |
| substient (misspelling often)!! | مجموعة استبدال |
| substition | استبدال |
| substituations | استبدالات |
| substitue | بها استبدال |
| substituent | مجموعة استبدال |
| substitute | يستبدل، بديل |
| substituted indole derivatives | مشتقات إندول بها استبدال |
| substituted monophenyl monophosphonamidate | فوسفوناميدات مونوفينيل به استبدال |
| substituted or unsubstituted | بها استبدال أو بدون استبدال |
| substituted or unsubstituted atom | ذرة بها استبدال أو بدون استبدال |
| substituted or unsubstituted compound | مركب به استبدال أو بدون استبدال |
| substitutes | مواد بديلة |
| substitution | استبدال |
| substitution in meta | استبدال في الموضع ميتا |
| substitutions at the c-5 position (= at the c5-position ) | استبدالات عند الموضع 5 |
| substoichiometric | شبه متكافئ العناصر |
| substoichiometric zinc oxide | أكسيد زنك شبه متكافئ العناصر |

| | |
|---|---|
| substoichiometric; sub-stoichiometric | شبه المتكافئ |
| substrate | ركيزة؛ طبقة تحتية |
| substratum | طبقة تحتية |
| subsurface | تحت سطحي |
| subsurface hydrocarbon containing formation | تكوين جوفي يحتوي على الهيدروكربون |
| sub-systems | النظم الفرعية |
| subtenancy | استئجار من الباطن |
| subtenant | مستأجر من الباطن |
| subtending circuits | دوائر متقابلة |
| sub-terrain mines | المناجم الموجودة تحت الأرض |
| sub-terrain mining of the oil sands | استخراج الرمال النفطية من تحت الأرض؛ استخلاص الرمال النفطية من تحت الأرض |
| subterranean | جوفي |
| subterranean formation | تكوين جوفي |
| subterranean formation having reservoirs therein | تكوين جوفي يحتوي على مخزونات |
| subterranean water | مياه جوفية |
| subtle energy | طاقة لطيفة |
| subtracter | وحدة طرح |
| subtype | نوع فرعي |
| subversive activity | نشاط هدام |
| success | نجاح |
| successive | متتالي |
| successive invention | اختراع لاحق |
| successively | على التتابع |
| such a combination therapy achieves synergy effect | مثل هذا العلاج بالتوليفة يؤدي إلى تحقيق تأثير تآزري |
| such as postherpetic neuralgia | مثل الألم العصبي التالي لمرض الحلاء |
| such as shown by/indicated by numeral 412 | كما هو مبين بالرقم 412 |
| sucker rods | قضبان ماصة |
| suction | وحدة امتصاص |
| suction filtration | ترشيح بالشفط |
| suction means | وسائل الشفط |
| suction mode | وضع شفط |
| suction pressure | ضغط المص |
| suction-dry | يجفف بالشفط |
| suction-filter | يرشح بالشفط |
| sud | وتد |
| sudden release of accumulated strains | حصول انفراج مفاجيء لانفعالات متراكمة |
| sufficiently clear disclosure of invention | إفصاح لاختراع واضح وضوحا كافيا |
| suffix (-aemia or -emia) | متعلق بالدم |
| suffix (-based) | لاحقة بمعنى: أساسه كذا (مثال: محفز أساسه التيتانيوم titanium-based catalyst) |
| suffix (-constrained) | مقيدة بـ |
| suffix (-fold) | مرة (أضعاف كذا) |
| suffix (-fold) | أضعاف (كذا) |
| suffix (-fold) | لمرتين؛ لثلاث مرات؛ إلخ |
| suffix (-gated) | عن طريق بوابة؛ على اتصال بـ (بوابة) |
| suffix (-gated) | معتمد على |
| suffix (-loaded) | محمَّل بكذا |
| suffix (-meter) | مقياس؛ جهاز قياس |
| suffix (-tagged) | معلَّم ب؛ مرقم بـ |
| suffix (-terminated) | منتهي بـ |
| suffix (-ylate) | يرتبط بكذا: يرتبط بالمركب، المادة إلخ (على سبيل المثال الارتباط بالمانوز mannosylation؛ الارتباط بالجليكوزيل glycosylation) |
| sugar beet | سكر البنجر |
| sugar rearrangment oligosaccharides | قليلات السكريدات الناتجة عن إعادة تنظيم جزيء السكر |
| suit | دعوى |
| suitable acid-scavenging base | قاعدة مناسبة لكسح الحمض |
| sulfanyl | سلفانيل |
| sulfidation | التحويل إلى كبريتيد |
| sulfidation of the catalysts | إدخال كبريتيد إلى المحفزات |
| sulfide | كبريتيد |
| sulfides | مركبات الكبريتيد |
| sulfinate | سلفينات |
| sulfitation | معالجة بالكبريتيت |
| sulfite | كبريتيت |
| sulfite pulp | الاستخلاص بطريقة الكبريتيت، الاستخلاص الكيميائي للألياف حيث يتم استخدام الكبريتيت والبيكبريتيت ككيماويات طبخ أساسية |
| sulfolane | سالفولين |
| sulfonamide | سلفوناميد |
| sulfonate esters | إسترات سلفونات |
| sulfonated | مُسلفن |
| sulfonyl | سلفونيل |
| sulfuric acid;sulphuric acid | حمض الكبريتيك (ويسمى أيضا حمض السلفوريك) |
| sulphate ; sulfate | كبريتات |
| sulphation | وجود الكبريت |
| sulphide | كبريتيد |
| sulphide(s) | كبريتيد(ات)..؛ سلفيد(ات) |
| sulphonate | كبريتونات |
| sulphonic | سلفونيك |
| sulphur cement-aggregate composites | تركيبات الأسمنت الكبريتي مع الركام |
| sulphur-extended asphalt | أسفلت محتوي على كبريت |
| summary judgment | حكم مستعجل |
| summing device | جهاز جمعي |
| sump | حوض تجميع |
| sun solaris | نظام التشغيل صن سولاريز |
| sunburn | السفعة الشمسية |
| super bowl | مباريات كرة القدم الأمريكية |
| super fine | فائقة |
| super macro mode | وضع التصوير شديد القرب |
| superacid | شديدة الحموضة |
| supercomputer ; super computer | سوبر كمبيوتر |
| superconducting | توصيل فائق |
| superconductor | موصل فائق التوصيل |
| supercritical | فوق الحرج |
| super-critical | فوق الحرج |

| | |
|---|---|
| superfamily | طائفة |
| superficial | سطحية |
| superfusion | انصهار شديد |
| superheated temp. | درجة حرارة التسخين الفوقي |
| superimposable | متراكب |
| superimposeable | قابلة للتراكب |
| superimposcable | متراكب |
| super-leads | LEADs فائقة: بروتينات طافرة قيادية فائقة |
| supermarket | مجمع تجارى |
| supernumeraries (extras) | كومبارس |
| superoxide | أكسيد فائق |
| supersatuarated | مفرط التشبع |
| supersonic | أسرع من الصوت |
| supersonic speed | سرعة فوق الصوت |
| super-spike period | فترة الارتفاع الرهيب (للأسعار إلخ) |
| supplement (with) | يستكمل (ب) |
| supplementation | استكمال |
| supplemented | مكملة |
| support | مادة حاملة؛ دعامة؛ يدعم، دعم |
| support (on) | يُحمل على |
| support blocks | كتل أو وحدات داعمة: قد تكون كتل خشبية داعمة إلخ |
| support device | وسيلة الدعم |
| support gas | الغاز الحامل |
| support grant | منحة داعمة |
| support system | نظام دعم (مساندة) |
| support track | المسار الحامل |
| supportability | قابلية الشيء للدعم |
| supportable | قابل للدعم |
| supported catalyst | محفز محمول - محفز تحمّل |
| supporting | دعم |
| supporting industries | صناعات معاونة |
| supportive | داعم |
| supportive bandages | أربطة تجبير |
| suppositories | تحاميل |
| suppository | تحميلة |
| suppressing crystal formation | منع؛ تثبيط |
| suppressor | كابت |
| supra-maximal blocking concentration | أقصى تركيز إغلاق |
| supranuclear | فوق النواة |
| supremacy clause | بند السمو، بند العلو. بند تعاقدي يبين درجات المستندات وأيها يكون أعلى من الآخر في حالة التناقض |
| supreme commander of the armed forces | القائد الأعلى للقوات المسلحة |
| supreme court fellow | زميل المحكمة العليا |
| surface | يبرز على السطح، سطح |
| surface active agent | عامل نشط عند السطح |
| surface active toxin | توكسين نشط عند سطح الخلية |
| surface anchors | وسائل تثبيت سطحية؛ مثبتات سطحية {زراعة الخلايا} |
| surface area | مساحة السطح |
| surface controlled subsurface safety valve (scssv) | صمام أمان تحت سطحي يتم التحكم فيه من السطح |
| surface plasmon resonance assay | اختبار رنين البلازمون السطحي |
| surface region | منطقة سطحية |
| surface strain | إجهاد على السطح |
| surface tention | التوتر السطحي |
| surface texture | النسيج السطحي |
| surface tracker | رادار أرضي |
| surface-active ; surface active | نشط عند السطح (وبخاصة نشط عند سطح الخلية {كيمياء}) |
| surface-to-take point borehole | ثقب حفر من سطح إلى نقطة أخذ |
| surfactant | مادة خافضة للتوتر السطحي؛ خافض للتوتر السطحي |
| surge margin | أداة التحكم في حد التمور |
| surge pressure injector system | نظام حاقن متمور الضغط |
| surge tank | خزان تنظيم التدفق |
| surgeon | جراح |
| surgery | جراحة |
| surrender | يستسلم |
| surrogate | دواء بديل |
| surveillance device | جهاز مراقبة |
| surveillance software | برنامج للمراقبة |
| surveying | مسح |
| surveyor | مساح، مختص بالمسح |
| survivable infrastructure information system | نظام معلوماتي خاص بالبنية التحتية الناجية. نظام معلوماتي خاص بالبنية التحتية التي تنجو من الهجمات والأعطال |
| survival clause | البند الخاص ببقاء بعض الالتزامات |
| survival upon termination clause | البند الخاص ببقاء بعض الالتزامات بعد الإنهاء |
| susceptibility to developing a disease or condition ; susceptibility to a disease or condition | قابلية الإصابة بمرض أو حالة |
| susceptible × insusceptible | متأثر × غير متأثر بـ |
| susceptible control plant | نبات عياري عرضة للإصابة (بفطر؛ إلخ) |
| suspect | المشتبه فيه |
| suspend by | يتدلى من |
| suspended ceiling | سقف معلق |
| suspending agents and thickening agents | عوامل تعليق وعوامل مكسبة للقوام |
| suspense | أفلام الإثارة |
| suspension | معلق؛ وقف مؤقت (تأديبي) |
| sustain | يساند، يؤازر، يمد بأسباب الحياة، يديم |
| sustainability | قابلية الشيء للاستدامة، استدامة |
| sustainability driven innovation | ابتكار تسوقه الاستدامة. جهد ابتكاري غايته إدامة الاختراع والنشاط التجاري المرتبط به |
| sustainable | مستدام؛ دائم |
| sustainable energy | طاقة مستدامة |
| sustainable growth | نمو مستدام، نمو يمكن إدامته |
| sustainable innovation | إبداع مستدام |
| sustainable patent system | نظام براءات يمكن إدامته، نظام |

| | |
|---|---|
| | براءات مستدام |
| sustained release | إطلاق مستمر |
| sustained release form | صورة إطلاق مستمر |
| sustained-release base | القاعدة مستمرة الإطلاق، المادة الأساسية مستمرة الإطلاق |
| sustenance | رزق، معيشة، طعام، مساندة، مؤازرة، إعالة، سند |
| sutured contact | اتصال متشابك |
| suzuki coupling | إقران سوزوكي |
| svc | دائرة افتراضية مبدلة |
| svc(s) | خدمة (خدمات) |
| svd | وثيقة نسخة البرنامج |
| sw | برامج |
| swarming (namely the so-called phenomena "surge") of the liquid medium | احتشاد (بمعنى أكثر تحديداً ما يسمى بظاهرة "اندفاع") الوسط السائل |
| swbs | هيكل تفاصيل أعمال المقاول |
| swbsd | قاموس هيكل تفاصيل أعمال المقاول |
| sweet potatoes | بطاطا |
| sweet spots | مناطق حساسة |
| sweeteners | مواد تحلية: مواد مكسبة للمذاق الحلو |
| swing in conditions | ظروف متأرجحة |
| swirl | دوامة؛ حركة دوامية؛ يتحرك أو يحرّك في دوامة |
| swirling means | وسيلة تدويم |
| switch | مفتاح "كهرباء"؛ محول؛ مفتاح؛ يحول |
| switch box | صندوق التبديل |
| switch tripper | مفتاح فصل |
| switch valve | صمام تحويل |
| switched movement alarm | جهاز إنذار بتحول الحركة |
| swivelably | على نحو دوّار |
| swivelling | حركة دوارة؛ دوران |
| swoop down on | ينقض على |
| swordsmith | الخطاطون بالنقوش |
| syllabus | خطة دراسية |
| symbol index | معامل رمز |
| symmetric | متماثل |
| symmetrical folds | الثنيات المحدبة والمقعرة المتماثلة |
| symmetrization | تماثل |
| symmetry column | عمود متماثل |
| sympathetic blockade | حصار السمبثاوي |
| sympathetic nervous system | الجهاز العصبي السمبثاوي |
| sympathomimetic | شبيه بالسمبثاوي |
| symples tactical harness blk | طقم حماية أسود |
| sympotomatic | عرضي |
| synallagmatic contract | عقودٌ تبادليَّةٌ |
| synapic | متشابك |
| synaptogenesis | تكوُّن الاشتباك |
| synch | تزامن |
| synchronous system | نظام متزامن |
| syn-depositional structures | بنيات أثناء الترسيب |
| syndicated | منشورة |
| syndiotactic | منتظم التناوب |
| synergistic | تآزري؛ تعاوني؛ مؤازر؛ معاون |
| synergistic advantage | ميزة مؤازرة |
| synergy | تعاون؛ تآزر |
| syngas (synthesis gas) | غاز تخليق |

| | |
|---|---|
| syngeneic | متماثلة جينيًا |
| synonyms | حقوق الدخول المكافئة |
| synovial | زلالي |
| synthesis | تركيب، تأليف، اصطناع، الجميعة |
| synthesize | يركب، يؤلف |
| synthesizer | مولف |
| synthetic | تركيبي، تأليفي |
| synthetic examdple numbers | أرقام المثال التخليقي |
| synthetic fibers | ألياف صناعية |
| synthetic fuel | وقود توليفي |
| synthetic methods | طرق التخليق |
| synthetics | اللدائن |
| syringe | محقنة |
| syringe barrel | أنبوب المحقنة |
| syringe filter | مرشح محقنة |
| syrups | الشراب |
| system | نظام |
| system and apparatus for jet-fluid cutting nozzle | نظام وجهاز لفوهة قطع بتدفق المائع |
| system bandwidth | عرض نطاق النظام |
| system bus | ناقل نظام |
| system catalog | دليل (كتالوج) النظام |
| system controller | أداة تحكم في النظام |
| system failure | تعطّل نظام |
| system global area (sga) | منطقة النظام العالمية (عبارة عن هياكل ذاكرة) |
| system memory | ذاكرة جهاز |
| system status | حالة النظام |
| system status led | LED حالة النظام |
| systematic name | اسم علمي: اسم منهجي (في التسمية الكيميائية عندما يتوافق مع التركيب) |
| systemic | جهازي؛ منهاجي |
| systemic cachexia | الهزال العام |
| systemic exposure | تعرض جهازي |
| systemic lupus | الذئبة الإحمرارية الشاملة |
| systemic lupus erythematosis | مرض الذئبة الحمامية المجموعي |
| systemic treatment | معالجة بطريقة تعم (توثر على) الجسم كله |
| systemic vasculitis | الالتهاب الوعائي الشامل |
| systems engineering | هندسة نظم |
| systems-level delivery | توصيل مستوى الأنظمة |
| systolic | انقباضي |

# T

| | |
|---|---|
| tab | سُطيح تحكم؛ عروة |
| tab screen | فهارس جداول |
| tabacosis | السحار التبغي |
| tabbouleh | التبولة |
| table cloths [not of paper] | مفارش المناضد [ليست من الورق] |
| table cloths of paper | مفارش المناضد من الورق |
| table cutlery [knives, forks and spoons] | الأدوات الخاصة بالمائدة [السكاكين والشوك والملاعق] |
| table forks | شوك المائدة |
| table indexes | مساحات الجداول |
| table linen [not of paper] | مفروشات المائدة [ليست من الورق] |
| table linen of paper | مفروشات المائدة من الورق |
| table mats [not of paper] | القطع التي توضع تحت الأطباق على المائدة [ليست من الورق] |
| table mats of paper | القطع التي توضع تحت الأطباق على المائدة وتكون من الورق |
| table napkins of paper | فوط المائدة من الورق |
| table napkins of textile | فوط المائدة من القماش |
| table plates of precious metal | أطباق المائدة من معدن نفيس |
| table plates, not of precious metal | أطباق المائدة ليست من معدن نفيس |
| table runners | أغطية المائدة |
| table spaces | كمبيوتر لوحي |
| table tennis (tables for -) | تنس الطاولة (طاولات للعب تنس الطاولة) |
| table tops | أغطية المائدة |
| table waters | ماء المائدة |
| tables | موائد |
| tables (arithmetical -) | الجداول (الجداول الرياضية) |
| tables (calculating -) | الجداول (الجداول الحسابية) |
| tables (operating -) | طاولات (طاولات للعمليات الجراحية) |
| tables for indoor football | طاولات للعب كرة القدم داخلياً |
| tables for machines | طاولات للماكينات |
| tables for table tennis | طاولات للعب تنس الطاولة |
| tables of metal | طاولات من المعدن |
| tablet pc | الكمبيوتر اللوحي؛ رقعات لبطاقات الفهارس |
| tablet punch | سطح ضغط القرص |
| tableting press; tablet press | مكبس تصنيع أقراص |
| tablets | أقراص |
| tabletting lubricants | مادة تزليق الأقراص (مزلقات) |
| tableware [knives, forks and spoons] | أدوات المائدة [السكاكين والشوك والملاعق] |
| tableware [other than knives, forks and spoons] not of precious metal | أدوات المائدة [بخلاف السكاكين والشوك والملاعق] ليست من معدن نفيس |
| tabs (monogram -) for marking linen | تطريز (تطريز للمونوجرام) لتعليم المفروشات |
| tachometers | مقاييس سرعة الدوران |
| tachyarrhythmias | سرعة النبض |
| tachycardia | إسراع القلب |
| tack | التصاق؛ لصق |
| tackifier | عوامل مكسبة للزوجة |
| tackifying agent | عامل لاصق |
| tackle (fishing -) | عدة (عدة صيد السمك) |
| tacks [nails] | المسامير |
| tacos | سندوتشات التاكو |
| taffeta [cloth] | بفتاه [قماش] |
| taffeta plasters (gummed -) | ضمادات من بفتاه (ضمادات لاصقة من بفتاه) |
| tag | علامة |
| tag (with) | يعلِّم ب؛ يرقّم بـ |
| tag detacher | مزيل الملصق التعريفي |
| tag epitope sequence | متوالية تعليم للقمة اللاصقة |
| tagging | تعليم؛ ترقيم |
| tags for index cards | التقاط صورة |
| tahini [sesame seed paste] | طحينة [عجين من بذور السمسم] |
| tail current reversal potential | الجهد العاكس للتيار الطرفي |
| tail gas | غاز ذيلي؛ غاز متخلف؛ غاز النفث |
| tailboard lifts [parts of land vehicles] | الأجزاء الرافعة للأبواب الخلفية [أجزاء من المركبات الأرضية] |
| tailgates (am.) (elevating -, power -) [parts of land vehicles] | الأبواب الخلفية في عربات النقل (أبواب خلفية رافعة) و(أبواب خلفية آلية) [أجزاء من المركبات الأرضية] |
| tailing processing system | نظام معالجة للبقايا |
| tailored design | تصميم مصمم حسب الحاجة |
| tailors' chalk | طباشير الخياطين |
| tailors' dummies | النماذج المستخدمة للتفصيل للخياطين |
| tailors' wax | شمع الخياطين |
| tailplane (also horizontal stabilizer) | ذيل الطائرة |
| take a picture | زمن المكالمة: عدد الدقائق / الساعات من الكلام المتواصل (سواءً كانت المكالمة صادرة أو واردة) التي تستمر خلالها البطارية مشحونة بالكامل في حالة التشغيل |
| take fingerprints | يرفع البصمات |
| take the oath | يقسم اليمين |
| take the product out of the reactor tube | سحب المنتج من أنبوب المفاعل |
| take up | تمت إذابته؛ إذابة |
| take-off | إقلاع |
| talc [magnesium silicate] | تلك [سيليكات الماغنسيوم] |
| talcum powder, for toilet use | مسحوق تلك للاستخدام في التجميل |
| talkie = sound film | فيلم ناطق |
| tallow | الشحم الحيواني |
| tambourines | دفوف صغيرة |
| tambours for embroidery machines | إطارات لماكينات التطريز |

| | |
|---|---|
| tamper resistence | مقاومة التلاعب |
| tamper technology | تقنية العبث، تقنية التلاعب |
| tampered dosage form | صورة جرعة معالَجة |
| tampering of formulations | التلاعب بالصيغ |
| tan | أسمر ضارب إلى الصفرة؛ لحاء دبغ الجلود |
| tan solid | مادة صلبة سمراء مصفرة |
| tangental contact | اتصال نقطة |
| tangy cheese | الجبن الحريف |
| tank truck | شاحنة صهريجية |
| tankards of precious metal | أباريق من معدن نفيس |
| tankards, not of precious metal | أباريق ليست من معدن نفيس |
| tanker | فرد المدرعات |
| tanks | الدبابات |
| tanks [indoor aquaria] | أحواض [أحواض لعرض الأسماك داخل المنزل] |
| tanks [weapons] | دبابات [أسلحة] |
| tanks of masonry | خزانات من الطوب أو الحجارة |
| tanks of metal | خزانات من المعدن |
| tanks, not of metal nor of masonry | خزانات ليست من المعدن أو الطوب أو الحجارة |
| tannic acid | حمض التنيك |
| tannin | حمض التنيك |
| tanning apparatus [sun beds] | أجهزة إكساب البشرة اللون الأسمر [حمامات شمسية] |
| tanning substances | مواد للدباغة |
| tantalum [metal] | تنتالم [فلز] |
| tan-wood | خشب للدباغة |
| tap wrenches | مفاتيح ربط ذكر اللولبة |
| tape (insulating -) | شريط (شريط عازل) |
| tape; adhesive tape | شريط لاصق |
| tape backup | النسخ الاحتياطي على شريط |
| tape cartridge | خرطوشة الأشرطة |
| tape liberary | مكتبة أشرطة |
| tape recorder | جهاز تسجيل الصوت على شرائط |
| tape storage | التخزين على أشرطة |
| tape units (magnetic -) [for computers] | وحدات للشرائط (وحدات الشرائط المغناطيسية) [للحاسبات الآلية] |
| tapered | مُسْتَدَقّ |
| tapering | تشكيل بحيث تكون مستدقة الطرف |
| tapers | الشموع الرفيعة والطويلة |
| tapes (adhesive -), for medical purposes | شرائط (شرائط لاصقة) للأغراض الطبية |
| tapes (demagnetizing apparatus for magnetic -) | شرائط (جهاز لإزالة المغنطة للاستخدام مع الشرائط المغناطيسية) |
| tapes for curtain headings | شرائط للأجزاء العلوية من الستائر |
| tapestry [wall hangings], not of textile | أنسجة مطرَّزة [ما يعلق على الجدران لتزيينها] من مواد غير نسيجية |
| tapestry [wall hangings], of textile | أنسجة مطرَّزة [ما يعلق على الجدران لتزيينها من مواد نسيجية] |
| tapioca | التابيوكا |
| tapioca flour for food | دقيق التابيوكا للطعام |
| tapping doors | أبواب سحب |
| taps [cocks, spigots] [faucets (am.)] for pipes | صنابير [حنفيات، سدادات] للمواسير |
| taps [faucets] | صنابير [حنفيات] |
| taps [hand tools] | صنابير أو سدادات [أدوات يدوية] |
| taps [parts of machines, engines or motors] | صنابير أو سدادات [أجزاء من الآلات أو المحركات أو الموتورات] |
| taps for casks [not of metal] | صنابير للأوعية [ليست من المعدن] |
| taps for casks [of metal] | صنابير للأوعية [من المعدن] |
| tar | القطران [قار] |
| tar-brushes, long handled | فُرش الطلاء بالقطران ذات مقابض طويلة |
| target (sth to sth) | يتم توجيه كذا إلى كذا |
| target binding domain (tbd) | نطاق ربط مستهدف |
| target chemical entities or target biological entities | العوامل الكيميائية المستهدفة أو العوامل البيولوجية المستهدفة |
| target conditional error rate | معدل أخطاء شرطية مستهدَفة |
| target inlet air temperature | درجة حرارة هواء الدخول المستهدفة |
| target snr | جودة الإشارة المستقبَلَة المستهدفة |
| target to (i.e. target sth to) | يوجه إلى |
| targetable | مستهدف |
| targets | أهداف للتسديد |
| tarpaulins | تربولين (قماش مشمع) |
| tarred brattice cloth | فاصل من قماش مطلي بالقار |
| tarred felt (coatings for -) [paints] | لباد مطلي بالقار (طلاء للباد المغطى بالقار) [دهانات] |
| tarred strips, for building | شرائح مطلية بالقار لأغراض البناء |
| tarring | دوران المحرك |
| tarring machines | ماكينات للطلاء بالقطران |
| tars | القطرانات؛ مركبات القطران |
| tarsal tunnel syndrome | متلازمة النفق الرصغي |
| tart scoops | ملاعق للكعك المحشو بالمربى أو الفاكهة |
| tartar | طرطرات |
| tartaric acid | حامض الطرطير |
| taser stun guns | البنادق/المسدسات الصاعقة من ماركة تاسر |
| task | اختبار؛ مهمة |
| task system | نظام مهام |
| tassels [haberdashery] | شُرَّابات [خردوات] |
| taste | مذاق |
| tautomeric forms | صور صنوية |
| tautomerism | تزامر ديناميكي(تكون في صورة صنوية) |
| tautomers | مركبات صنوية |
| tax and regulatory instruments | الضرائب والأنظمة الضابطة للسوق |
| tax feasibility | الجدوى الضريبية |
| tax limits | الحدود الضريبية |
| tax offset | التعويض الضريبي |
| tax price | سعر الضريبة |
| taxable income | دخل خاضع للضريبة؛ دخل خاضع للضرائب |
| taxable wealth | الثروة الخاضعة للضريبة |
| taxiing | دروج |
| taximeters | عدادات التاكسي |

| | |
|---|---|
| tbaf | تترا بيوتيل أمونيوم فلوريد |
| tbq | تيرا بكريل |
| t-cell | الخلية T؛ خلية تائية |
| td = triplet of doublets | ثلاثي الثنائيات |
| tdma | وصول متعدد بالتقسيم الزمني: عبارة عن نظام معالجة يستخدم بواسطة الهواتف المحمولة الرقمية يتيح لعدد من الهواتف اليدوية في المنطقة امكانية استخدام نفس الذبذبة. وكل مكالمة يخصص لها فترتها الزمنية الخاصة بها- فأنت بالفعل تسمع المحادثة لكسر من كل ثانية ولكن بما |
| tea | الشاي؛ تراي إيثيل أمين |
| tea (iced -) | شاي (مثلج) |
| tea balls, not of precious metal | كرات الشاي ليست من معدن نفيس |
| tea caddies of precious metal | علب صغيرة لأوراق الشاي من معدن نفيس |
| tea caddies, not of precious metal | علب صغيرة لأوراق الشاي ليست من معدن نفيس |
| tea carts | مناضد صغيرة ذات عجلات تستخدم لتقديم الشاي |
| tea cosies | أغطية من القماش لأباريق الشاي |
| tea infusers of precious metal | أدوات لصب الشاي مصنوعة من معدن نفيس |
| tea infusers, not of precious metal | أدوات لصب الشاي ليست من معدن نفيس |
| tea services of precious metal | أطقم شاي من معدن نفيس |
| tea services, not of precious metal | أطقم شاي ليست من معدن نفيس |
| tea strainers of precious metal | مصفاة للشاي من معدن نفيس |
| tea trolleys | عربات الشاي |
| tea-based beverages | مشروبات لها أساس من الشاي |
| teacher | مدرس |
| teacher homage | جائزة تكريم المعلم؛ جائزة المعلم المثالي |
| teacher supply | توفير المدرسين |
| teaching apparatus | جهاز تعليمي |
| teaching materials [except apparatus] | مواد تعليمية [باستثناء الأجهزة] |
| teaching/instructing | تدريس |
| teapots of precious metal | أباريق الشاي من معدن نفيس |
| teapots, not of precious metal | أباريق الشاي ليست من معدن نفيس |
| tear strength | مقاومة التمزق |
| tear-gas weapons | أسلحة غاز مسيل للدموع |
| tear-off calendars | نتائج التقويم اليومية يمكن انتزاع أوراقها |
| teaser campaign | حملة تشويقية؛ حملة إغراء؛ حملة جذب انتباه |
| teat cups for milking machines | أكواب ذات حلمات لماكينات الحلب |
| teats | حلمات |
| teats (feeding bottle -) | حلمات (حلمات لزجاجات |

إرضاع الأطفال)

| | |
|---|---|
| tech sergeant | رقيب فني |
| technetium | تكنتيوم |
| technical director | المدير الفني |
| technical equivalences | المكافئات الفنية |
| technical printing | الطباعة الفنية |
| technical solutions | حلول تقنية |
| technique | أسلوب تقني |
| techniques | تقنيات |
| techniques | أساليب تقنية |
| techniques in site-directed mutagenesis | أسلوب إحداث الطفرة بأسلوب موجه إلى الموقع |
| technological creativity | إبداع تقني |
| technological empowerment | تمكين تقني |
| technological empowerment of marginalized individuals | تمكين تقني لأفراد مهمشين |
| technological gap | فجوة تقنية |
| technologically-based empowerment of indigenous peoples | تمكين مرتكز على التقنية للشعوب المحلية |
| technologically-driven country | بلد تقوده التقنية |
| technologist | تقني |
| technology area | مجال من مجالات التقنية |
| technology driven innovation | ابتكار تقوده التقنية |
| technology infrastructure | البنية التحتية للتقنية |
| technology licensability | قابلية تقنية للترخيص |
| technology licensing | ترخيص تقنية |
| technology licensing agreement | اتفاق ترخيص تقنية |
| technology operation | عملية تقنية |
| technology pundit | خبير تكنولوجي |
| technology secrets | أسرار التقنية |
| technology transfer | نقل التقنية |
| technology transfer management | إدارة نقل التقنية |
| technology-based growth | نمو مؤسس على التقنية |
| technology-driven business model | نموذج تجاري تقوده التقنية |
| technology-driven business solutions | حلول تجارية تسوقها التقنية |
| technology-driven entrepreneurship | مضاربة تقودها التقنية |
| technology-driven society | مجتمع تسوقه التقنية |
| technology-enabled government operation | عملية حكومية ممكنة تقنيا |
| technology-intensive industry | صناعة يعد حضور التقنية فيها كثيفا |
| techonomy | تعبير يطلق على اقتصاد التقنية |
| tectonic breccia | الرواهص التكتونية |
| teddies [undergarments] | قمصان [ملابس تحتية] |
| tedding machines | ماكينات لنشر التبن بغية تجفيفه |
| teddy bears | دمى على شكل دببة محشوة |
| tee-shirts | قمصان قصيرة الأكمام [تي شيرت] |
| teeth (artificial -) | أسنان (أسنان صناعية) |
| teeth filling material | مادة لحشو الأسنان |
| teeth protectors | واقيات للأسنان |
| teething (preparations to | ظهور الأسنان (مستحضرات |

| | |
|---|---|
| facilitate -) | لتسهيل ظهور الأسنان) |
| teething rings | حلقات الأسنان [عضاضات] |
| teflon | مادة التفلون: واحدة من أفضل المواد المضادة للمياه |
| tel | هاتف |
| telco | شركة الاتصالات |
| teleangiectasia | التوسع الوعائي البعيد |
| telecast | يذيع بالتلفزيون |
| telecommunications | المواصلات السلكية واللاسلكية |
| telecommunications operator | شركة الاتصالات؛ مشغل الاتصالات |
| telecommuting | العمل من خلال التواصل الآلي. العمل مع الآخرين عبر تقنيات الاتصالات التقنية |
| telecoms | الاتصالات |
| telegraph [apparatus] | تلغراف [جهاز التلغراف] |
| telegraph posts of metal | صناديق التلغراف من المعدن |
| telegraph posts, not of metal | صناديق التلغراف ليست من المعدن |
| telegraph wires | أسلاك التلغراف |
| telehealth technology | تقنية رعاية صحية عن بعد |
| telemarketing | التسويق عبرالهاتف. |
| telematics | نظام تيليماتيكس: نظام اتصال لاسلكي مصمم لتجميع ونشر البيانات التي يمكن أن تستخدم في مجال الهاتف المحمول، متابعة السيارات، تحديد المواقع، خدمات الملاحة والمعلومات المباشرة والمساعدة في حالات الطوارئ |
| telemedicine | تعبير يطلق على مجال طبي جديد يتسم بتوظيف عالٍ للتقنية التفاعلية في تقديم العلاج |
| telemeter | تليمتر؛ جهاز قياس عن بُعد |
| telephone & video-conferencing interpreting | ترجمة فورية عبر الهاتف الصوتي والمرئي؛ (ترجمة فورية عن بعد) |
| telephone apparatus | جهاز الهاتف |
| telephone booths of metal | حجرات صغيرة مقفلة للهاتف من المعدن |
| telephone booths, not of metal | حجرات صغيرة مقفلة للهاتف ليست من المعدن |
| telephone boxes of metal | حجرات الهاتف من المعدن |
| telephone boxes, not of metal | مقصورة الهاتف ليست من المعدن |
| telephone receivers | سماعات الهاتف |
| telephone transmitters | ميكروفونات الهاتف |
| telephone wires | أسلاك الهاتف |
| telephones (portable -) | هواتف (هواتف محمولة) |
| teleprompters | ملقنات عن بُعد |
| telerupter | جهاز للفصل عن بُعد |
| telescope | جهاز تلسكوب |
| telescope for firearms (sighting -) | جهاز تلسكوب للأسلحة النارية الصغيرة (جهاز تلسكوب للمراقبة) |
| telescopic arm | ذراع تلسكوبي |
| telescopic lens | عدسة تلسكوبية |
| teletypewriters/teleprinters | طابعات عن بُعد |
| television | تلفزة |
| television apparatus | جهاز تليفزيوني |
| teller machine | آلة صرف النقود |
| tellurium | تلوريوم |
| telpher cables | كبلات العربات المعلَّقة [التلفريك] |
| telpher railways [cable cars] | سكك حديدية للعربات المعلقة [عربات تجرها كبلات متحركة] |
| temper | يقسي؛ يقوي |
| temperature equilibration | تعادل درجة الحرارة |
| temperature indicator | جهاز لبيان درجات الحرارة |
| temperature sensor | جهاز إحساس بدرجة الحرارة |
| temperature sensors | أجهزة إحساس بدرجة حرارة |
| temperature versus depth profile | منحنى درجة الحرارة بالنسبة للعمق |
| tempered glass | الزجاج المقسى: أنظر الزجاج المسطح المعالج حرارياً |
| tempered glass sheets | ألواح زجاج مقسى |
| tempered water | ماء مخفف |
| tempering of steel | تقسية الفولاذ (تقويته) |
| tempering preparations (metal -) | مستحضرات للسقي (مستحضرات فلزية للسقي) |
| template | قالب |
| template amino acid | قالب حمض نووي |
| template dna | قالب DNA |
| template peptide | ببتيد قالب |
| temporal cortex=temporal lobe | الفص الصدغي |
| temporary channel disturbance | اضطراب مؤقت للقناة |
| temporary monopoly | احتكار مؤقت. تقوم فكرة الملكية الفكرية المعاصرة على منح صاحب الحق في الممتلك الفكري احتكاراً مؤقتاً |
| temporary storing of information | تخزين مؤقت للمعلومات |
| temprature field | مجال حراري |
| tender | عطاء |
| tendonitis | التهاب الوتر |
| tenecteplase | تينيكتيبلاز |
| tenement | عقار |
| tennis ball throwing apparatus | جهاز لقذف كرات التنس |
| tennis nets | شبكات التنس |
| tenoning machines | ماكينات تلسين |
| tenosynovitic | متعلق بالتهاب غشاء الوتر الزلالي |
| tenosynovitis | التهاب غشاء الوتر الزلالي |
| tensile force | قوة شد |
| tensile srength | مقاومة الشد |
| tensile testing | اختبار الشد |
| tensioactive agents | عوامل نشطة تجاه الشد |
| tension | جهد (كهربائي)؛ توتر (عصبي)؛ شد (حبل، كبل) إلخ |
| tension links | وصلات الشد |
| tensioner | شدادة |
| tensioner h.d. | شدادة الخدمة الشاقة |
| tensor | العضلة الموترة؛ العضلة الشادَّة: تعمل على تمدد المفصل. |
| tent pegs of metal | أوتاد الخيام من المعدن |

| | |
|---|---|
| tent pegs, not of metal | أوتاد الخيام ليست من المعدن |
| tenth grader | طلبة الصف العاشر |
| tents | الخيام |
| teratoma | الورم المسخي |
| terbium | تربيوم |
| terephthalic acid | حمض الترفثاليك |
| term °c refers to degrees celsius | درجة مئوية |
| term note | سند إذني لأجل محدد |
| terminal | طرفي؛ طرف؛ وحدة طرفية |
| terminal end | نهاية طرفية |
| terminal peptide | ببتيد طرفي: ببتيد يقع عند طرف |
| terminal purity or contamination levels | مستوى النقاء أوالتلوث النهائيين |
| terminals [electricity] | أطراف توصيل [للكهرباء] |
| terminate | ينهي |
| termination clause | البند الخاص بإنهاء العقد |
| terminus | نهاية |
| terms | بنود، شروط، أحكام |
| terpenes [essential oils] | تربينات [زيوت عطرية] |
| terpolymer | بوليمر ثلاثي |
| terra alba | طين أرضي |
| terra cotta | طين نضيج |
| terrain | تربة؛ أرض |
| terrariums (indoor -) [plant cultivation] | مربى للأحياء البرية (مربي للأحياء البرية داخل المنزل) [للعناية بالنباتات] |
| terrariums (indoor -) [vivariums] | مربى للأحياء البرية (مربي للأحياء البرية داخل المنزل) [مربى يابس] |
| terrestrial globes | كرات أرضية |
| terrigenous conglomerates | مدملكات أرضية (قارية) |
| territorial | إقليمي، محلي |
| territorial claims, gains, water | مطامع، مكاسب، المياه إقليمية |
| territorial dispute | نزاع حول الأرض |
| territorial exclusivity | حصرية إقليمية |
| territoriality | إقليمية |
| territoy | إقليم |
| tert-butyl acetate | أسيتات t- بيوتيل |
| tertiary amine amides | مركبات أميد الأمين الثلاثية |
| tertiary amino azabicyclic alcohols | كحولات t- أمينو- آزا باي سيكلو الثلاثية |
| tertiary recovery method | طريقة الاستخلاص الثالثة |
| tes | تراي إيثيل سيلان |
| test | تجربة؛ يختبر؛ إختبار |
| test board | لوحة الاختبار |
| test paper, chemical | ورقة اختبار كيميائية |
| test stage | مرحلة الاختبارر |
| test substrate | المادة الخاضعة للتفاعل في الاختبار |
| test tubes | أنابيب اختبار |
| testability | القابلية للاختبار |
| testable | قابل للاختبار |
| testable idea | فكرة قابلة للاختبار |
| tester | أداة اختبار |
| testicular | خصوي |
| testicular cancer | سرطان الخصية |
| testing apparatus | جهاز اختبار |
| tetanus | تتنوس |
| tether | حبل؛ مِطوَل؛ مطاولة |
| tetra | تترا |
| tetra armed backbones | مجموعات رئيسية مدرعة في الموضع تترا |
| tetraazol | تترا أزول |
| tetrabodies | أجسام مضادة رباعية التكافؤ |
| tetrachlorides | رابع الكلوريدات |
| tetrahedral | رباعي |
| tetrahydrocannabinol | تترا هيدروكانابينول |
| tetramer | تترامر: وحدة بنائية رباعية |
| tetrameric | رباعي الوحدات البنائية |
| tetramers | ترامیرات |
| tetramethyluronium hexafluorophosphate | تترا ميثيل يورونيوم هكسا فلورو فوسفات |
| tetrasubstituted | به أربع استبدالات |
| tetrazole | تترا زول |
| text message (messaging) | رسالة نصية |
| textile (raw fibrous -) | نسيج (نسيج من ألياف خام) |
| textile fibers [fibres] | ألياف نسيجية [ألياف] |
| textile oil | زيوت نسيجية |
| textile-brightening chemicals | مواد كيميائية لتزهية النسيج |
| textile-impregnating chemicals | مواد كيميائية لتشريب النسيج |
| textile-waterproofing chemicals | مواد كيميائية لجعل النسيج مقاوماً للماء |
| textural maturity | النضوج النسيجي |
| tfa | حمض تراي فلورو أسيتيك |
| tfaa | أنهيدريد تراي فلورو أسيتيك |
| tg | درجة حرارة التحول الزجاجي؛ نقطة تحول الزجاج؛ درجة حرارة التزجج |
| thalassaemia = thalassemia | أنيميا البحر الأبيض |
| thallium | ثاليوم |
| than ever before | أكثر دقة من أي وقت مضى |
| thaw | يذيب، يفك تجميد |
| the chartered institute for patent attorneys | المعهد المعتمد لوكلاء البراءات |
| the clinical trial ip clause | بند الملكية الفكرية المنبثقة عن المحاولات السريرية. المادة التي تنظم ملكية الاختراعات المنبثقة عن الاختبارات السريرية |
| the coders rights project | مشروع حقوق المشفرين |
| the convents on human rights | مواثيق حقوق الإنسان |
| the earth | الأرض |
| the french national assembly | الجمعية الوطنية البريطانية |
| the fuel supply department | إدارة الوقود |
| the general assembly | الجمعية العامة |
| the geneva conventions | معاهدات جنيف |
| the house of representatives | مجلس النواب |
| the interference (directed) to any particular base station | التداخل (الموجه) إلى أي محطة قاعدية محددة |
| the intermediate product | المركب الوسيط |
| the international committee of the red cross | الهيئة الدولية للصليب الأحمر |
| the international court o justice (icj) | محكمة العدل الدولية |

| | |
|---|---|
| the international monetary fund (imf) | صندوق النقد الدولي |
| the international olympic committee, ioc | اللجنة الأوليمبية الدولية؛ اللجنة الأوليمبية العالمية |
| the inter-parliamentary union | الاتحاد البرلماني الدولي |
| the launch of london's bid | تقديم عرض مدينة لندن لأستضافة |
| the low glass transition temperature (tg) resin | الراتنج الذي له درجة حرارة تحول زجاجي منخفضة (Tg) |
| the medical & veterinary authority | الهيئة الطبية والبيطرية |
| the military academy | الكلية الحربية |
| the military police dep | إدارة الشرطة العسكرية |
| the military technical academy | الكلية الفنية العسكرية |
| the missing | المفقودون |
| the national assembly | مجلس الأمة |
| the naval academy | الكلية البحرية |
| the navy | البحرية |
| the order of merit | وسام الاستحقاق |
| the ordnance dep | إدارة المهمات |
| the people's assembly | مجلس الشعب |
| the personnel authority | هيئة شئون الأفراد |
| the police academy | كلية الشرطة |
| the printing and publishing dep | إدارة المطبوعات والنشر |
| the prior art | التقنية السابقة: أي ما تم إنجازه في المجال في الأوقات/الاختراعات السابقة |
| the rations dep | إدارة التعيينات |
| the reserve officers academy | كلية ضباط الاحتياط |
| the scheduler interlace table | جدول تشابك وحدة الجدولة |
| the security council | مجلس الأمن |
| the senate | مجلس الشيوخ |
| the shura council | مجلس الشورى |
| the supply and provitions auth | هيئة الإمداد والتموين |
| the third world | العالم الثالث |
| the united states district court for the middle district of georgia | محكمة الولايات المتحدة الإقليمية لإقليم جورجيا القضائي الأوسط |
| the universal declaration of human rights | الإعلان العالمي لحقوق الإنسان |
| the west german boundestage | برلمان ألمانيا الغربية |
| the world bank | البنك الدولي |
| the world peace council, wpc, helsinki | مجلس السلام العالمي |
| theatre mode | عرض بملء الشاشة: لمشاهده واجهه البرنامج بملأ الشاشه وغالبا يستخدم في حاله مشاهده ملفات الفيديو يختفي شريط الأدوات في حاله عدم تحريكنا للماوس لمده خمس ثواني وفي حاله الرغبه في العوده للواجهه المعتاده نضغط على Return أو زرار F7" |
| theatrical masks | أقنعة مسرحية |
| thecal hyperplasia | فرط التنسج الغمدي |
| theft | سرقة براءات |
| theft prevention installations electric | تركيبات كهربائية للحماية ضد السرقة |
| thematic instruction | التعليم الموضوعي |
| theodolites | أدوات لقياس الزوايا [تيودوليت] |
| therapeutic | علاجي |
| therapist | معالج |
| therapy | علاج |
| thermal analyzer (ta) | جهاز التحليل الحراري |
| thermal conductivity | موصلية حرارية |
| thermal contact | تلامس حراري |
| thermal destruction device | وسيلة إتلاف حرارية |
| thermal efficiency | فعالية حرارية |
| thermal expansion valve | صمام تمدد حراري |
| thermal imaging | تصوير حراري، نوع من أنواع التصوير الذي يستعمل الأشعة تحت الحمراء |
| thermal packs for first aid purposes | كمادات حرارية للاستخدام في أغراض الإسعافات الأولية |
| thermal tempering | المعالجة الحرارية؛ التقوية الحرارية: معالجة حرارية للتقوية |
| thermal water | ماء حراري |
| thermally conductive material ; thermally conduction material | مادة موصلة للحرارة |
| thermally insulated containers for food | عبوات معزولة حرارياً للأطعمة |
| thermally insulating material | مادة عازلة للحرارة |
| thermic lances [machines] | مشارط حرارية [ماكينات] |
| thermionic lamps and tubes | مصابيح وأنابيب أيونية حرارية |
| thermionic valves [radio] | صمامات أيونية حرارية [لأجهزة الراديو] |
| thermo gravimetric analysis (tga) | تم استخدام التحليل الحراري الوزني |
| thermo-chemistry | كيمياء حرارية |
| thermocouple | زوج حراري؛ مزدوجة حرارية |
| thermodynamically meta-stable | ثابتة في الموضع ميتا بصورة حرارية ديناميكية |
| thermo-dynamics | ديناميات حرارية |
| thermo-electric compresses [surgery] | ضمادات كهربية حرارية [للجراحة] |
| thermogram | مخطط حراري |
| thermogravimetric analysis (tga) | التحليل الوزني الحراري |
| thermogravi-metric and infrared analysis (tg/ir) | التحليل الوزني الحراري والأشعة تحت الحمراء |
| thermo-mechanical pulping . | الاستخلاص الحراري-الميكانيكي |
| thermometer | ترمومتر |
| thermophilic | آلفة للحرارة؛ محبة للحرارة |
| thermoplastic | تتلدن بالحرارة؛ حرارية التلدن |
| thermoplastic resins | راتنجات تتلدن بالحرارة |
| thermoplastics | لدائن حرارية |
| thermoregulation | التنظيم الحراري |
| thermosetting | تتصلب بالحرارة؛ متصلب بالحرارة؛ متصلد بالحرارة؛ حرارية التصلب |
| thermosiphon | مثعب حراري |
| thermosiphon reboilers | مراجل إعادة غلي مزودة بممص |

| | |
|---|---|
| | حراري |
| thermostatic valves [parts of heating installations] | صمامات ترموستاتية [أجزاء من تركيبات التسخين] |
| thermostat-regulation fluid | مائع تنظيم الحرارة؛ مائع تثبيت الحرارة؛ مائع تنظيم ثرموستاتي |
| thermostats | ترموستات [مثبتات أوتوماتيكية لدرجات الحرارة] |
| thermostats for vehicles | ترموستات للمركبات |
| thf | تترا هيدروفيوران |
| thick or fat client/server | عميل/خادم (متكامل أو ثقيل)؛ عميل/خادم معالجة بيانات |
| thickeners | مواد لتغليظ القوام؛ مكسبات للقوام؛ مغلظات |
| thickeners for paints | مواد لتغليظ القوام للاستخدام مع الدهانات |
| thickening agents for cooking foodstuffs | مواد لتغليظ القوام لطهي المواد الغذائية |
| thicket | دغل |
| thieno | ثيينو |
| thigh | فخذ |
| thimbles (rope -) of metal | عراوي (عراوي للحبال) من المعدن |
| thimbles (sewing -) | عراوى (عراوي للحياكة) |
| thin client/server | عميل/خادم (بسيط أو رفيع)؛ عميل/خادم عرض بيانات |
| thin film holey carbon supports | مواد حاملة كربونية مثقبة في صورة طبقة رقيقة |
| thinking | تفكير |
| thinking machine | آلة مُفكرة. يطلق هذا التعبير على الآلات شديدة التطور وعلى الروبوتات |
| thin-layer chromatography ("tlc") | كروماتوجراف الطبقة الرقيقة ("TLC") |
| thinners | مُرَقِّقَاتٌ لِلْقِوَامِ |
| thinners for lacquers | مرققات القوام للاستخدام مع اللاكية |
| thinners for paints | مرققات القوام للاستخدام مع الدهانات |
| thiocarbanilide | ثيوكربانيليد |
| thionating agent | عامل إدخال مجموعة ثيو |
| thionyl bromide | بروميد ثيونيل |
| thiophenecarboxylate | ثيو فين كربوكسيلات |
| thiourethane prepolymer | بوليمر ثيو يوريثان أولي |
| third fuel line | خط وقود ثالث |
| third party (third-party) | (شركة) طرف ثالث؛ شركة متعاونة |
| thistle extirpators [hand tools] | أدوات اقتلاع الأشواك [أدوات يدوية] |
| thixotropic agent | عامل تسيلي بالرج |
| thomson staff | فريق عمل thomson |
| thoracic | صدري |
| thoracotomy | شق الصدر |
| thorium | ثوريوم |
| thought | فكر، فكرة |
| thought-provoking environment | بيئة مثيرة للفكر |
| thread | سلسلة من العمليات؛ سن ملولب؛ خيط؛ يتم مده (مثل سن ملولب) (خلال) |
| thread (leather -) | خيوط (خيوط من الجلد المدبوغ) |
| thread [surgical] | خيوط [جراحية] |
| thread counters | عدادات أسنان اللوالب |

| | |
|---|---|
| thread of metal for embroidery | خيط من المعدن للتطريز |
| thread of metal for tying-up purposes | خيوط من المعدن لأغراض الربط |
| thread, not of metal, for wrapping or binding | خيط ليس من المعدن للتغليف أو الحزم |
| thread, oil crops, sesame | خيط، محاصيل زيتية، السمسم |
| threadably | كسن ملولب؛ على نحو ذي أسنان ملولبة |
| threaded | ملولب؛ ذو أسنان ملولبة؛ كسن ملولب |
| threaded engagement | تعشيق لولبي |
| threaded portion | جزء ذو أسنان ملولبة |
| threaded screw | مسمار ملولب ذو أسنان لولبية |
| threadedably | كسن ملولب؛ على نحو ذي أسنان ملولبة |
| threaders | أدوات تشكيل الخيوط |
| threading (compositions for -) | تشكيل الخيوط (تركيبات لتشكيل الخيوط) |
| threading machines | ماكينات لتشكيل الخيوط |
| threads (identification -) for electric wires | خيوط لونية رفيعة (خيوط تمييز) للأسلاك الكهربية |
| threads of plastic for soldering | خيوط من البلاستيك للحام |
| threads of plastic materials for textile use | خيوط من مواد بلاستيكية للاستخدام في النسيج |
| threads of plastic materials, not for textile use | خيوط من مواد بلاستيكية ليست للاستخدام في النسيج |
| threads of precious metal [jewellery, jewelry (am.)] | خيوط من معدن نفيس [للمجوهرات] |
| threads of rubber, not for use in textiles | خيوط من المطاط ليست للاستخدام في المنسوجات |
| threat assessment report | تقرير تقييم التهديدات |
| three-wheeled vehicle | مركبة ذات ثلاث عجلات |
| threshing machines | ماكينات دراس |
| threshold | القيمة الحدية: (توصف القيمة الحدية بأنها أكبر larger/higher، وأقل lower (كبيرة high، صغيرة low) |
| threshold distance | مسافة حدّية |
| threshold temperature | درجة حرارة حدّية |
| thriller | أفلام الإثارة والبوليسية |
| thrip | تربس |
| thrombocytopenia | نقص الصفائح الدموية |
| thrombocytopenic | منقص الصفائح الدموية |
| thromboembolism | انسداد الأوعية |
| thrombophlebitis | التهاب الوريد الخثاري |
| thrombosis | تخثر؛ تجلط |
| thrombotic | متجلط |
| throttle ; throttle valve | صمام خانق |
| throttling | تمرير (الخليط، إلخ) في صمام خانق |
| throttling service | خدمة تمرير تدفق محدود عبر الصمام |
| through hole | ثقب نافذ |
| throughput | ناتج؛ إنتاجية |
| thrust | دفع |
| thryroiditis | التهاب الغدة الدرقية |
| thulium | ثوليوم |
| thumbnail | صورة مصغرة |
| thumbtacks | مسامير الخرائط |

| | |
|---|---|
| thymocyte | خلية تيموسية |
| thymol | ثيمول [مادة تستخرج من الزعتر] |
| thymoma | ورم الغدة التيموسية |
| thymoregulators | منظمات توتية |
| thymus | الغدة التيموسية |
| thyroiditis | التهاب الدرقية |
| tibia | عظم القصبة |
| tibial | قصبي |
| tibiofibular | قصبي شظي |
| tick [linen] | قماش أغلفة الوسائد [قماش] |
| ticket dispensers | موزعات التذاكر |
| ticketing solutions | حلول إصدار تذاكر |
| tickets | تذاكر |
| tickets (instruments for punching -) | تذاكر (أدوات تثقيب التذاكر) |
| ticks [mattress covers] | أكياس [أغطية للمراتب] |
| tid | ثلاث مرات في اليوم |
| tidal flats | مسطحات المد والجزر |
| tidal power | طاقة المد |
| tie | وصلة |
| tie clips | دبابيس أربطة العنق |
| tie plates | ألواح للربط |
| tie presses | مكابس لكي أو فرد رباط العنق |
| tie-in ad | إعلان مرتبط بحملة؛ إعلان منوط بحملة إعلانية |
| tiering | تدرُّج؛ تدريج الأسعار؛ تدرج أسعار الخدمات |
| ties of metal (railroad -) | عوارض من المعدن (عوارض لخطوط السكك الحديدية) |
| ties, not of metal (railroad -) | عوارض ليست من المعدن (عوارض لخطوط السكك الحديدية) |
| tiff | صيغة ملف الصور المختارة |
| tights | رداء مُحكَم (على الجسم) |
| tile draining | الصرف المغطى |
| tile floorings of metal | مواد لتبليط الأرضيات من المعدن |
| tile floorings, not of metal | مواد لتبليط الأرضيات ليست من المعدن |
| tiles (mirror -) | بلاط (بلاط من المرايا) |
| tiles (preservatives for -), except paints and oils | بلاط (مواد واقية للبلاط) باستثناء الدهانات والزيوت |
| tiles of metal | بلاط من المعدن |
| tiles of metal for building | بلاط من المعدن للبناء |
| tiles, not of metal | بلاط ليس من المعدن |
| tiles, not of metal, for building | بلاط ليس من المعدن للبناء |
| till hardness | حتى الصلابة؛ حتى يصلب |
| tilt down | الحركة بالكاميرا إلى أسفل |
| tilt hammers | مطارق ثقيلة تتحرك بشكل عمودي (تستخدم في طرق الحديد) |
| tilt sensors | أجهزة إحساس بالميلان |
| tilt up | الحركة بالكاميرا إلى أعلى |
| tilting-carts | عربات قلّابة |
| timber (building -) | أخشاب (أخشاب للبناء) |
| timber (manufactured -) | أخشاب (أخشاب مصنّعة) |
| timber (sawn -) | أخشاب (أخشاب منشورة) |
| timber (undressed -) | أخشاب (أخشاب غير مشكّلة) |
| timber (unsawn -) | أخشاب (أخشاب غير منشورة) |
| timber (worked -) | أخشاب (أخشاب مشغولة) |
| timber industry, glass industry | صناعة الأخشاب؛ صناعة الزجاج |
| timbers [frames] for ships | أخشاب [هياكل] للسفن |
| time clocks [time recording devices] | ساعات الدوام [أجهزة لتسجيل الوقت] |
| time constant | ثابت زمني |
| time division multiple access (tdma) system | نظام الوصول المتعدد بالتقسيم الزمني TDMA |
| time division multiplexed pilot transmission scheme | مخطط إرسال إشارة دليلية متضاعفة بالتقسيم الزمني |
| time domain electromagnetic signal | إشارة كهرومغناطيسية في مجال الزمن |
| time efficient solutions | حلول فعالة على مستوى الوقت |
| time is of the essence clause | البند الخاص بكون الوقت أمراً جوهرياً. بند تعاقدي تتضمنه معظم العقود الصناعية يبين أن التزام طرف بالمدة المقررة لتنفيذ التزامه ضروري من أجل أن يقوم الطرف الآخر بالتزام مقابل |
| time on stream (tos) | زمن التفاعل (TOS) |
| time point | نقطة زمنية |
| time recording apparatus | أدوات لتسجيل الوقت |
| time switches, automatic | مفاتيح كهربائية زمنية أوتوماتيكية |
| time varying electromagnetic force | قوة كهرومغناطيسية متغيرة مع الزمن |
| time-, frequency-, or code division multiplexed signal | إشارة بالإرسال التعاقبي المتعدد بتقسيم الزمن أو التردد أو الشفرة |
| time-consuming system | نظام مستهلك للوقت |
| timed 25 foot walk test (t25fw) | المشي 25 قدم حسب توقيت زمني |
| timed 25-foot walk test (t25fw) | اختبار المشي 25 قدم حسب توقيت زمني |
| timed walk responders | المستجيبون للمشي حسب توقيت زمني |
| time-domain ; time domain | مجال الزمن |
| time-of-flight mass spectrometer | مقياس ثقل الجزيئات وتركيبها النووي |
| timestamp | خاتم الوقت |
| timetables (printed -) | جداول زمنية (جداول زمنية مطبوعة) |
| time-varying electromagnetic field (tvemf) ; time varying electromagnetic field (tvemf) | مجال كهرومغناطيسي متغير مع الزمن (TVEMF) |
| timing differences | الفروقات الزمنية المؤقتة |
| tin | قصدير |
| tin (ii) chloride dihydrate | ثنائي هيدرات كلوريد القصدير (II) |
| tin (ii) or (iv) esters | إسترات القصدير II أو IV |
| tin cans | عُلب من القصدير |
| tin openers, electric | فتاحات كهربائية للعلب |
| tin openers, non-electric | فتاحات غير كهربائية للعلب |
| tincture of iodine | صبغة يود |
| tinctures for medical purposes | أصباغ للأغراض الطبية |
| tinder | مواد سريعة الاشتعال |
| tinfoil | رقاقات من القصدير |

| | |
|---|---|
| tingling | نخز |
| tinplate | ألواح مطلية بالقصدير |
| tinplate packings | حشو الألواح المطلية بالقصدير |
| tins | علب من القصدير |
| tinsels [trimmings for clothing] | خيوط أو أشرطة لتزيين المنسوجات [زركشة للملابس] |
| tinted glass | زجاج ملون: زجاج شفاف أو نصف شفاف، ويعتمد ذلك على نوع الزجاج، حيث أن الزجاج ملون بالكامل |
| tinted windows | نوافذ ذات زجاج عاتم/معتم |
| tiny sensor | جهاز إحساس دقيق |
| tip | طرف |
| tip speed | سرعة طرفية (لمروحة، لعضو دوار إلخ) |
| tipping apparatus, parts of trucks and waggons | أجهزة قلابة، أجزاء من الشاحنات والعربات |
| tipping bodies for lorries [trucks] | هياكل قلابة لعربات النقل [الشاحنات] |
| tipranavir | تيبرانافير |
| tips (billiard cue -) | نهايات مستدقة (نهايات مستدقة لعصىّ البليارد) |
| tips (cigarette -) | أطراف (أطراف للسجائر) |
| tips for crutches for invalids | رؤوس للعكاز للمعوقين |
| tips for footwear | أطراف لملبوسات القدم |
| tips of yellow amber for cigar and cigarette holders | أطراف من الراتنج الأصفر لأدوات حمل السيجار والسجائر |
| tire repairing compositions | تركيبات لإصلاح الإطارات |
| tires (automatic indicators of low pressure in vehicle -) | إطارات (مؤشرات أتوماتيكية لبيان الضغط المنخفض في إطارات المركبات) |
| tires (flanges of railway wheel -) | إطارات (حواف ناتئة لإطارات عجلات السكك الحديدية) |
| tires (mastic for -) | إطارات (صمغ المصطكا للإطارات) |
| tires (non-skid devices for vehicle -) | إطارات (وسائل مضادة للانزلاق لإطارات المركبات) |
| tires for bicycles, cycles | إطارات للدراجات والدراجات الثلاثية |
| tires for vehicle wheels | إطارات لعجلات المركبات |
| tires, solid, for vehicle wheels | إطارات صلبة لعجلات المركبات |
| tissue chopper | قاطع أنسجة |
| tissue paper | ورق رقيق شبه شفاف |
| tissue replacement | إحلال أنسجة |
| tissue-cultured ; tissue cultured | زراعة أنسجة |
| tissues | أنسجة |
| tissues (surgical -) | أنسجة (أنسجة جراحية) |
| tissues impregnated with cosmetic lotions | مناديل مشبعة بغسول للتجميل |
| tissues impregnated with pharmaceutical lotions | مناديل مشبعة بغسول صيدلاني |
| tissues of paper for removing make-up | مناديل ورقية لإزالة مستحضرات التجميل |
| tissues of textile for removing make-up | مناديل من النسيج لإزالة مستحضرات التجميل |
| titanite | تيتانيت |
| titanium | تيتانيوم |

| | |
|---|---|
| titanium dioxide [pigment] | ثاني أكسيد التيتانيوم [صباغ] |
| titanium iron | حديد التيتانيوم |
| titanium tetrachloride | رابع كلوريد التيتانيوم |
| titer | عيار حجمي |
| title | يعنون، عنوان |
| title compound | المركب المذكور في العنوان |
| titrant | المحلول المعاير |
| titres | عيارات حجمية |
| tiw | ثلاث مرات في الأسبوع |
| tlc = thin-layer chromatography | كروماتوجراف الطبقة الرقيقة |
| t-learning | التعليم عن بعد بواسطة التلفاز |
| tlt | معاهدة قانون العلامات |
| tm | كتيب فني |
| tm ( temprature ) | درجة حرارة |
| tmn | شبكة إدارة الاتصالات السلكية واللاسلكية |
| to an equivalent extent | إلى حد متعادل |
| to barbecue | يشوي |
| to bypass around | يمر في مسار فرعي حول ؛ يمر جانبيا حول |
| to nitride | نترت |
| to transfer a gene to a certain site, etc. | نقل؛ تغيير الموضع؛ الانتقال |
| toasters | محمّصات خبز كهربائية |
| tobacco | تبغ |
| tobacco (cooling installations for -) | تبغ (تركيبات تبريد للتبغ) |
| tobacco (sauce for preparing -) | تبغ (نكهة لتحضير التبغ) |
| tobacco extracts [insecticides] | مستخرجات من التبغ [مبيدات حشرية] |
| tobacco industry | صناعة السجائر |
| tobacco jars of precious metal | جِرار للتبغ من معدن نفيس |
| tobacco jars, not of precious metal | جِرار للتبغ ليست من معدن نفيس |
| tobacco pipes | غليون لتدخين التبغ |
| tobacco pouches | أكياس التبغ |
| tobacco processing machines | ماكينات معالجة التبغ |
| tobacco roasters | محمّصات التبغ |
| tobacco-free cigarettes for medical purposes | سجائر خالية من التبغ لأغراض طبية |
| tod | الوقت من اليوم |
| toddy | تودي (أنواع مشروبات روحية) |
| tofu | طوفو |
| togas | ثياب فضفاضة |
| together with | سويا مع كذا |
| toggle | وصلة مفصلية |
| toilet bowls | سلاطين المراحيض |
| toilet brushes | فُرش المراحيض |
| toilet cases | عُلب التجميل |
| toilet paper | ورق المراحيض |
| toilet paper holders | أدوات حمل ورق المراحيض |
| toilet seats | مقاعد المرحاض |
| toilet sponges | إسفنج للمراحيض |
| toilet utensils | أدوات المراحيض |
| toilet water | ماء التواليت [كولونيا] |

| | |
|---|---|
| toiletries | مستحضرات الزينة |
| toilets [water-closets] | مراحيض [بيوت الخلاء] |
| toilets, portable | مراحيض متنقلة |
| token | رمز |
| token device | جهاز تشفير؛ جهاز ترميز |
| tokens (copper -) | عملات معدنية صغيرة (عملات معدنية صغيرة من النحاس) |
| tolerate | يتقبل؛ يتحمل؛ يسمح |
| toll like receptor | مستقبلات بروتينية لتنشيط المناعة |
| toll transport services | خدمات نقل المعلومات لمسافات بعيدة |
| toluene | التولوين |
| tomato juice [beverage] | عصير الطماطم [مشروب] |
| tomato juice for cooking | عصير الطماطم للطهي |
| tomato purée | حساء مركز من الطماطم |
| tomato sauce | صلصة الطماطم |
| tomb or grave enclosures, not of metal | سياج للقبور أو المدافن ليست من المعدن |
| tombac | سبائك من النحاس والزنك لصنع الحلي الرخيصة |
| tombs (enclosures of metal for -) | مدافن (سياج من المعدن للمدافن) |
| tombs (monuments of bronze for -) | مدافن (نُصب من البرونز للمدافن) |
| tombs (monuments of metal for -) | مدافن (نُصب من المعدن للمدافن) |
| tombs [monuments], not of metal | قبور [شواهد قبور] ليست من المعدن |
| tombs of metal | مدافن (قبور) من المعدن |
| tombs, not of metal | قبور (مدافن) ليست من المعدن |
| tombstone plaques of metal | شواهد القبور من المعدن |
| tombstone plaques, not of metal | ألواح لشواهد القبور ليست من المعدن |
| tombstone stelae of metal | بلاطة معدنية تحمل نقشاً تذكارياً توضع على القبور |
| tombstone stelae, not of metal | شواهد القبور ليست من المعدن |
| tombstones | شواهد للقبور |
| tombstones of metal | شواهد للقبور من المعدن |
| tomography | رسم سطحي |
| tom-toms | طبل صغير |
| ton | طن |
| tone arms for record players | أذرع الفونوغراف لأدوات الأسطوانات الفونغرافية |
| toner cartridge recycling | تدوير |
| toner cartridges [filled] for printers and photocopiers | خراطيش محلول التونر (الحبر) [معبأة] للطابعات وماكينات تصوير المستندات |
| toners [ink] for photocopiers | تونر [حبر] لماكينات تصوير المستندات |
| tongs | ملقاط |
| tongue | نتوء لساني |
| tongue scrapers | مكشطة للسان |
| tonicity | تقوية |
| tonicity agents | عوامل ضبط التوتر |
| tonics [medicine] | عقاقير مقوية أو منشطة [دواء] |
| toning baths [photography] | مغاطس تلوين |
| toning salts [photography] | أملاح تلوين |
| tonsils | اللوزتين |
| too good to be true | تفوق حد التصديق |
| tool bags of leather | حقائب للعُدد من الجلد |
| tool belts [holders] | سيور للعُدد [حوامل] |
| tool boxes of metal | صناديق للعُدد من المعدن |
| tool chests of metal | صناديق كبيرة للعُدد من المعدن |
| tool handles of metal | مقابض للعُدد من المعدن |
| tool handles, not of metal | مقابض للعُدد ليست من المعدن |
| toolbox ; tool kits | شنطة أدوات؛ شنطة العدة؛ صندوق العدة؛ صندوق الأدوات؛ طقم أدوات: مجموعة الأدوات |
| toolface ; tool face | اتجاه أدوات الحفر |
| tools (divot repair -) [golf accessories] | عُدد (عُدد لإصلاح كتل الأعشاب الموجودة في ملاعب الجولف) [كماليات للعبة الجولف] |
| tools (hand-held -), other than hand-operated | عُدد (عدد تُحمل باليد) بخلاف الأدوات التي يتم تشغيلها يدوياً |
| tools (holding devices for machine -) | عُدد (وسائل حاملة لعُدد الماكينات) |
| tools [parts of machines] | عُدد [أجزاء من الماكينات] |
| toothbrushes | فُرش الأسنان |
| toothbrushes, electric | فُرش أسنان كهربائية |
| toothpick holders of precious metal | أدوات حاملة لعيدان تنظيف (خلال) الأسنان [أعواد يتخلل بها الأسنان] من معدن نفيس |
| toothpick holders, not of precious metal | أدوات حاملة لعيدان تنظيف (خلال) الأسنان [أعواد يتخلل بها الأسنان] ليست من معدن نفيس |
| toothpicks | عيدان تنظيف (خلال) الأسنان [أعواد يتخلل بها الأسنان] |
| top hats | قبعات رسمية |
| top management | الإدارة العليا |
| top resistivity | المقاومية عند القمة |
| top sheet | رقاقة علوية |
| top up with | يغذي إلى أقصى حد؛ يزود إلى أقصى حد؛ يرفع إلى أقصى حد |
| topcoats | معاطف خفيفة |
| topical use | استخدام موضعي |
| topically-applied | يتم إعطاؤه |
| top-knots [pompoms] | حلي للرأس [حزم من الخيوط كحلي للقبعات] |
| topoisomerase | توبوأيزومراز |
| topological information | معلومات طوبولوجية |
| topology | طوبولوجيا |
| tops (spinning -) [toys] | أدوات أسطوانية أو مخروطية ذات طرف مكسو بالصلب (حلزونية) [لُعب] |
| top-secret invention | اختراع شديد السرية |
| top-tier turn-around artists | كبار فناني التحولات المبدِعين |
| top-up | رفع قيمة؛ تزويد إلى أقصى حد |
| top-up distribution server | خادم توزيع شحن |
| torch | مِشْعَلٌ |
| torches (pocket -), electric | بطاريات إضاءة صغيرة كهربية (للجيب) |
| torches for lighting | مشاعل للإضاءة |
| toroid | ملف حلَقي |
| toroidal | حلَقي |
| torpedo boat | زورق طوربيدو |

| | |
|---|---|
| torque | عزم الدوران |
| torque converters | محولات عزم الدوران |
| torque converters for land vehicles | محولات عزم الدوران للمركبات الأرضية |
| torr | تور (مقياس الضغط الفراغي للبخار ) |
| torsades de pointes | إلتواء النقط في مخطط كهرباء القلب: هي أحد أنواع عدم انتظام ضربات القلب تظهر في المخطط كموجات منتظمة متلوية حول خط الصفر |
| torsion bar | قضيب التوائي |
| torsion bars for vehicles | قضبان ليّ للمركبات |
| torsion spring | نابض التوائي |
| torsional | التوائي |
| tort | أذى؛ ضرر |
| tortillas | كعك مسطح مدور من دقيق الذرة |
| tortoiseshell | صدفة (عظم ظهر) السلحفاة |
| tortoiseshell imitation | تقليد صدفة (عظم ظهر) السلحفاة |
| toshiba companion diskette | قرص توشيبا للطوارئ ( قرص Toshiba المرفق) |
| tosyl chloride | كلوريد توسيل |
| total c5 and c7 asphaltene content | إجمالي محتوى الأسفلتين C5 وC7 (وأيضا محتوى الأسفلتين C5 وC7 الكلي) |
| total commingled production of a cluster of wells | إجمالي الإنتاج الممتزج لمجموعة من الآبار |
| total exclusivity | حصرية كاملة |
| total past-due support amount | إجمالي مستحقات الإعالة المتأخرة |
| total, limited, cold, civil, verbal war | حرب شاملة، محدودة، باردة، أهلية، كلامية |
| totality | إجمالي |
| totality test | اختبار الكلية. اختبار لاستطلاع التشابه الجوهري بين عملين فكريين، وذلك من خلال إعمال معيار المراقب الصورة الكلية للعمل |
| totalizators | ماكينات تسجيل مبالغ الرهان المشترك |
| totals formulas | معادلات التجميع |
| tote bags | حقائب يد كبيرة للتسوق |
| touch pad | لوحة تعمل باللمس |
| touch screen keyboard | لوحة مفاتيح بتقنية اللمس |
| touchscreen | يلمس الشاشة، لمس الشاشة |
| touchscreen technology | تقنية لمس الشاشة |
| touchscreenable | قابلية الشيء أن يدار بلمس الشاشة |
| touch-tone calling | طلب بالطنين |
| toupees | خصلات من الشعر المستعار |
| tourist | سائح |
| tourmaline | التورمالين |
| tow | نسالة الكتان |
| towel dispensers, fixed, not of metal | موزعات المناشف، مثبتة وليست من المعدن |
| towel dispensers, fixed, of metal | موزعات المناشف، مثبتة ومن المعدن |
| towel holders of precious metal | حوامل للمناشف من معدن نفيس |
| towels (sanitary -) | فوط (فوط صحية) |
| towels of paper | مناشف ورقية |
| towels of textile | مناشف من النسيج |
| tower structure | هيكل البرج |
| town gas | غاز الاستصباح |
| townhouse | بيوت متصلة |
| townhouses | بيوت من نوع أو على شكل تانون-هاوس |
| toxic | سام |
| toxic gas neutralizers | مواد لإبطال فعل الغازات السامة |
| toxic gas sensor | جهاز إحساس بالغازات السامة |
| toxic shock syndrome | متلازمة الصدمة الناتجة عن التسمم |
| toxic to wildlife | سام للحياة البرية |
| toxin | توكسين |
| toxoplasmosis | داء المقوسات |
| toy inventor | مخترع ألعاب |
| toy masks | أقنعة للعب |
| toy pistols | مسدسات للعب |
| toy vehicles | عربات للعب |
| toys | دمى |
| toys for domestic pets | دمى للحيوانات الأليفة المنزلية |
| tr | إرسال - استقبال |
| trace amount | كمية ضئيلة |
| trace element | عناصر شحيحة |
| trace elements (preparations of -) for human and animal use | عناصر نادرة (مستحضرات من العناصر النادرة) |
| trace elements (preparations of -) for plants | عناصر نادرة (مستحضرات من العناصر النادرة) للنباتات |
| traced cloths for embroidery | أقمشة مشجرة للتطريز |
| tracer | عامل تتبع |
| traces | مسارات؛ تتبعات |
| traces [harness] | السيور التي تجر بها الحيوانات العربات [أطقم الحيوانات] |
| trachea | القصبة الهوائية |
| tracheotomy | ثقب أو فتح القصبة الهوائية |
| tracing | اقتفاء أو تقصي |
| tracing bulletys | طلقات كاشفة |
| tracing cloth | قماش الاستشفاف [الشف] |
| tracing needles for drawing purposes | إبر الاستشفاف لأغراض الرسم |
| tracing paper | ورق الاستشفاف |
| tracing patterns | نماذج الاستشفاف |
| track | جنزير؛ يتعقب |
| track record | سجل انجازاتنا |
| trackability | قابلية الشيء للتعقب |
| trackball | كرة تعقب |
| tracker | متعقب |
| tracking | تعقب |
| tracking device | جهاز تعقب |
| tracking system | نظام تتبع |
| traction | سحب |
| traction apparatus | جهاز سحب |
| traction engines | قاطرات جر |
| tractors | جرارات |
| trade secret license agreement | اتفاق بشأن ترخيص سر تجاري. اتفاق ينظم قيام طرف بمنح |

| | |
|---|---|
| | طرف آخر الحق في استعمال سر تجاري بشروط معينة ولمدة معينة |
| tradebook ; trade book | كتاب مطبوع؛ كتاب تجاري؛ كتاب للقراءة |
| trademark and patent agent | وكيل براءات وعلامات تجارية |
| trademark know-how | دراية الكيفية في مجال العلامات |
| trademarks and patents registration services | خدمات تسجيل العلامات التجارية والبراءات |
| trading partner | الأطراف الشركاء |
| traditional knowledge | معرفة تقليدية. مجمل العلوم والمعارف والابتكارات والممارسات الخاصة بالمجتمعات التقليدية والأصيلة والمحلية التي تراكمت عبر العصور وتناقلتها الأجيال على نحو تلقائي وتجلت في شكل عادات وأعراف وممارسات وطقوس وطرائق وممارسات ذات طابع مادي و/أو معنوي. ونظراً لكون المعرفة التقليدية تعد ممتلكا فكرياً ذا قيمة كبرى لأصحابها وقيمة نوعية للإنسانية، وفي ضوء ما تعرضت له خلال القرون الماضية من تعديات واستيلاء غير شرعي وانتهاك، فقد قامت المنظمة العالمية للملكية الفكرية وحدها، وبالتعاون مع منظمات دولية أخرى وهيئات ومؤسسات ثقافية، بالسعي لحماية حقوق الملكية الفكرية المنبثقة عن تلك المعارف التقليدية. |
| traditional knowledge related to genetic resources | معرفة تقليدية متصلة بالموارد الجينية. مجمل الخبرات والطرائق المتوارثة من جيل إلى جيل في مجتمع تقليدي يعيش في اتصال وثيق بالطبيعة بما في ذلك المجتمعات البدائية والريفية التي تتسم بتمتعها بنظام إدارة ذاتية فيما يتصل بموارد الجينات والتأثير في سلالاتها. |
| traditional techniques | أساليب تقنية تقليدية. هي تحديثات وتغييرات وإدخالات تكنولوجية حديثة لما هو تقليدي من أعمال وأمور، فنية كانت أو صناعية، لتتناسب والعصر الذي تطبق فيه. |
| traffic | حركة إرسال واستقبال الرسائل (كمبيوتر) |
| traffic accidents (reflecting discs, for wear, for the prevention of -) | حوادث المرور (أقراص عاكسة للارتداء لمنع حوادث المرور) |
| traffic builder | منشط للحركة؛ مروّج للموقع أو للمحل؛ وسيلة اجتذاب الزوار أو الزبائن أو العملاء |
| traffic department | قسم الحركة؛ قسم حركة الإعلانات |
| traffic generation software | برنامج لتوليد حركة سير. برنامج يستخدم لزيادة توجه مستخدمي الشبكة البينية نحو موقع شبكي معين |

| | |
|---|---|
| tragacanth gum for use in manufactures | صمغ الكثيراء للاستخدام في الصناعة |
| trailer hitches for vehicles | وصلات ربط المقطورات للاستخدام في المركبات |
| trailers [vehicles] | مقطورات [مركبات] |
| trailing edge | حافة خلفية |
| trailing edge | الطرف الخلفي |
| train | سلسلة؛ يدرب؛ يسحب |
| trainee patent attorney | وكيل براءات متدرب |
| trait ; traits | صفة؛ صفات |
| trajectory | مسار |
| tramcars | عربات الترام |
| tranche | فئة سندات |
| tran-esterification | إسترة عبرية |
| tranquilizers | مهدئات |
| tranquillizers | عقاقير مهدئة للأعصاب |
| trans - isomers | أيزومرات ترانس- |
| trans- configuration | الصورة ترانس |
| trans enantiomer a | متشاكل ترانس A |
| trans reaction | تفاعل انتقالي؛ تفاعل تحويلي؛ إلخ |
| trans time | زمن الانتقال |
| trans:cis isomers | أيزومرات سيس:ترانس |
| transaction | معاملات (كمبيوتر) |
| transaction processing system | نظام معالجة التعاملات. نظم لمعالجة التعاملات الاعتيادية والروتينية مثل إرسال إشعارات السداد للمستهلكين، وسداد الرواتب الأسبوعية والشهرية والضرائب |
| transalkylation | ألكلة متبادلة |
| transceiver | مُرْسِلٌ-مُسْتَقْبِل؛ وحدة إرسال-استقبال |
| transcript | نسخة طبق الأصل؛ صورة؛ نسخ |
| transcription | استنساخ |
| transcutaneous | الحقن تحت الجلد |
| transdermal (including electrotransport) patches | والضمادات (بما في ذلك النقل الكهربي) عبر الجلد |
| transdermal patches | ضمادة عبر الجلد |
| transdermal platforms | صور التوصيل عبر الجلد |
| transducer | محول (طاقة) {بترول وصناعة}؛ ناقل المحددات الوراثية (مثل ناقل إشارة بين الجزيئات، إلخ) |
| transduction | نقل؛ تحول |
| transesterification | تحويل إستر إلى آخر؛ أسترة تحويلية |
| transesterification | أسترة إنتقالية |
| transesterify | تمت أسترتها بطريقة تبادلية |
| transfected | تم نقل العدوى إليها |
| transfer | يحول، ينقل، تحويل، نقل |
| transfer agreement | اتفاق تحويل |
| transfer pump | مضخة نقل |
| transferability | القابلية للتحويل، القابلية للنقل |
| transferable | قابل للتحويل، قابل للنقل |
| transferable patent | براءة قابلة للتحويل |
| transferee | المحول إليه، المنقول إليه |
| transferor | المحول، الناقل |
| transfers (decorative -) for cosmetic purposes | رسوم منقولة من سطح إلى آخر بالاحتكاك (رسوم زخرفية) |

| | |
|---|---|
| | لأغراض التجميل |
| transfers [decalcomanias] | رسوم منقولة من سطح إلى آخر بالاحتكاك [صور منقولة من ورق معد لذلك إلى الزجاج أو الخشب .. الخ] |
| transform | يحول |
| transformability | قابلية الشيء للتحول |
| transformable | قابل للتحول |
| transformants ; transformed cells | الخلايا المتحولة |
| transformer | محول |
| transformers (insulating oil for -) | محولات (زيوت عازلة للمحولات) |
| transformers [electricity] | محولات [كهرباء] |
| transfusion | نقل الدم |
| transgenic | متحور وراثيًا |
| transgenic methods (e.g. by transformation) | طرق التحوير الوراثي (مثل التحويل الوراثي) |
| transient | انتقالي |
| transient electro magnetic soundings | أنظمة سبر عمق كهرومغناطيسية عابرة |
| transient expression | التعبير الوراثي العابر (عكس التعبير الوراثي الثابت stable) |
| transistor | مقحل، ترانزيستور |
| transistors [electronic] | ترانزيستور [إلكتروني] |
| transit advertising | إعلانات سيارة؛ دعايات جوالة |
| transition metal | فلز انتقالي أو تحولي |
| transition metal cations and transition metal complex cations and anions, transition metal oxy anions | كاتيونات فلز انتقالي وكاتيونات وأنيونات معقد فلز انتقالي، وأوكسي أنيونات فلز انتقالي |
| transition phrase ; transition term ; transitional term ; transitional phrase | مصطلح متعدي؛ مصطلح انتقالي |
| transitional cell | خلية متدرجة |
| translation | ترجمة وراثية؛ ترجمة |
| translator | مترجم |
| translocation | إزاحة؛ انتقال الموضع |
| translucent glass | زجاج نصف شفاف: الزجاج الذي يسمح بنفاذية الضوء بدرجات مختلفة من الانتشار مما يجعل الرؤية غير واضحة |
| transmission | إرسال؛ نقل |
| transmission chains for land vehicles | سلاسل نقل الحركة للمركبات الأرضية |
| transmission chains other than for land vehicles | سلاسل نقل الحركة لغير المركبات الأرضية |
| transmission electron microscopes (tem) | الميكروسكوب الإلكتروني النافذ |
| transmission fluid | مائع نقل الحركة |
| transmission frequency | تردد النقل/الإرسال: التردد الحامل لأى معلومه سـواء كانت صوتيه أو معلوماتيه (داتا) أو تليفزيونيه إلخ |
| transmission means | وسيلة نقل |
| transmission shafts (bearings for) | أعمدة تشغيل ناقل الحركة (أجزاء حاملة لأعمدة تشغيل ناقل الحركة) |
| transmission shafts for land vehicles | أعمدة تشغيل ناقل الحركة للمركبات الأرضية |
| transmissions | عمليات إرسال؛ عمليات نقل |
| transmissions for land vehicles | آليات نقل الحركة للمركبات الأرضية |
| transmissions for machines | آليات نقل الحركة للماكينات |
| transmit power on control channel | قدرة الإرسال على قناة تحكم |
| transmit telemetry | يرسل عن بعد |
| transmittability | قابلية الشيء للنقل |
| transmittal | نقل |
| transmitter | مرسل (ج: مرسلات)؛ جهاز إرسال (ج: أجهزة إرسال)؛ ناقل: مثل مرسل/ناقل عصبي neurotransmitter |
| transmitters of electronic signals | أجهزة إرسال للإشارات الإلكترونية |
| transmitting sets [telecommunication] | أجهزة إرسال [للاتصالات عن بُعد] |
| transmucosal | عن طريق الغشاء المخاطي |
| transonic speed | سرعة حول صوتية |
| transparencies [photography] | شرائح مصورة شفافة |
| transparencies [stationery] | شرائح مصورة شفافة [قرطاسية] |
| transparency projection apparatus | جهاز لعرض الشرائح المصورة الشفافة |
| transparent glass | زجاج شفاف: الزجاج الذي يسمح بنفاذية الضوء بالكامل ويمكن من الرؤية الواضحة من خلاله |
| transplants | عضو أو نسيج مزروع (طعم، غريسة) |
| transponding device | جهاز تلقٍّ |
| transport apparatus and installations (cable -) | أجهزة وتركيبات للنقل (أجهزة وتركيبات للنقل ذات كبلات) |
| transport pallets of metal | منصات نقالة من المعدن |
| transport pallets, not of metal | منصات نقالة ليست من المعدن |
| transporter | طائرة نقل |
| transporters | ناقلات |
| transporters (pneumatic -) | ناقلات (ناقلات تعمل بالهواء المضغوط) |
| transposon | عنصر ناقل |
| transurethral | عن طريق قناة مجرى البول |
| transversally | عرضيا؛ مستعرضا |
| transverse | مستعرض؛ عرضي |
| transverse shear waves | الموجات القصية المستعرضة |
| trap | جزء احتجاز |
| trapezohedron | مسطح المعين المنحرف |
| trapezoidal summation of the plasma concentration-time profile | التراكم شبه المنحرف لمنحنى التركيز - الزمن في البلازما |
| traps | مصائد |
| traps (clay pigeon -) | أداة لإطلاق أطباق الرماية في الهواء (للحمامة الطينية) [والحمامة الطينية هي قرص فخاري يقذف في الهواء ليتخذ هدفاً للرماة] |
| traps (insect -) | شراك (شراك للحشرات) |

| | |
|---|---|
| traps (rat -) | مصيدة (مصيدة للفئران) |
| traps (steam -) | مانع تسرب (مانع تسرب البخار) |
| traps for wild animals | شراك للحيوانات البرية |
| traps of plastic (drain -) [valves] | مصيدة من البلاستيك (مصيدة من البلاستيك لهواء المجارى) [صمامات] |
| trash cans | صفائح معدنية للنفايات |
| trash compacting machines | ماكينات لضغط النفايات |
| trash seals | موانع تسريب نفايات |
| trastuzumab | الجسم المضاد تراست زوماب المضاد لـ erB2 |
| trauma | رضوض |
| traumatic arthritis | التهاب المفاصل الناتج عن الإصابات |
| travel | ينتقل، يسافر، انتقال، سفر؛ يتحرك |
| travel assistance package | برنامج للمساعدة في شئون السفر |
| traveler | مسافر، منتقل |
| traveling block | وحدة متحركة |
| traveling valve | صمام متنقل |
| travelling | تحرك |
| travelling bags | حقائب السفر |
| travelling rugs [lap robes] | أغطية السفر: أغطية مثل البطاطين للأرجل والأقدام للمسافرين |
| travelling sets [leatherware] | أطقم السفر [مصنوعات جلدية] |
| travelling trunks | صناديق الثياب للسفر |
| travelling wave reactor | مفاعل بالموجات المتنقلة |
| travelling waves | موجات منتقلة |
| traversability | القابلية للتحرك جيئة وذهابا |
| traverse | يتحرك جيئة وذهابا، يجتاز، يعبر، يتحرك على محور، التحرك جيئة وذهابا، اجتياز، عبور |
| traverse (across) | يمتد بصورة مستعرضة (عبر) |
| traverse notch impact toughness | متانة صدم ثلمة مستعرضة |
| traverse robot | روبوت قادر على التحرك جيئة وذهابا |
| travertine | رواسب الينابيع الحارة |
| tray | صينية |
| tray drier | حوض تجفيف مسطح |
| tray tower | برج يحتوي على صينية |
| trays (litter -) [for pets] | صواني (صواني من القش) [للحيوانات الأليفة لترقد عليها] |
| trays for domestic purposes, of paper | صواني للأغراض المنزلية من الورق |
| trays for sorting and counting money | صواني لتصنيف وعد النقود |
| trays of precious metal, for household purposes | صواني من معدن نفيس للأغراض المنزلية |
| tray-type container | حاوية على شكل صينية |
| tread of the step | الجزء الأفقي العلوي من درجة السلم |
| treads for retreading tires [tyres] | الأسطح المحيطة بالإطارات لتلبيس الإطارات بالمطاط |
| treads for vehicles [roller belts] | دواسات للمركبات [سيور دوارة] |
| treads for vehicles [tractor type] | دواسات للمركبات [من نوع الجرارات] |
| treatable material | مادة قابلة للمعالجة |
| treatment | معالجة؛ علاج |
| tree cavity fillers [forestry] | حشو لتجاويف الأشجار [غابات] |
| tree protectors of metal | واقيات للأشجار من المعدن |
| tree pruners | مقصات لتشذيب الأشجار |
| tree-banding (glutinous preparations for -) | تطويق الأشجار (مستحضرات غروية لتطويق الأشجار) |
| trees (trunks of -) | أشجار (جذوع الأشجار) |
| trehalose | تريهالوز |
| trellis | عريشة تشابكية |
| trellis of metal | تعريشة من المعدن |
| trellises, not of metal | تعريشات ليست من المعدن |
| tremor | رعشة |
| trenches | خنادق |
| trends | توجهات، نزعات |
| tresses of hair | ضفائر الشعر |
| trestles [furniture] | مساند [أثاث] |
| tri -band | الهواتف ثلاثية الموجات: يمكن أن تعمل على حيزات التردد الثلاثية للهاتف الجوال: ترددات GSM1800 & GSM900 المستخدمة في أكثر من 150 بلدا في العالم، إضافة إلى الحيز الترددي Gsm1900 الذي يتم تطبيقه بشكل متزايد في الولايات المتحدة الأمريكية، وكندا وبعض أجزاء أمريكيا |
| triabodies | أجسام مضادة ثلاثية التكافؤ |
| trial by jury | المحاكمة بنظام المحلفين |
| trial dock | قفص الاتهام |
| trialkyl silanethiol | تراي ألكيل سيلان ثيول |
| trialkyltin | قصدير ثلاثي الألكيل |
| triamerisation | بلمرة ثلاثية |
| triangles [musical instruments] | مثلثات [أدوات موسيقية] |
| triarchic theory | نظرية الذكاء الثلاثية |
| triaxial test | اختبار ثلاثي المحاور |
| triazol | تريازول |
| tribal war | حرب قبلية |
| triboelectrically | كهربي بالحك |
| tribunal | محكمة عسكري |
| trichuriasis | داء شعيرات الذيل |
| tricks and special effects | الخدع والمؤثرات الخاصة |
| triclinic | ثلاثي الميَلان |
| tricycles (carrier -) | دراجات ثلاثية (للنقل) |
| tri-cyclic amines (tca) | الأمينات ثلاثية الحلقات |
| triethanolamine oleate | أوليات تراي إيثانول أمين |
| triflate | تريفلات |
| trifluoroaceticacid anhydride | أنهيدريد حمض تراي فلورو أسيتيك |
| triflyl- or nonaflyl group | مجموعة تريفليل- أو نونافليل |
| trigeminal neuralgia | ألم العصب ثلاثي التوائم |
| trigger | الزناد |
| trigger guards for guns and rifles | واقيات الزناد للمسدسات والبنادق |
| triggering | بدء؛ إحداث |
| triggering element | عنصر تشغيل |

| | |
|---|---|
| triggers | الأوامر |
| trihydrate | هيدرات ثلاثية |
| tri-iso-propyl silanethiol | تراي-إسو-بروبيل سيلان ثيول |
| trilobe | شكل ثلاثي الفصوص |
| trim | تلبيس؛ موازن (صمامات) |
| trimer | ترايمر: وحدة بنائية ثلاثية |
| trimers | ترميرات |
| trimming machines | ماكينات تهذيب بالقطع |
| trimmings for clothing | بطانة للملابس |
| trimmings of leather for furniture | قصاصات من الجلد للأثاث |
| trimodality | طريقة؛ وسيلة العلاج |
| trinkets [jewellery, jewelry (am.)] | حلى صغيرة [مجوهرات] |
| trinometric | ثلاثي الحدود |
| triol | ترايول |
| trip device | جهاز فصل |
| tripe | كروش الحيوانات المجترة |
| tripeptide | ثلاثي الببتيدات |
| triple doublet | ثنائيات ثلاثية |
| tripod socket | فتحة الحامل ثلاثي القوائم |
| tripods for cameras | حوامل ثلاثية القوائم للكاميرات |
| tripoli stone for polishing | حجر طرابلسي للصقل |
| tripping auxiliary | ملحق فصل |
| tripping means | وسيلة فصل |
| tris | تريس (هيدروكسي منثيل) أمينو ميثان |
| tris(dibenzylideneacetone)dipalladium | تريس(داي بنزيليدين أسيتون)داي بالاديوم |
| tri-substituted | بها استبدال ثلاثي |
| tritiate | يعاير |
| triturate | يسحن |
| trivets [table utensils] | حوامل ثلاثية القوائم [أدوات المائدة] |
| trivial name | الاسم الشائع: في التسمية الكيميائية؛ عندما لايتوافق مع التركيب |
| trnsfer of technology | نقل التكنولوجيا |
| trocar | جهاز بزل |
| troches | قرصات |
| trojan ; trojan horse | حصان طروادة: هذا النوع من الفيروسات يكون مرفقا مع أحد البرامج أي يكون جزء من برنامج ما. فعندما يبدأ البرنامج تنفيذ عمله ويصل الى مرحلة ما الفيروس يبدأ العمل والتخريب وقد لا يكون هدف الفيروس التخريب هنا قد يكون هدفه ربحي |
| troll tracking blog | تعبير يطلق على المدونة المتخصصة في تعقب صاحب الحق في براءةٍ الذي يُنْفذ البراءة لكي يستهدف ـ على نحو استغلالي ـ منتهك مزعوم وليس لاستخدامها استخداما اعتياديا ويسعى إلى كشفه على الملأ |
| trolleys for computers [furniture] | حوامل متحركة لأجهزة الكمبيوتر [أثاث] |
| trombones | متردات [آلات موسيقية] |
| troop | فصيلة/قوة (فصائل/قوات) (مدفعية أو مدرعات) |
| troop carrier | ناقة جنود |
| tropical spastic paraparesis | الشلل الجزئي التشنجي المداري |
| tropo | تشتت الموجة اللاسلكية في طبقة التروبوسفير |
| trouble ticket | تذكرة دعم فني |
| troubleshoot | يزيل الخلل |
| troubleshooting | إزالة الخلل |
| troughs for livestock | أوعية العلف للدواجن أو الماشية |
| troughs of metal for mixing mortar | أوعية من المعدن لخلط الملاط |
| troughs, not of metal, for mixing mortar | أوعية ليست من المعدن لخلط ملاط |
| trouser clips for cyclists | مشابك السراويل لراكبي الدراجات |
| trouser presses | مكابس (مكاوي) السراويل |
| trouser straps | شرائط السراويل |
| trouser stretchers | أدوات فرد السراويل |
| trousers | سراويل |
| trowel | مالج؛ مسطرين: لتوزيع الأسمنت وخلافه |
| trowels [gardening] | أدوات لرفع النباتات الصغيرة [بساتين] |
| truck lifts | رافعات سيارات الشحن |
| trucks (luggage -) | سيارات شحن (سيارات شحن للأمتعة) |
| true creativity | ابتكارية حقيقية |
| trueing machines | ماكينات تسوية |
| truffles, fresh | ثمار درنية طازجة |
| truffles, preserved | ثمار درنية محفوظة |
| trumpets | أبواق |
| truncated trucks | شاحنات مبتورة |
| truncheons | عُصي |
| trunk of the motor vehicle | صندوق السيارة |
| trunks (bathing -) | سراويل قصيرة [شورت] للرجال (للسباحة) |
| trunks [luggage] | صناديق للثياب [أمتعة] |
| trunks of trees | جذوع الأشجار |
| trunnions for heavy weapons | مرتكزات الدوران للأسلحة الثقيلة |
| truss | جملون |
| truss tomatoes | طماطم عنقودية |
| trusses | أحزمة الفتق |
| trussing apparatus for hay | جهاز لحزم القش |
| trust | شركة ائتمان |
| trust company | شركة ودائع؛ مصرف ودائع؛ مصرف ائتمان؛ مصرف أمانات |
| trusted network detection | اكتشاف شبكة موثوق فيها |
| trusteeship council (tc) | مجلس الوصاية |
| trypanosomiasis | داء المثقبيات |
| tscl | كلوريد توسيل |
| t-squares (drawing -) | مساطر على شكل حرف T (للرسم) |
| tubbing of metal | بطانة بأطواق معدنية |
| tube | أنبوب، إطار داخلي، قناة |
| tube conveyors, pneumatic | ناقلات للأنابيب تعمل بضغط الهواء |
| tube cutters [hand tools] | أدوات قطع الأنابيب [أدوات يدوية] |
| tube cutting instruments | آلات قطع الأنابيب |

| | |
|---|---|
| tube packs | مجموعات أنابيب |
| tube sealed at its lower end with end cap | أنبوب مغلق بإحكام عند طرفه السفلي بواسطة غطاء طرفي |
| tube sheet | لوح الأنبوب السفلي |
| tube-bundle reactors | مفاعلات مزودة بمجموعة أنابيب |
| tubeless tires [tyres] for bicycles, cycles | إطارات بدون إطارات داخلية مختزنة بالهواء للدراجات والدراجات البخارية |
| tuberculosis | السل |
| tubes | أنابيب |
| tubes (boiler -) [parts of machines] | أنابيب (أنابيب للغلاية) [أجزاء من الماكينات] |
| tubes (cardboard -) | أنابيب (أنابيب من الورق المقوى) |
| tubes (discharge -), electric, for lighting | أنابيب (أنابيب تفريغ) كهربية للإضاءة |
| tubes (drainage -) | أنابيب (أنابيب تصريف) |
| tubes (electric discharge -), other than for lighting | أنابيب (أنابيب تفريغ كهربية) بخلاف تلك الخاصة بالإضاءة |
| tubes (flexible -), not of metal | أنابيب (أنابيب مرنة) ليست من المعدن |
| tubes (luminous -) for lighting | أنابيب (أنابيب مضيئة) للإضاءة |
| tubes of metal | أنابيب من المعدن |
| tubing | مجموعة أنابيب |
| tubing head | رأس الأنابيب |
| tubing head pressure (thp) | ضغط الأنابيب العلوية |
| tubular | أنبوبيات |
| tubular anchor seal assemblies | تجميعات منع تسرب أنبوبية مثبتة |
| tubular joint | وصلة أنبوبية |
| tufa | توفة [حجر مسامي] |
| tulle | تول [حرير رقيق] |
| tuna fish | سمك التونة |
| tundish | مسكبة |
| tungsten | تنجيتسن |
| tungsten iron | حديد التنجستين |
| tungstic acid | حمض تنجستينى |
| tuning forks | شوكة رنانة |
| tuning hammers | مطارق رنانة |
| tunnel pasteurization | البسترة النفقية |
| tuple | مجموعة قيم |
| tuple spaces | مسافات مجموعة القيم |
| turbans | عمامة |
| turbid solution | محلول غير رائق |
| turbine blades | شفرات التوربين |
| turbine engine | محرك توربيني |
| turbines (hydraulic -) | توربينات (توربينات هيدروليكية) |
| turbines for land vehicles | توربينات للمركبات الأرضية |
| turbines other than for land vehicles | توربينات بخلاف تلك الخاصة بالمركبات الأرضية |
| turbo expander turbine / turbo expander | توربين وسيلة تمديد |
| turbocompressors | ضاغط توربيني |
| turbofan engine | محرك عنفي مروحي |
| turbojet engine | محرك عنفي نفاث |
| turboprop engine | محرك عنفي ذو داسر |
| turbulent flow | تدفق مضطرب |
| turf (artificial -) | مروج (مروج صناعية) |
| turf removing ploughs | محاريث لإزالة المروج |
| turf, natural | مروج (مروج طبيعية) |
| turkish bath cabinets, portable | حجرات خصوصية صغيرة للحمام التركي، متنقلة |
| turmeric [colorant] | كركم [مادة ملوِّنة] |
| turmeric for food | كركم للطعام |
| turn rate equation | معادلة تغير السمت |
| turn ratio | نسبة اللف |
| turn signals for vehicles | إشارات الانعطاف للمركبات |
| turn the mode dial to movie mode. | قم بتدوير قرص تحديد الوضع على وضع الأفلام |
| turn-around tales | قصص التحولات |
| turnaround time | الزمن المستغرق (في المعالجة)؛ زمن المعالجة |
| turning apparatus for sheet music | جهاز تصفح النوتة الموسيقية |
| turning mirrors | مرايا دوّارة |
| turnip cutters [machines] | أدوات قطع اللفت [آلات] |
| turnover | انقلاب |
| turns in the antenna | اللفات في الهوائي |
| turnstiles, automatic | بوابات دوارة رباعية الأطر، أوتوماتيكية |
| turnstiles, non-automatic | بوابات دوارة رباعية الأطر غير أتوماتيكية |
| turntables [railways] | مناضد دوارة [سكك حديدية] |
| turpentine [thinner for paints] | تربنتين [مرققات لقوام الدهانات] |
| turpentine for pharmaceutical purposes | تربنتين للأغراض الصيدلانية |
| turpentine, for degreasing | تربنتين لإزالة الشحم |
| turret | برج الدبابة |
| tv | تلفزيون |
| tv piracy | قرصنة التلفزة |
| tweak | يعدل: يغير في المكونات والخصائص الأساسية |
| tweaking | تعديل؛ عبث |
| tweezers | ملقاط صغير: من أجل تثبيت بعض العناصر الإلكترونية الدقيقة. |
| twine for nets | خيوط مجدولة للشباك |
| twine made of paper | خيوط مجدولة من الورق |
| twinkie defense | حُجّة توينكي - نسبة إلى توينكي وهي وجبات غنية بالسكريات |
| twirling batons | عُصىّ القذف |
| two 155 amino acid chains | سلسلتين حمض أميني 155 |
| two bird densities | كثافتين مختلفتين للطيور |
| two-cylinder non-opposed petrol engine | محرك بترولي ذو سلندرين غير متعارضين |
| two-loop reactor | مفاعل ثنائي الحلقات |
| two-necked flask | دورق مزدوج العنق |
| two-phase flow | تدفق له طورين |
| two-unit dental bridge | جسر أسنان بين وحدتين |
| two-way radios | جهاز إرسال واستقبال لاسلكي |
| two-wheeled trolleys | عربات ترولي ذات عجلتين |
| two-wheeled vehicle | مركبة ذات عجلتين |

| | |
|---|---|
| tympans [parts of printing presses] | غشاء لجعل الضغط متساويا في المطبعة اليدوية [أجزاء من الآلات الطابعة] |
| type [numerals and letters] | حروف مطبعية [أرقام وحروف] |
| type i diabetes | الداء السكري النوع 1 |
| type ii diabetes mellitus | داء البول السكري من النوع 2 |
| typecasting machines | ماكينات سبك وصب حروف الطباعة |
| type setting machines [photocomposition] | ماكينات تنضيد الحروف المطبعية [ماكينات جمع تصويري] |
| type-setting machines [printing] | ماكينات تنضيد الحروف المطبعية [طباعة] |
| typewriter keys | مفاتيح الآلات الكاتبة |
| typewriter ribbons | شرائط الآلات الكاتبة |
| typewriters [electric or non-electric] | آلات كاتبة [كهربائية أو غير كهربائية] |
| typical alkylation procedures | إجراءات الألكلة النمطية |
| typical ester exchange catalysts | محفزات تبادل الإستر النمطية |
| typical trellis coding scheme | مخطط تشفير نمطي على شكل عريشه تشابكية |
| typically | بصورة نمطية |
| typing desks | مكاتب لاستعمال الآلات الكاتبة |
| typographic machines | ماكينات مطبعية |
| typographic presses | مكابس طباعة |
| tyre repairing compositions | تركيبات لإصلاح الإطارات |
| tyres (automatic indicators of low pressure in vehicle -) | إطارات (مؤشرات أتوماتيكية لبيان انخفاض الضغط في إطارات المركبات) |
| tyres (flanges of railway wheel -) | إطارات (حواف ناتئة لإطارات عجلات السكك الحديدية) |
| tyres (mastic for -) | إطارات (صمغ مصطكا للإطارات) |
| tyres (non-skid devices for vehicle -) | إطارات (وسائل لمنع انزلاق إطارات المركبات) |
| tyres (rubber material for recapping -) | إطارات (مواد مطاطية لإعادة تلبيس الإطارات) |
| tyres for bicycles, cycles | إطارات للدراجات والدراجات الثلاثية |
| tyres for vehicle wheels | إطارات لعجلات المركبات |
| tyres, solid, for vehicle wheels | إطارات صلبة لعجلات المركبات |
| tyrosine kinase | كيناز التيروسين |
| tyrosine phosphatase | فوسفاتاز التيروزين |
| tyrosine residues | وحدات التيروسين البنائية |

# U

| | |
|---|---|
| ulcer | قرحة |
| ulceration | تقرح |
| ulcerative colitis | التهاب القولون التقرحي |
| ulcerogenic | مقرح |
| ulcus duodeni | قرحة الاثنا عشر |
| ulcus ventriculi / ventriculus | قرحة المعدة |
| ulnar neuropathy | الاعتلال العصبي الزندي |
| ultra - low dose | جرعة فائقة الانخفاض |
| ultra dense memory chip | شريحة ذاكرة ذات كثافة عالية |
| ultra high molecular weight polyethylene | البولي إثيلين ذي وزن جزيئي مرتفع جدا |
| ultra low consistency alpha- and beta-blend stucco | خليط ألفا وبيتا من جبس بتماسك فائق الانخفاض |
| ultrafiltration | وحدة ترشيح فائق |
| ultrasonic bath | حمام بالموجات فوق الصوتية |
| ultrasonic pressure sensor | جهاز إحساس بالضغط فوق صوتي |
| ultrasound identification systems | نظم تعريف الموجات فوق الصوتية |
| ultrasound imaging | تصوير بواسطة الموجات فوق الصوتية أو الموجات فوق السمعية |
| ultraviolet ray lamps | مصابيح بالأشعة فوق البنفسجية |
| ultraviolet rays for medical purposes (filters for -) | الأشعة فوق البنفسجية للأغراض الطبية (مرشحات للأشعة فوق البنفسجية) |
| umami | مذاق حريف |
| umber | بني مصفر |
| umbilical belts | أحزمة سُرية |
| umbrella covers | أغطية المظلات |
| umbrella handles | مقابض المظلات |
| umbrella or parasol ribs | دعامات المظلات أو الشماسي |
| umbrella rings | حلقات المظلات |
| umbrella stands | حوامل المظلات |
| umbrella sticks | عُصي المظلات |
| umbrellas | المظلات |
| umts | نظام الاتصالات المتنقلة العام: نظام اتصالات متنقلة من الجيل الثالث يقدم تطبيقات الصوت والبيانات والوسائط المتعددة. الخلف النهائي للهاتف الجوال. أول شبكة UMTS في المملكة المتحدة، 3، تم إطلاقها في عام 2003 |
| un | الأمم المتحدة |
| un charter | ميثاق الأممم المتحدة |
| un children's fund, unicef | صندوق الأمم المتحدة الدولي لرعاية الطفولة (نيويورك) |
| un committee on the elimination of racial discrimination | لجنة الأمم المتحدة المناهضة للتمييز العنصري |
| un conference on trade and development, unctad | مؤتمر الأمم المتحدة للتجارة والتنمية |
| un decolonisation committee, undc | لجنة تصفية الاستعمار |
| un development programme, undp | برنامج الأمم المتحدة للتنمية (نيويورك) |
| un educationa, scientific and cultural organization, unesco | اليونسكو، منظمة الأمم المتحدة للتعليم والعلوم والثقافة |
| un environment programme, unep | برنامج الأمم المتحدة للبيئة |
| un fund for drug abuse control, unfdac | صندوق الأمم المتحدة لرقابة استخدام العقاقير المخدرة |
| un fund for population activities, unfpa | صندوق الأمم المتحدة للأنشطة السكانية |
| un high commissioner for fefugees, unhcr | المندوب السامي لشئون اللاجئين |
| un industrial development organization, unido | منظمة الأمم المتحدة للتنمية الصناعية |
| un institute of training and research, (unitary) | معهد الأمم المتحدة للتدريب والأبحاث |
| un peacekeeping forces | قوات حفظ السلام التابعة للأمم المتحدة |
| un relief and works agency, unrwa | وكالة الأمم المتحدة للإغاثة والتشغيل |
| un truce supervision organization in palestine, unstop | هيئة مراقبة الهدنة في فلسطين التابعة للأمم المتحدة |
| unalloyed | نقي |
| unary | أحادي: ومثل نظام العد هذا يكون التالي: ثنائي binary، ثلاثي ternary إلخ |
| unauthorized storing of confidential information | تخزين غير مخول للمعلومات السرية |
| unawardable patent | براءة لا يمكن الموافقة عليها |
| unbundling | تفكيك |
| uncertainties | الشكوك |
| uncommercializable invention | اختراع غير قابل أن يوضع في إطار تجاري |
| uncommercializable patent | براءة غير قابلة أن تكون موضعا لتطبيقات تجارية |
| uncommercialized invention | اختراع لم يتم وضعه في إطار تجاري |
| unconditional surrender | استسلام بلا شروط |
| unconsolidated | غير مدمج؛ غير متماسك |
| unconventional invention | اختراع غير معهود |
| uncover | يكشف عن |
| uncovered prior art | فن سابق تم الكشف عنه |
| uncovering | الكشف عن |
| uncovering prior art | الكشف عن الفن السابق |
| uncreatable software | برنامج حاسوبي غير قابل للابتكار |
| undec | يونديك |
| undefendable patent | براءة لا يمكن الدفاع عنها |
| under acidic conditions | في ظل ظروف حمضية |
| under demanding test conditions | في ظروف اختبار قاسية |

| | |
|---|---|
| under down hole conditions | في ظل الظروف السائدة أسفل البئر |
| under fisher-indolization conditions | في ظل ظروف فيشر القياسية لإدخال مجموعة إندول، في ظل ظروف فيشر القياسية لتخليق الإندول |
| under high vacuum | تحت ضغط شديد الانخفاض؛ في وسط عالي التفريغ |
| under licence | بترخيص من |
| under mukaiyama condition | في ظل ظروف Mukaiyama |
| under nitrogen | في جو من النيتروجين |
| under nitrogen flow | تحت تدفق من النيتروجين؛ في جو من النيتروجين |
| under protest | مع الاعتراض |
| under reduced pressure | تحت ضغط منخفض |
| under secretary | وكيل وزارة |
| under the force of gravity ; under gravity force | تحت تأثير الجاذبية |
| under undrained conditions | في ظل ظروف عدم التصريف |
| under use of the intellectual property system | استعمال أقل مما يجب لنظام الملكية الفكرية. عدم الاستخدام الكامل لنظام الملكية الفكرية وما يوفره من ضمانات وحماية |
| under vaccum | تحت ضغط منخفض؛ في وسط مفرغ |
| under-age ; minor ; juvenile | قاصر؛ حدث |
| underbalanced drilling | الحفر تحت مستوى التوازن؛ حفر بطريقة الخلخلة |
| underburden | طبقة ما تحت الهيدروكربون: تكوين تحت الهيدروكربون |
| undercarriages for vehicles | هياكل حمل المركبات: الجزء الذي يرتكز عليه بدن السيارة |
| underclothing | ملابس داخلية |
| underclothing (anti-sweat -) | ملابس داخلية (ملابس داخلية مضادة للعرق) |
| undercoating for vehicle chassis | طليات سفلية لهياكل المركبات |
| underground | جوفي؛ تحت (سطح) الأرض |
| underground (clandestine) organisation | تنظيم سري |
| underground deposits | رواسب جوفية أو تحت الأرض |
| underlined | مميز بوضع خط تحته؛ تحته خط |
| underlying | تحتي؛ أساسي |
| underlying layer | الطبقة التحتية |
| underpants | سراويل تحتية |
| underpayment | دفعة أولى |
| undersampling | استخدام تردد عينة منخفض |
| undersealing for vehicle chassis | وسائل إحكام سفلية لهياكل المركبات |
| undersigned | الموقع أدناه |
| undertaking for collective investment in transferable securities | تعهّد للإستثمارِ الجَماعي في السندات المالية القابلة للتحويلِ |
| under-voltage or shunt releases | وسائل تحرير (مُعتِقات) عند انخفاض الجهد أو موصَّلة على التوازي |
| underwear | ملابس داخلية |
| undisclosable design | تصميم يتوجب عدم الإفصاح عنه |
| undisclosed invention | اختراع غير مفصح عنه |
| undisputed originality | أصالة غير متنازع عليها |
| undressed timber | خشب غير مكسو |
| undue experimentation | تجريب غير ضروري |
| undue experimentation | اختبار في غير محله |
| undue use of indigenous people's creations | استعمال في غير محله للابتكارات الخلاقة الخاصة بالشعوب المحلية |
| unenergized magnets | مغناطيسات غير منشَّطة |
| unenforced patent | براءة غير مُنفذة. |
| unesco report | تقرير اليونسكو |
| unethical patent lobbying | استمالة غير أخلاقية فيما يتصل بسياسات البراءات |
| unethical subject matter | مادة غير أخلاقية |
| unethical use | استعمال غير أخلاقي |
| unexamined patent application | طلب براءة اختراع لم يتم فحصه بعد |
| unexecutable agreement | اتفاق غير قابل للتنفيذ |
| unexecuted agreement | اتفاق غير مبرم، اتفاق غير مُنفذ |
| unexploited patent | براءة غير مستغلة |
| unfeasible technology | تقنية غير مجدية |
| unfinalized | لم يتم إنهاؤه |
| unfolding of protein, etc. | فك طي |
| unfunctionalized | ليس به مجموعة وظيفية |
| ungluing agents [chemical preparations for liquifying starch] | مواد لإزالة التغرية [مستحضرات كيميائية لإسالة النشا] |
| ungluing preparations | مستحضرات لإزالة التغرية |
| ungranted patent application | طلب براءة غير ممنوح |
| uni | واجهة شبكة المستخدم |
| uniaxial | أحادي المحور |
| unicast | خدمة البث الأحادية: خدمة الـ Unicast |
| unidustrializable invention | اختراع غير قابل للتصنيع |
| unidustrializable patent | براءة غير قابلة للتصنيع |
| unified modelling language | لغة النمذجة الموحدة |
| uniform | متجانس؛ منتظم |
| uniform distribution | التوزيع المتجانس |
| uniforms | ملابس موحدة |
| unindustrialized invention | اختراع لم يتم وضعه في إطار صناعي |
| union or joint high school district | مقاطعات المدارس الثانوية الاتحادية أو المشتركة |
| unique inventive concept | مفهوم اختراعي فريد |
| unique sales proposition (usp) | عروض مبيعات فريدة من نوعها |
| unique users | أفراد الزوار |
| unit area | وحدة المساحة |
| unit cell | خلية وحدية |
| unit cell size | حجم خلية الوحدة |
| unit dosage | وحدة جرعة |
| unit dosing, unit doses | وحدة جرعات |
| unit vector | وحدة متجه |
| united nations | الأمم المتحدة |
| united nations emergency force, unef | قوة الطوارئ الدولية للأمم المتحدة |
| united nations industrial | صندوق الأمم المتحدة للتنمية |

| | |
|---|---|
| development fund | الصناعية |
| united nations interim force in lebanon, unifil | قوة الأمم المتحدة المؤقتة في لبنان |
| united nations peacekeeping force in cyprus, unficyp | قوة الأمم المتحدة لحفظ السلام في قبرص |
| united nations special fund (unsf) | الصندوق الخاص للأمم المتحدة |
| united nations university, unu | جامعة الأمم المتحدة |
| unity | وحدة |
| unity of invention | وحدة الاختراع |
| universal framework | إطار عام |
| universal joints [cardan joints] | وصلات عامة الحركة [وصلات "كردان"] |
| universal postal union, upu | الاتحاد العالمي للبريد (برن) |
| university invention | اختراع جامعي |
| university patent policy | سياسة الجامعة بالنسبة للبراءات |
| unjust enrichment | ثراء غير مشروع |
| unknown prior art | تقنية سابقة غير معلوم |
| unknown soldier's memorial | نصب الجندي المجهول |
| unlawful acts | أعمال (عمل) غير قانونية |
| unlawful use of a person's voice | استعمال غير قانوني لصوت شخص يعد شكلا من أشكال انتهاك حق منصب على ممتلك فكري، كما قد يعد في حالات معينة شكلاً من أشكال سرقة الهوية |
| unlawful use of signature | استعمال غير قانوني لتوقيع شخص. يعد شكلا من أشكال انتهاك حق منصب على ممتلك فكري، كما قد يعد في حالات معينة شكلاً من أشكال سرقة الهوية. |
| unleavened bread | خبز غير مخمر |
| unless context requires otherwise | ما لم يقتضي سياق النص معنى آخر |
| unless explicity claimed | ما لم يُطلب حمايته بوضوح |
| unless expressly claimed | ما لم يُذكر/يُطلب ذلك صراحةً في عناصر الحماية |
| unless otherwise indicated | ما لم يُذكر خلاف ذلك؛ ما لم يُنص خلاف ذلك؛ ما لم يشار إلى ذلك |
| unless otherwise stated or clearly contradicted by context | ما لم يُنص خلاف ذلك أو يقتضي سياق النص معنى آخر |
| unlicenced weapon possession | حيازة سلاح بدون ترخيص |
| unlicensed software | برنامج حاسبي غير مرخص |
| unlimited patentability | إمكانية غير محدودة لصدور براءة |
| unlimited reselling (mr) | إمكانية إنشاء مواقع تجارة إلكترونية بدون حدود |
| unloading of the natural gas | تفريغ الغاز الطبيعي |
| unmarketable invention | اختراع غير قابل للتسويق |
| unmaterializable idea | فكرة غير قابلة للتحقق |
| unmodified vehicle | مركبة لم يتم إجراء تعديل فيها |
| unmonitizable idea | فكرة لا يمكن أن تتحول إلى مال |
| unnecessary invention | اختراع غير ضروري |
| unnecessary patenting | استصدار براءات غير ضروري |
| unopposed | بلا مقاومة |
| unoriginal idea | فكرة غير أصيلة |
| unoriginal invention | اختراع غير أصيل |
| unoriginal thought | فكرة غير أصيلة |
| unpatentability | عدم قابلية الاختراع أن يصدر عنها براءة |
| unpatentable | غير قابل أن يصدر عنه براءة |
| unpatentable idea | فكرة لا يمكن أن يصدر عنها براءة |
| unpatented drug | دواء غير صادرة عنه براءة |
| unpatented idea | فكرة لم يصدر عنها براءة |
| unpatented product | منتج لم تصدر عنه براءة |
| unprecedented invention | اختراعات غير مسبوق |
| unpredictable invention | اختراع غير متوقع |
| unprivileged belligerent | المحارب غير الحاصل على الامتياز |
| unprocurable patent | براءة لا يمكن شراؤها |
| unprofitable idea | فكرة غير مربحة |
| unprotected storage | مخزن مفتقر للحماية. مخزن معلومات دون حمايتها |
| unpublished opinion | رأي غير منشور. وفق القانوني الأمريكي هو رأي يصدره قاض لتفسير حكم صادر مع تقرير عدم نشره لكونه لا يحمل قيمة سبقية فلا ينظر له كحكم سبقي يمكن الالتزام به مستقبلا في قضايا أخرى |
| unqualified legal opinion | رأي قانوني غير مسبب |
| unreasoned arbitral award | حكم تحكيم غير مسبب |
| unrecovered liquid hydrocarbon | هيدركربون سائل غير مستخلص |
| unrecovered liquid hydrocarbons | هيدركربونات سائلة غير مستخلصة |
| unrelated patent documents | مستندات براءة غير ذات علاقة |
| unreliable patent search | بحث براءتي لا يعول عليه |
| unrest | قلاقل |
| unsafe use of an invention | استعمال غير آمن لاختراع |
| unsalable idea | فكرة غير قابلة للبيع |
| unsaturated natural source oil | زيت غير مشبع من مصدر طبيعي |
| unsawn timber | خشب غير منشور |
| unscannable document | مستند غيرقابل للمسح للضوئي |
| unscramble | يفك شفرة |
| unsecure usage | استعمال غير آمن |
| unsettleable patent dispute | نزاع بشأن براءات غير قابل للتسوية |
| unsolvated | غير مذاب |
| unspotable | غير ممكن رصده |
| unsticking and separating preparations | مستحضرات فاصلة غير لاصقة |
| unsubstituted or substituted | بها استبدال أو بدون استبدال |
| unsustainable patent | براءة غير قابلة للاستدامة |
| un-tapered | غير مستدق |
| until complete | حتى اكتماله |
| until dryness | حتى الجفاف؛ حتى يجف |
| untreatable material | مادة غير قابلة للمعالجة |
| unusable | غير قابل للاستعمال |
| unused invention | اختراع غير مستخدم |
| unused patent | براءة غير مستخدمة |

unwind (a reel, roller, etc.) يفك (بكرة إلخ)
up block تحميل
up to ph3 حتى وصل الرقم الهيدروجيني إلى 3
up/down volume key مفتاح مستوى الصوت العلوي/السفلي
upconverter محول رفع
up-flow mode وضع تدفق إلى أعلى
upgradability القابلية للتحسين
upgradeable solutions حلول لرفع مستوى الأداء
uphole ; up-hole قمة البئر؛ أعلى البئر
upholstering (grasses for -) تنجيد (عشب للتنجيد)
upholstery (feathers for stuffing-) تنجيد (ريش لحشو التنجيد)
upholstery (straw for stuffing -) تنجيد (قش لحشو التنجيد)
upholstery fabrics أقمشة للتنجيد
upholstery for vehicles تنجيد للمركبات
upholstery wool [stuffing] صوف التنجيد [للحشو]
uplink ; up-link اتصال صاعد أو بـ (الوصلة الصاعدة)
upload تحميل؛ إرسال
upon renounciation بناءا علي هذا التنازل
upper flammability limit أعلي مدي للاشتعال
upper limit حد أعلى
upper respiratory tract inflammatory disorders (urid) الاضطرابات الالتهابية بالجهاز التنفسي العلوي (URID)
upper well of trans well عين علوية من عيون متفرقة
uppers (footwear -) فَرعة [الجزء العلوي من ملبوسات القدم]
upregulate ; up-regulate يزيد بشكل متحكم فيه
upregulation ; up-regulation زيادة متحكم فيها
upright قائم إنشائي (بناء)
ups تغذية مستمرة بالقدرة الكهربائية
upsell بيع فوق البيع؛ بيع إضافي؛ بيع على بيع
upstanding قائم؛ منتصب
upstream الاتجاه العلوي
upstream activating signals إشارات تنشيط قبلية
upstream multiphase flow measurements قبل قياسات التدفق
upstream of قبل
uptake امتصاص؛ يمتص
up-time زمن التشغيل؛ الزمن الاعلى
upward thrust الدفع العلوي
upwardly facing flow surface سطح التدفق المتجه لأعلى
uranium يورانيوم
uranium oxide أكسيد يورانيوم
urban مدني
urban schools المدارس المدنية
ureido يوريدو
urethane associative thickener محسن قوام ترابطي يوريثان
urethral probes مجسات لمجرى البول
urethral syringes محقن لمجرى البول
uric acid حمض اليوريك (البوليك في براءات مصر)
urinals [sanitary fixtures] مبولة [تركيبات صحية]
urinals [vessels] مبولة [أواني للتبول]
urinary calculus الحصوة البولية
urinary incontinence سلس البول
urinarycarcinoma الورم السرطاني البولي
urinometers مقاييس كثافة البول النوعية
urn جَرّة: إناء له قائم كآنية الزهور إلخ
urns (funerary -) جرار (جرار لحفظ رماد الموتى)
urns of precious metal جرار من معدن نفيس
urns, not of precious metal جرار ليست من معدن نفيس
urological apparatus and instruments أجهزة وأدوات للمسالك البولية
urticaria الارتيكاريا؛ الشرى؛ الطفح الجلدي
us agency for international development, usaid الوكالة الأمريكية للتنمية الدولية
us civil administrator الحاكم المدني الأمريكي
usability قابلية الشيء للاستعمال
usability test اختبار القابلية للاستعمال
usable قابل للاستعمال
usable idea فكرة قابلة للاستعمال
usable patent براءة قابلة للاستعمال
usage استعمال
usage-based licensing ترخيص قائم على الاستعمال
usb cable كبل USB
usb key مفتاح USB
usb ports منافذ USB
usb( universal serial bus) الناقل التسلسلي العالمي
use يستعمل، استعمال، فائدة
used in the next reaction without further purification تم استخدامها في التفاعل التالي دون مزيد من التنقية
useful invention اختراع مفيد
useful invention اختراع مفيد
useless invention اختراع لا فائدة منه
useless patent براءة لا فائدة منها
usenet يوزنت: مجموعات الأخبار مجهولة الهوية
user account حساب المستخدم؛ حق الدخول الخاص بالمستخدم
user content license ترخيص للمستعمل بوضع محتوى
user datagram protocol بروتوكول مخطط بيانات المستخدم
user driven innovation ابتكار يسوقه وضع المستعمل. جهد ابتكاري يسير على هدى من موقف المستعمل وملاءمات الاستعمال ومعوقاته
user equipment معدة مستخدم
user friendly سهل الاستخدام
user innovation ابتكار مستعمل
user terminal وحدة طرفية للمستخدم
user/operator مستخدم / قائم بالتشغيل
user-defined معرَّف من قبل المستخدم
user-friendly invention اختراع ملائم للمتستخدم
user's guide دليل المستخدم
uses استعمالات، فوائد
usi واجهة نظام المستخدم
usmtf صيغة أمريكية لنص رسالة
usp دستور الأدوية الأمريكي
uspto مدير مكتب البراءات والعلامات التجارية
ussd بيانات الخدمات المكمّلة غير المركبة
usual interstitial and cryptogenic organizing pneumonia الالتهاب الرئوي الخلالي المعتاد والمنظم لتولد الخلايا
usufruct حق الانتفاع

| | |
|---|---|
| usurping of indigenous peoples' traditional medicines and knowledge | الاستيلاء على الأدوية والمعارف التقليدية الخاصة بالشعوب المحلية |
| utensils for household purposes | أدوات للأغراض المنزلية |
| uterine corpus carcinoma | الورم السرطاني بالجسم الرحمي |
| uterine syringes | محقن للرحم |
| uterus | رحم |
| utility of the invention | استخدام الاختراع |
| utilization | توظيف |
| utilization of indigenous peoples' knowledge and their biological resources | توظيف معرفة الشعوب المحلية ومواردهم البيولوجية |
| utilization of knowledge-based resource | توظيف موارد مؤسسة على المعرفة |
| utilize | يستخدم |
| utilized | موضوع موضع التوظيف، مُوظف |
| utilized patent | براءة مستخدمة |
| utp | يوريدين تراي فوسفات |
| uv detection diode array | كشف بالأشعة البنفسجية لمجموعة الصمام الثنائي |
| uv/visible spectrophotometer | جهاز قياس الطيف الضوئي للأشعة المرئية والفوق بنفسجية: يستخدم في قياس درجة الامتصاص من مركبات عن الأطوال الموجية المرئية والفوق بنفسجية كما أنه يستخدم في تقدير تركيزات المركبات من خلال برنامج الكمبيوتر. كما أنه يستخدم في عمل مسح ضوئي للمركبات |
| uveitis | التهاب العنبية |
| uvmap | خريطة متجهات حضرية |
| uv-visible spectrophotometer | جهاز قياس الطيف المرئي وفوق البنفسجي (UV-Vis) |

# V

| | |
|---|---|
| va | مسئول العرض المرئي |
| va benefit | إعانة المحاربين القدامى |
| vacate | يبطل، يلغي، يشغر، يخليـ يتخلى عن |
| vaccinal | لقاحي، تلقيحي |
| vaccinate | يلقح، شخص تلقيحي |
| vaccinator | ملقح، أداة تلقيح |
| vaccine | لقاح |
| vacillate | يتذبذب، يتخطر، يترجح، يتردد |
| vacillating | متذبذب، متخطر، مترجح، متذبذب |
| vacuolar myelopathy | اعتلال النخاع الفجوي |
| vacuous | فارغ، متبطل |
| vacutainer | أنبوب مفرغ من الهواء |
| vacuum | فراغ، خوائي، مكنسة كهربية؛ وسط التفريغ |
| vacuum distillation | التقطير تحت ضغط منخفض |
| vacuum drying | تجفيف تحت ضغط منخفض |
| vacuum energy | طاقة الفراغ |
| vacuum gas | غاز تحت ضغط منخفض |
| vacuum oven | فرن تحت ضغط منخفض |
| vacuum pump | مضخة تفريغ |
| vacuum residue | مادة متبقية تحت ضغط منخفض: مواد متبقية ناتجة عن التقطير تحت ضغط منخفض |
| vacuum vessel for treatment of oils | وعاء تحت ضغط منخفض لمعالجة الزيوت |
| vacuum-dry | يجفف تحت ضغط منخفض |
| vacuumize | يخوي، يحدث خواء |
| vagi | أعصاب حائرة |
| vaginitis | التهاب المهبل |
| vagus nerve | العصب الحائر |
| vaild | صالح؛ صحيح؛ شرعي، ساري المفعول |
| valid admin contact email clause | بند سلامة بريد الشخص المدير: أن مسجل (مالك اسم النطاق) يتوجب عليه أن يكون مسجلاً بحسبانه الجهة التي تدير اسم النطاق، وأنه يتوجب عليه أن يكون لديه عنوان بريد مستقل عن شركة التسجيل |
| valid agreement | اتفاق نافذ |
| valid or invalid vote | صوت انتخابي صحيح أو غير صحيح |
| valid patent | براءة شرعية، براءة صالحة، براءة فعالة |
| valid prior art | تقنية سابقة صحيحة |
| validate | يجعل الشيء شرعيا، يُثَبت شرعية الشئ؛ يتحقق من |
| validation | تثبيت شرعية الشئ |
| validation of the ticket | تحديث التذكرة أو تجديد صلاحيتها |
| validity | شرعية، سريان المفعول |
| validity opinion | الرأي بشأن القابلية للإنفاذ. الرأي بشأن صحة البراءة. |
| valuation | تقييم |
| value | يثمن، ثمين |
| value model | نموذج قيمة |
| value of intangible assets | قيمة الأصول غير الملموسة |
| value of intangibles | قيمة المواد غير الملموسة |
| value of intellectual capital | قيمة رأس المال الفكري |
| value-added | ذات القيمة المضافة |
| value-focused thinking | تفكير متركز حول القيمة |
| valve | صمام |
| valve metal | فلز صمامي |
| valve seat | مقعد صمام |
| valved | مُصَرَع، ذو مصاريع، ذو صمامات |
| valveless | لا صمامي، لا مصراعي، غير مزود بمصاريع، غير مزود بصمامات |
| valvula | صميم، مصيريع، صمام صغير |
| valvular | صمامي، مصراعي |
| vanity | علبة مكياج |
| vapor | يتبخر، بخار |
| vapor byproduct | منتج ثانوي في صورة بخار |
| vaporific | مولد للبخار، بخاري |
| vaporimeter | مبخار، ميزان لقياس ضغط البخار وحجمه |
| vaporish | بخاري، رقيق، ناعم، كثير البخار |
| vaporizability | قابلية الشيء للتبخر |
| vaporizable | قابل للتبخر |
| vaporization | تبخير، تبخر |
| vaporization system | نظام تبخير |
| vaporize | يبخر، يتبخر |
| vaporizer | مبخر |
| vaporous | بخاري، متطاير، طيار، رقيق |
| vaporware | برامج وهمية |
| vapory | بخاري، ضبابي |
| vapour pressure | ضغط البخار |
| variability | القابلية للتغير |
| variable | متغير |
| variant | صورة متغيرة؛ متغير؛ صورة بديلة: صورة أخرى لنموذج، لمثال من النظام أو للطريقة التي يقدمها الاختراع |
| variant flap | صورة متغيرة من (جين) FLAP |
| variation | تغيير؛ تغير؛ اختلاف |
| variation coefficient | معامل الاختلاف: أحد مقاييس المستخدمة لقياس درجة التشتت |
| variation embodiment | تجسد لأحد أشكال الشيء. تجسد لأحد أشكال الاختراع موضوع البراءة |
| variations | اختلافات |
| varicella | جدري الدجاج |
| variety programme | برنامج منوعات |
| variety shows | عروض أو برامج المنوعات |
| vary | يتغير |
| vascular damaging agent | عوامل متلفة للأوعية |

| | |
|---|---|
| vascular dementia | الخرف الوعائي |
| vascular endothelial cells | خلايا بطانية وعائية |
| vascular endothelial growth factor (vegf) | عامل النمو البطاني الوعائي |
| vascularization | تكون الأوعية |
| vasculature | الجهاز الوعائي |
| vasculitides | التهاب الأوعية الدموية |
| vasculitis (morbus wegener) | الالتهاب الوعائي (Morbus Wegener) |
| vasculogenesis | تكوين الأوعية |
| vaso | وعائي |
| vasoconstriction | انقباض الأوعية |
| vasodilation | توسع الأوعية |
| vasodilator | موسع أوعية |
| vasomotor rhinitis | التهاب الأنف الحركي الوعائي |
| vastus lateralis | المتسعة الوحشية |
| v-blender | خلاط على شكل حرف V |
| vbr | معدل بت متغير |
| vc | قناة افتراضية؛ دائرة افتراضية؛ مؤتمر فيديو؛ |
| vcc | توصيل قناة افتراضية |
| vce | معدات التحكم في الصوت |
| vcr | مسجل شريط مرئي |
| vcri | مؤشر فهرس الإسناد الترافقي للتحقق |
| vdd | وثيقة وصف النسخة،SDRL SO8S |
| vdi-meg | جمعية ماكس إيث التابعة لرابطة المهندسين الألمان |
| vds | سونار متغير العمق |
| vector | ناقل؛ متجه |
| vector borne diseases | الأمراض المحمولة بوسيط ناقل للعدوى |
| vectorial capacity | سعة الوسيط |
| vegetable oil | زيت نباتي |
| vegetable oil economy | اقتصاد مرتكز على الزيت الغذائي |
| vegetable oil refining | تنقية زيوت الخضروات |
| vegetable protein, sugar cane, beetroot, coffee | بروتين نباتي، قصب السكر، البنجر، البن |
| vegetative | إنباتية |
| vehicle | مادة ناقلة؛ مركبة، وسيلة |
| vehicle dynamics | ديناميات المركبات |
| vehicle transmission | ناقل حركة السيارة |
| vena cordis minimae | أوردة قلبية صغيرة |
| venereum | المنقول جنسيًا |
| venetian strip silvering | سقاية شرائح الزجاج الفينيسى بالفضة: العملية التي يتم بواسطتها إنتاج ألواح من الزجاج النقي من جهة والمغطى بالفضة من الجهة الأخرى وهو ما يسمى بالزجاج ذو الرؤية من جهة واحدة، أنظر أيضا الزجاج المغطى بالفضة. |
| venipuncture | وخز الوريد |
| vent | تصريف |
| vent (gas etc.) | يصرف (الغاز) |
| vent gas | الغاز المنصرف |
| ventilation band dryer | جهاز تجفيف شريطي بالتهوية |
| ventilator | جهاز تهوية |
| ventilator induced lung injury | إصابة الرئة المستحثة بواسطة الجهاز التنفسي |
| ventral | بطني |
| ventral and dorsal striatum | الجسم المخطط البطني والظهري |
| venturi | أنبوب فنتوري (لقياس السائل أو الغاز) |
| venule | وُرَيْد؛ وريد صغير |
| verbal and spatial memory and sustained attention | الذاكرة اللغوية والمكانية فضلا عن الانتباه المتواصل |
| verdict of the jury | قرار المحلفين |
| verifiability | قابلية الشيء للتحقق |
| verification | تحقق |
| verifier | متحقق |
| verifying device | جهاز تحقق |
| vermiculite | فيرميكيوليت |
| vernal conjunctivitis | الرمد الربيعي |
| version | نسخة |
| vertebrate | فقاري |
| vertical | رأسي؛ عمودي؛ المحور الرأسي |
| vertical axis | المحور الرأسي |
| vertical dimension | بعد رأسي |
| vertical drop | سقوط رأسي |
| vertical industry | الصناعة الرأسية (الصناعة التخصصية أو النوعية) |
| vertical market | السوق الرأسية (الصناعة التخصصية أو النوعية) |
| vertically integrated monopoly | الاحتكار ذو التكامل الرأسي |
| vertical-specific supplier | موردو السلاسل رأسية |
| very high profile event | مناسبة على أرفع المستويات |
| very high stringency conditions | الظروف عالية الصرامة جدا |
| very long acting ; long-acting | طويل المفعول |
| vesicle | حويصلة |
| vest | يقلد، يخول، يلبس، ثوب، صدرة |
| vf | تردد صوتي |
| vgo | نفط غاز تحت ضغط منخفض |
| vh | المتغير ثقيل السلسلة |
| vhf | تردد عال جدا |
| via | عبر |
| viability | البقاء حية؛ القدرة على مواصلة الحياة؛ جدوى، قابلية الشئ للتنفيذ |
| viable | قادر على مواصلة الحياة |
| viable invention | اختراع قابل للتطبيق على نحو مجدٍ |
| viable inventive concept | مفهوم اختراعي ممكنٌ تنفيذه |
| viable patent | براءة ذات فعالية |
| vial | قارورة؛ قنينة |
| vibrate | يهز، يهتز، يتردد |
| vibrating screen | غِرْبَالٌ هَزَّازٌ |
| vibration | هز |
| vibration sensing device | جهاز إحساس اهتزازي |
| vibration sensor | جهاز إحساس بالاهتزازات |
| vic | الجوار |
| vice admiral | لواء بحري |
| vice bench | نَضَد المِلْزَمة |
| vice squad | بوليس الآداب |
| victim | مجني عليه |
| victim information and | موظف الاستعلامات والمشورة |

| | |
|---|---|
| advice officer | للضحايا |
| victimisation | ايذاء؛ قتل؛ خداع |
| victimise | يوقع في براثن |
| video card | كارت الفيديو |
| video door entry station | محطة تصوير مدخل بوابة |
| video play mode | وضع Video Play (تشغيل الفيديو) |
| video port | منفذ فيديو |
| videoconferencing | عقد مؤتمرات الفيديو |
| video-out jack | مقبس خروج فيديو |
| videophone ; video phone | الهاتف المرئي |
| view | عرض؛ طريقة عرض؛ منظر |
| view definition | تعريف العرض |
| village bank | بنك القرية |
| violation of third parties' rights clause | البند الخاص بانتهاك حقوق الغير. بند تعاقدي يبين أن أطراف العقد بإبرامهم العقد لا يقصدون انتهاك حقوق الغير |
| vip | شخصية هامة جدا / أشخاص مهمين جدا |
| viral encephalitis | التهاب الدماغ الفيروسي |
| viral marketing | تسـويق فيروسي |
| viral oncoproteins | بالبروتينات المولدة للأورام الفيروسية |
| viral- or bacterial exacerbation of asthma | تفاقم الربو الفيروسي أو البكتيري |
| virology | دراسة الفيروسات |
| virosomal | جسم فيروسي |
| virtual circuit | دائرة افتراضية |
| virtual economy | اقتصاد افتراضي |
| virtual ict solutions | حلول تقنية اتصالات ومعلومات افتراضية |
| virtual infringement | انتهاك افتراضي |
| virtual machine | آلة افتراضية. جعل برنامج حاسوبي يعمل عمل الشبكة |
| virtual mobile technology | تقنية محمول افتراضي |
| virtual reality | الواقع الافتراضي |
| virtual reality technology | تقنية الواقع الافتراضي |
| virtual world | العالم الافتراضي |
| virtualizable operating system | نظام تشغيل يمكن جعله افتراضيا |
| virtualization infrastructure | بنية تحتية لجعل الشئ افتراضيا |
| virtualization software | برنامج حاسبي لتأسيس حالة افتراضية |
| virtualization technology | تقنية تأسيس الحالة الافتراضية |
| virtualized it infrastructure | بنية تحتية لتقنية المعلومات تم جعلها افتراضية |
| virulence | مقاومة |
| virus | فيروس: برنامج تنفيذي يعمل بشكل منفصل ويهدف الى احداث خلل في نظام الحاسوب وتتراوح خطورتة حسب مهمته فمنه الخبيث ومنه الحميد وكلاهما خبيث. |
| virus detection | اكتشاف الفيروسات |
| virus protection | الحماية ضد الفيروسات |
| visa activities | معاملات التأشـيرات؛ إجراءات التأشيرات |
| visbreaking | خفض اللزوجة |
| visceral | حشوي؛ متعلق بالأحشاء |

| | |
|---|---|
| visceral pain | الألم الأحشائي |
| viscoelastic | لزجة مرنة |
| viscose fibres, modal fibres, polynosic fibres and lyocell | ألياف الفيسكوز، وألياف المودال، وألياف البولينيزيا، وألياف الليوسيل |
| viscosified fluids | موائع مرتفعة اللزوجة |
| viscosifier | عامل إكساب اللزوجة |
| viscosifying agent | عامل زيادة اللزوجة |
| viscosity | لزوجة |
| viscosity index | دليل اللزوجة |
| viscosupplements | مكملات اللزوجة : علاج للمفصل |
| visibility | رؤية |
| visible | مرئي، منظور |
| visible light | ضوء مرئي |
| visible light emitter | باعث ضوء مرئي |
| vision | رؤيا، رؤية، شيء مرئي |
| vision correction | تصحيح البصر |
| vision device | جهاز رؤية |
| vision quest | البحث عن الرؤية |
| vision technology | تقنية الرؤية |
| visitors centre | مركز الزوار |
| visual representation | تمثيل مرئي |
| visual signals | إشارات بصرية |
| visual technology | تقنية بصرية |
| visualizability | قابلية الشيء للتصور |
| visualization | تصور |
| visualize | يتصور |
| vitd | بيانات منطقة فاصلة لمنتج متجه |
| vl | المتغير خفيف السلسلة |
| vlan | شبكة اتصالات محلية افتراضية |
| vmap | خريطة متجهات |
| vocal energy | طاقة صوتية |
| vocational training | التدريب المهني |
| voice pattern | أنماط الصوت |
| voice recognition | التعرف على الصوت: إمكانية تقدمها الآن عدة هواتف يدوية تتيح إمكانية تنفيذ مكالمات باستخدام أوامر صوتية بدلا من إدخال أرقام. وبإمكان المستخدمين برمجة الذاكرة لتخزين وتعريف الأسماء التي نطقت في الهاتف اليدوي والاتصال بالأرقام المتصلة بها. |
| voice recognition | التعرف إلى الصوت |
| voice record mode | وضع تسجيل الصوت |
| voice travel | انتقال الصوت |
| voicemail | رسالة صوتية |
| void arbitral award | حكم تحكيمي باطل |
| void of any legal standing | خالية من أي سند قانوني |
| void per particle | فراغ لكل جسيم |
| voip | بروتوكول نقل الصوت عبر الإنترنت |
| volatiles | المواد المتطايرة |
| volcanic ashes | الرماد البركاني |
| volcanic bombs | القنابل البركانية |
| volcanic breccia | الرواهص البركانية |
| volcanic cone | المخروط البركاني |
| volcanic crater | فوهة البركان |
| volcanic neck | عنق البركان |

| | |
|---|---|
| volcanic plateaus | هضاباً بركانية |
| voltage | جهد |
| voltage clamp | مشبك الجهد |
| voltage potential | الجهد |
| voltage relative to the environment | جهد بالنسبة للبيئة |
| voltage-clamped | فولتية مثبتة؛ جهد مثبَّت |
| voltage-gated sodium channel | قناة الصوديوم المعتمدة على الجهد |
| voltammeter | مقياس الجهد |
| voltammogram | مقياس فرق الجهد الكهربائي |
| voltamperometry | قياس الجهد والتيار |
| volume control | التحكم في مستوى الصوت |
| volume control buttons | أزرار تحكم في الصوت |
| volume estimation techniques | تقنيات تقدير الحجم |
| volume fraction of a compound | نسبة حجم المركب |
| volume indicator | مؤشر مستوى الصوت |
| volume of water | مقدار المياه |
| volume ppm benzoquinone solution | جزء في المليون بالحجم من محلول بنزو كينون |
| volume reduction | اختزال الحجم ( تقليله) |
| volumetric | حجمي |
| volumetric centroid | مركز وسطي حجمي |
| volumetric ratio | نسبة حجمية |
| voluntary arbitration | تحكيم طوعي |
| volunteer | نبات تلقائي (نبات)؛ متطوع |
| vortex (pl. vortices) | دوامة؛ دوامات (أو تدويم؛ تدويمات) |
| vortex mixer | خلاط دوامي |
| vortex shedder | وسيلة سكب دوامية |
| vortex-shedding device | وسيلة سكب دوامي |
| vote a law | يصوت بالموافقة على (قانون) |
| vote counting ; sorting out of votes | فرز الأصوات |
| vote down | يصوت ضد |
| voting | اقتراع |
| voxel correlation | ارتباط الفوكسلات |
| vp | مسار افتراضي |
| vpc | توصيل المسار الافتراضي |
| vpn | الشبكات الشخصية الافتراضية |
| vsat | وحدة طرفية فتحة صغيرة جدا |
| vt | الكمية الإجمالية |
| vtc | مؤتمر فيديو عن بعد |
| vtol | إقلاع وحط عمودي |
| vtp | بروتوكول ترنك افتراضي |
| vugy porosity | مسامية الثقب |
| vulcanized rubber | المطاط المصلّد |
| vulnerabilities | ثغرات: مشكلات اختراق |
| vulnerability assessment report | تقرير تقييم الهشاشة |
| vulnerable | سهلة الاختراق؛ معرضة للهجوم |
| vulvodynia | ألم الفرج |

# W

| | |
|---|---|
| wackes | أحجار الواكي |
| wad | يسطم، سطام، حشوة |
| wadable | ممكن التخويض |
| wadding | حشوة |
| wadding | مواد للحشو أو السطم |
| wafer | برشام |
| waft | يدفع، يسوق فوق الماء أو عبر الهواء، ينبعث أو ينطلق |
| waivable license | ترخيص قابل للتنازل عنه |
| waiver of default | التنازل عن التقصير |
| walkers | مشايات |
| walking robot | روبوت سيارة |
| wall | جدار |
| wallboard | لوح جداري |
| wallpapers | خلفية لسطح المكتب |
| walnut | جوز |
| wan | شبكة واسعة المدى |
| wane | يتضاءل، يتناقص، يبهت، ينحسر |
| wang resin-based carbamate linker | مادة ربط أساسها الراتنج Wang |
| wany | متضائل، متناقص |
| wap | إجراء التطبيقات اللاسلكية: عبارة عن نظام يمكن الهواتف النقالة المتطابقة مع هذا النظام من الوصول إلى خدمات الانترنت النصية، مثل البريد الالكتروني، الأخبار، السفر، التسليةو الترفيه، المال، الرياضة، الخ. وتستخدم أيضا كحامل للتقنية للمميزات المتطورة مثل MMS |
| war crimes court | مَحْكَمَة جَرَائِم حَرْب |
| war dead cemetery | مقابر الشهداء |
| war games | تدريبات عسكرية (نيران صديقة (friendly fires |
| war of attrition | حرب الاستنزاف |
| war of nerves | حرب أعصاب |
| warfare technology | تثنية حروب |
| waring blender | خلاط طحن |
| warm lime softener | وحدة إزالة العسر المسبب بواسطة الجير الداقئ |
| warmback | المؤخرة الدافئة |
| warm-blooded ; warm blooded | من ذوات الدم الحار |
| warning | تحذير |
| warning and note indicator | مؤشر التحذير والملاحظة |
| warrant officer (wo) | مساعد |
| warranty card | بطاقة الضمان |
| warsaw treaty organization, | منظمة حلف وارسو |
| wto | |
| wart | ثلول؛ بثرة؛ نتوء صغير |
| wash | يغسل |
| washer | حلقة: تُعرف أيضا باسم "وردة" |
| wassail | وسال (أنواع مشروبات روحية) |
| waste | يضيع، يلقي بالفضلات، نفايات، فضلات |
| waste disposal | تصريف النفايات |
| waste heat | حرارة متبددة |
| waste land | أرض بور |
| waste recovery | الاستخلاص من المخلفات |
| wasted circulation | جمهور بلا جدوى شرائية؛ توزيع مبدد |
| wastes | نفايات |
| waste-water | ماء الصرف |
| wasting | مصيب بالهزال |
| water | يسقي، ماء |
| water circuit | دورة مائية |
| water drive | دفع بالماء |
| water flooding | غمر بالماء |
| water gas | غاز الماء: مزيج من غازي الهيدروجين وأول أكسيد الكربون، ويسمى أحياناً الغاز الصناعي، وينتج من تفاعل الميثان مع بخار الماء عند درجة 700-800 درجة مئوية بوجود عامل مساعد . يمكن تحضيره أيضاً من تفاعل بخار الماء مع الفحم. |
| water gas shift reaction | تفاعل إزاحة الغاز بالماء |
| water hose | خراطيم المياه |
| water or gas coning | تكوين مخروطي مائي أو غازي |
| water purifier | منقي ماء |
| water reservoir | خزان الماء، احتياطي الماء |
| water sealing | مانع للتسرب المائي |
| water tube boiler | غلاية ماء أنبوبية |
| water vapour transmission rate (wvtr) | معدل انتقال بخار الماء |
| water-absorbing | ممتص للماء |
| water-based mud invasion | تغلغل وحل أساسه الماء |
| water-borne | محمول بواسطة الماء؛ محمول مائيا |
| waterborne | طافٍ علي سطح الماء، منتقل بالماء |
| watercolor | ألوان ماء؛ رسم مائي؛ لوحة مائية |
| water-gas shift reaction | تفاعل إزاحة الغاز بالماء |
| water-miscible x water-immiscible | قابل للمزج بالماء × غير قابل للمزج بالماء |
| waterpipes | أنابيب مياه |
| waterpower | قوة مائية تستخدم في الألات |
| waterproof pad | وسادة صامدة للماء |
| water-proof; water proof | مقاوم للماء؛ عازل للماء |
| water-repellent | صاد للماء |
| water-resistant | مقاوم للماء |
| waters pda 2996 diode array detector | كاشف Waters PDA 2996 به مجموعة من الدايودات |
| water-tight ; water tight | مضاد للماء |
| water-wet' and 'oil-wet' and 'mixed-wet' | مبلل بالماء" و"مبلل بالنفط" و"مبلل بشكل مختلط" |
| watery | مائي، رطب، سبخ |
| wave | يلوح، يرفرف، يموج، يتموج، تموج، موجة |

| | |
|---|---|
| wave length/nm | طول موجي / نانو متر |
| wave-front sensor | جهاز إحساس بالموجات الأمامية |
| waveguide | دليل موجي |
| wavelet | موجة صغيرة |
| wavelike | موجي الحركة أو الشكل |
| waves | موجات |
| wax | يتقوى، يتعاظم، شمع، إفراز شمعي |
| waxy | شمعي، مشمع |
| wc | مرحاض |
| wcdma | نظام الربط المعدد عريض النطاق بالتقسيم الزمني، وهو نظام ربط هوائي يمكن الهواتف المتنقلة من الجيل الثالث من دعم خدمات النطاق العريض والوسائط المتعددة عالية السرعة، مثل الاتصال المرئي. |
| w-cdma | النفاذ المتعدد عريض النطاق بالتقسيم الشفري |
| wct | معاهدة الويبو بشأن حق المؤلف |
| weapon guidance technology | تقنية توجيه السلاح |
| weapons of mass destruction; mass destruction weapons | أسلحة التدمير (الدمار) الشامل |
| wear | يرتدي، يحدث تدريجيا بالاحتكاك، لباس، زي |
| wear limits data | بيانات الحد الأقصى للبلي |
| wearability | قابلية الشيء للارتداء |
| wearable | قابل للارتداء |
| wearable alarm | جهاز إنذار يمكن ارتداؤه |
| wearable appliances | أدوات يمكن ارتداؤها |
| wearable computers | حاسوبيات يمكن ارتداؤها |
| wearable computing | تعبير يطلق على الأجهزة الحاسوبية التي يمكن ارتداؤها |
| wearable device | جهاز قابل للارتداء |
| wearable health monitoring technology | تقنية مراقبة صحية قابلة للارتداء |
| wearable technology | تقنية قابلة للارتداء |
| wearer | مرتدٍ |
| weather forecast | التنبؤات الجوية |
| weathering | التجوية |
| weaving industry | صناعة الغزل |
| weaving waste | عوادم الغزل |
| web | شبكة؛ الويب |
| web designer | مصمم شبكي |
| web offset press | طباعة الأوفست الشريطية |
| web page | صفحة ويب |
| webmaster | مسؤول الويب |
| website | موقع ويب؛ موقع على الإنترنت |
| web-site awareness | الإحاطة بالموقع الشبكي. إدراك وجود موقع شبكي معين |
| web-site optimization | رفع كفاءة الموقع الشبكي إلى المستويات القصوى |
| website optimization software | برنامج رفع كفاءة موقع شبكي إلى المستويات القصوى |
| wedge | إسفين. وتد أو ضرب |
| wedged | إسفيني الشكل، علق أو منحشر |
| wedgy | إسفيني الشكل |
| weed killer; weedicide | قاتل أو مبيد للأعشاب الضارة؛ مبيد الطحالب (طحلب) |
| weighable | قبل للوزن |
| weight average molecular weight; weight-average molecular weight | متوسط وزن الوزن الجزيئي؛ الوزن الجزيئي بناء على متوسط الوزن |
| weight average particle diameter | متوسط قطر الجسيم بالوزن |
| weight fraction of a compound | نسبة مركب بالوزن |
| weight ratio | النسبة بالوزن؛ النسبة الوزنية |
| weight space velocity | السرعة الفراغية للكتلة. |
| weight-bearing exercices | تمارين احتمال الوزن |
| weighted average | متوسط مرجح |
| weighted probability distribution | التوزيع الاحتمالي المرجح |
| weightless | عضيم الوزن |
| weighty | خطير أو ثقيل |
| weir | قنطرة احتجاز |
| weld | يلحم، وصلة ملحومة، التحام |
| weld seam | لحام طرفي |
| weld/welding seam | درزة لحام |
| welding | لحام |
| welding technology | تقنية لحم |
| weldment | لحم، الحم وحدة مؤلفة من عدة قطاع مالحومة |
| well | بئر |
| well boring; well drilling | حفر الآبار |
| well completions | عمليات إكمال بئر؛ عمليات تجهيز بئر: عمليات لإعداد حفرة البئر لإنتاج النفط أو الغاز من خزان. |
| well effluent streams | تيارات متدفقات البئر |
| well head | فوهة البئر |
| well header | رأس البئر |
| well impairment | خلل التدفق في البئر |
| well log output record | سجل مخرجات قياسات بئر |
| well logging tool | أداة تسجيل أداء البئر؛ أداء تسجيل القياسات البئرية |
| well logs | سجلات قياسات بئر |
| well models | نماذج البئر |
| well operation system | نظام عمليات بئر |
| well placement | تحديد موقع بئر |
| well servicing combination unit | وحدة مدمجة لصيانة بئر |
| wellbore | حفرة البئر؛ تجويف البئر |
| wellheads of the wells | فوهات الآبار |
| well-known prior art | فن سابق مشهور |
| west african development bank, wadb | بنك التنمية لغرب أفريقيا |
| western blot = western blotting | بقعة ويسترن (بقعة Western)؛ اختبار التشرب البقعي لويسترن |
| wet | بليل، رطب بليل غير جاف |
| wet gas | الغاز الرطب |
| wet natural gas | غاز طبيعي رطب |
| wet scrubbing and dry scrubbing processes | عمليات الغسل الرطب والغسل الجاف (للغازات إلخ) |
| wet-end | النهاية المبللة: جزء من عملية صناعة الورق قبل تكون نسيج الورق |
| wet-pulverizing | طحن في وجود ماء |

| | |
|---|---|
| wettability | قابلية الابتلال |
| wettability logging tool | أداة تسجيل أداء قابلية الابتلال |
| wettability logs | سجلات قابلية الابتلال |
| wetting agent | مادة ترطيب |
| wg | مجموعة عمل |
| wgs | النظام الجيوديسي العالمي |
| wgs-72 | النظام الجيوديسي العالمي 72 |
| wgs-84 | النظام الجيوديسي العالمي 84 |
| wh | وات في الساعة |
| wheat starch | نشا القمح |
| wheat, maize, barely, rice | القمح الذرة الشعير الأرز |
| wheel walkers | مشايات ذات عجلات |
| wheeze | أزيز |
| wheezy-infant syndrome | متلازمة أزيز التنفس بالأطفال |
| whey | الشرش |
| whipcord | حبل رفيع، المبرع، المضلع |
| whipstock | إسفين إمالة |
| white balance | توازن اللون الأبيض |
| white balance indicator | مؤشر (موازنة اللون الأبيض) |
| white hat security researcher | باحث في مجال الحماية |
| white opacifying hiding pigments | خضابات إخفاء بيضاء معتمة |
| white water | المياه البيضاء: مصطلح عام لكل مياه مصنع الورق التي تم فصلها من معلق اللب، سواء في ماكينة الورق أو في معدات ثانوية، مثل المثخنات، الغسالات، معدات استرجاع الألياف، أو من مطاحن اللب |
| whiteboard | لوح أبيض = برنامج تفاعلي مماثل للسبورة |
| whole and flattened tablets | أقراص سليمة (كاملة) ومسطحة |
| whole-school reform | إصلاح المدارس بالكامل |
| whsv | السرعة الفراغية الوزنية في الساعة؛ السرعة الفراغية للكتلة في الساعة |
| wick | فتيلة، فتيل، ذبالة |
| wide therapeutic spectrum | مجال علاجي واسع |
| wideband code division multiple access | الوصول المتعدد عريض النطاق بتقسيم الشفرة |
| wideband pilot | إشارة فحص عريضة النطاق |
| wide-cut gasoline | بنزين منخفض الأوكتين |
| widely held bank | مصرف مشاع الملكية |
| wifi ; wi-fi | واي فاي؛ تقنية واي فاي |
| wild | بري |
| wild accession | صنف بري |
| wild type | نمط بري |
| willful patent infringement | انتهاك براءة إرادي |
| willful patent theft | سرقة عمدية لبراءة |
| wimax | تقنية واي ماكس (الموجة الواسعة اللاسلكية): تتيح لتغطية الشبكات اللاسلكية أن تصل إلى حوالي 30 ميلا، وتنقل البيانات والصوت والفيديو بسرعة تفوق بكثير خط المشترك الرقمي DSL والكبل |
| winch | رافعة |
| wind energy | طاقة ريح |
| wind power | قوة الريح |
| wind tunnel | نفق هوائي |

| | |
|---|---|
| winder | ماكينة لف؛ ملفاف |
| winding | لف، منعطف، لولبي؛ ملف |
| window of system availability, and the criticality of the data | نافذة إتاحة النظام، وحرجية البيانات. |
| windows logo key | مفتاح شعار ويندوز |
| windscreen wipers | ممسحات الزجاج |
| wing | جناح |
| wing commander | مقدم طيار |
| wing nut | صامولة مجنحة |
| wink | إشارة ومضية |
| wipe | يمسح، ينطف، ينشف، يزيل بالمسح، مسحة، منديل |
| wiper | ممسحة، منديل |
| wipers | ممسحات |
| wipo creative heritage project | مشروع الويبو للتراث الإبداعي. هو ما تتخذه المنظمة العالمية للملكية الفكرية (الويبو) من إجراءات وترتيبات نحو تنفيذ مخطط حفظ وترتيب الأعمال التراثية الفكرية الإبداعية والمحافظة على التراث الثقافي والمعارف التقليدية التي تستحق الحماية. وذلك لأجل الاستفادة منها لأقصى حد ممكن خلال الحاضر والمستقبل |
| wipo patent information services | خدمات معلومات البراءات الخاصة بوايبو. برنامج أسسته المنظمة العالمية للملكية الفكرية في 1975 لتوفير معلومات البراءات على أوسع نطاق لاسيما للبلدان النامية للاستفادة منها في نهضتها الابتكارية |
| wire | يزود بأسلاك كهربية، يسلك، يبرق، سلك، سلك معدنين سك كهربي أو هاتفي |
| wire coil | ملف سلكي |
| wire drum | مكب أسلاك |
| wire mesh | شبكة سلكية |
| wire thermocouple | مزدوج حراري بسلك |
| wired | مسلك، مقوى بالأسلاك، مزود بأسلاك كهربية؛ سلكي |
| wired glass | زجاج مقوى بأسلاك: الزجاج الذي يحتوى على شبكة من السلك مدفونة بداخله لتقويته |
| wired patterned glass | زجاج مشكل (المزخرف) المقوى بأسلاك: زجاج نصف شفاف مقوى بأسلاك وسطحه مزخرف |
| wireless application protocol (wap) | بروتوكول التطبيقات اللاسلكي |
| wireless controller | وحدة التحكم اللاسلكية |
| wireless customers | الزبائن اللاسلكيون |
| wireless links | وصلات لاسلكية |
| wireless personal area networks (wpans). | الشبكات الشخصية اللاسلكية |
| wireless power connection | اتصال القدرة اللاسلكي |

| | |
|---|---|
| wireless power transmission | نقل/إرسال قدرة لاسلكياً؛ نقل/إرسال الطاقة الكهربائية اللاسلكية |
| wireless power transmissions | إشارات إرسال قدرة لاسلكية |
| wireless power transmitter | مرسل قدرة لاسلكي |
| wireless transmission | الاتصال اللاسلكي |
| wireless world | العالم اللاسلكي |
| wireline | كبل حفر |
| wireline inspection unit | وحدة فحص كبل حفر |
| wires | أسلاك |
| with a high distinction recognition | بتقدير إمتياز مع مرتبة الشرف |
| with an over travel stop | وقف، ابطال اثناء التشغيل |
| with cycling | مع التكرار |
| with minimal after-cooling | باستخدام الحد الأدنى من التبريد اللاحق |
| with the provisos that | بشروط أن |
| withold or maintain (position) | يتمسك بموقع؛ يحتفظ بموقع |
| without bail | بدون كفالة |
| without being limited by theory | بدون التقيد بنظرية |
| without further purification | بدون تنقية إضافية؛ بدون مزيد من التنقية |
| witness | يشهد |
| witness for the defence | شهود النفي |
| witness for the presecution | شهود الإثبات |
| wlans | الشبكات المحلية اللاسلكية |
| wood anemone | شَقَائِق النُّعْمان |
| wood flour | نشارة الخشب |
| wood sorrel | نبات الحماض |
| wood violets | شجر البنفسج |
| wood-containing board | الكرتون الذي يحتوى على خشب |
| wood-free board | الكرتون الخالي من الخشب |
| woodruff key | المفتاح الهلالي |
| woodwork | أشغال الخشب أو أجزاء مصنوعة من خشب |
| wool yarn | خيط من الصوف |
| word-recognition technology | أسلوب النص التنبؤي T9 |
| work | يعمل، عمل، مصنف، شغل؛ يعمل، يشتغل، مصنف فكري |
| work bench | نَضَد العمل |
| work coil | ملف تحريض |
| work up | يعالج؛ يشغل (خطوة، إجراءً، إلخ) |
| workability | قابلية الشئ للتشغيل |
| workable | قابل للتشغيل |
| workable invention | اختراع قابل للإعمال |
| workbox | علبة لأدوات الشغل أو مواده |
| worker | عامل |
| workers compensation commission | لجنة التعويضات العمالية |
| workflow | سير العمل |
| workforce management software | برنامج لإدارة قوة العمل |
| workforce management solutions | حلول لإدارة قوة العمل |
| workforce software | برنامج لتنظيم أعمال فرق العمل |
| working | إعمال، تشغيل |
| working connections child care (wccc) | برنامج رعاية الطفل للأقارب العاملين |
| working the invention | إعمال الاختراع، تشغيل الاختراع. من الأمور المطلوبة في طلبات استصدار البراءات إرفاق شرح للاختراع يمكن الغير من أصحاب الدراية العادية غير المتخصصين أن يشغلوا الاختراع |
| working volume | الحجم أثناء التشغيل |
| workover | أعمال الصيانة وزيادة الإنتاج في بئر منتجة؛ إعادة البئر المتوقفة إلى الإنتاج |
| workover operations | عمليات اعداد البئر للانتاج |
| workover rig | منصة صيانة البئر |
| workplace optimization solutions | حلول لرفع كفاءة مقر العمل إلى المستويات القصوى |
| work-up | معالجة؛ تشغيل [بخاصة في التحضيرات الكيميائية] |
| world economy | اقتصاد العالم |
| world food council, wfc | مجلس الغذاء العالمي |
| world food programme, wfp | برنامج الغذاء العالمي (روما) |
| world health organization, who | منظمة الصحة العالمية (جنيف) |
| world intellectual property organization, wipo | المنظمة العالمية للملكية الأدبية (جنيف) |
| world intellectual wealth organization | المنظمة العالمية للثروة الفكرية. مفهوم تم طرحه عام 2004 ليكون بديلاً لمفهوم المنظمة العالمية للملكية الفكرية خلال مناقشة مستقبل المنظمة. وهو مفهوم يقوم على فكرة أن تسهم هذه المنظمة الجديدة في إدارة الحقوق الفكرية، لكن بجانب ذلك عليها أن تسهم في مجالات أخرى |
| world meteorological organization, wmo | المنظمة العالمية للأرصاد الجوية (جنيف) |
| world power | قوة عالمية |
| world super power | قوة عالمية عظمى |
| world-shaking invention | تعبير يطلق على الاختراع و التأثير الشديد |
| worldwide license | ترخيص عالمي النطاق |
| worldwide patent | براءة عالمية |
| worldwide patent data provider | مقدم خدمة التزويد ببيانات براءات عبر العالم |
| worm | الدودة: فيروس ينتشر فقط عبر الشبكات والانترنت ويعمل على الانتشار على الشبكات عن طريق دفتر عنواين البريد الالكتروني مثلا فعند اصابة الجهاز يبحث البرنامج الخبيث عن عناوين الاشخاص المسجلين في دفتر العناوين على سبيل المثال ويرسل نفسه الى كل شخص وهكذا |
| worm drive | إدارة بترس دودي |
| worm gear | ترس دودي |

| | |
|---|---|
| worn anodes | الأقطاب الموجبة البالية |
| wp | تخطيط المياه؛ معالجة الكلمات |
| wppt | معاهدة الويبو بشأن الاداء والتسجيل الصوتي |
| wrap | يلف؛ يغطي، يغلف، يرزم، يقيد، مادة تغليف، لفة |
| wrap knitting ring | حلقة حياكة باللف |
| wraparound | ملفوف |
| wraparound | دثار، إزار |
| wrapper | غلاف، مغلف |
| wreck | يتلف، حطام، محطم، تحطم، خراب |
| wreckage | حطام، محطم، تحطم، خراب |
| wrench | ذراع |
| wrench ; spanner | مفتاح ربط (زي اللي مع بتاع الأنابيب) |
| wrest | يسحب، يلوي، يغتصب، ينتزع، لي، لوي، ملوي، مفتاح الدوزنة |
| writing data | جارٍ كتابة البيانات... |
| wrongful death | الوفاة نتيجة فعل غير مشروع |
| ws | محطة عمل |
| wtppm | جزء في المليون بالوزن |
| wtrsuppt | نقطة إمداد مياه |

# X

| | |
|---|---|
| xanthane | زانثان |
| xanthate salt | ملح زانثات |
| xanthic | أصفر، صفراوي، صفراويك |
| xanthin | زنتاين. مركب نيروجي متبلر وثيق الصلة بالحامض البولي، يوجد في البول و الدم و بعض الأنسجة الحيوانية والنباتية |
| xanthine | زانثين |
| x-axis | المحور السيني |
| xenobiotic | مادة كيميائية غريبة حيويا |
| xenogamy | إخصاب تهجيني |
| xenogeneic cell transplant | نقل خلايا من مصدر خارجي |
| xenogeneic cell transplant | نقل خلايا من مصدر خارجي: عملية نقل خلايا من مانح إلى مستقبل حيث يكون المستقبل عبارة عن نوع يختلف عن ذلك الخاص بالمانح |
| xenograft | طُعم خارجي |
| xenon | عنصر جهازي ثقيل خامل عديم اللون يوجد في الهواء و يستعمل في بعض المصابيح الكهربائية |
| xenopus oocytes | خلايا مأخوذة من بويضات الضفادع الطينية |
| xenotypic | ذو نمط خارجي |
| xerogel | جل جاف |
| xerography | التصوير الجاف. طريقة في التصوير تشبه الفوتوغرافية ولكنها لا تطلب أوراقا أو رقائق ذات حساسية |
| xerostomia | جفاف الفم |
| xiphoid | سيفي، سيفي الشكل |
| x-ray beam | حزمة أشعة سينية |
| x-ray crystal structure | بنية بللورية بالأشعة السينية |
| x-ray diffraction patterns | أنماط حيود الأشعة السينية |
| x-ray film | فيلم أشعة سينية |
| x-ray powder diffraction pattern | نمط حيود الأشعة السينية في المسحوق |
| x-ray powder diffractogram | مخطط حيود الأشعة السينية في المسحوق |
| xrpd | حيود الأشعة السينية في المسحوق، حيود أشعة X في المسحوق |
| xrpd fumaric acid salt 2:1 g-form | مخطط حيود الأشعة السينية في المسحوق لصورة g لملح حمض الفيوماريك 2: 1 |
| x-vivo | خارج الجسم الحي. قارن in-vivo |
| xx-negative patients | المرضى الذين لديهم نتيجة سلبية لـ XX |
| xylograph | نقش على الخشب |
| xylography | فن النقش على الخشب |
| xylotomous | ثاقب للخشب |
| Xylotomy | قطع الخشب |

# Y

| | |
|---|---|
| yankee cylinder | اسطوانة اليانكي: أسطوانة ضخمة منفردة بعد عملية الاستخلاص و/أو التبييض أو إزالة الأحبار معبرا عنها كنسبة مئوية من الألياف الخام |
| yard | ياردة |
| yardage | مقدار من الياردات |
| yarn | غزل |
| yarn clamp assembly | مجموعة مشابك تثبيت خيط |
| yarn loop | بكرة الخيط |
| yarn looping position | وضع حلقي للخيط |
| yawing | انعراج |
| y-axis | المحور الصادي |
| year-in and year-out | سنة تلو سنة |
| year-round education | التعليم على مدار العام |
| yeast vector | ناقل خمائري |
| yeasty | خميري: منسوب إلى الخمر أو شبيه بها |
| yellow amber | كهرمان أصفر |
| yellow dog contract | عقدٌ يحظر عُضوية الاتحادات العمالية |
| yellowish | ميال إلى الصفرة |
| yellowness | كون الشيء أصفر |
| yellow-tan | لون أسمر مصفر |
| yield | حصيلة؛ يعطي؛ ينتج |
| yield point | نقطة الخضوع |
| yielding | لدن، مائع |
| yields | نواتج |
| yoghurt, yogurt | الزبادي |
| yosarcoma | الورم السرطاني العضلي |
| you will not find wanting | لن تجد به أي نقص؛ لن تجده مفتقراً لأي شيء |
| yttria | إتريا (أكسيد الإتريوم) |
| yttrium | إتريوم |
| y-zeolite; y zeolite | زيوليت Y أو زيوليت من نوع Y |

# Z

| | |
|---|---|
| zamindar | ملتزم - متعهد - صاحب الامتياز |
| zap | يزيل؛ يدمر؛ يهاجم |
| zeolitic | زيوليتية |
| zero-emission engine | محرك ذو انبعاثات صفرية |
| zero-emission technology | تقنية ذات انبعاث صفري |
| zg | زيتا جرام |
| zinc | عنصر فلزي أبيض مزرق، يزنك، يخرضن، يعالج بالزنك أو الخارصين |
| zinc blend | كبر يتيد الزنك |
| zinc oxide based guard bed | طبقة واقية أساسها أكسيد الزنك |
| zinc oxycarbide inclusive layer | طبقة متضمنة أوكسي كربيد زنك |
| zinc white | أبيض الزنك، صبغ أبيض مؤلف من أكسيد |
| zinc-air battery | بطارية زنك هوائية |
| zincic | خارصيني |
| zincite | الزنكيت، أكسيد الزنك الأحمر |
| zincography | الحفر بالزينكوجارف |
| zincoid | زنكي، شبيه بالزنك أو الخار الصيني |
| zink plates | صفائح الزنك |
| zip | يندفع، ينطلق، حيوية، نشاط |
| zip code | كود المنطقة |
| zip fastener | زمام المنزلق |
| zipper | زمام منزلق: ببتيد ربط |
| zippered | مزملق، مزود يزمام منزلق |
| zipping | فتح أو غلْق الزّمام |
| zircon | الزركون |
| zirconate | ملح حامض الزيركوني |
| zirconia | أكسيد الزركونيوم |
| zirconic | زركوني |
| zirconium | زركونيوم، عنصر فلزي نادر |
| zirconium chloride | كلوريد زركونيوم |
| zirconium oxide | أكسيد الزركونيوم |
| zmd single quadrupole mass spectrometer | مقياس طيفي للكتلة ذو قطب رباعي مفرد ZMD |
| zmogolist | زيمولوجي، العالم بالزيمولوجيا أو علم الخمائر |
| zonal | نطاقي، منطقي |
| zonation | تَوزُّع إلى مناطق |
| zone | يمنطق، منطقة، نطاق |
| zone of proximal development | المنطقة القصوى للتطوير |
| zoned | ممنطق، مقسم غلى مناطق، مقسم إلى مناطق أو متنطق |
| zoom bar | شريط التكبير/التصغير |
| zoom button | زر التكبير/التصغير |
| zoom camera | كاميرا مقربة؛ كاميرا لتقريب الصورة |
| zoom in | يكبر؛ تكبير الشيء: تصويره مقربا |
| zoom in/ out indicator | مؤشر التكبير/التصغير |
| zoom-out | يصغر؛ تصغير الشيء: تصويره بعيدا |
| zwitterion | شاردة ثنائية القطب: أيون ثنائي القطب |
| zymogen | زيموجين، مولدة الخمائر |
| zymogenic | متعلق بمولدة الخمائر |
| zymology | زيمولوجيا، علم الخمائر |
| zymolysis | الأنزيمية، فعل الخمائر الهضمي و التخميري |
| zymometer | الزيمومتر، المخمار، أداة تبين مادة التخمير أو الاختمار |
| zymoplastic | مخمر، مولد للخمائر |
| zymoscope | زيموسكوب، مقياس للتخمير، جهاز يقيس قدرة الخميرة على التخمير |

Made in the USA
Monee, IL
05 November 2026

67808627R00168